CENTRE DE PHYSIQUE DES HOUCHES

1982

RAYONNEMENT GRAVITATIONNEL

GRAVITATIONAL RADIATION

NATO ASI

CENTRE DE PHYSIQUE DES HOUCHES

M. T. Béal-Monod and D. Thoulouze Directors

2 June - 21 June 1982

RAYONNEMENT GRAVITATIONNEL

GRAVITATIONAL RADIATION

edited by

NATHALIE DERUELLE AND TSVI PIRAN

INSTITUT D'ÉTUDES AVANCÉES DE L'OTAN

NATO ADVANCED STUDY INSTITUTE

N·H
P.C

1983

NORTH-HOLLAND PUBLISHING COMPANY

AMSTERDAM · NEW YORK · OXFORD

ISBN: 0 444 86560 8

Publishers:
NORTH-HOLLAND PUBLISHING COMPANY
AMSTERDAM · NEW YORK · OXFORD

Sole distributors for the U.S.A. and Canada:
ELSEVIER SCIENCE PUBLISHING COMPANY, INC.
52 VANDERBILT AVENUE
NEW YORK, N.Y. 10017

Library of Congress Cataloging in Publication Data

NATO Advanced Study Institute (1982 : Centre de physique des Houches)
Rayonnement gravitationnel.

At head of title: NATO ASI, Centre de physique des Houches, 2 June-21 June 1982.
Includes bibliographical references and indexes.
1. Gravitational radiation--Congresses. I. Deruelle, Nathalie, 1952- . II. Piran, Tsvi, 1949- . III. Centre de physique des Houches. IV. Title: Gravitational radiation.
QC179.N37 1982 531'.14 82-24625
ISBN 0-444-86560-8 (U.S.)

Printed in The Netherlands

CONTENTS

PARTICIPANTS

ABRAMOVICI Alex	: Weizmann Institute of Science, Department of Nuclear Physics 76100 Rehovot, Israël
ASHTEKAR Abhay	: Syracuse University, Department of Physics, 201 Physics Building Syracuse, New York, 13210 U.S.A.
BARDEEN James	: University of Washington, Department of Physics, Seattle, Washington, 98195 U.S.A.
BASSAN Massimo	: Stanford University, Department of Physics, Stanford, California, 94305 U.S.A.
BILGE Hümeyra	: Middle East Technical University, Department of Physics, Metu, Ankara, Turkey
BLAIR David	: University of Western Australia, Department of Physics, Nedlands, 6009 Western Australia
BRILL Dieter	: University of Maryland, Department of Physics & Astronomy College Park, Maryland, 20742 U.S.A.
BRILLET Alain	: Université Paris Sud, Lab. de l'Horloge Atomique, Bât. 221 91405 Orsay, France
CARTER Brandon	: Observatoire de Paris Meudon, G.A.R. 92190 Meudon, France
CAVES Carlton	: Caltech, Theoretical Astrophysics 130-33 Pasadena, California, 91125 U.S.A.
CHOQUET Yvonne	: Université Paris VI, Département de Mécanique, Tours 55-66 11 Quai St. Bernard, 75007 Paris, France
DAMOUR Thibaut	: Observatoire de Paris Meudon, G.A.R. 92190 Meudon, France
DERUELLE Nathalie	: Institut Henri Poincaré, 11 rue Pierre et Marie Curie 75005 Paris, France
DREVER Ronald	: Caltech, Department of Physics 130-33 Pasadena, California 91125 U.S.A. University of Glasgow, Natural Philosophy Department Glasgow, G12 8QQ U.K.
EARDLEY Douglas	: Center for Astrophysics, 60 Garden Street Cambridge, Massachusetts, 02138 U.S.A.
FITCHETT Michael	: Institute of Astronomy, Madingley Road, Cambridge, CB3 OHA, U.K.
FRIEDRICH Helmut	: Hochschule der Bundeswehr, Holstenhofweg 85, 2000 Hamburg 70, R.F.A.
FUSTERO Xavier	: Universitat Autonoma de Barcelona, Dept. de Fisica Teorica Bellaterra, Barcelona, Spain

FUTAMASE Toshifumi : Max Planck Inst. Für Physik und Astrophysik, Karl Schwarzschild Strasse 1, 8046 Garching bei München, R.F.A.

HAMILTON William : Louisiana State University, Dept. of Physics & Astronomy Baton Rouge, Louisiana, 70803 U.S.A.

HAUGAN Mark : Cornell University, Center for Radiophysics & Space Research Space Science Building, Ithaca, New York, 14853 U.S.A.

HELLINGS Ronald : Jet Propulsion Laboratory, 4800 Oak Drive Pasadena, California 91103 U.S.A.

HERELD Mark : Caltech, Department of Physics 130-33 Pasadena, California 91125 U.S.A

HOBILL David : Institut Henri Poincaré, 11 rue Pierre et Marie Curie 75005 Paris, France

HOROWITZ Garry : Institute for Advanced Study Princeton, 08540 New Jersey, U.S.A.

HOUGH James : University of Glasgow, Natural Philosophy Department Glasgow, G12 8QQ U.K.

ISAACSON Richard : National Science Foundation Washington, D.C. 20550 U.S.A.

ISRAEL Werner : University of Alberta, Department of Physics Edmonton, Alberta, T6G 2J1 Canada

KATES Ron : Max Planck Inst. für Physik und Astrophysik, Karl Schwarzschild Strasse 1, 8046 Garching bei München, R.F.A.

KRISHNASAMY Ilangkovan : University College, Dept. of Applied Mathematics & Astronomy P.O. BOX 78, Cardiff, CF1 1XL, U.K.

LUN Antony : Hong Kong Polytechnic, Dept. of Mathematic Studies Hung Hom, Kowloon, Hong Kong

MAN Nary : Université Paris Sud, Lab. de l'Horloge Atomique, Bât. 221 91405 Orsay, France

MANN Patrick : University of Oxford, Dept. of Astronomy, South Park Road Oxford, OX1 3RQ, U.K.

MASHHOON Bahram : Universität zu Köln, Institut für Theoretische Physik Zülpicher Strasse 77, 500 Köln 41, R.F.A.

MEERS Brian : University of Glasgow, Natural Philosophy Department Glasgow, G12 8QQ, U.K.

MICHELSON Peter : Stanford University, Department of Physics Stanford, California, 94305 U.S.A.

NAKAMURA Takashi : Kyoto University, Department of Physics 606 Kyoto, Japan

NARICI Livio : University of Rochester, Dept. of Physics & Astronomy River Campus Station, Rochester, New York 14627 U.S.A.

NEUHAUSER Dany : The Hebrew University, Racah Institute of Physics Jerusalem, Israël

PALLOTTINO Giovanni : Universita di Roma, IST. di Fisica G. Marconi Piazzale Aldo Moro 5, 00185 Roma, Italia

PAPAPETROU Achille : Institut Henri Poincaré, 11 rue Pierre et Marie Curie 75005 Paris, France

Piran Tsvi : The Hebrew University, Racah Institute of Physics Jerusalem, Israël
Institute for Advanced Study, Princeton, New Jersey 08540 U.S.A.

PORTILLA Miguel : Institut Henri Poincaré, 11 rue Pierre et Marie Curie 75005 Paris, France

REES Martin : Institute of Astronomy, Madingley Road Cambridge, CB3 OHA, U.K.

REULA Oscar : University of Chicago, Enrico Fermi Institute, 5630 Ellis Avenue Chicago, Illinois 60637 U.S.A.

RUIZ CARRERO Eduardo : Universidad de Salamanca, Dept. de Fisica Teorica Salamanca, Espana

SCHILLING Roland : Max Planck Inst. für Physik und Astrophysik, Karl Schwarzschild Strasse 1, 8046 Garching bei München, R.F.A.

SCHMIDT Bernd : Max Planck Inst. für Physik und Astrophysik, Karl Schwarzschild Strasse 1, 8046 Garching bei München, R.F.A.

SCHUMAKER Bonny : Caltech, Department of Theoretical Physics, Pasadena, California, 91125 U.S.A.

SCHUTZ Bernard : University College, Dept. of Applied Mathematics & Astronomy PO. BOX 78, Cardiff, CF1 1XL, U.K.

SHAW William : Mathematical Institute, 24-29 Saint Giles, Oxford, OX1 3LB, U.K.

STARK Richard : The Hebrew University, Racah Institute of Physics, Jerusalem, Israël

THORNE Kip : Caltech, Theoretical Astrophysics 130-33 Pasadena, California, 91125 U.S.A.

TOURRENC Philippe : Institut Henri Poincaré, 11 rue Pierre et Marie Curie 75005 Paris, France

UNRUH William : University of British Columbia, Dept. of Physics 2075 Wesbrook Mall, Vancouver, BC, V6T 2A6, Canada

VAN DER WOERD Hans : University of Amsterdam, Astronomical Institute, Roetersstraat 15 1018 WB Amsterdam, The Netherlands

VEITCH Peter : University of Western Australia, Department of Physics Nedlands, 6009, Western Australia

WALKER Martin : Max Planck Inst. für Physik und Astrophysik, Karl Schwarzschild Strasse 1, 8046 Garching bei München, R.F.A.

WARD Henry : University of Glasgow, Natural Philosophy Department, Glasgow, G12 8QQ, U.K.

YORK James : University of North Carolina, Dept. of Physics & Astronomy Phillips Hall 039 A, Chapel Hill, North Carolina 27514 U.S.A.

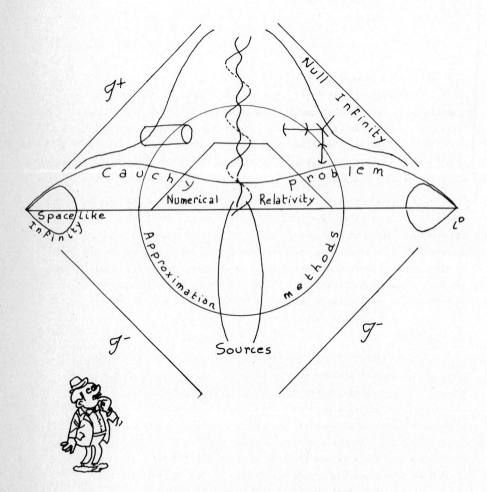

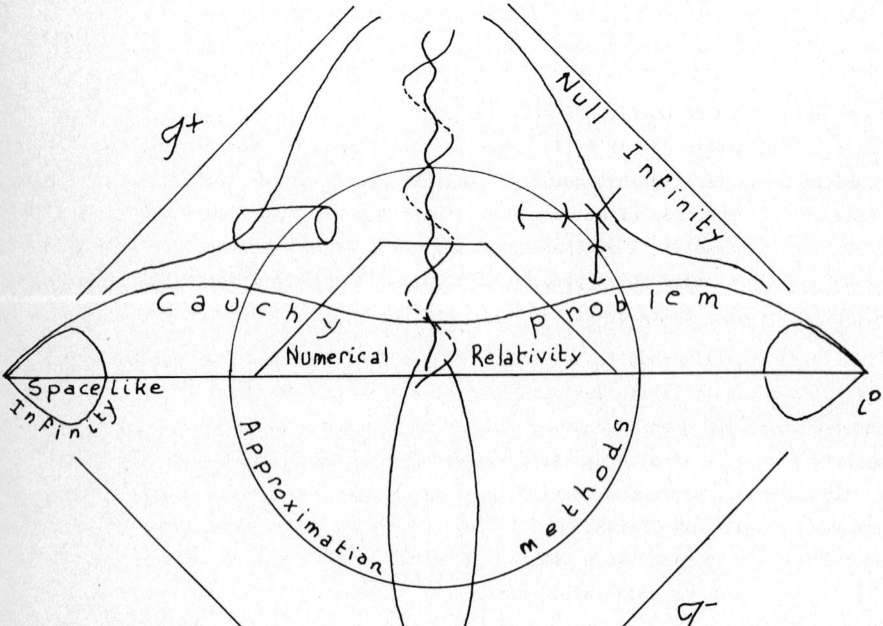

THE PATCHWORK OF GRAVITATIONAL RADIATION RESEARCH

INTRODUCTION

Einstein découvrit une solution radiative des équations du vide de la Relativité générale dès 1916 [1]. Mais il fallut près de quarante ans pour que le problème de la réalité physique des ondes gravitationnelles soit éclairci. N'étaient-elles pas qu'un simple effet de coordonnées comme le pensait Infeld [2] ? Quelle était leur vitesse si elle dépend de changements de coordonnées qui peuvent "se propager à la vitesse de la pensée" ainsi que l'a écrit Eddington [3] ? Transportaient-elles de l'énergie, et dans quel sens ?

La bataille pour la reconnaissance de l'existence du rayonnement gravitationnel s'acheva à la fin des années cinquante. Pour Hawking et Israël [4] l'année décisive fut 1962 quand "Bondi, Sachs, Newmann et Penrose, et leurs collaborateurs, montrèrent que la masse d'un système (mesurée à l'infini) devait décroître si le système émettait des ondes gravitationnelles". Mais trois ans plus tôt déjà, P. Bergmann pouvait dire lors de la clotûre de la conférence de Royaumont [5] : "C'est peut-être dans la discussion des ondes (gravitationnelles) que nous regrettons le plus l'absence de Leopold Infeld car il est presque le seul à affirmer qu'il n'y en a pas" [6].

Pour J. Weber c'était le moment d'aller de l'avant. En 1961 il écrivit[7]: "Considérons pour un instant le problème du point de vue d'un expérimentateur (...) Partons de l'hypothèse que les ondes gravitationnelles existent [et] (...) discutons d'abord du principe du dispositif de détection de telles ondes". Dans les années qui suivirent il établit les fondements théoriques décrivant l'intéraction d'une onde gravitationnelle et d'un détecteur [8-11] et, surtout, il construisit un détecteur. C'était là une attitude de pionnier. En effet, les ondes gravitationnelles ne pouvant être produites sur Terre à un niveau suffisant, il fallait les chercher dans le ciel. Or les connaissances théoriques sur les sources possibles étaient alors très minces et aucune source réaliste de rayonnement gravitationnel n'était même conçue.

Ce travail d'avant-garde fut cependant vite conforté par la découverte dans les années soixante d'une profusion de nouveaux objets astrophysiques comme les quasars, les pulsars et les sources de rayonnement X [12]. Il fut alors possible de concevoir des phénomènes aussi relativistes que les pulsations, l'accrétion ou la collision de trous noirs, que le collapse d'étoiles ou l'effondrement d'un système double d'étoiles à neutrons, phénomènes qui pouvaient être des sources importantes de rayonnement gravitationnel [13]. Ce fut une période d'enthousiasme pour la physique et l'astrophysique des objets collapsés et au début des années soixante-dix J. Weber annonça qu'il avait détecté des flux d'ondes gravitationnelles [14].

Cette nouvelle suscita une floraison de travaux astrophysiques sur les sources de rayonnement gravitationnel ainsi que la construction de la première génération de détecteurs opérant à la température ambiante. Il s'avéra alors que les flux détectés par J. Weber étaient beaucoup plus importants que ceux que l'on pouvait attendre des conceptions couramment admises en Astrophysique [15] et que les nouveaux détecteurs ne reproduisaient pas ses résultats [16].

Cette période s'acheva donc par la conviction que la détection des ondes gravitationnelles était une tâche bien plus ardue que ce que l'on pensait primitivement. Il devint aussi clair que l'étude de sources puissantes de rayonnement gravitationnel nécessitait la mise au point de modèles plus élaborés. Il fallait donc développer de nouveaux "outils" aussi bien théoriques qu'expérimentaux pour aboutir.

Ces dernières années apparaissent ainsi comme une période de maturation. Le but des expérimentateurs et des théoriciens n'est en effet plus tant de détecter des ondes gravitationnelles "sur le champ" que d'établir des bases solides à "l'astronomie des ondes gravitationnelles" à venir.

Dans le domaine expérimental le but est d'accroître la sensibilité des détecteurs de 6 à 8 ordres de grandeur. Les efforts n'ont pas été épargnés et une quinzaine de groupes se sont lancés dans l'entreprise. De nouvelles technologies ont été développées - dans le domaine des transducteurs et en cryogénie en particulier ; de nouveaux détecteurs ont été conçus - comme des interféromètres à laser ou des satellites suivis par effet Doppler ; et de nouveaux concepts ont même été introduits - comme la non-démolition quantique. Aucun de ces détecteurs de "seconde génération" n'est encore opérationnel mais on espère qu'ils le seront prochainement, malgré les innombrables difficultés auxquelles il faut faire face.

Sur le plan théorique l'objectif a été de concevoir et d'étudier des sources "réalistes" de rayonnement gravitationnel. Le domaine des modèles résolubles par des méthodes d'approximation analytiques ou semi-analytiques ayant été défriché, des méthodes numériques d'intégration des équations d'Einstein durent être développées, dans le but d'étudier des modèles de sources astrophysiques hautement dynamiques et asymétriques. Ceci implique non seulement la mise en oeuvre pratique de techniques de résolution de systèmes d'équations différentielles non-linéaires mais aussi, pour ce faire, une étude mathématique approfondie de la formulation des équations d'Einstein. Un tel programme inclut une analyse du problème aux valeurs initiales, la construction de systèmes de coordonnées d'espace-temps appropriés et l'étude de l'évolution du champ gravitationnel. Etant donné la somme de travail mathématique et théorique qui est ici en jeu, la "Relativité numérique", même si elle est devenue une branche de la Relativité générale à part entière, en est encore à ses débuts.

En Astrophysique enfin, les travaux ont surtout consisté d'une part à donner des limites plus précises à la fréquence et à l'efficacité des événements galactiques susceptibles de produire des ondes gravitationnelles et d'autre part à explorer les possibilités d'existence de sources extragalactiques susceptibles de produire un fond stochastique de rayonnement. La difficulté de telles estimations est considérable d'autant plus qu'aucune expérience franchement positive de détection ne vient guider les recherches.

La Physique réserve néanmoins d'agréables surprises. L'une d'elles fut la découverte en 1974 par Hulse et Taylor [17] du pulsar double PSR 1913+16. Qu'un système d'étoiles double doive rayonner de l'énergie gravitationnelle était connu depuis longtemps mais que l'effet sur le mouvement soit observable semblait hors de question. Or ce système de deux objets compacts s'avéra être un "laboratoire" idéal où tester la Relativité générale. Après cinq ans d'observations continues une diminution de la période orbitale du système fut mesurée [18], observation qui fut tout de suite interprétée comme la réaction sur le mouvement d'un rayonnement d'ondes gravitationnelles. Cependant des problèmes théoriques importants devaient être éclaircis avant de pouvoir affirmer que des ondes gravitationnelles avaient été, du moins indirectement, observées pour la première fois. En effet l'utilisation faite de la "formule du quadrupole" d'Einstein pour relier la diminution de période au rayonnement n'était pas, dans le cas considéré d'un système auto-gravitant, rigoureusement justifiée [19]. Cette découverte alimenta donc une controverse animée et permit d'éclaircir d'épineux problèmes théoriques restés dans l'ombre jusqu'alors.

Un autre événement marquant de ces dernières années, fut la preuve de la positivité de l'énergie gravitationnelle totale d'un système. Ce résultat assure qu'un système isolé ne peut rayonner plus d'énergie que sa masse au repos initiale. Si de nombreux arguments physiques simples soutenaient cette conjecture, une preuve rigoureuse manquait. Elle fut fournie récemment à partir de travaux de Schoen et Yau [20] ainsi que de Witten [21].

Au vu de ce résumé rapide de l'évolution et des développements des travaux sur le rayonnement gravitationnel, on ne peut s'empêcher de se poser la question : toutes ces recherches forment-elles encore un tout cohérent ? Ou bien se sont-elles éparpillées en une myriade de spécialités disjointes d'autant moins reliées au problème du rayonnement gravitationnel qu'aucune confirmation expérimentale directe concluante ne permet d'en resserrer l'éventail ?

Le but de l'école des Houches de 1982 sur le rayonnement gravitationnel fut par conséquent de "faire le point". Les cours consistèrent en revues approfondies des différentes branches de la Physique touchant au rayonnement gravitationnel, allant de l'étude du cadre mathématique et des modèles théoriques de sources à l'Astrophysique observationnelle et aux expériences de détection. Ils couvrirent donc un large éventail de sujets, non pas seulement dans le but de rendre compte des réalisations, problèmes et perspectives dans chaque branche mais aussi de mettre l'accent sur leurs interconnections, et les chaînons manquants le cas échéant. C'est aux participants de l'école et aux lecteurs de ces comptes-rendus de juger si cet objectif a été atteint ou non. A notre avis cependant les résultats qui furent présentés par les conférenciers et les discussions qui eurent lieu entre les participants ont montré que le but final n'a pas été oublié : "l'astronomie des ondes gravitationnelles" c'est-à-dire l'ouverture sur le ciel d'une fenêtre entièrement nouvelle. Comme le dit un participant : "Je travaille sur les "squids", tu travailles sur " $\mathcal{I}$ ", mais nous cherchons la même chose !".

*

* *

Ces comptes-rendus s'ouvrent sur une introduction à la théorie du rayonnement gravitationnel par K. Thorne qui résume les outils théoriques nécessaires pour aborder le sujet. Il présente une série de méthodes de calcul des ondes gravitationnelles émises par des sources astrophysiques et d'analyse de la propagation des ondes et de leur intéraction avec des détecteurs. Ces méthodes seront à la base de l'interprétation des ondes gravitationnelles lorsqu'elles auront été détectées.

T. Damour fait ensuite une revue approfondie du problème du rayonnement gravitationnel et du mouvement d'objets compacts. Cette contribution, où les équations du mouvement à l'ordre c^{-5} sont données pour la première fois, met fin à la controverse sur la "formule du quadrupole" d'Einstein qui fut soulevée par la découverte du pulsar double PSR 1913+16 (dont les propriétés sont rappelées par D. Eardley dans sa contribution). Les discussions animées qui entourèrent ces conférences ainsi que des approches parallèles sont résumées dans le rapport d'A. Ashtekar : "Les équations du mouvement : l'état de l'art".

Dans ses cours M. Walker décrit la structure asymptotique de l'espace-temps et présente une preuve de la positivité de la masse qui jusqu'à récemment n'était qu'une conjecture. Il montre que l'énergie-impulsion mesurée asymptotiquement à des temps retardés est orientée vers le futur et du genre temps. On savait que l'impulsion-énergie de Bondi-Sachs décroissait au cours du temps lorsque le système rayonne et il était certainement important de montrer qu'elle restait pointée vers le futur et du genre temps. Autrement il aurait fallu envisager la possibilité d'extraire une quantité infinie d'énergie d'un système isolé. Le problème de la définition de l'énergie gravitationnelle est considérée par Y. Choquet-Bruhat qui définit, dans deux situations différentes, une quantité positive conservée qui peut être interprétée comme l'énergie du champ gravitationnel. H. Friedrich examine la notion d'espace asymptotiquement vide et plat de Penrose qui sert de base aux discussions sur les champs asymptotiques. Il montre que non seulement elle permet de traiter l'infini isotrope en termes de géométrie différentielle locale mais aussi de discuter l'existence de solutions des équations de champ d'Einstein du vide, régulières à l'infini isotrope, en résolvant des problèmes aux valeurs initiales locaux.

J. York fait une revue de l'approche dynamique ou "trois plus un" de la théorie d'Einstein. Cette approche qui consiste à considérer la Relativité générale comme une théorie dynamique de la gravitation dans laquelle on dispose d'une surface de données initiales, d'équations de contraintes sur les données et d'équations d'évolution, fournit le cadre mathématique nécessaire pour résoudre numériquement les équations d'Einstein. La "Relativité numérique" est ensuite présentée par T. Piran qui insiste sur les problèmes techniques et théoriques auxquels il faut faire face ainsi que sur les résultats déjà obtenus ou auxquels on peut s'attendre dans un avenir proche. Le problème du choix d'une jauge appropriée lorsqu'on traite numériquement l'émission de rayonnement gravitationnel par des objets compacts est considérée par J. Bardeen. T. Nakamura présente des résultats numériques décrivant le collapse d'étoiles supermassives et d'étoiles en rotation.

D. Eardley, dans ses cours sur les modèles théoriques de sources de rayonnement gravitationnel, présente les résultats les plus récents concernant le collapse des noyaux stellaires en étoiles à neutrons ou trous noirs et l'émission d'ondes gravitationnelles par les étoiles à neutrons ou les trous noirs une fois qu'ils sont formés ainsi que par des systèmes binaires (dont le pulsar double PSR 1913+16). M. Rees, dans sa revue des sources extragalactiques de rayonnement gravitationnel, se montre pessimiste en ce qui concerne la possibilité de détecter des ondes gravitationnelles en provenance des noyaux galactiques. Il montre en revanche que si la majeure partie de la masse "invisible" de l'Univers est constituée d'étoiles massives de la "population III", un fond stochastique devrait alors exister qui pourrait être détectable.

Enfin, l'état de l'art dans le domaine expérimental est traité extensivement.

La catégorie des antennes coupléesélectromagnétiquement est étudiée par R. Drever qui décrit les prototypes actuels d'interféromètres à laser. R. Hellings montre comment le suivi par effet Doppler d'un vaisseau spatial pourrait donner des informations sur la partie à basses fréquences du spectre gravitationnel et A. Brillet et P. Tourrenc, dans la perspective de définir un projet de construction d'une antenne à large bande, comparent les interféromètres actifs et passifs et examinent les techniques de détection spectroscopique. La catégorie des antennes couplées acoustiquement d'autre part est traitée de façon approfondie par D. Blair et V. Braginski. P. Michelson fait un rapport sur le détecteur d'ondes gravitationnelles à basse température de l'Université de Stanford où une sensiblilité de 10^{-18} a été atteinte, ce qui est le meilleur résultat obtenu à ce jour. Quelques aspects théoriques de ces expériences sont considérés par B. Carter qui présente une analyse rigoureuse de l'interaction d'une onde gravitationnelle avec un milieu solide élastique et par W. Unruh qui décrit un aspect de la barrière de non-démolition quantique qui attend les expérimentateurs.

⁂

Cette école d'été des Houches n'aurait pas été possible sans l'impulsion initiale et les nombreux conseils de Cécile de Witt et sans l'aide constante de Marie-Thérèse Béal-Monod ainsi que de Daniel Thoulouze et André Landesman.

Essentiel également fut le support financier de la Division des Affaires Scientifiques de l'OTAN (qui inclut cette session dans son programme d'Instituts d'Etude Avancée), de l'Université Scientifique et Médicale de Grenoble et du CNRS.

Nous remercions également Nicole Coiffier et Annie Battendier pour leur rôle dans l'administration de la session ainsi qu'Henri Coiffier et son équipe pour s'être occupés de nos problèmes matériels.

Nous tenons enfin à remercier les conférenciers pour les nombreuses heures passées à préparer leurs cours et leurs manuscrits qui, nous l'espérons, feront de ce livre un outil utile à la communauté scientifique.

Nathalie Deruelle

N.B. : Références en page xx.

INTRODUCTION

Einstein discovered a radiative solution of the vacuum equations of general relativity as early as 1916 [1]. However it took about fourty years before the problem of the physical reality of gravitational waves could be settled. Were they anything more than a mere coordinate effect as Infeld thought they were [2] ? What was their speed if it may be affected by coordinate changes that we can "propagate" with "the speed of thought" as Eddington put it [3] ? Were they carrying energy, and in what sense ?

The battle for the recognition of the existence of gravitational waves was over in the late fifties. Hawking and Israël [4] put the landmark in 1962 when "Bondi, Sachs, Newmann and Penrose, and their collaborators, showed that the mass of a system (measured at infinity) would decrease if the system emitted gravitational waves". However, already three years earlier, P. Bergmann could say in his concluding remarks of the conference held in Royaumont [5] : "Perhaps at no point do we feel the absence of Leopold Infeld as keenly as we do in the discussion of (gravitational) waves, where he is almost the only worker who insists that there are not any" [6].

To J. Weber the time was ripe to go forward. In 1961 he wrote [7] : "Let us for a moment consider the problem from the standpoint of an experimentalist. (...) Proceed on the assumption that there are gravitational waves [and] (...) discuss first the theory of apparatus to detect the presence of such waves". In the following years he laid down the theoretical foundations describing the interaction of a gravitational wave and a detector [8-11] but, moreover, he also built a detector. This was a pioneering attitude. Indeed strong gravitational waves cannot be produced on Earth so one must look for them in the sky. Now the theoretical knowledge about possible sources was then very scarce and no realistic source of gravitational radiation was even conceived.

This pioneering work was however soon backed up by the discovery in the sixties of a wealth of new astrophysical objects such as quasars, pulsars and binary X-ray sources [12]. It was then possible to conceive highly relativistic events such as pulsating, accreating or colliding black holes, collapsing stars or merging neutron stars binaries which could be strong sources of gravitational radiation [13]. In this period of enthusiasm for the physics and astrophysics of collapsed objects J. Weber announced in the early seventies that he had detected fluxes of gravitational waves [14].

This news led to a wave of work on the gravitational radiation from astrophysical sources and to the construction of the first generation of (room temperature) detectors. It turned out that Weber's event rate was much larger than expected from current astrophysical ideas [15] and was not reproduced by the new detectors [16].

This period ended then with the realization that the detection of gravitational waves was a much more difficult task than what was originally expected. It also became clear that in order to study strong sources of gravitational radiation more elaborate models had to be worked out. This meant that new experimental, as well as theoretical tools had to be developped in order to succeed.

The recent years then appear as a period of maturation. The aim of the experimentalists and the theoreticians is indeed no longer to detect gravitational waves "right away" but rather to lay down sound basis for the "gravitational wave astronomy" to come.

In the experimental domain the goal is to increase the sensitivity of the detectors by 6 to 8 orders of magnitude. Efforts have not been spared and about fifteen groups have embarked in this task. New technologies, like squids and large cryogenic systems, are developped ; new detectors, like laser interferometers and spacecraft doppler tracking are designed, and even new physical concepts, like quantum non-demolition, are considered. None of these second generation detectors is yet operational but it is expected that they will soon be, in spite of the tremendous difficulties that must be faced.

In the theoretical domain the objective was to conceive and study "realistic" sources of gravitational radiation. The array of models that can be solved by analytic or semi-analytic approximation methods being explored, numerical methods for integrating Einstein's equations had to be developped, in order to study highly dynamical and asymmetric astrophysical sources. This implies not only the setting of practical techniques for solving non-linear differential equations but also a careful mathematical analysis of the formulation of Einstein's equations for this purpose. This includes an analysis of the initial value problem, the construction of suitable space-time coordinate systems and the evolution of the gravitational field. In view of the mathematical and theoretical work involved, "Numerical Relativity", although it has become a branch of general relativity in its own right, is still in its infancy.

In Astrophysics finally, the work mainly consisted in setting more precise limits to the galactic event rate and to examine extragalactic sources which, if they exist, would produce a stochastic background of gravitational radiation. Such estimates are all the more difficult as no really positive detection experiment is here to lead the research.

Physics however has its good surprises. The discovery by Hulse and Taylor [17] of the binary pulsar PSR 1913+16 was one of these. That a binary system should radiate gravitational energy had been known for a long time but the observability of this effect seemed out of the question. Now it turned out that this system of two compact objects was a perfect "laboratory" for testing general relativity. After five years of continuous observations a decrease in the orbital period of the system was measured [18]. This was immediately interpreted as the back action on the motion by the gravitational radiation emitted by the system. However, serious theoretical problems had to be cleared up before being sure that the existence of gravitational radiation had been, at least indirectly, shown for the first time. Indeed the use of the Einstein "quadrupole formula" to link the decrease of the period to the radiation had not been fully justified in this case of a self-gravitating system [19]. This discovery therefore gave rise to a lively controversy and helped to clear up difficult unsolved problems.

Another prominent issue of the recent years was the proof of the positivity of the total gravitational energy. This result ensures that an isolated system cannot radiate more energy than its initial rest mass. Simple physical arguments supported this conjecture. However a rigourous proof was given only recently, based on work by Shoen and Yau [20] and by Witten [21].

In view of this brief summary of the evolution and developments of research on gravitational radiation, one cannot help asking the question : is all the research work still forming a coherent whole ? Has it not scattered into a myriad of disjoint specialities all the less related to the problem of gravitational radiation as it is not restricted by any concluding and direct experimental detection ?

The aim of the 1982 les Houches school on gravitational radiation was therefore to survey the current state of the field and to "determine the ship's position". It consisted of thorough reviews of the different branches of physics concerned with gravitational radiation including the mathematical framework, theoretical models of sources, observational astrophysics and experimental detection schemes. It therefore covered a wide range of subjects not only in order to review the achievements, problems and prospects in each branch but also to emphasize the interconnections and the missing links, should the occasion arise. It is up to the participants of the school and the readers of these proceedings to judge whether this goal was fulfilled or not. In our opinion however, the results which were presented by the lecturers and the discussions which took place among the participants show that the final objective has not been forgotten : "gravitational wave astronomy" that is the opening of an entirely new window to the sky. As one of the participants put it : "I'm working on "squids" ; you're working on " $\mathscr{I}$ " ; still we are looking for the same thing !".

⁂

These proceedings start with K. Thorne's introduction to the theory of gravitational radiation which summarizes the theoretical tools one needs to approach the subject. He presents various methods for calculating gravitational waves emitted by astrophysical sources and for analysing the propagation of the waves and their interaction with detectors. These methods will be essential for interpreting gravitational waves when they are detected.

Then T. Damour make a comprehensive review of the problem of the gravitational radiation and the motion of compact bodies. This contribution, where the equations of motion up to order c^{-5} are given for the first time, clears up the controversy about Einstein's "quadrupole formula" which arose after the discovery of the binary pulsar PSR 1913+16 (whose properties are reviewed by D. Eardley in his contribution). The lively discussions that followed these lectures and alternative approaches are summarized in A. Ashtekar's report : "the equations of motion, the state of the art".

M. Walker in his lectures describes the asymptotic structure of space-time and presents a proof of the positive mass conjecture. He shows that the energy-momentum measured asymptotically at retarded times is future directed and time-like. The Bondi-Sachs energy-momentum was known to decrease in time when the system radiates and it was indeed important to show that it remained future directed and time-like. Otherwise one would have had to face the possibility of extracting an infinite amount of energy from an isolated system. The problem of defining the gravitational energy is considered by Y. Choquet-Bruhat who defines, in two different situations, a positive conserved quantity that can be considered as the energy of the gravitational field. H. Friedrich investigates the appropriatness of Penrose's notion of asymptotically flat and empty space which is the basis for the discussion of far fields. He shows that it not only allows to investigate null infinity in terms of local differential geometry but also to discuss the existence of solutions of Einstein's vacuum field equations which have a smooth structure at null infinity by solving local initial value problems.

J. York gives a review of the dynamical or "three plus one" approach to Einstein's theory. This approach consists in considering general relativity as a dynamical theory of gravitation in which one is given an initial data surface, constraints equations on the data and evolution equations. It so provides us with the mathematical framework one needs for solving numerically Einstein's equations. "Numerical relativity" is then presented by T. Piran who emphasizes the technical and theoretical problems to be faced and the results already obtained or to be expected in a near future. The problem of choosing a suitable gauge when treating numerically the emission of gravitational radiation by compact sources is considered by J. Bardeen. T. Nakamura exhibits numerical results describing the collapse of supermassive stars and rotating stars.

D. Eardley, in his lectures on the theoretical models of sources of gravitational radiation presents up-to-date results about the collapse of stellar cores to neutron stars or black holes and the emission of gravitational radiation by already formed neutron stars and black holes as well as by binary systems (including the binary pulsar PSR 1913+16). M. Rees, in his review of extragalactic sources is pessimistic about the possibility of the detection of gravitational radiation from galactic nuclei. On the other hand he shows that if most of the "unseen" mass of the universe consists in massive "population III" stars, a stochastic background of radiation should then exist, which could be detectable.

Finally the state of the art in the experimental domain is thoroughly reviewed. The class of electromagnetically coupled antennae is treated by R. Drever who describes the existing laser interferometers prototypes. R. Hellings shows how a deep-space doppler tracking of spacecraft could give some information on the low frequency part of the gravitational wave spectrum and A. Brillet and P. Tourrenc, with the idea of proposing a wideband antenna, compare active and passive interferometers and evaluate spectroscopic detection techniques. The class of acoustically coupled antennae on the other hand is treated extensively by D. Blair and V. Braginski. P. Michelson reports on the low temperature gravitational wave detector at Stanford University, where a dimensionless strain sensitivity of 10^{-18} has been achieved, the best result at present. Some theoretical aspects of these experiments are considered by B. Carter who presents a rigorous analysis of the interaction of a gravitational wave with an elastic solid medium and by W. Unruh who describes one aspect of the quantum non-demolition barrier awaiting for the experimentalists.

⁂

This les Houches summer school would not have been possible without the initial impulse and the numerous advices of Cécile de Witt and without the constant help from Marie-Thérèse Béal-Monod as well as Daniel Thoulouze and André Landesman.

Essential too was the financial support from the NATO Scientific Affairs Division (which included the session in its Advanced Study Institutes Programme), from the Université Scientifique et Médicale de Grenoble and from the CNRS.

We also acknowledge the rôle of Nicole Coiffier and Annie Battendier in the administration of the session as well as Henri Coiffier and his staff for looking after our material needs.

Finally we thank the lecturers for the many hours which went into the preparation of their lectures and their manuscripts, which we hope will make the present volume a useful instrument for the scientific community.

Nathalie Deruelle

References :

[1] A. Einstein, Sitzker. Preuss. Akad. Wiss., p. 688 (1916) ; p. 154 (1918).

[2] L. Infeld, A. Plebanski, "Motion and Relativity", Pergamon (1960).

[3] A. Eddington, "The Mathematical Theory of Relativity", Cambridge Press (1923).

[4] "General relativity, an Einstein centenary survey", S. Hawking, W. Israël edts, Cambridge Press (1979).

[5] "Les théories relativistes de la gravitation", edts CNRS (1962).

[6] Note however that Infeld subsequently changed his positions.

[7] "Evidence for gravitational theories", Proceedings of the 1961 Varenna School, Møller edt, Academic Press (1962).

[8] J. Weber, Gravity research Foundation Prize essays (New Boston, N.H. April 1958 and April 1959).

[9] J. Weber, Phys. Rev., 117, 306 (1960).

[10] J. Weber, "General relativity and gravitational waves", N.Y. (1961).

[11] J. Weber in the proceedings of the 1963 les Houches school on "Relativity Groups and Topology", de Witt Edts, N.Y. (1964).

[12] For a review of these discoveries, cf. e.g. the proceedings of the 1975 Varenna school on "Physics and astrophysics of neutron stars and black holes", R. Giacconi, R. Ruffini Edts, North Holland (1978).

[13] For a review of the sources of gravitational radiation conceived in the early seventies, cf. e.g. the proceedings of the 1972 les Houches summer school on "Black holes", de Witt edts, North Holland (1973) or "Gravitation", Misner, Thorne et Wheeler, Freeman San Francisco (1973).

[14] J. Weber, Phys. Rev. Lett., 22, 1320 (1969).

[15] See e.g. "Black holes, gravitational waves and cosmology", M. Rees, R. Ruffini, J. Wheeler, Gordon Breach edts (1974).

[16] A few examples of coincidences have however since be reported. See e.g. V. Ferrari et al., Phys. Rev. D25, 2471 (1982) and J. Weber in "General Relativity and Gravitation", A. Held edt, Plenum Press (1980), vol. II, p. 435.

[17] R. Hulse and J. Taylor, Astrophys. J., 195, L51 (1975).

[18] J.H. Taylor, L.A. Fowler, P.M. McCulloch, Nature, 277, 437 (1979).

[19] See e.g. J. Ehlers, A. Rosenblum, J. Goldberg, P. Havas, Astrophys. J., 208, L77 (1976).

[20] R. Schoen, S.T. Yau, Comm. Math. Phys., 65, 45 (1979).

[21] E. Witten, Comm. Math. Phys., 80, 381 (1981).

THE THEORY OF GRAVITATIONAL RADIATION: AN INTRODUCTORY REVIEW*

KIP S. THORNE

California Institute of Technology, Pasadena, California
and
Institute for Theoretical Physics, University of California, Santa Barbara

TABLE OF CONTENTS

*Supported in part by the National Science Foundation [AST79-22012 and PHY77-27084].

1. INTRODUCTION AND OVERVIEW

1.1 The nature of these lectures

These lectures are an introduction to and a progress report on the effort to bring gravitational-wave theory into a form suitable for astrophysical studies — a form for use in the future, when waves have been detected and are being interpreted. I will not describe all aspects of this effort. Several of the most important aspects will be covered by other lecturers, elsewhere in this volume. These include the computation of waves from models of specific astrophysical sources (lectures of Eardley); the techniques of numerical relativity — our only way of computing waves from high-speed, strong-gravity, large-amplitude sources (lectures of York and Piran); and a full analysis of radiation reaction and other relativistic effects in binary systems such as the binary pulsar — our sole source today of quantitative observational data on the effects of gravitational waves (lectures of Damour).

My own lectures will provide a sort of framework for those of Eardley, York and Piran, and Damour: I shall present the mathematical description of gravitational waves in a form suitable for astrophysical applications (§2); I shall describe a variety of methods for computing the gravitational waves emitted by astrophysical sources (§3); I shall describe methods for analyzing the propagation of waves from their sources, through our lumpy universe, to earth (§2); and I shall describe methods of analyzing the interaction of gravitational waves with earth-based and solar-system-based detectors (§4). Here and there in my lectures I shall sketch derivations of the methods of analysis and of the formulas presented; but in most places I shall simply refer the reader to derivations elsewhere in the literature and/or pose the derivations as exercises for the reader.

1.2 What is a gravitational wave?

A gravitational wave is a ripple in the curvature of spacetime, which propagates with the speed of light (Fig. 1). In the real universe gravitational waves propagate on the back of a large-scale, slowly changing spacetime curvature created by the universe's lumpy, cosmological distribution of matter. The background curvature is characterized, semiquantitatively, by two length scales

$$\mathcal{R} \equiv \begin{pmatrix}\text{radius of curvature}\\ \text{of background spacetime}\end{pmatrix} \equiv \begin{vmatrix}\text{typical component } R_{\hat\alpha\hat\beta\hat\gamma\hat\delta} \text{ of Rieman}\\ \text{tensor of background in a local Lorentz frame}\end{vmatrix}^{-\frac{1}{2}} ,$$

$$\mathcal{L} \equiv \begin{pmatrix}\text{inhomogeneity scale of}\\ \text{background curvature}\end{pmatrix} \equiv \begin{pmatrix}\text{length scale on which}\\ R_{\hat\alpha\hat\beta\hat\gamma\hat\delta} \text{ varies}\end{pmatrix} \lesssim \mathcal{R} \, ; \tag{1.1}$$

and the gravitational waves are characterized by one length scale

$$\lambdabar \equiv \begin{pmatrix}\text{reduced wavelength of}\\ \text{gravitational waves}\end{pmatrix} = \frac{1}{2\pi} \times (\text{wavelength } \lambda). \tag{1.2}$$

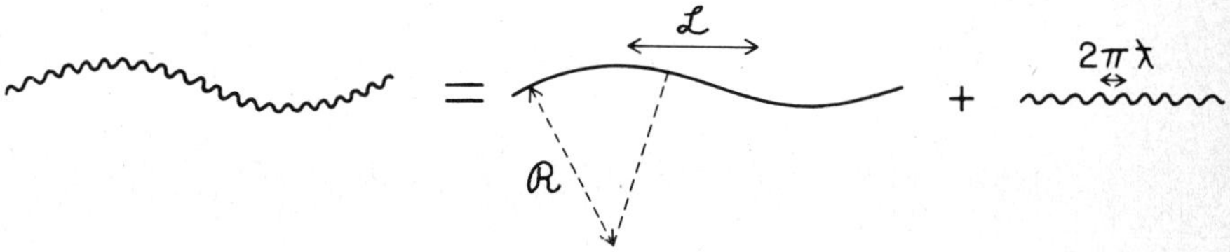

Fig. 1 A heuristic embedding diagram for the decomposition of curve spacetime into a background spacetime plus gravitational waves.

(Of course $\bar{\lambda}$, $\mathcal{L}$, and $\mathcal{R}$ are not precisely defined; they depend on one's choice of coordinates or reference frame. But in typical astrophysical situations there are preferred frames — e.g. the "asymptotic rest frame" of the source of the waves, or the "mean local rest frame" of nearby galaxies; and these permit $\bar{\lambda}$, $\mathcal{L}$, and $\mathcal{R}$ to be defined with adequate precision for astrophysical discussion.) The separation of spacetime curvature into a background part $R^{(B)}_{\alpha\beta\gamma\delta}$ and a wave part $R^{(W)}_{\alpha\beta\gamma\delta}$ depends critically on the inequality

$$\bar{\lambda} \ll \mathcal{L}. \tag{1.3}$$

The waves are the part that varies on the lengthscale $\bar{\lambda}$; the background is the part that varies on the scale $\mathcal{L}$; the separation is impossible if $\bar{\lambda} \sim \mathcal{L}$. See Figure 1.

In constructing the theory of gravitational waves one typically expands the equations of general relativity in powers of $\bar{\lambda}/\mathcal{L}$ and $\bar{\lambda}/\mathcal{R}$. In the real universe these expansions constitute perturbation theory of the background spacetime (these lectures and that of Yvonne Choquet). In an idealized universe consisting of a source surrounded by vacuum (so that $\mathcal{L} \equiv r$ = distance to source) these expansions constitute "asymptotic analyses of spacetime structure near future timelike infinity $\mathscr{I}^+$" (lectures of Martin Walker).

1.3 Regions of space around a source of gravitational waves

I shall characterize any source of gravitational waves, semiquantitatively, by the following length scales as measured in the source's "asymptotic rest frame".

$$L \equiv \begin{pmatrix}\text{size of}\\ \text{source}\end{pmatrix} = \begin{pmatrix}\text{radius of region inside which the stress-energy } T^{\alpha\beta}\\ \text{and all black-hole horizons are contained}\end{pmatrix},$$

$$2M \equiv \begin{pmatrix}\text{gravitational}\\ \text{radius of source}\end{pmatrix} = \begin{pmatrix}2\times\text{mass of source in}\\ \text{units where } G=c=1\end{pmatrix},$$

$$\bar{\lambda} \equiv (\text{reduced wavelength of the waves emitted}), \tag{1.4}$$

$$\left.\begin{array}{l} r_I \equiv (\text{inner radius of local wave zone}) \\ r_O \equiv (\text{outer radius of local wave zone}) \end{array}\right\} \text{(see below).}$$

Corresponding to these length scales, I shall divide space around a source into the following regions (Fig. 2):

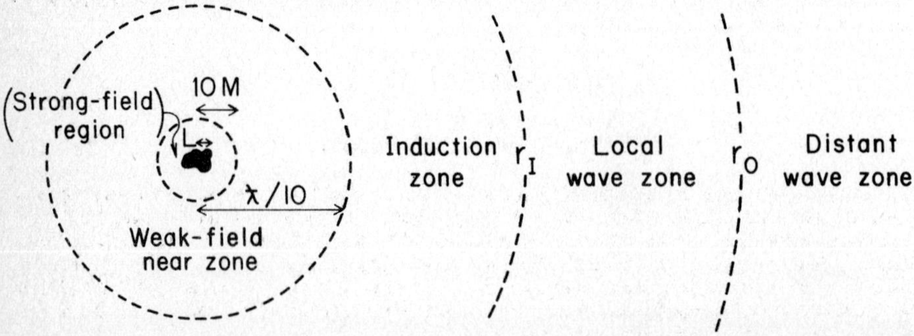

Fig. 2 Regions of space around a source of gravitational waves.

$$
\begin{array}{ll}
\text{Source:} & r \lesssim L, \\
\text{Strong-field region:} & r \lesssim 10\,M \text{ if } 10\,M \gtrsim L, \\
 & \text{typically does not exist if } L \gg 10\,M, \\
\text{Weak-field near zone:} & L < r,\ 10\,M < r < \lambda\!\!\!^{-}/10, \\
\text{Induction zone:} & L < r,\ \lambda\!\!\!^{-}/10 < r < r_I \\
\text{Local wave zone:} & r_I < r < r_O \\
\text{Distant wave zone:} & r_O < r.
\end{array}
\tag{1.5}
$$

Although Figure 2 suggests the lengthscale ordering $L < 10\,M < \lambda\!\!\!^{-}/10$, no such ordering will be assumed in these lectures. Thus, we might have $\lambda\!\!\!^{-} \gg L$ and M ("slow-motion source"), or $\lambda\!\!\!^{-} \ll L$ and M (high-frequency waves from some small piece of a big source; weak field near zone does not exist), or $\lambda\!\!\!^{-} \sim L$ or M; and we might have $L \gg M$ or perhaps $L \sim M$.

At radius r outside the source $(r > L)$ the background curvature due to the source has lengthscales

$$\mathcal{R}_s \simeq (r^3/M)^{\frac{1}{2}} \quad , \quad \mathcal{L}_s \simeq r. \tag{1.6}$$

Consequently, the dynamically changing part of the curvature can be regarded as "gravitational waves" (i.e. has $\lambda\!\!\!^{-} \ll \mathcal{L}$) only in the "wave zone" $r \gg \lambda\!\!\!^{-}$. I split the wave zone up into two parts, the local wave zone and the distant wave zone, so as to facilitate a clean separation of two mathematical problems: the generation of waves by the source, and the propagation of those waves through the lumpy, real universe to earth. The local wave zone $(r_I \lesssim r \lesssim r_O)$ will serve as a matching region for the two problems: the theory of wave generation will cover the local wave zone and all regions interior to it; the theory of wave propagation will cover the local wave zone and its exterior.

To facilitate the matching I shall choose r_I and r_O in such a manner that throughout the local wave zone the background curvature can be ignored and the background metric can thus be approximated as that of flat Minkowskii spacetime. More specifically, the inner edge of the local wave zone (r_I) is the location at which one or more of the following effects becomes important: (i) the waves cease to be waves and become a near-zone field, i.e., r becomes $\lesssim \lambda\!\!\!^{-}$; (ii) the gravitational pull of the source produces a significant red shift, i.e., r becomes $\sim 2M$ = (Schwarzschild radius of source); (iii) the background curvature produced by the source distorts the wave fronts and backscatters the waves significantly, i.e., $(r^3/M)^{1/2}$ becomes $\lesssim \lambda\!\!\!^{-}$; (iv) the outer limits of the source itself are encountered, i.e., r becomes $\lesssim L$ = (size of source). Thus, the inner edge of the local wave zone is given by

$$
\begin{aligned}
r_I &= \alpha \times \max\{\lambda\!\!\!^{-}, 2M, (M\lambda\!\!\!^{-2})^{1/3}, L\}\,, \\
\alpha &\equiv \begin{pmatrix} \text{some suitable number} \\ \text{large compared to unity} \end{pmatrix}.
\end{aligned}
\tag{1.7}
$$

The outer edge of the local wave zone r_O is the location at which one or more of the following effects becomes important: (i) a significant phase shift has been produced by the "M/r" gravitational field of the source, i.e., $(M/\lambda\!\!\!^{-}) \times \ln(r/r_I)$ is no longer $\ll \pi$; (ii) the background curvature due to nearby masses or due to the external universe perturbs the propagation of the waves, i.e., r is no longer $\ll \mathcal{R}_u$ = (background radius of curvature of universe). Thus, the outer edge of the local wave zone is given by

$$r_O = \min[r_I \exp(\lambdabar/\beta M),\ \mathcal{R}_u/\gamma],$$
$$\beta,\gamma = \begin{pmatrix}\text{some suitable numbers}\\ \text{large compared to unity}\end{pmatrix}. \tag{1.8}$$

Of course, we require that our large numbers α,β,γ be adjusted so that the thickness of the local wave zone is very large compared to the reduced wavelength:

$$r_O - r_I \gg \lambdabar\ . \tag{1.9}$$

In complex situations the location of the local wave zone might not be obvious. Consider, for example, a neutron star passing very near a supermassive black hole. The tidal pull of the hole sets the neutron star into oscillation, and the star's oscillations produce gravitational waves [Mashhoon (1973); Turner (1977)]. If the hole is large enough, or if the star is far enough from it, there may exist a local wave zone around the star which does not also enclose the entire hole. Of greater interest — because more radiation will be produced — is the case where the star is very near the hole and the hole is small enough ($M_h \lesssim 100\ M_\odot$) to produce large-amplitude oscillations, and perhaps even disrupt the star. In this case, before the waves can escape the influence of the star, they get perturbed by the background curvature of the hole. One must then consider the entire star-hole system as the source, and construct a local wave zone that surrounds them both.

* * * * *

Exercise 1. Convince yourself that for all astrophysical sources except the big-bang singularity (e.g., for the neutron-star/black-hole source of the last paragraph) α, β, and γ can be so chosen as to make condition (1.9) true.

1.4 Organization of these lectures; Notation and conventions

Section 2 of these lectures will discuss the propagation of gravitational waves from the local wave zone out through our lumpy universe to the earth. Section 3 will discuss the generation of gravitational waves, including their propagation into the local wave zone where they can be matched onto the propagation theory of Section 2. Section 4 will discuss the detection of gravitational waves on earth and in the solar system.

My notation and conventions are those of Misner, Thorne, and Wheeler (1973) (cited henceforth as "MTW"): I use geometrized units ($c = G = 1$); Greek indices range from 0 to 3 (time and space), Latin indices from 1 to 3 (space only); the metric signature is +2; $\eta_{\alpha\beta} \equiv \mathrm{diag}(-1,1,1,1)$ is the Minkowskii metric; $\epsilon_{\alpha\beta\gamma\delta}$ and ϵ_{ijk} are the spacetime and space Levi-Civita tensors with $\epsilon_{0123} > 0$ in a right-hand-oriented basis; and the signs of the Riemann, Ricci, Einstein, and stress-energy tensors are given by

$$R^{\alpha}{}_{\beta\gamma\delta} = \Gamma^{\alpha}{}_{\beta\delta,\gamma} - \Gamma^{\alpha}{}_{\beta\gamma,\delta} + \text{"}\Gamma\Gamma\text{"} - \text{"}\Gamma\Gamma\text{"}\ , \qquad R_{\alpha\beta} \equiv R^{\mu}{}_{\alpha\mu\beta}\ ,$$
$$G_{\alpha\beta} \equiv R_{\alpha\beta} - \tfrac{1}{2} R g_{\alpha\beta} = 8\pi\, T_{\alpha\beta}\ , \qquad T^{00} > 0\ . \tag{1.10}$$

Much of the viewpoint embodied in these lectures I have adopted or developed since 1972 when Misner, Wheeler and I completed MTW. However, many of the new aspects of my viewpoint are contained in my 1975 Erice lectures (Thorne 1977) and/or in a recent Reviews of Modern Physics article (Thorne 1980a; cited henceforth as "RMP").

2. THE PROPAGATION OF GRAVITATIONAL WAVES

2.1 Gravitational waves in metric theories of gravity: Description and propagation speed

Gravitational waves are not unique to Einstein's theory of gravity. They must exist in any theory which incorporates some sort of local Lorentz invariance into its gravitational laws. Many such theories have been invented; see, e.g., Will (1982) for examples and references.

Among the alternative theories of gravity there is a wide class — the so-called "metric theories" — whose members are so similar to general relativity that a discussion of their gravitational waves brings the waves of Einstein's theory into clearer perspective. Thus, I shall initiate my discussion of wave propagation within the framework of an arbitrary metric theory, and then shall specialize to Einstein's general relativity.

A metric theory of gravity is a theory (i) in which gravity is characterized, at least in part, by a 4-dimensional, symmetric spacetime metric $g_{\alpha\beta}$ of signature +2; and (ii) in which the Einstein equivalence principle is satisfied — i.e., all the nongravitational laws of physics take on their standard special relativistic forms in the local Lorentz frames of $g_{\alpha\beta}$ (aside from familiar complications of "curvature coupling"; chapter 16 of MTW).

Examples of metric theories are: general relativity [$g_{\alpha\beta}$ is the sole gravitational field]; the Dicke-Brans-Jordan theory (e.g., Dicke 1964) [contains a scalar gravitational field Φ in addition to $g_{\alpha\beta}$; matter generates Φ via a curved-spacetime wave equation; then Φ and the matter jointly generate $g_{\alpha\beta}$ via Einstein-like field equations]; and Rosen's (1973) theory [a "bimetric" theory with a flat metric $\eta_{\alpha\beta}$ in addition to the physical metric $g_{\alpha\beta}$; the matter generates $g_{\alpha\beta}$ via a flat-spacetime wave equation whose characteristics are null lines of $\eta_{\alpha\beta}$]. See Will (1982) for further details, references, and other examples.

The Einstein equivalence principle guarantees that in any metric theory, as in general relativity, freely falling test particles move along geodesics of $g_{\alpha\beta}$, and that the separation vector ξ^α between two nearby test particles (separation $\ll$ $\lambda\!\!\!^{-}$) is governed by the equation of geodesic deviation:

$$D^2\xi^\alpha/d\tau^2 + R^\alpha{}_{\beta\gamma\delta}\, u^\beta\, \xi^\gamma\, u^\delta = 0 \,. \tag{2.1a}$$

Here u^α is the 4-velocity of one of the test particles; τ is proper time measured by that particle;

$$D^2\xi^\alpha/d\tau^2 \equiv (\xi^\alpha{}_{;\beta}\, u^\beta)_{;\gamma}\, u^\gamma \tag{2.1b}$$

is the relative acceleration of the particles; and $R^\alpha{}_{\beta\gamma\delta}$ is the Riemann curvature tensor associated with $g_{\alpha\beta}$. Throughout Sections 2 (wave propagation) and 3 (wave generation) I shall use geodesic deviation and the Riemann tensor to characterize the physical effects of gravitational waves. Only in Section 4 (wave detection) will I discuss other physical effects of waves.

The Riemann tensor $R_{\alpha\beta\gamma\delta}$ contains two parts: background curvature and wave curvature

$$R_{\alpha\beta\gamma\delta} = R^{(B)}_{\alpha\beta\gamma\delta} + R^{(W)}_{\alpha\beta\gamma\delta} \,. \tag{2.2}$$

As discussed in §1.2 $R^{(B)}_{\alpha\beta\gamma\delta}$ varies on a long lengthscale $\mathcal{L}$, while $R^{(W)}_{\alpha\beta\gamma\delta}$ varies on a short lengthscale $\lambda\!\!\!^{-}$. Consequently, if by $\langle\ \rangle$ we denote an average over spacetime regions somewhat larger than $\lambda\!\!\!^{-}$ but much smaller than $\mathcal{L}$ ("Brill-Hartle average";

Exercise 35.14 of MTW), then we can write

$$R^{(B)}_{\alpha\beta\gamma\delta} \equiv \langle R_{\alpha\beta\gamma\delta} \rangle \quad , \quad R^{(W)}_{\alpha\beta\gamma\delta} \equiv R_{\alpha\beta\gamma\delta} - \langle R_{\alpha\beta\gamma\delta} \rangle \; . \tag{2.3a}$$

Similarly we can define the background metric, of which $R^{(B)}_{\alpha\beta\gamma\delta}$ is the Riemann tensor, by

$$g^{(B)}_{\alpha\beta} \equiv \langle g_{\alpha\beta} \rangle \; . \tag{2.3b}$$

[For a discussion of delicacies which require the use of "steady coordinates" in the averaging of $g_{\alpha\beta}$ see Isaacson (1968), or more briefly §35.13 of MTW.]

In general relativity and in the Dicke-Brans-Jordan theory gravitational waves propagating through vacuum are governed by the wave equation

$$R^{(W)}_{\alpha\beta\gamma\delta|\mu\nu} \, g^{\mu\nu}_{(B)} = 0 \; , \tag{2.4}$$

whereas in Rosen's theory they are governed by

$$R^{(W)}_{\alpha\beta\gamma\delta,\mu\nu} \, \eta^{\mu\nu} = 0 \; . \tag{2.5}$$

Here "|" denotes covariant derivative with respect to $g^{\mu\nu}_{(B)}$ while "," denotes covariant derivative with respect to the flat matric $\eta^{\mu\nu}$. These equations imply that in general relativity and in Dicke-Brans-Jordan theory gravitational waves propagate through vacuum with precisely the speed of light, $c_{GW} = c_{EM}$, but in Rosen's theory they propagate with a different speed, $c_{GW} \neq c_{EM}$. As a rough rule of thumb, whenever a theory of gravity possesses "prior geometry" such as a flat auxiliary metric (MTW, §17.6), it will have $c_{GW} \neq c_{EM}$; often when there is no prior geometry, $c_{GW} = c_{EM}$.

High-precision experiments to test $c_{GW} = c_{EM}$ will be possible if and when electromagnetic waves and gravitational waves are observed from outbursts in the same distant source. For example, for a supernova in the Virgo cluster of galaxies (about 4×10^7 light years from earth; distance at which several supernovae are seen each year) one can hope to discover the light outburst within one day (of retarded time) after the explosion is triggered by gravitational collapse. If gravitational waves from the collapse are observed, then a test is possible with precision

$$\left|\frac{\Delta c}{c}\right| = \left|\frac{c_{GW} - c_{EM}}{c}\right| \sim \frac{1 \text{ day}}{4 \times 10^7 \text{ yr}} \simeq 1 \times 10^{-10} \; . \tag{2.6}$$

Actually, there already exists strong observational evidence that gravitational waves do not propagate more slowly than light. If they did, then high-energy cosmic rays with speeds v in the range $c_{GW} < v < c_{EM}$ would emit gravitational Cerenkov radiation very efficiently and would be slowed quickly by gravitational radiation reaction to $v = c_{GW}$. Since cosmic rays are actually detected with v as large as $c_{EM} \times (1-10^{-18})$, c_{GW} presumably is no smaller than this. (For further details and for a discussion of whether we really understand gravitational Cerenkov radiation in alternative theories of gravity see Caves (1980); also earlier work by Aichelburg, Ecker, and Sexl (1971).

2.2 Plane waves on a flat background in metric theories with $c_{GW} = c_{EM}$

Henceforth I shall restrict attention either to metric theories that have $c_{GW} = c_{EM}$ always (e.g., general relativity and Dicke-Brans-Jordan); or, for theories like Rosen's, to regions of spacetime where c_{GW} happens to equal c_{EM}.

In this section and the next several, I shall make a further restriction to spacetime regions of size $\ll \mathcal{R}$ (but $\gg \lambda\!\!\!^{-}$). In such regions with good accuracy I can ignore the curvature of the background; i.e., I can and will introduce global Lorentz frames of the background metric, in which

$$g^{(B)}_{\alpha\beta} = \eta_{\alpha\beta} \ . \tag{2.7}$$

Far from their source gravitational waves will have wave fronts with radii of curvature large compared to $\lambda\!\!\!^{-}$, i.e., they will be locally plane fronted. Thus, with good accuracy I can and shall approximate $R^{(W)}_{\alpha\beta\gamma\delta} = R_{\alpha\beta\gamma\delta}$ as precisely plane fronted; and by correctly orienting my spatial axes I shall make the waves propagate in the $x^3 = z$ direction. Since they propagate with the speed of light, the waves are then functions of $t - z$:

$$R_{\alpha\beta\gamma\delta} = R_{\alpha\beta\gamma\delta}(t-z). \tag{2.8}$$

The analysis of such waves in arbitrary metric theories of gravity, as described below, is due to Eardley, Lee, Lightman, Wagoner, and Will (1973), cited henceforth as ELLWW. For greater detail see Eardley, Lee, and Lightman (1973).

2.2.1 Bianchi identities and dynamical degrees of freedom

Because the Riemann tensor of any metric theory is derivable from a metric $g_{\alpha\beta}$, it must satisfy the Bianchi identities $R_{\alpha\beta[\gamma\delta;\epsilon]} = 0$. For the plane-wave Riemann tensor (2.8) on a flat background (2.7) the total content of the Bianchi identities is

$$\begin{aligned} R_{\alpha\beta12,0} &= 0 & &\Rightarrow & R_{\alpha\beta12} &= 0 \ , \\ R_{\alpha\beta13,0} - R_{\alpha\beta10,3} &= 0 & &\Rightarrow & R_{\alpha\beta13} &= -R_{\alpha\beta10} \ , \\ R_{\alpha\beta23,0} - R_{\alpha\beta20,3} &= 0 & &\Rightarrow & R_{\alpha\beta23} &= -R_{\alpha\beta20} \ . \end{aligned} \tag{2.9}$$

Recalling the pair-wise symmetry $R_{\mu\nu\alpha\beta} = R_{\alpha\beta\mu\nu}$ we see from (2.9) that any purely spatial pair of indices (12 or 13 or 23) either vanishes or can be converted into a space-time pair (10 or 20 or 30). This means that the six quantities

$$R_{i0j0}(t-z) = R_{j0i0}(t-z) \tag{2.10}$$

are a complete set of independent components of our plane-wave Riemann tensor. All other components of Riemann can be expressed algebraically in terms of these.

In a general metric theory of gravity these six quantities represent six independent degrees of freedom of the gravitational field — i.e., six independent polarizations of a gravitational wave.

In the special case of general relativity a vacuum gravitational wave must have vanishing Ricci tensor

$$R_{\mu\nu} = R^{\alpha}{}_{\mu\alpha\nu} = 0 \tag{2.11}$$

(Einstein field equations). One can show easily that this reduces the number of independent degrees of freedom from six to two:

$$R_{x0x0} = -R_{y0y0} \qquad \text{and} \qquad R_{x0y0} = R_{y0x0} \ . \tag{2.12}$$

* * * * *

Exercise 2. Show that the Bianchi identities for a plane wave on a flat background imply equations (2.9) and that they, in turn, guarantee that R_{i0j0} are a complete set of independent components of the Riemann tensor.

Exercise 3. Show that the vacuum Einstein field equations (2.11) reduce the independent plane-wave components of Riemann to (2.12).

2.2.2 Local inertial frames (side remarks)

In the next section I shall use geodesic deviation to elucidate the physical nature of the six gravity-wave polarizations. But as a foundation for that discussion I must first remind you of the mathematical and physical details of local inertial frames (LIF); see, e.g., §§8.6, 11.6, and 13.6 of MTW.

Physically an LIF is the closest thing to a global inertial frame that an experimenter can construct. The central building block of an LIF is a freely falling test particle ("fiducial particle"), which carries with itself three orthogonally pointing gyroscopes. The experimenter attaches a Cartesian coordinate grid to the gyroscopes. Because of spacetime curvature, this grid cannot be precisely Cartesian; but deviations from Cartesion structure can be made second order in the spatial distance r from the fiducial particle:

$$g_{\alpha\beta} = \eta_{\alpha\beta} + O(r^2 R_{\mu\nu\rho\sigma}) \,. \qquad (2.13)$$

From an experimental viewpoint the details of the $O(r^2 R_{\mu\nu\rho\sigma})$ corrections often are unimportant. Those corrections actually produce geodesic deviation, if one calculates geodesics directly from $g_{\alpha\beta}$; but geodesic deviation is more clearly described as the effect of $R_{\mu\nu\rho\sigma}$ in the geodesic deviation equation (2.1a), which now reads for a test particle at spatial location $x^j = \xi^j$ = (separation from fiducial test particle) and, as always in geodesic deviation, with velocity $|dx^j/dt| \ll 1$:

$$d^2x^j/dt^2 = -R_{j0k0}\, x^k \,. \qquad (2.14)$$

It is this "experimenter's version" of geodesic deviation to which I shall appeal in discussing gravitational waves.

* * * * *

Exercise 4. Show that in an LIF with metric (2.13) the fiducial particle (at rest at the spatial origin) moves along a geodesic. Show further that if $\xi^j = x^j$ is the separation vector between the fiducial test particle and another test particle, the equation of geodesic deviation (2.1a) takes on the form (2.14).

Exercise 5. One realization of an LIF is a "Fermi normal coordinate system" obtained by letting the spatial coordinate axes be spacelike geodesics that start out along the directions of the three gyroscopes. Show that in such a coordinate system

$$\begin{aligned} ds^2 = {} & -dt^2(1 + R_{0\ell 0m}\, x^\ell x^m)dt^2 - \tfrac{4}{3} R_{0\ell 0m}\, x^\ell x^m\, dt dx^j \\ & + (\delta_{ij} - \tfrac{1}{3} R_{i\ell jm}\, x^\ell x^m) dx^i dx^j . \end{aligned} \qquad (2.15)$$

For details see, e.g., §13.6 of MTW.

Exercise 6. Show that in the de Donder gauge of §3.1.3 below and in the vacuum of general relativity a mathematical realization of an LIF is

$$ds^2 = -dt^2(1 + R_{0\ell 0m}x^\ell x^m)dt^2 - \frac{4}{3} R_{0\ell jm}x^\ell x^m dtdx^j$$
$$+\delta_{ij}(1 - R_{0\ell 0m}x^\ell x^m)dx^i dx^j \ . \qquad (2.16)$$

(Note: neither this nor (2.15) requires any assumption of a plane-wave Riemann tensor.) For details see, e.g., Hartle and Thorne (1983).

2.2.3 Physical description of plane-wave polarizations

Consider a cloud of test particles surrounding a central, fiducial test particle. Initially the cloud resides in flat spacetime, all its particles are at rest with respect to each other, and its shape is precisely spherical with radius a. Then a gravitational wave hits and deforms the cloud. The deformations can be analyzed using the equation of geodesic deviation only if the cloud is small compared to the inhomogeneity scale of the Riemann tensor, $a \ll \lambdabar$. Assume this to be the case, and analyze the cloud's deformations in the LIF of the fiducial particle:

$$d^2x^j/dt^2 = -R_{j0k0}(t)x^k. \qquad (2.17)$$

Here $x^j(t)$ is the location, in the LIF, of some specific test particle at time t; and $R_{j0k0}(t\text{-}z)$ is evaluated at the fiducial particle's location $(x,y,z) = 0$. Consider, in turn, and with the help of Figure 3, the six independent polarizations of the wave (further details in ELLWW):

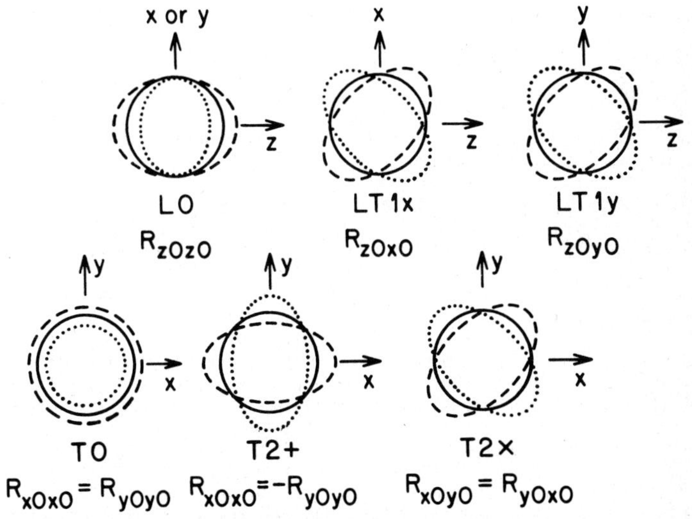

Fig. 3. The deformations of a sphere of test particles produced by gravitational waves with each of six polarizations. As the wave oscillates, the sphere (solid) first gets deformed in the manner shown dashed; then in the manner shown dotted.

R_{z0z0} produces deformations

$$\ddot{x} = 0, \ \ddot{y} = 0, \ \ddot{z} = -R_{z0z0}z. \tag{2.18a}$$

As $R_{z0z0}(t)$ alternately oscillates negative and positive this expands and then squeezes the sphere longitudinally (i.e., along the direction of wave propagation, z), while leaving its transverse cross section unchanged. In this sense the wave is "purely longitudinal". At any moment of time the deformed sphere is invariant under rotations about the propagation direction $\vec{e}_z$. This means, in the language of "canonical field theory", that the wave has "spin zero" (or "helicity zero"). These properties are summarized by saying that the wave is "L0" (longitudinal and spin zero).

$R_{z0x0} = R_{x0z0}$ produces deformations

$$\ddot{x} = -R_{x0z0}z, \ \ \ddot{y} = 0, \ \ \ddot{z} = -R_{x0z0}x. \tag{2.18b}$$

As $R_{x0z0}(t)$ oscillates this expands and then squeezes the sphere at a 45 degree angle to $\vec{e}_z$ in the "logitudinal-transverse" z-x plane, while leaving it undeformed in the y direction. At any moment the deformed sphere is invariant under a 360° rotation about the propagation direction, a property that it shares with the electric or magnetic field of an electromagnetic wave. Thus, this gravitational wave like an electromagnetic wave has spin one — but whereas the electromagnetic wave is "T1" (transverse, spin one), this gravitational wave is "LT1" (longitudinal-transverse, spin one).

$R_{z0y0} = R_{y0z0}$ produces deformations

$$\ddot{x} = 0, \ \ \ddot{y} = -R_{y0z0}z, \ \ \ddot{z} = -R_{y0z0}y, \tag{2.18c}$$

and is thus also "LT1". It is the LT1 polarization orthogonal to R_{z0x0}.

A wave with $R_{x0x0} = R_{y0y0}$ and all other R_{j0k0} zero produces deformations

$$\ddot{x} = R_{x0x0}x, \ \ \ddot{y} = R_{x0x0}y, \ \ \ddot{z} = 0. \tag{2.18d}$$

This wave alternately expands and compresses the sphere in the transverse plane while leaving it transversely circular and leaving it totally unchanged in the longitudinal direction. Thus, this wave is T0 ("transverse, spin-zero").

A wave with $R_{x0x0} = -R_{y0y0}$ and all other R_{j0k0} zero produces deformations

$$\ddot{x} = -R_{x0x0}x, \ \ \ddot{y} = +R_{x0x0}y, \ \ \ddot{z} = 0. \tag{2.18e}$$

As $R_{x0x0}(t)$ oscillates this wave expands the sphere in the x direction and squeezes it in y, then expands it in y and squeezes it in x. Thus the deformations are purely transverse, and at any moment the deformed sphere is invariant under a 180° rotation about the propagation direction. The "spin" ("helicity") S of any wave which propagates with the speed of light is determined by the angle Θ of rotations about the propagation direction that leave all momentary physical effects of the wave unchanged:

$$S = 360^\circ/\Theta.$$

Thus, this wave has spin S = 2, i.e., it is a T2 ("transverse, spin 2) wave. The orientation of the polarization is identified as "+" (x and y; horizontal and vertical).

$R_{x0y0} = R_{y0x0}$ produces deformations

$$\ddot{x} = R_{x0y0}y, \quad \ddot{y} = R_{x0y0}x, \quad \ddot{z} = 0 \tag{2.18f}$$

which are also T2; but the orientation of the polarization is "×". This is the T2 wave orthogonal to "+".

That the spin 0 waves have just one polarization state while the spin 1 and spin 2 waves each have two orthogonal polarization states is familiar both from quantum mechanics and from canonical, classical field theory. It is a consequence of the fact that the waves propagate with the speed of light — i.e., their quanta have zero rest mass.

This familiar feature is deceptively reassuring. Actually, a nasty surprise awaits us if we try to check the fundamental tenet of canonical field theory that the spin of a wave must be Lorentz invariant. If we begin in one Lorentz frame with a gravitational wave that is pure T0 or pure T2, we will find it to be pure T0 or pure T2 in all other Lorentz frames. However, if we begin with a pure LT1 wave in one frame, we will find a mixture of LT1, T0, and T2 in other frames; and if we begin with pure L0 in one frame, we will find a mixture of L0, LT1, T0, and T2 in other frames. See Eardley, Lee, and Lightman (1973) for proofs.

This means that any metric theory of gravity possessing L0 or LT1 waves violates the tenets of canonical field theory and cannot be quantized by canonical methods, even in the weak-gravity limit. Rosen's theory is an example (in the special case $c_{GW} = c_{EM}$ to which our discussion applies; when $c_{GW} \neq c_{EM}$ there exist eight polarizations, not six [C. M. Caves, private communication]). By contrast, metric theories with purely transverse, speed-of-light gravity waves obey the canonical tenets and are quantizable by canonical means, at least in the weak-gravity limit. Examples are general relativity which has pure T2 waves (Exercise 3 above) and the Dicke-Brans-Jordan theory which has both T2 waves and T0 waves.

* * * * *

Exercise 7. Verify the claims made above about the behavior of polarization states under Lorentz transformations. (See Eardley, Lee, and Lightman 1973 for solution.)

2.3 Plane waves on a flat background in general relativity

2.3.1 The gravitational-wave field h^{TT}_{jk}

Specialize now and henceforth to general relativity. Then a plane wave on a flat background has precisely two orthogonal polarization states: T2+ and T2× (denoted simply "+" and "×" henceforth).

Choose a specific Lorentz frame of the flat background space, and in that frame define a "gravitational-wave field" h^{TT}_{jk} by

$$R_{j0k0}(t-z) = -\tfrac{1}{2} h^{TT}_{jk,tt} \tag{2.19}$$

with $h^{TT}_{jk} = 0$ before any waves ever arrive. Then the waves are fully characterized equally well by R_{j0k0} or by h^{TT}_{jk}. Note that the only nonzero components of h^{TT}_{jk} are

$$h^{TT}_{xx} = -h^{TT}_{yy} \equiv A_{+}(t-z), \qquad h^{TT}_{xy} = h^{TT}_{yx} = A_{\times}(t-z), \tag{2.20}$$

A_+ being the "amplitude function" for the + polarization state and $A_\times$ being that for the × state. Note that h^{TT}_{jk} is purely spatial, symmetric, transverse to the propagation direction $\vec{n} = \vec{e}_z$, and also traceless (hence the TT superscript)

$$h^{TT}_{jk} = h^{TT}_{kj}, \qquad h^{TT}_{jk}\, n^k = 0, \qquad \delta^{jk}\, h^{TT}_{jk} = 0. \tag{2.21}$$

Note further that the experimenter's version of the equation of geodesic deviation (eq. 2.17) can be integrated to give

$$\delta x^j = \tfrac{1}{2}\, h^{TT}_{jk}\, x^k \tag{2.22}$$

for the change in location, in an LIF, of a test particle initially at x^k. This equation suggests the common interpretation of h^{TT}_{jk} as a "dimensionless strain of space".

2.3.2 Behavior of h^{TT}_{jk} under Lorentz transformations

A single gravitational wave is described, in different Lorentz frames of the flat background, by different h^{TT}_{jk} fields, each one purely spatial and TT in its own frame. How are these gravitational-wave fields related to each other? I shall state the answer in this section, leaving the proof as an exercise for the reader.

Begin in some fiducial background Lorentz frame, in which h^{TT}_{jk} is described by equations (2.20) above. Define

$$\psi \equiv t - z = \text{"retarded time"}, \tag{2.23a}$$

regard ψ as a scalar field in spacetime (a sort of "phase function" for the wave), and regard the amplitude functions A_+ and $A_\times$ of equations (2.20) as scalar fields which are known functions of ψ. From the scalar field ψ construct the "propagation vector"

$$\vec{k} \equiv -\vec{\nabla}\psi, \quad \text{so} \quad k^0 = k^z = 1, \quad k^x = k^y = 0 \text{ in fiducial frame.} \tag{2.23b}$$

This propagation vector and the basis vector $\vec{e}_x$, which determines the orientations of the + and × polarization states, together define a "fiducial 2-flat" (plane)

$$\overleftrightarrow{f} \equiv \vec{k} \wedge \vec{e}_x \equiv (\text{2-flat spanned by } \vec{k} \text{ and } \vec{e}_x). \tag{2.23c}$$

Now choose some other background Lorentz frame with 4-velocity $\vec{u}'$. In that frame define basis vectors

$$\vec{e}_{0'} \equiv \vec{u}', \qquad \vec{e}_{z'} \equiv \begin{bmatrix}\text{unit vector obtained by projecting } \vec{k} \\ \text{orthogonal to } \vec{u}' \text{ and renormalizing}\end{bmatrix},$$

$$\vec{e}_{x'} \equiv [\text{unit vector lying in } \overleftrightarrow{f} \text{ and orthogonal to } \vec{u}'], \tag{2.24a}$$

$$\vec{e}_{y'} \equiv \begin{bmatrix}\text{unit vector such that } \vec{e}_{0'}, \vec{e}_{x'}, \vec{e}_{y'}, \vec{e}_{z'} \text{ are a right-hand} \\ \text{oriented, orthonormal frame}\end{bmatrix}.$$

Then in this basis the gravitational-wave field has components

$$h'^{TT}_{x'x'} = -h'^{TT}_{y'y'} = A_+(\psi), \qquad h'^{TT}_{x'y'} = h'^{TT}_{y'x'} = A_\times(\psi), \tag{2.24b}$$

where A_+ and $A_\times$ are the same scalar fields as describe the waves in the fiducial frame. Note, however, that ψ is not t'-z'; rather, it differs from t'-z' by the standard doppler-shift factor:

$$\psi = t-z = (\nu'/\nu)(t'-z'), \qquad (2.24c)$$

$$\frac{\nu'}{\nu} = \left[\begin{array}{c}\text{ratio of frequencies of photons, propagating in } \vec{k} \text{ direction,} \\ \text{as measured in the two reference frames}\end{array}\right].$$

Thus, under a Lorentz transformation the gravitational-wave frequencies get doppler shifted just like those of light, but the amplitude functions are left unchanged and the polarization directions change only by a projection that keeps them spatial (eq. 2.24a for $\vec{e}_x'$). The fact, that h^{TT}_{jk} is a "spin-2" quantity with amplitude functions A_+ and $A_\times$ that are Lorentz invariant is embodied in the statement that "$A_+ + iA_\times$ has spin-weight 2 and boost-weight 0" [language of Geroch, Held, and Penrose (1973); $i \equiv \sqrt{-1}$].

It is often convenient to define polarization tensors

$$\overset{\leftrightarrow}{e}{}_+' \equiv \vec{e}_{x'} \otimes \vec{e}_{x'} - \vec{e}_{y'} \otimes \vec{e}_{y'} \quad , \quad \overset{\leftrightarrow}{e}{}_\times' \equiv \vec{e}_{x'} \otimes \vec{e}_{y'} + \vec{e}_{y'} \otimes \vec{e}_{x'} , \qquad (2.24d)$$

and to rewrite equations (2.24b) as

$$\overset{\leftrightarrow}{h}{}'^{TT} = A_+(\psi)\overset{\leftrightarrow}{e}{}_+' + A_\times(\psi)\overset{\leftrightarrow}{e}{}_\times' . \qquad (2.24e)$$

Another useful relation is

$$R_{\alpha'\beta'\gamma'\delta'} = \tfrac{1}{2}\left(\ddot{h}'^{TT}_{\alpha'\delta'}k_{\beta'}k_{\gamma'} + \ddot{h}'^{TT}_{\beta'\gamma'}k_{\alpha'}k_{\delta'} - \ddot{h}'^{TT}_{\beta'\delta'}k_{\alpha'}k_{\gamma'} - \ddot{h}'^{TT}_{\alpha'\gamma'}k_{\beta'}k_{\delta'}\right), \qquad (2.24f)$$

where $^{\bullet} = d/d\psi$.

* * * * *

Exercise 8. Show that in the fiducial frame of this section, equation (2.19) is equivalent to $R_{j0k0} = -(1/2)\ddot{h}^{TT}_{jk}k_0k_0$ where the dot means $d/d\psi$. Show further that in the fiducial frame the full Riemann tensor is given by equation (2.24f) without the primes. (Hint: use equations 2.9).

Exercise 9. Show that the Riemann tensor of (2.24f) with the primes and with $h'^{TT}_{\alpha'\gamma'}$ given by (2.24a,b) is obtained from that of Exercise 8 (no primes) by a standard Lorentz transformation. Convince yourself that this fully justifies the claimed behavior of h^{TT}_{jk} under a change of frames (eqs. 2.24a,b).

2.3.3 Relationship of h^{TT}_{jk} to Bondi news function

Consider gravitational waves propagating radially outward from a source, and approximate the background as flat. Introduce spherical polar coordinates and denote the associated orthonormal basis vectors by,

$$\vec{e}_{\hat{r}} = \partial/\partial r, \quad \vec{e}_{\hat{\theta}} = r^{-1}\partial/\partial\theta, \quad \vec{e}_{\hat{\varphi}} = (r\sin\theta)^{-1}\partial/\partial\varphi. \qquad (2.25a)$$

Let $\vec{e}_{\hat{\theta}}$ be the fiducial direction (analog of $\vec{e}_x$ above) used in defining the polarization base states, so that

$$\overset{\leftrightarrow}{e}_+ = \vec{e}_{\hat{\theta}} \otimes \vec{e}_{\hat{\theta}} - \vec{e}_{\hat{\varphi}} \otimes \vec{e}_{\hat{\varphi}} \quad , \quad \overset{\leftrightarrow}{e}_\times = \vec{e}_{\hat{\theta}} \otimes \vec{e}_{\hat{\varphi}} + \vec{e}_{\hat{\varphi}} \otimes \vec{e}_{\hat{\theta}} ; \qquad (2.25b)$$

$$h^{TT}_{jk} = A_+ \overleftrightarrow{e}_+ + A_\times \overleftrightarrow{e}_\times \, . \qquad (2.25c)$$

Because the wave fronts are spherical (though very nearly plane on length scales $\lambda\!\!\!^{-} \ll r$), A_+ and $A_\times$ die out as $1/r$ (Exercise 14 below)

$$A_+ = r^{-1} F_+(\psi;\theta,\varphi), \quad A_\times = r^{-1} F_\times(\psi;\theta,\varphi), \quad \psi = t-r. \qquad (2.25d)$$

In gravitational-wave studies near "future timelike infinity" $\mathscr{I}^+$, mathematical physicists often use instead of h^{TT}_{jk} a different description of the waves due to Bondi, van der Burg, and Metzner (1962) and to Sachs (1962): The role of the gravitational-wave amplitude is played by the "Bondi News Function"

$$N \equiv \tfrac{1}{2} \frac{\partial}{\partial t} (F_+ + i F_\times) = \tfrac{1}{2} r \frac{\partial}{\partial t} (A_+ + i A_\times), \qquad (2.26a)$$

where $i \equiv \sqrt{-1}$. This complex News function has the advantage of depending only on angles θ, φ, and retarded time ψ ($1/r$ dependence factored out); but for this it pays the price of not being a scalar field. In the language of Geroch, Held, and Penrose, it has "boost weight 2", whereas $A_+ + iA_\times$ has "boost weight 0". It is conventional in the Bondi-Sachs formalism to introduce the complex vector

$$\vec{\bar{m}} = (1/\sqrt{2}) \, (\vec{e}_{\hat{\theta}} - i \vec{e}_{\hat{\varphi}}). \qquad (2.26b)$$

In terms of N and $\vec{\bar{m}}$ the gravitational-wave field is

$$\frac{\partial}{\partial t} h^{TT}_{jk} = \text{Real} \left\{ \frac{4N}{r} \bar{m}_j \bar{m}_k \right\} . \qquad (2.26c)$$

Several lecturers in this volume will use the Bondi-Sachs formalism (e.g., M. Walker, A. Ashtekar, and R. Isaacson).

2.4 Weak perturbations of curved spacetime in general relativity

2.4.1 Metric perturbations and Einstein field equations

Abandon, now, the approximation that the background spacetime is flat. As a foundation for discussing gravitational waves in curved spacetime, consider the general problem of linear perturbations of a curved background metric:

$$\mathbf{g}_{\mu\nu} = g^{(B)}_{\mu\nu} + h_{\mu\nu} \, . \qquad (2.27)$$

In analyzing the metric perturbations $h_{\mu\nu}$, I shall not make explicit the small dimensionless parameter that underlies the perturbation expansion. It might be $\lambda\!\!\!^{-}/\mathscr{L}$ (gravitational wave expansion, §2.4.2 below); it might be the dimensionless amplitude of pulsation of a neutron star, $\delta R/R$ (linear pulsation-theory expansion, Thorne and Campolattaro 1967); it might be the mass ratio m/M of a small body m falling into a Schwarzschild black hole M and generating gravitational waves as it falls (linear perturbations of Schwarzschild geometry; Davis et al. 1971). In the latter two cases, near the star and hole $\lambda\!\!\!^{-}/\mathscr{L}$ is not $\ll 1$; but nevertheless the linearized equations of this section are valid.

The perturbed Einstein field equations for $h_{\mu\nu}$ are expressed most conveniently in terms of the "trace-reversed" metric perturbation

$$\bar{h}_{\mu\nu} \equiv h_{\mu\nu} - \tfrac{1}{2} h \, g^{(B)}_{\mu\nu} \quad , \quad h \equiv h_{\mu\nu} \, g^{\mu\nu}_{(B)} \, . \qquad (2.28)$$

A straightforward calculation (cf. §§35.13 and 35.14 of MTW) gives for the first-order perturbations of the field equations

$$\bar{h}_{\mu\nu|\alpha}{}^{\alpha} + g^{(B)}_{\mu\nu}\,\bar{h}^{\alpha\beta}{}_{|\beta\alpha} - 2\bar{h}_{\alpha(\mu|}{}^{\alpha}{}_{\nu)} + 2R^{(B)}_{\alpha\mu\beta\nu}\,\bar{h}^{\alpha\beta} - 2R^{(B)}_{\alpha(\mu}\bar{h}_{\nu)}{}^{\alpha} = -16\pi\delta T_{\mu\nu}. \tag{2.29}$$

Here a slash "|" denotes covariant derivative with respect to $g^{(B)}_{\mu\nu}$; indices on $\bar{h}_{\alpha\beta}$ are raised and lowered with $g^{(B)}_{\mu\nu}$; $R^{(B)}_{\alpha\beta\gamma\delta}$ and $R^{(B)}_{\alpha\beta}$ are the Riemann and Ricci tensors of the background, and $\delta T_{\mu\nu}$ is the first-order perturbation of the stress-energy tensor.

The first-order perturbed field equation (2.29) can be used to study a wide variety of phenomena, including wave generation (§3.5 below), wave propagation on a curved vacuum background (§2.4.2), absorption and dispersion of waves due to interaction with matter (§2.4.3), and scattering of waves off background curvature and the resulting production of wave tails (§2.4.2).

2.4.2 Wave propagation on a curved vacuum background

Consider gravitational waves of reduced wavelength $\lambdabar$ propagating on a curved vacuum background with radius of curvature $\mathcal{R}$ and inhomogeneity scale $\mathcal{L}$. In keeping with the discussion in §1.2 assume $\lambdabar \ll \mathcal{R}$, but for the moment do not assume $\lambdabar \ll \mathcal{L}$. Then "vacuum" implies $\delta T_{\mu\nu} = 0$ in the field equations (2.29); and $\lambdabar \ll \mathcal{R}$ implies that the terms involving $R^{(B)}_{\alpha\mu\beta\nu}$ and $R^{(B)}_{\alpha\beta}$, which are of size $h/\mathcal{R}^2$, can be neglected compared to the first three terms, which are of size $h/\lambdabar^2$. Simplify the resulting field equations further by an infinitesimal coordinate change ("gauge change")

$$x^{\alpha}_{new} = x^{\alpha}_{old} + \xi^{\alpha}, \qquad h^{new}_{\mu\nu} = h^{old}_{\mu\nu} - \xi_{\mu|\nu} - \xi_{\nu|\mu} \tag{2.30}$$

so designed as to make

$$\bar{h}_{\mu}{}^{\alpha}{}_{|\alpha} = 0 \qquad (\text{"Lorentz gauge"}). \tag{2.31a}$$

(See, e.g., §35.14 of MTW for discussion of such gauge changes.) The first-order field equations (2.29) then become a simple source-free wave equation in curved spacetime:

$$\bar{h}_{\mu\nu|\alpha}{}^{\alpha} = 0. \tag{2.31b}$$

The Riemann curvature tensor associated with these waves

$$R^{(W)}_{\alpha\mu\beta\nu} = \tfrac{1}{2}\,(h_{\alpha\nu|\mu\beta} + h_{\mu\beta|\nu\alpha} - h_{\mu\nu|\alpha\beta} - h_{\alpha\beta|\mu\nu}) \tag{2.32}$$

will also satisfy the wave equation

$$R^{(W)}_{\alpha\mu\beta\nu|\sigma}{}^{\sigma} = 0 \tag{2.33}$$

(covariant derivatives "|" commute because $\lambdabar \ll \mathcal{R}$). Note that although we require $\lambdabar \ll \mathcal{L}$ in order to give a clear definition of "wave", we need not place any restriction on $\lambdabar/\mathcal{L}$ in order to derive the wave equation (2.31b).

The Lorentz gauge condition (2.31a) is preserved by any gauge change (2.30) whose generating function ξ_{α}, like $\bar{h}_{\mu\nu}$, satisfies the wave equation $\xi_{\alpha|\mu}{}^{\mu} = 0$. One of the four degrees of freedom in such a gauge change can be used to make $\bar{h}_{\mu\nu}$ trace-free everywhere

$$\bar{h}_{\alpha}{}^{\alpha} = 0 \quad \text{so} \quad \bar{h}_{\mu\nu} = h_{\mu\nu} \qquad (\text{"trace-free Lorentz gauge"}) \tag{2.34}$$

(MTW exercise 35.13); and the other three degrees of freedom can be used <u>locally</u> (in a local inertial frame of the background $g^{(B)}_{\mu\nu}$) to guarantee that

$$h_{0\alpha} = 0, \quad h_{ij} = h^{TT}_{ij} \quad (\text{"local TT gauge"}), \tag{2.35}$$

where h^{TT}_{ij} is the gravitational-wave field defined, in the background LIF, by

$$R^{(W)}_{i0j0} \equiv -\tfrac{1}{2} h^{TT}_{ij,00} \ . \tag{2.36}$$

If the background is approximated as flat throughout the wave zone, then one can introduce a global inertial frame of $g^{(B)}_{\mu\nu}$ throughout the wave zone and one can impose the TT gauge globally. However, if the background is curved, a global TT gauge cannot exist (MTW exercise 35.13).

One often knows $h_{\alpha\beta}$ or $\bar{h}_{\alpha\beta}$ in a Lorentz but non-TT gauge and wants to compute its "gauge-invariant part" h^{TT}_{ij} in some LIF of the background. Such a computation is performed most easily by a "TT projection", which is mathematically equivalent to a gauge transformation (MTW Box 35.1): One identifies the propagation direction n_j in the LIF as the direction in which the wave is varying rapidly (on length scale $\lambda\!\!\!^{-}$). One then obtains h^{TT}_{ij} by discarding all parts of h_{ij} or $\bar{h}_{ij}$ along n_j and by then removing the trace:

$$h^{TT}_{ij} = P_{ia}h_{ab}P_{bj} - \tfrac{1}{2} P_{ij}P_{ab}h_{ab} = (\text{same expression with } h_{ab} \rightarrow \bar{h}_{ab}), \tag{2.37}$$

where $P_{ab} = \delta_{ab} + n_a n_b$. WARNING: This projection process gives the correct answer only in an LIF of the background and only if $h_{\mu\nu}$ is in a Lorentz gauge.

* * * * * *

Exercise 10. Show that the infinitesimal coordinate change (2.30) produces the claimed gauge change of $h_{\mu\nu}$. Show further that the Riemann tensor of the waves is correctly given by (2.32) in any gauge, and that this Riemann tensor is invariant under gauge changes (2.30).

Exercise 11. Show that a gauge change with $\xi_{\alpha|\mu}{}^{\mu} = 0$ can be used to make a Lorentz-gauge $h_{\mu\nu}$ trace-free globally (eq. 2.34) and TT locally (eq. 2.35). Show further that the TT projection process (2.37) produces the same result as this gauge transformation.

<u>2.4.3 Absorption and dispersion of waves by matter</u>

When electromagnetic waves propagate through matter (e.g., light through water, radio waves through the interplanetary medium), they are partially absorbed and partially scatter off charges; and the scattered and primary waves superpose in such a way as to change the propagation speed from that of light in vacuum ("Dispersion"). A typical model calculation of this absorption and dispersion involves electrons of charge e, mass m, and number density n, each bound to a "lattice point" by a 3-dimensional, isotropic, damped, harmonic-oscillator force:

$$\ddot{\mathbf{z}} + (1/\tau_*)\dot{\mathbf{z}} + \omega_o^{\,2}\mathbf{z} = (e/m)\mathbf{E} = -(e/m)\dot{\mathbf{A}}, \tag{2.38a}$$

where $\mathbf{A}$ is the vector potential in transverse Lorentz gauge and a dot denotes $\partial/\partial t$. These electrons produce a current density $\mathbf{J} = ne(d\mathbf{z}/dt)$, which enters into Maxwell's equations for wave propagation $\Box\mathbf{A} = -4\pi\mathbf{J}$ to give waves of the form $\mathbf{E} = \mathbf{E}_0 \exp(-i\omega t + i\mathbf{k}\cdot\mathbf{x})$ with the dispersion relation (for weak dispersion)

$$\frac{\omega}{k} = (\text{phase speed}) = 1 - \frac{2\pi ne^2/m}{\omega_o^2 - \omega^2 - i\omega/\tau_*} . \tag{2.38b}$$

This dispersion relation shows both absorption (imaginary part of ω/k) and dispersion (real part), and in real situations either or both can be very large.

When gravitational waves propagate through matter they should also suffer adsorption and dispersion. However, in real astrophysical situations the absorption and dispersion will be totally negligible, as the following model calculation shows. (For previous model calculations similar to this one see Szekeres 1971.)

The best absorbers or scatterers of gravitational waves that man has devised are Weber-type resonant-bar gravitational-wave detectors (§§4.1.2 and 4.1.4). On larger scales, a spherical self-gravitating body such as the earth or a neutron star is also a reasonably good absorber and scatterer (good compared to other kinds of objects such as interstellar gas). Consider, then, as idealized "medium" made of many solid spheres (spheres to avoid anisotropy of response to gravity waves), each of which has quadrupole vibration frequency ω_o, damping time (due to internal friction) τ_*, mass m and radius R. For ease of calculation (and because we only need order of magnitude estimates) ignore the self gravity and mutual gravitational interactions of the spheres, and place the spheres at rest in a flat background spacetime with number per unit volume n. Let h_{ij}^{TT} be the gravitational-wave field and require $\lambda\!\!\!^{-} > n^{-1/3} > R$. The waves' geodesic deviation force drives each sphere into quadrupolar oscillations with quadrupole moment $\mathcal{I}_{jk}$ satisfying the equation of motion (Exercise 22 in §4.1.4 below)

$$\ddot{\mathcal{I}}_{jk} + (1/\tau_*)\dot{\mathcal{I}}_{jk} + \omega_o^2 \mathcal{I}_{jk} = (1/5)mR^2\ddot{h}_{jk}^{TT} \tag{2.39a}$$

(analog of the electromagnetic equation 2.38a). As a result of these oscillations each sphere reradiates. The wave equation for h_{jk}^{TT} with these reradiating sources (analog of $\Box \underset{\sim}{A} = -4\pi \underset{\sim}{j}$) is

$$\Box h_{jk}^{TT} \equiv \eta^{\alpha\beta} h_{jk,\alpha\beta}^{TT} = -8\pi n \ddot{\mathcal{I}}_{jk} \tag{2.39b}$$

(Exercise 12). By combining equations (2.39a,b) and assuming a wave of the form $h_{jk} \propto \exp(-i\omega t + i\underset{\sim}{k}\cdot\underset{\sim}{x})$ we obtain the gravitational-wave dispersion relation

$$\frac{\omega}{k} = (\text{phase speed}) = 1 - \frac{(4\pi/5)nmR^2\omega^2}{\omega_o^2 - \omega^2 - i\omega/\tau_*} . \tag{2.39c}$$

To see that the absorption and dispersion are negligible, compare the length scale $\ell = |(1-\omega/k)\omega|^{-1}$ for substantial absorption or for a phase shift of $\sim \pi/2$ with the radius of curvature of spacetime produced by the scatterers (i.e., the maximum size that the scattering region can have without curling itself up into a closed universe), $\mathcal{R} = (nm)^{-1/2}$:

$$\frac{\ell}{\mathcal{R}} = \underbrace{\left|\frac{\omega_o^2 - \omega^2 - i\omega/\tau_*}{(4\pi/5)\omega^2}\right|}_{\substack{\gtrsim 1 \text{ off resonance} \\ \sim(1/Q) \text{ on resonance}}} \frac{1}{\underbrace{(nR^3)^{1/2}}_{\lesssim 1}\underbrace{(m/R)^{1/2}}_{<1/\sqrt{2}}\underbrace{(\omega R)}_{<1}} . \tag{2.40}$$

Here $Q = 1/\omega\tau_*$ is the quality factor of a scatterer, $nR^3 \lesssim 1$ because the scatterers cannot be packed closer together than their own radii, $m/R < 1/2$ because a scatterer cannot be smaller than a black hole of the same mass, and $\omega R = R/\lambda\!\!\!^{-} < 1$

was required to permit a geodesic-deviation analysis (see above). In the most extreme of idealized universes $\ell/\Re$ can be no smaller than unity off resonance (dispersion) and $1/Q$ on resonance (absorption); and such extreme values can be achieved only for neutron stars or black holes ($m/R \sim 1$) packed side by side ($nR^3 \sim 1$) with $R \sim \lambdabar$. In the real universe, $\ell/\Re$ will always be $\ggg 1$; i.e., absorption and dispersion will be negligible regardless of what material the waves encounter and regardless of how far they propagate through it.*

For this reason, henceforth in discussing wave propagation through astrophysical matter (e.g., the interior of the Earth or Sun) I shall approximate $\bar{h}_{\mu\nu}|_\alpha{}^\alpha = -16\pi\delta T_{\mu\nu}$ by $\bar{h}_{\mu\nu}|_\alpha{}^\alpha = 0$. The matter will influence wave propagation only through the background curvature it produces (covariant derivative "|"), not through any direct scattering or absorption ($\delta T_{\mu\nu}$); see §2.6.1 below.

*   *   *   *   *

Exercise 12. For non-self-gravitating matter in flat spacetime and in Lorentz coordinates, show that $T^{\alpha\beta}{}_{,\beta} = 0$ implies $T^{jk} = (1/2)(\rho x^j x^k)_{,00}$ + (perfect spatial divergence), where ρ is mass density. Average this over a lattice of oscillating spheres with number density $n > \lambdabar^{-3}$ to get $T^{jk} = (1/2)n\ddot{I}_{jk}$, where $I_{jk} = \int \rho x^j x^k d^3x$ is the second moment of the mass distribution of each sphere. Passing gravitational waves excite the oscillations in accord with equation (2.39a) (result to be proved in Exercise 22). These oscillations involve no volume changes, so $\ddot{I}_{jk} = \ddot{\mathcal{I}}_{jk}$ = (trace-free part of $\ddot{I}_{jk}$); moreover, equation (2.39a) shows that $\mathcal{I}_{jk}$ is transverse and traceless. Show that this permits TT gauge to be imposed in the field equations (2.29) in the presence of the oscillating, reradiating spheres (usually it can be imposed only outside all sources), and that the resulting field equations reduce to (2.39b). Then derive the gravitational-wave dispersion relation (2.39c) and the estimate (2.40) of the effects of dispersion and absorption.

2.4.4 Scattering of waves off background curvature, and tails of waves

A self-gravitating body of mass m and size R will typically generate gravitational waves with reduced wavelength

$$\lambdabar \sim (R^3/m)^{\frac{1}{2}} \sim \Re_s = (\text{radius of curvature of spacetime near source}). \tag{2.41}$$

If the body has strong self gravity, $m/R \sim 1$ (neutron star or black hole), then $\lambdabar \sim \Re_s$ in the innermost parts of the wave zone; and the curvature coupling terms must be retained in the first-order Einstein equations (2.29). These terms cause the waves to scatter off the background curvature; and repetitively backscattered waves superimposing on each other produce a gravity-wave "tail" that lingers near the source long after the primary waves have departed, dying out as $t^{-(2\ell+2)}$ for waves of multipole order ℓ. See, e.g., Price (1972) for a more detailed discussion, and Cunningham, Price, and Moncrief (1978) for an explicit example.

I regard these backscatterings and tails as part of the wave generation problem and as irrelevant to the problem of wave propagation. In fact, I have defined the inner edge of the "local wave zone" to be so located that throughout it, and throughout the wave propagation problem, $\lambdabar \ll \Re$ and backscatter and tails can be ignored (eq. 1.7 and associated discussion).

---

*For description of a physically unrealistic but conceivable material in which dispersion is so strong that it actually reflects gravitational waves see Press (1979).

2.4.5 The stress-energy tensor for gravitational waves

Gravitational waves carry energy and momentum and can exchange them with matter, e.g., with a gravitational-wave detector. Isaacson (1968) (see also §35.15) has quantified this by examining nonlinear corrections to the wave-propagation equation (2.31b). In this section I shall sketch the main ideas of his analysis.

Consider a gravitational wave with $\lambda\!\!\!^{-} \ll \mathcal{L} \lesssim \mathcal{R}$, and expand the metric of the full spacetime in a perturbation series

$$g_{\mu\nu} = \underset{1,\mathcal{L}}{g^{(B)}_{\mu\nu}} + \underset{\mathcal{a},\lambda\!\!\!^{-}}{h_{\mu\nu}} + \underset{\mathcal{a}^2,\lambda\!\!\!^{-}}{j_{\mu\nu}} + \dots \quad . \tag{2.42a}$$

Below each term I have written the characteristic magnitudes $(1, \mathcal{a}, \mathcal{a}^2)$ of the metric components, and the lengthscales $(\mathcal{L}, \lambda\!\!\!^{-})$ on which they vary in the most "steady" of coordinate systems. Note that $j_{\mu\nu}$ is a nonlinear correction to the propagating waves. By inserting this perturbation series into the standard expression (MTW eqs. 8.47-8.49) for the Einstein curvature tensor $G_{\mu\nu}$ in terms of $g_{\mu\nu}$ and its derivatives, and by grouping terms according to their magnitudes and their lengthscales of variation, one obtains

$$G_{\mu\nu} = \underset{\leq 1/\mathcal{R}^2,\mathcal{L}}{G^{(B)}_{\mu\nu}} + \underset{\mathcal{a}/\lambda\!\!\!^{-2},\lambda\!\!\!^{-}}{G^{(1)}_{\mu\nu}(h)} + \underset{\mathcal{a}^2/\lambda\!\!\!^{-2},\lambda\!\!\!^{-}}{G^{(2)}_{\mu\nu}(h)} + \underset{\mathcal{a}^2/\lambda\!\!\!^{-2},\lambda\!\!\!^{-}}{G^{(1)}_{\mu\nu}(j)} + \dots \quad . \tag{2.42b}$$

Here $G^{(B)}_{\mu\nu}$ is the Einstein tensor of the background metric $g^{(B)}_{\mu\nu}$; $G^{(1)}_{\mu\nu}(h \text{ or } j)$ is the linearized correction to $G_{\mu\nu}$ (MTW eq. 35.58a, trace-reversed); and $G^{(2)}_{\mu\nu}(h)$ is the quadratic correction (MTW eq. 35.58b), trace-reversed).

Isaacson splits the Einstein equations into three parts: a part which varies on scales $\mathcal{L}$ (obtained by averaging, "$\langle\ \rangle$", over a few wavelengths)

$$G^{(B)}_{\mu\nu} = 8\pi\left(T^{(B)}_{\mu\nu} + \langle T^{(2)}_{\mu\nu}\rangle + T^{(W)}_{\mu\nu}\right), \quad T^{(W)}_{\mu\nu} \equiv -(1/8\pi)\,\langle G^{(2)}_{\mu\nu}(h)\rangle ; \tag{2.43a}$$

a part of magnitude $\mathcal{a}/\lambda\!\!\!^{-2}$ which varies on scales $\lambda\!\!\!^{-}$ and averages to zero on larger scales

$$G^{(1)}_{\mu\nu}(h) = 8\pi\, T^{(1)}_{\mu\nu} \iff \bar{h}_{\mu\nu|\alpha}{}^{\alpha} = -16\pi\, T^{(1)}_{\mu\nu} \text{ in Lorentz gauge;} \tag{2.43b}$$

and a part of magnitude $\mathcal{a}^2/\lambda\!\!\!^{-2}$ which varies on scales $\lambda\!\!\!^{-}$ and averages to zero on larger scales

$$G^{(1)}_{\mu\nu}(j) = -G^{(2)}_{\mu\nu}(h) + \langle G^{(2)}_{\mu\nu}(h)\rangle + 8\pi\left(T^{(2)}_{\mu\nu} - \langle T^{(2)}_{\mu\nu}\rangle\right). \tag{2.43c}$$

Here $T^{(B)}_{\mu\nu}$ is the stress-energy tensor of the background; $T^{(1)}_{\mu\nu}$ and $T^{(2)}_{\mu\nu}$ are its first- and second-order perturbations; $T^{(W)}_{\mu\nu} \equiv -(1/8\pi)\langle G^{(2)\mu\nu}_{\mu\nu}(h)\rangle$ is a stress-energy tensor associated with the gravitational waves; and the averaging $\langle\ \rangle$ can be performed in the most naive of manners if the coordinates are sufficiently "steady", but must be performed carefully, by Brill-Hartle techniques (MTW exercise 35.14), if they are not. The "smoothed" field equations (2.43a), together with the contracted Bianchi identities $G^{\mu\nu}_{(B)}|_{\nu} \equiv 0$, imply a conservation law for energy and momentum in the presence of gravitational waves:

$$T^{\mu\nu}_{(B)}|_\nu + \langle T^{\mu\nu}_{(2)}\rangle|_\nu + T^{\mu\nu}_{(W)}|_\nu = 0. \qquad (2.44)$$

(Here and throughout this section indices are raised and lowered with $g^{(B)}_{\mu\nu}$.)

To understand the physics of the field equations (2.43) and conservation law (2.44), let us reconsider the propagation of waves through a cloud of spherical oscillators (§2.4.3). Equation (2.43b) is the wave equation (2.39b) for h, which we used to calculate the absorption and dispersion of the waves. In this wave equation $T^{(1)}_{\mu\nu}$ is the part of $T_{\mu\nu}$ that is linear in the oscillators' amplitude of motion; in Exercise 12 its spatial part (after averaging over scales $< \lambdabar$) was shown to be $T^{(1)}_{jk} = \frac{1}{2} n \ddot{\mathcal{I}}_{jk}$. Equation (2.43c) describes the generation of nonlinear corrections $j_{\mu\nu}$ to the propagating waves. In Lorentz gauge it takes the explicit form

$$j_{\mu\nu}|_\alpha{}^\alpha = \begin{pmatrix} \text{source terms quadratic in } h_{\alpha\beta} \text{ and in} \\ \text{the amplitude of oscillator motion} \end{pmatrix}. \qquad (2.45)$$

In §2.6.2 we shall see that these nonlinear corrections, like absorption and dispersion, are negligible in realistic astrophysical circumstances. Equation (2.43a) describes the generation of smooth, background curvature by the stress-energy of the gravitational waves $T^{(W)}_{\mu\nu}$ and of the matter. Note that the waves contribute an amount of order $\mathcal{A}^2/\lambdabar^2$ to the background curvature $1/\mathcal{R}^2$, and that therefore $1/\mathcal{R}^2 \gtrsim \mathcal{A}^2/\lambdabar^2$; i.e.,

$$\mathcal{A} \lesssim \lambdabar/\mathcal{R}. \qquad (2.46)$$

Since $\lambdabar/\mathcal{R} \ll 1$ for propagating waves, such waves must necessarily have dimensionless amplitudes $\mathcal{A} \ll 1$. If ever $\mathcal{A}$ were to become of order unity, the wave would cease to be separable from the background curvature; the two would become united as a dynamically vibrating spacetime curvature to which the theory of propagating gravitational waves cannot be applied. Equation (2.44) describes the exchange of energy and momentum between matter and waves. In this conservation law $T^{\mu\nu}_{(B)} = mnu^\mu u^\nu$ is the stress-energy of the unperturbed spheres (number density n, mass m, 4-velocity u^μ) and by itself has vanishing divergence. The term $\langle T^{\mu\nu}_{(2)}\rangle$ is the quadratic-order stress-energy associated with the spheres' oscillations, averaged spatially over a few wavelengths and temporally over a few periods of the waves. In an LIF of the oscillators the only nonzero components are the energy density $\langle T^{00}_{(2)}\rangle$ which includes the kinetic energy and the potential energy of oscillation and the thermal energy produced when the oscillations are damped by internal friction [$1/\tau_*$ term in oscillators' equation of motion (2.39a)], and a transverse stress of magnitude comparable to $\langle T^{00}_{(2)}\rangle$. Thus, for our idealized problem the conservation law (2.44) describes the absorption of gravitational-wave energy by the oscillators and the subsequent conversion of oscillation energy into heat.

The gravitational-wave stress-energy tensor $T^{(W)}_{\mu\nu}$ "lives in" the background spacetime and is manipulated using background-spacetime mathematics [e.g., covariant derivative "|" in the conservation law (2.44)]. Because of the averaging $\langle\ \rangle$ in its definition, $T^{(W)}_{\mu\nu}$ gives a well-defined localization of the waves' energy and momentum only on lengthscales somewhat larger than $\lambdabar$ (no way to say whether the energy is in the "crest" of a wave or in its "trough"); no more precise localization of gravitational energy is possible in general relativity. Like $R^{(W)}_{\alpha\beta\gamma\delta}$ and unlike $h_{\alpha\beta}$, the stress-energy tensor $T^{(W)}_{\alpha\beta}$ is gauge invariant. Explicit calculations (Isaacson 1968; MTW §35.15) give

$$T^{(W)}_{\mu\nu} = \frac{1}{32\pi}\left\langle \bar{h}_{\alpha\beta}|_\mu \bar{h}^{\alpha\beta}|_\nu - \tfrac{1}{2}\bar{h}|_\mu \bar{h}|_\nu - 2\,\bar{h}^{\alpha\beta}|_\beta\,\bar{h}_{\alpha(\mu|\nu)}\right\rangle \quad \text{in any gauge}$$

$$= \frac{1}{32\pi}\left\langle \bar{h}_{\alpha\beta}|_\mu \bar{h}^{\alpha\beta}|_\nu\right\rangle \quad \text{in trace-free Lorentz gauge} \qquad (2.47)$$

$$= \frac{1}{32\pi} \left\langle h^{TT}_{jk,\mu} \, h^{TT}_{jk,\nu} \right\rangle \quad \text{in LIF of any observer.}$$

2.5 Wave propagation in the geometric optics limit

2.5.1 Differential equations of geometric optics

Return now to the explicit problem of the propagation of gravitational waves from the local wave zone of a source out through the lumpy universe toward earth. Throughout the local wave zone, and almost everywhere in the universe, not only will $\lambda\!\!\!^{-}$ be very small compared to the background radius of curvature $\mathcal{R}$, but also it will be small compared to the scale $\mathcal{L}$ on which the background curvature varies

$$\lambda\!\!\!^{-} \ll \mathcal{L}. \tag{2.48}$$

Here, as in the above discussion of the waves' stress-energy, I shall assume that $\lambda\!\!\!^{-} \ll \mathcal{L}$; later (§2.6.1) I shall relax that assumption. Here I shall also assume that $\lambda\!\!\!^{-} \ll \mathcal{L}^{(W)} \equiv$ (radius of curvature of the wave fronts of the waves or any smaller scale length for transverse variation of the waves).

The assumptions $\lambda\!\!\!^{-} \ll \mathcal{L}$ and $\lambda\!\!\!^{-} \ll \mathcal{L}^{(W)}$ permit us to solve for the propagation using the techniques of geometric optics (e.g., MTW Exercise 35.15): Introduce trace-free Lorentz gauge everywhere, and ignore the effects of direct interaction between the propagating waves and matter (negligible absorption and dispersion). Then

$$h^{\alpha}{}_{\alpha} = 0, \qquad h^{\mu\alpha}{}_{|\alpha} = 0, \qquad h_{\mu\nu|\alpha}{}^{\alpha} = 0. \tag{2.49}$$

The solution of these gauge and propagation equations is a rapidly varying function of retarded time ψ and a slowly varying function of the other spacetime coordinates:

$$h_{\mu\nu} = h_{\mu\nu}(\psi, x^{\alpha}) \tag{2.50}$$

(x^{α}: variation on scales $\mathcal{L}^{(W)}$, $\mathcal{L}$, $\mathcal{R}$; ψ: variation on scale $\lambda\!\!\!^{-}$.)

As in the discussion of waves in flat spacetime (§2.3.2), define the propagation vector

$$\vec{k} \equiv -\vec{\nabla}\psi . \tag{2.51a}$$

Then, aside from fractional corrections of order $\lambda\!\!\!^{-}/\mathcal{L}^{(W)}$, $\lambda\!\!\!^{-}/\mathcal{L}$, $\lambda\!\!\!^{-}/\mathcal{R}$ the gauge and field equations (2.49) imply

$$k_{\alpha}k^{\alpha} = 0 \text{ and } k_{\beta|\alpha}k^{\alpha} = 0 \Longleftrightarrow \vec{k} \text{ is tangent to null geodesics ("rays")}, \tag{2.51b}$$

$$h_{\alpha}{}^{\alpha} = 0,\ h_{\alpha\beta}k^{\beta} = 0 \quad \Longleftrightarrow h_{\alpha\beta} \text{ is trace free and orthogonal to } \vec{k}, \tag{2.51c}$$

$$h_{\mu\nu|\alpha}k^{\alpha} = -\tfrac{1}{2}(\vec{\nabla}\cdot\vec{k})h_{\mu\nu} \qquad \text{(propagation equation for } h_{\mu\nu}). \tag{2.51d}$$

Had we been analyzing the propagation of electromagnetic waves rather than gravitational, our Lorentz gauge equations for the vector potential would have been

$$A^{\alpha}{}_{|\alpha} = 0, \qquad A_{\mu|\alpha}{}^{\alpha} = 0 \tag{2.52a}$$

(MTW eq. 16.5' with curvature coupling term removed because $\lambda\!\!\!^{-} \ll \mathcal{R}$) (cf. eq.

2.49); our geometric-optics ansatz would have been

$$A_\mu = A_\mu(\psi;\ x^\alpha) \tag{2.52b}$$

(cf. eq. 2.50); and in the geometric optics limit the gauge and wave equations (2.52a) would have reduced to

$$k_\alpha k^\alpha = 0, \qquad k_{\beta|\alpha}k^\alpha = 0, \qquad A_\alpha k^\alpha = 0, \qquad A_{\mu|\alpha}k^\alpha = -\tfrac{1}{2}(\vec{\nabla}\cdot\vec{k})A_\mu \tag{2.52c}$$

(cf. eqs. 2.51c,d).

*   *   *   *   *

Exercise 13. Show that in the geometric optics limit $\lambda\!\!\!{}^{-} \ll \mathcal{L} \lesssim \mathcal{R}$ and $\lambda\!\!\!{}^{-} \ll \mathcal{L}^{(W)}$, and with the geometric optics ansatz (2.50), the gravitational gauge and propagation equations (2.49) reduce to the geometric optics equations (2.51). Similarly show that for electromagnetic waves (2.52a) reduce to (2.52c).

2.5.2 Solution of geometric optics equations in local wave zone

In the local wave zone of the source introduce (flat-background) spherical coordinates (t,r,θ,φ). The waves propagate radially outward from the source along the null-geodesic rays

$$\psi = t-r,\ \theta,\ \varphi \text{ all constant}, \qquad k^0 = k^r = 1. \tag{2.53a}$$

Throughout the local wave zone introduce transverse basis vectors $\vec{e}_{\hat\theta} = r^{-1}\,\partial/\partial\theta$ and $\vec{e}_{\hat\varphi} = (r\sin\theta)^{-1}\,\partial/\partial\varphi$ and polarization tensors

$$\overleftrightarrow{e}_+ \equiv \vec{e}_{\hat\theta}\otimes\vec{e}_{\hat\theta} - \vec{e}_{\hat\varphi}\otimes\vec{e}_{\hat\varphi}, \qquad \overleftrightarrow{e}_\times \equiv \vec{e}_{\hat\theta}\otimes\vec{e}_{\hat\varphi} + \vec{e}_{\hat\varphi}\otimes\vec{e}_{\hat\theta}\ . \tag{2.53b}$$

Then it turns out (Exercise 14) that in TT gauge the general solution to the gauge and propagation equations (2.51c,d) is

$$\begin{aligned} \overleftrightarrow{h}^{TT} &= A_+(\psi;r,\theta,\varphi)\,\overleftrightarrow{e}_+ + A_\times(\psi;r,\theta,\varphi) \\ A_+ &= r^{-1}F_+(\psi;\theta,\varphi), \qquad A_\times = r^{-1}F_\times(\psi;\theta,\varphi); \end{aligned} \tag{2.53c}$$

and similarly for electromagnetic waves

$$\begin{aligned} \vec{A} &= A_{\hat\theta}(\psi;r,\theta,\varphi)\,\vec{e}_{\hat\theta} + A_{\hat\varphi}(\psi;r,\theta,\varphi)\,\vec{e}_{\hat\varphi} \\ A_{\hat\theta} &= r^{-1}F_{\hat\theta}(\psi;\theta,\varphi), \qquad A_{\hat\varphi} = r^{-1}F_{\hat\varphi}(\psi;\theta,\varphi). \end{aligned} \tag{2.54}$$

Stated in words: In polarization bases $\overleftrightarrow{e}_+$, $\overleftrightarrow{e}_\times$ and $\vec{e}_{\hat\theta}$, $\vec{e}_{\hat\varphi}$ which are parallel transported along the rays, the amplitude functions A_+, $A_\times$ of gravitational waves and $A_{\hat\theta}$, $A_{\hat\varphi}$ of electromagnetic waves die out as $1/r$ but otherwise are constant along the rays.

The precise forms of $F_+(\psi;\theta,\varphi) = rA_+$ and $F_\times(\psi;\theta,\varphi) = rA_\times$ are to be determined by solution of the wave generation problem (§3 below). The local-wave-zone waves (2.53) are then to be used as "starting conditions" for propagation out through the universe.

* * * * *

Exercise 14. Show that equations (2.53) are the general solution of the gravitational geometric optics equations (2.51) specialized to TT gauge, for waves propagating radially outward through the local wave zone of a source. Similarly show that equations (2.54) are the solution of the electromagnetic equations (2.52c).

2.5.3 Solution of geometric optics equations in distant wave zone

Suppose that the wave generation problem has been solved to give h_{jk}^{TT} in the form (2.52) throughout the local wave zone. These waves can then be propagated throughout the rest of the universe (assuming $\lambda\!\!\!^{-} \ll \mathcal{L}$ and $\lambda\!\!\!^{-} \ll \mathcal{L}^{(W)}$) using the following constructive method [solution of geometric optics equations (2.51)]:

First extend the radial null rays (2.53a) of the local wave zone out through the universe by solving the geodesic equation. Continue to label each ray by ψ,θ,φ and parametrize it by an affine parameter denoted r (and equal to the radial coordinate in the local wave zone):

$$\text{rays are } (\psi,\theta,\varphi) = \text{const}; \qquad \vec{k} \equiv -\vec{\nabla}\psi = d/dr. \tag{2.55a}$$

Next, along each ray parallel propagate the fiducial basis vector $\vec{e}_{\hat{\theta}}$

$$\vec{\nabla}_{\vec{k}}\,\vec{e}_{\hat{\theta}} = 0 \text{ everywhere}, \qquad \vec{e}_{\hat{\theta}} = r^{-1}\,\partial/\partial\theta \text{ in local wave zone.} \tag{2.55b}$$

Together $\vec{e}_{\hat{\theta}}$ and $\vec{k}$ form a fiducial 2-flat $\vec{k}\wedge\vec{e}_{\hat{\theta}}$ to be used below in defining the polarization of the waves. Next, propagate A_+ and $A_\times$ along each ray by solving the ordinary differential

$$(\partial A/\partial r)_{\psi,\theta,\varphi} = -\tfrac{1}{2}(\vec{\nabla}\cdot\vec{k})A, \qquad A = [\text{expression (2.53c) in local wave zone}]. \tag{2.55c}$$

The resulting A_+, $A_\times$, and fiducial 2-flat $\vec{k}\wedge\vec{e}_{\hat{\theta}}$ determine the gravitational-wave field in the manner of §2.3.2: At any event in the distant wave zone introduce an observer with 4-velocity $\vec{u}$; introduce an orthonormal basis

$$\vec{e}_0 \equiv \vec{u}, \qquad \vec{e}_z \equiv \begin{bmatrix}\text{unit vector obtained by projecting } \vec{k} \\ \text{orthogonal to } \vec{u} \text{ and renormalizing}\end{bmatrix},$$

$$\vec{e}_x \equiv [\text{unit vector lying in } \vec{k}\wedge\vec{e}_{\hat{\theta}} \text{ and orthogonal to } \vec{u}]. \tag{2.55d}$$

$$\vec{e}_y \equiv \begin{bmatrix}\text{unit vector such that } \vec{e}_0, \vec{e}_x, \vec{e}_y, \vec{e}_z \text{ are a right-hand oriented,} \\ \text{orthonormal frame}\end{bmatrix};$$

and introduce corresponding polarization tensors

$$\overleftrightarrow{e}_+ \equiv \vec{e}_x\otimes\vec{e}_x - \vec{e}_y\otimes\vec{e}_y, \qquad \overleftrightarrow{e}_\times \equiv \vec{e}_x\otimes\vec{e}_y + \vec{e}_y\otimes\vec{e}_x. \tag{2.55e}$$

Then the gravitational-wave field in this LIF is

$$\overleftrightarrow{h}^{TT} = A_+\,\overleftrightarrow{e}_+ + A_\times\,\overleftrightarrow{e}_\times\,; \tag{2.55f}$$

and the Riemann tensor and stress-energy tensor associated with the waves are

$$R^{(W)}_{\alpha\beta\gamma\delta} = \tfrac{1}{2}(\ddot{h}^{TT}_{\alpha\delta} k_\beta k_\gamma + \ddot{h}^{TT}_{\beta\gamma} k_\alpha k_\delta - \ddot{h}^{TT}_{\beta\delta} k_\alpha k_\gamma - \ddot{h}^{TT}_{\alpha\gamma} k_\beta k_\delta),$$

$$T^{(W)}_{\alpha\beta} = \frac{1}{16\pi}\langle \dot{A}_+^{\,2} + \dot{A}_\times^{\,2}\rangle k_\alpha k_\beta, \quad \text{where} \quad \dot{} \equiv \partial/\partial\psi. \tag{2.56}$$

For electromagnetic waves the geometric optics equations (2.52c) have a similar solution. In a basis $\vec{e}_{\hat\theta}$, $\vec{e}_{\hat\varphi}$ obtained by parallel transport (eqs. 2.55b) along the rays (eqs. 2.55a) the components of the vector potential, $A_{\hat\theta}$ and $A_{\hat\varphi}$, satisfy identically the same propagation equation (2.55c) as the gravitational-wave amplitude functions A_+ and $A_\times$. Moreover, an observer with 4-velocity $\vec{u}$ can always put the waves into purely spatial Lorentz gauge (no component of $\vec{A}$ along $\vec{u}$) by a gauge change, which produces

$$\vec{A}^S = A_{\hat\theta}\,\vec{e}_x + A_{\hat\varphi}\,\vec{e}_y \tag{2.57}$$

(analog of eq. 2.55f) with $\vec{e}_x$, $\vec{e}_y$ given by equations (2.55d). The electromagnetic field tensor, and the stress-energy tensor of the waves averaged over several wavelengths (analogs of eqs. 2.56) are

$$F_{\alpha\beta} = \dot{A}^S_\beta k_\alpha - \dot{A}^S_\alpha k_\beta,$$

$$\langle T_{\alpha\beta}\rangle = \frac{1}{4\pi}\langle A_{\hat\theta}^{\,2} + A_{\hat\varphi}^{\,2}\rangle k_\alpha k_\beta . \tag{2.58}$$

* * * * * *

Exercise 15. Show that equations (2.55) constitute a solution of the gravitational geometric optics equations (2.51), transformed locally to TT gauge. Show further that this solution joins smoothly onto the local-wave-zone solution (2.53), and that the Riemann tensor and stress-energy tensor of these waves have the form (2.56). Similarly show that if $A_{\hat\theta}$ and $A_{\hat\varphi}$ are propagated via (2.55c), then $A_{\hat\theta}\vec{e}_{\hat\theta} + A_{\hat\varphi}\vec{e}_{\hat\varphi}$ is a solution of the electromagnetic equations (2.52c); (2.57) is this same solution in another gauge; and (2.58) are the field tensor and averaged stress-energy tensor of the waves.

2.5.4 Example: Propagation through a Friedmann universe

As an example of the geometric optics solution for wave propagation consider, as the background spacetime, a closed Friedmann universe with metric

$$g^{(B)}_{\alpha\beta}\, dx^\alpha dx^\beta = a^2(\eta)\,[-d\eta^2 + d\chi^2 + \Sigma^2\,(d\theta^2 + \sin^2\theta\, d\varphi^2)]$$

$$\Sigma = : \ \chi \text{ for } k = 0, \quad \sin\chi \text{ for } k = +1, \quad \sinh\chi \text{ for } k = -1. \tag{2.59}$$

Here k is the curvature parameter (k = 0 for a spatially flat universe, k = +1 for a closed universe, k = -1 for an open universe; see, e.g., chapters 27-29 of MTW). Orient the coordinates so the source of the waves is at $\chi = 0$, and let the source be active (emit waves) at a coordinate time $\eta \simeq \eta_e$ when the expansion factor of the universe is $a = a_e$ ("e" for "emission"). The flat, spherical coordinates of the local wave zone, and the retarded time are

$$t = a_e(\eta-\eta_e), \quad r = a_e\chi, \quad \theta, \quad \varphi; \qquad \psi = t-r = a_e(\eta-\chi-\eta_e); \tag{2.60}$$

and the waves in the local wave zone are described by equations (2.53b,c).

Throughout the wave zone (local and distant) the rays and propagation vector of equations (2.55a) are

$$\eta - \chi = \eta_e + \psi/a_e, \qquad k^\eta = k^\chi = \left(\frac{\partial\eta}{\partial r}\right)_{\psi,\theta,\varphi} = \left(\frac{\partial\chi}{\partial r}\right)_{\psi,\theta,\varphi} = \frac{a_e}{a^2}; \qquad (2.61a)$$

the parallel-propagated fiducial basis vector (eq. 2.55b) is

$$\vec{e}_{\hat\theta} = (1/a\Sigma)\,\partial/\partial\theta; \qquad (2.61b)$$

and the transported gravity-wave and electromagnetic-wave amplitude functions (eq. 2.55c) are

$$A_J = \frac{F_J(\psi;\theta,\varphi)}{a\Sigma}\ ; \ J = + \text{ or } \times \text{ (gravity)},\ J = \hat\theta \text{ or } \hat\varphi \text{ (electromagnetism)}. \qquad (2.61c)$$

If we approximate the earth as at rest in the Friedmann coordinate system at χ_o, θ_o, φ_o and we denote the present epoch by $\eta \simeq \eta_o$, $a = a_o$, then the basis vectors (2.53b) of the earth's LIF are

$$\vec{e}_0 = \frac{1}{a_o}\frac{\partial}{\partial\eta}, \quad \vec{e}_x = \frac{1}{a_o\Sigma_o}\frac{\partial}{\partial\theta}, \quad \vec{e}_y = \frac{1}{a_o\Sigma_o \sin\theta_o}\frac{\partial}{\partial\varphi}, \quad \vec{e}_z = \frac{1}{a_o}\frac{\partial}{\partial\chi}; \qquad (2.61d)$$

and the gravitational-wave field as measured at earth (eqs. 2.53b,c) is

$$\overleftrightarrow{h}^{TT} = \frac{1}{a_o\Sigma_o}\left[F_+(\psi;\theta_o,\varphi_o)(\vec{e}_x\otimes\vec{e}_x - \vec{e}_y\otimes\vec{e}_y) + F_\times(\psi;\theta_o,\varphi_o)(\vec{e}_x\otimes\vec{e}_y + \vec{e}_y\otimes\vec{e}_x)\right]. \qquad (2.61e)$$

The energy density in these waves as measured at earth (eq. 2.56) is

$$T_{00}^{(W)} = \underbrace{\frac{\langle \dot F_+^2 + \dot F_\times^2\rangle}{4\cdot 4\pi a_o^2\Sigma_o^2}}_{\uparrow\ \text{(surface area around source today)}}\ \underbrace{\left(\frac{a_e}{a_o}\right)^2}_{(1+Z)^{-2}}, \qquad \dot{} = \partial/\partial\psi, \qquad (2.62)$$

where Z is the cosmological redshift of the source. Similarly, for electromagnetic waves

$$\vec{A}^S = (1/a_o\Sigma_o)[F_{\hat\theta}(\psi;\theta_o,\varphi_o)\,\vec{e}_x + F_{\hat\varphi}(\psi;\theta_o,\varphi_o)\,\vec{e}_y], \qquad (2.63a)$$

$$\langle T_{00}\rangle = \frac{\langle \dot F_{\hat\theta}^2 + \dot F_{\hat\varphi}^2\rangle}{4\pi a_o^2\Sigma_o^2}\left(\frac{a_e}{a_o}\right)^2. \qquad (2.63b)$$

Note that the factor $1/a_o\Sigma_o$, by which the amplitudes of the waves die out as they recede from the source, is given in terms of cosmological parameters by

$$\frac{1}{a_o\Sigma_o} \equiv \frac{1}{R} = \frac{H_o q_o^2(1+Z)}{-q_o + 1 + q_oZ + (q_o-1)(2q_oZ+1)^{1/2}}$$

$$\approx \frac{H_o}{Z}\left[1 + \tfrac{1}{2}(1+q_o)Z + O(Z^2)\right] \qquad \text{for} \qquad Z \ll 1 \tag{2.64}$$

$$\approx H_o q_o \qquad \text{for } Z \gg 1 \text{ and } Z \gg 1/q_o$$

(MTW eqs. 29.28-29.33). Here H_o is the Hubble expansion rate; q_o is the deceleration parameter of the universe; Z is the cosmological redshift of the source; and I have assumed zero cosmological constant. For formulas with nonzero cosmological constant see MTW eqs. (29.32).

*   *   *   *   *

Exercise 16. Show that for propagation through a Friedmann universe equations (2.55)-(2.58) become (2.59)-(2.63).

2.6 Deviations from geometric optics

I have already discussed in detail several ways that wave propagation can differ from geometric optics: absorption and dispersion by matter (§2.4.3; almost always negligible for gravitational waves), and scattering of waves off background curvature with resulting production of tails (§2.4.4; important primarily near source, but also if waves encounter a sufficiently compact body — e.g., a neutron star or black hole). In this section I shall describe two other nongeometric-optics effects: diffraction and nonlinear interactions of the wave with itself.

2.6.1 Diffraction

As gravitational and electromagnetic waves propagate through the universe, they occasionally encounter regions of enhanced spacetime curvature due to concentrations of matter (galaxies, stars, ...) which produce a breakdown in $\lambda\!\!\!^{-} \ll \mathcal{L}$ and/or in $\lambda\!\!\!^{-} \ll \mathcal{L}^{(W)}$ and a resulting breakdown in geometric-optics propagation. Such a breakdown is familiar from light propagation, where it is called "diffraction".

Consider, as an example, the propagation of waves through the neighborhood and interior of the sun (Fig. 4), and ignore absorption and dispersion by direct interaction with matter (justified for gravitational waves, §2.4.3; not justified for electromagnetic waves). As they pass near and through the sun, rays from a distant source are deflected and forced to cross each other; i.e., they are

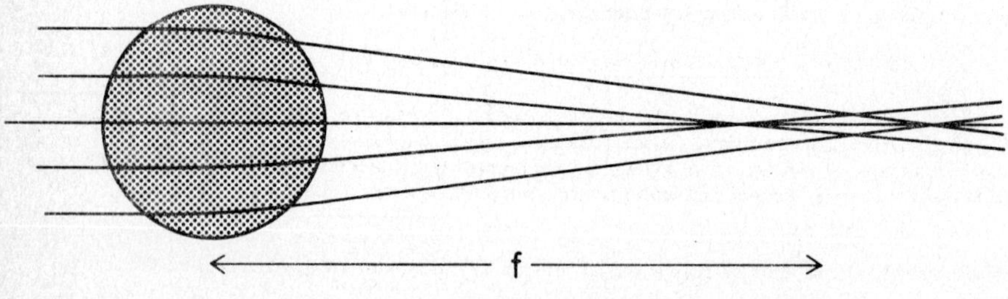

Fig. 4 The rays for geometric-optics wave propagation through the sun.

focussed gravitationally. The dominant source of deflection is the spacetime curvature of the solar core. It produces ray crossing ("caustics") along the optic axis at distances of order (and greater than) the "focal distance"

$$f \sim \frac{\mathcal{L}}{4M/\mathcal{L}} \simeq 20 \text{ AU} . \tag{2.65}$$

Here $\mathcal{L} \sim 10^5$ km is the inhomogeneity scale of the solar core, $M \sim 0.3\ M_\odot$ is the mass of the solar core, and the value 20 AU comes from detailed calculations with a detailed solar model (Cyranski and Lubkin 1974).

Geometric optics would predict infinite amplification of the waves at the caustics. However, geometric optics breaks down there because it also predicts $\mathcal{L}^{(W)} \rightarrow 0$. To understand the actual behavior of the waves near the caustics, think of the waves which get focussed by the solar core as a single wave packet that has transverse dimension $\Delta y \sim \mathcal{L}$ as it passes through the core. The uncertainty principle for waves $(\Delta y \Delta k_y \gtrsim 1)$ forces this wave packet to spread in a nongeometric optics manner with a spreading angle

$$\theta_s \sim \Delta k_y / k_x \sim \lambda\!\!\!^{-}/\mathcal{L} . \tag{2.66}$$

This spreading is superimposed on the geometric-optics focussing, and it spreads out the highly focussed waves near the caustics over a lateral scale y_s

$$y_s \sim (\lambda\!\!\!^{-}/\mathcal{L}) f \sim (\lambda\!\!\!^{-}/4M)\mathcal{L} . \tag{2.67}$$

If $y_s \ll \mathcal{L}$ (i.e., if $\lambda\!\!\!^{-} \ll 4M$) there is substantial focussing: the wave energy density increases near the caustics by a factor $\sim (y_s/\mathcal{L})^2$ and the amplitude increases by $\sim y_s/\mathcal{L} \sim \lambda\!\!\!^{-}/4M$. The details of this regime are described by the laws of "Fresnel diffraction". On the other hand, if $y_s \gtrsim \mathcal{L}$ (i.e., if $\lambda\!\!\!^{-} \gtrsim 4M$) there is negligible focussing; and the little focussing that does occur is described by the laws of "Fraunhoffer diffraction". For full details see Bontz and Haugan (1981) and references therein.

For the case of the sun the dividing line between substantial focussing and little focussing is $\lambda\!\!\!^{-} \sim$ (gravitational radius of sun), i.e., (frequency) $\sim 10^4$ Hz. Since all strong sources of gravitational waves are expected to have $\lambda\!\!\!^{-} \gtrsim$ (gravitational radius of source) $\gtrsim$ (gravitational radius of Sun), i.e., (frequency) $\lesssim 10^4$ Hz, they all lie in the "little focussing regime" — a conclusion that bodes ill for any efforts to send gravitational-wave detectors on spacecraft to the orbit of Uranus in search of amplified gravitational waves; cf. Sonnabend (1979).

Far beyond the focal region the geometric optics approximation becomes valid again, except for a smearing of lateral structure of the waves over an angular scale $\sim \theta_s$. For example, ray crossing may produce multiple images of a gravitational-wave source in this region; and those images can be computed by geometric optics methods aside from θ_s-smearing.

2.6.2 Nonlinear effects in wave propagation

Once a gravitational wave has entered and passed through the local wave zone, its nonlinear interactions with itself are of no importance. To see this consider the idealized problem of a radially propagating, monochromatic wave in flat spacetime. At linear order, in spherical coordinates write the wave field as

$$h_{\hat\theta\hat\theta} = -h_{\hat\varphi\hat\varphi} = A_o(\theta,\varphi) \frac{\lambda\!\!\!^{-}}{r} \cos\left(\frac{t-r}{\lambda\!\!\!^{-}}\right) , \tag{2.68}$$

where hats denote components in an orthonormal, spherical basis. Note that the angular function A_o is the amplitude of the wave in the induction zone, where it is just barely starting to become a wave. For any realistic source $A_o \lesssim 1$; see eq. (3.55b) below.

As these waves propagate, their nonlinear interaction with themselves produces a correction $j_{\mu\nu}$ to $h_{\mu\nu}$. Like $h_{\mu\nu}$, $j_{\mu\nu}$ has the outgoing-wave form

$$j_{\hat{\mu}\hat{\nu}} = J_{\hat{\mu}\hat{\nu}}(r,\theta,\varphi) \cos[(t-r)/\lambdabar + \text{phase}]. \tag{2.69}$$

Equations (2.43c) and (2.45) describe the growth of this correction as it propagates. They have the form $j_{\mu\nu|\alpha}{}^{\alpha} = (\text{source})$, which for $j_{\mu\nu}$ of the form (2.69) reduces to

$$\frac{1}{r\lambdabar}\frac{\partial}{\partial r}(r\, J_{\hat{\mu}\hat{\nu}}) = \alpha\left(\frac{A_o}{r}\right)^2 k_{\hat{\mu}}k_{\hat{\nu}} + 0\left(\frac{A_o{}^2\lambdabar}{r^3}\right), \tag{2.70}$$

where α is a constant of order unity and $k_{\hat{r}} = -k_{\hat{0}} = 1$ is the propagation vector.

The leading, $1/r^2$ source term in (2.70) produces a rapidly growing correction

$$J_{\hat{\mu}\hat{\nu}} = \alpha A_o{}^2 \frac{\lambdabar}{r} \ln\left(\frac{r}{\lambdabar}\right) k_{\hat{\mu}}k_{\hat{\nu}} ; \tag{2.71}$$

but this correction is purely longitudinal, i.e., it has no transverse-traceless part, i.e., it is purely a gauge change. The $1/r^3$ source term in (2.70) produces corrections of negligible size:

$$J_{\hat{\mu}\hat{\nu}} \sim A_o{}^2\lambdabar^2/r^2 \ll A_o\lambdabar/r \sim h_{\hat{\mu}\hat{\nu}} . \tag{2.72}$$

Thus, the effects of nonlinearities are negligible as claimed.

* * * * *

Exercise 17. Use equations (35.58) of MTW to show that the wave equation (2.43c) for $j_{\mu\nu}$ reduces to (2.70). Show that the solution has the form (2.71), (2.72).

3 THE GENERATION OF GRAVITATIONAL WAVES

Turn now from wave propagation to wave generation. Elsewhere (Thorne 1977) I have given a rather thorough review of the theory of gravitational wave generation, including a variety of computational techniques valid for a variety of types of sources. In these lectures I shall focus almost entirely on computational techniques that involve multipole-moment decompositions. My discussion in large measure will be an overview of a long treatise on "multipole expansions of gravitational radiation" which I published recently in Reviews of Modern Physics (Thorne 1980a; cited henceforth as "RMP").

3.1 Foundations for multipole analyses

3.1.1 Multipole moments of a stationary system in linearized general relativity

I shall motivate my discussion of multipole moments by considering a stationary (time-independent), weakly gravitating system surrounded by vaccum and described using the linearized approximation to general relativity (MTW chapters 18 and 19). In a Cartesion coordinate system and in Lorentz gauge the Einstein field equations and gauge conditions are

$$\nabla^2 \bar{h}^{00} = -16\pi\rho, \qquad \nabla^2 \bar{h}^{0j} = -16\pi\rho v^j, \qquad \nabla^2 \bar{h}^{jk} = -16\pi T^{jk},$$
$$\bar{h}^{0j}{}_{,j} = 0, \qquad \bar{h}^{ij}{}_{,j} = 0. \tag{3.1}$$

Here ∇^2 is the flat-space Laplacian, $\bar{h}^{\alpha\beta}$ is the trace-reversed metric perturbation, $\rho = T^{00}$ is the source's mass density, v^j is its velocity field, and T^{jk} is its stress tensor. These equations can be solved for $\bar{h}^{\alpha\beta}$ using the usual flat-space Green's function $-(1/4\pi)|\underset{\sim}{x}-\underset{\sim}{x}'|^{-1}$; and the resulting integrals can then be expanded in powers of $1/r$. By doing this and by then making gauge changes described in § VIII of RMP, one can bring the external gravitational field into the form

$$\bar{h}^{00} = \frac{4M}{r} + \frac{6}{r^3}\mathcal{I}_{jk}n_j n_k + \ldots + \frac{4(2\ell-1)!!}{\ell!\,r^{\ell+1}} \underbrace{\mathcal{I}_{a_1\ldots a_\ell}}_{\mathcal{I}_{A_\ell}} \underbrace{n_{a_1}\ldots n_{a_\ell}}_{N_{A_\ell}} + \ldots, \tag{3.2a}$$

$$\bar{h}^{0j} = \frac{2}{r^2}\epsilon_{jka}\mathcal{S}_k n_a + \ldots + \frac{4\ell(2\ell-1)!!}{(\ell+1)!\,r^{\ell+1}}\epsilon_{jka_\ell}\mathcal{S}_{kA_{\ell-1}}N_{A_\ell} + \ldots, \tag{3.2b}$$

$$\bar{h}^{ij} = 0. \tag{3.2c}$$

Here $r \equiv (\delta_{jk}x^j x^k)^{\frac{1}{2}}$ is radius, $n_j \equiv x^j/r$ is the unit radial vector, ϵ_{ijk} is the Levi-Civita tensor used to form cross products, $(2\ell-1)!!$ is the product $(2\ell-1)\cdot(2\ell-3)\cdots1$, shorthand notations have been introduced for strings of indices $a_1\ldots a_\ell \equiv A_\ell$ and for products of unit radial vectors $n_{a_1}\cdots n_{A_\ell} = N_{A_\ell}$, and spatial indices are moved up and down with impunity because the spatial coordinates are Cartesian. The "multipole moments" M, $\mathcal{I}_{A_\ell}$, $\mathcal{S}_{A_\ell}$ are given as integrals over the source by

$$M = (\text{mass}) = \int \rho\, d^3x, \tag{3.3a}$$

$$\mathcal{I}_{a_1\ldots a_\ell} = \begin{pmatrix}\text{mass } \ell\text{-pole}\\ \text{moment}\end{pmatrix} = \left[\int(\rho+T^{jj})x^{a_1}\ldots x^{a_\ell}d^3x\right]^{STF}, \tag{3.3b}$$

$$\mathcal{S}_{a_1\ldots a_\ell} = \begin{pmatrix}\text{current } \ell\text{-pole}\\ \text{moment}\end{pmatrix} = \left[\int(\epsilon_{a_\ell pq}x^p\rho v^q)x^{a_1}..x^{a_{\ell-1}}d^3x\right]^{STF}. \tag{3.3c}$$

Here "STF" means "symmetric, trace-free part", i.e., "symmetrize and remove all traces"; cf. equation (2.2) of RMP. Note that the mass moments, which produce Newtonian-type gravitational accelerations $\underset{\sim}{g} = (1/4)\underset{\sim}{\nabla}\bar{h}^{00}$, are generated by $\rho+T^{jj}$ = (mass density + trace of stress tensor). For a description of a possible future experiment to verify the role of T^{jj} see §IV.D of Braginsky, Caves, and Thorne (1977).

For any realistic, weakly gravitating astrophysical source $T^{jj} \ll \rho$, so $\mathcal{I}_{a_1\ldots a_\ell} = \mathcal{I}_{A_\ell}$ is the STF part of the ℓ'th moment of the mass density; and $\mathcal{S}_{A_\ell}$ is the STF part of the $(\ell-1)$'th moment of the angular momentum density (though I call it the "ℓ'th current moment"). Note that as in electromagnetism, so also here, the external gravitational field is fully characterized by just two families of moments: the "mass moments" $\mathcal{I}_{A_\ell}$ are analogs of electric moments, the "current moments" $\mathcal{S}_{A_\ell}$ are analogs of magnetic moments. In order of magnitude, for a source of mass M, size L, and characteristic internal velocity v,

$$|\mathcal{I}_{A_\ell}| \lesssim ML^\ell, \quad |\mathcal{S}_{A_\ell}| \lesssim MvL^\ell. \tag{3.4}$$

It is remarkable that, by an appropriate adjustment of gauge, $\bar{h}_{ij}$ can be made to vanish identically outside the source; and $\bar{h}_{00}$ is then determined fully by the mass moments while $\bar{h}_{0j}$ is determined fully by the current moments.

Note that the spatial coordinates of equations (3.2) have been "mass-centered" so the mass dipole moment $\mathcal{I}_j$ vanishes. I always mass-center my coordinates, thereby avoiding the issue of arbitrariness in the moments associated with arbitrariness in the origin of coordinates. Note further that the current dipole moment $\mathcal{S}_j$ is precisely the angular momentum of the source.

* * * * *

Exercise 18. Write down the solution of equations (3.1) using the Green's function $-(1/4\pi)|\underset{\sim}{x}-\underset{\sim}{x}'|^{-1}$, expanded in powers of $1/r$. Then specialize the discussion of §VIII of RMP to the stationary case and use its gauge changes to bring $\bar{h}^{\alpha\beta}$ into the form (3.2), (3.3).

3.1.2 Relation of STF tensors to spherical harmonics

The "STF" expansions (3.2) for $\bar{h}^{\alpha\beta}$ are mathematically equivalent to the more familiar expansions in terms of spherical harmonics $Y_{\ell m}(\theta,\varphi)$. The precise relationship between STF expansions and $Y_{\ell m}$ expansions is spelled out in §II of RMP. Here I shall describe only the flavor of that relationship.

Choose a specific value for the spherical-harmonic index ℓ. Then there are $2\ell+1$ linearly independent STF tensors of order ℓ ("STF-ℓ tensors"); and there are $2\ell+1$ linearly independent functions $Y_{\ell m}(\theta,\varphi)$. Moreover, the STF-$\ell$ tensors and the $Y_{\ell m}(\theta,\varphi)$ generate the same irreducible representation of the rotation group. Any scalar function $F(\theta,\varphi)$ can be expanded in two mathematically equivalent forms:

$$\begin{aligned} F(\theta,\varphi) &= \sum_{\ell,m} f_{\ell m} Y_{\ell m}(\theta,\varphi) \\ &= \sum_{\ell} \mathcal{F}_{A_\ell} N_{A_\ell} . \end{aligned} \tag{3.5}$$

In the first expansion the coefficients $f_{\ell m}$ are constant scalars, and the angular dependence is contained in the harmonics $Y_{\ell m}$. In the second expansion the coefficients $\mathcal{F}_{A_\ell}$ are constant STF-ℓ tensors, and the angular dependence is obtained by contracting the unit vectors $N_{A_\ell} \equiv n_{a_1}\ldots n_{a_\ell}$ into them.

STF expansions were widely used in the nineteenth century, before $Y_{\ell m}(\theta,\varphi)$ came into vogue; see, e.g., Kelvin and Tate (1879); Hobson (1931). In recent years they have been restored to common use by relativity theorists (e.g., Pirani 1964, RMP, Thorne 1981) because they are rather powerful when the spherical harmonics being manipulated are tensorial rather than scalar. In part, this power stems from the fact that the indices of $\mathcal{F}_{A_\ell}$ carry both angular dependence (implicitly) and tensorial component properties (explicitly), and carry them simultaneously. An example is the tensorial harmonic $\epsilon_{pqj}\mathcal{S}_{kqA_{\ell-2}} n_p N_{A_{\ell-2}}$. Harmonics of this form are second-rank tensors (two free indices j and k); they have harmonic order ℓ (ℓ indices on $\mathcal{S}$ implies these generate the same irreducible representation of the rotation group as do $Y_{\ell m}$); and they have parity $\pi = (-1)^{\ell+1}$ ("1" from ϵ_{pqj}, "ℓ" from $\mathcal{S}$).

3.1.3 The Einstein equations in de Donder (harmonic) gauge

In performing multipole decompositions of fully relativistic gravitational fields (the following sections) it is computationally powerful to work in de Donder (harmonic) gauge: Define the "gravitational field" $\bar{h}^{\alpha\beta}$ in terms of the "metric density" $\mathfrak{g}^{\alpha\beta}$ by

$$\mathfrak{g}^{\alpha\beta} \equiv (-g)^{\frac{1}{2}} g^{\alpha\beta} \equiv \eta^{\alpha\beta} - \bar{h}^{\alpha\beta}, \qquad g \equiv \det \| g_{\mu\nu} \| , \tag{3.6}$$

where $\eta^{\alpha\beta}$ is the Minkowski metric, diag(-1,1,1,1); and adjust the coordinates so as to impose the de Donder gauge conditions

$$\mathfrak{g}^{\alpha\beta}{}_{,\beta} = - \bar{h}^{\alpha\beta}{}_{,\beta} = 0. \tag{3.7}$$

Then the Einstein field equations take on the form (Landau and Lifshitz 1962, eq. 100.4; MTW eq. 20.21)

$$\underbrace{\mathfrak{g}^{\mu\nu} \bar{h}^{\alpha\beta}{}_{,\mu\nu}} = -16\pi(-g)(T^{\alpha\beta} + t^{\alpha\beta}_{LL}) - \bar{h}^{\alpha\mu}{}_{,\nu} \bar{h}^{\beta\nu}{}_{,\mu} \tag{3.8}$$

characteristics: null rays of metric $g_{\alpha\beta}$

or, equivalently

$$\underbrace{\eta^{\mu\nu} \bar{h}^{\alpha\beta}{}_{,\mu\nu}} = -16\pi(-g)(T^{\alpha\beta} + t^{\alpha\beta}_{LL}) - \bar{h}^{\alpha\mu}{}_{,\nu} \bar{h}^{\beta\nu}{}_{,\mu} + \bar{h}^{\alpha\beta}{}_{,\mu\nu} \bar{h}^{\mu\nu} \equiv W^{\alpha\beta}. \tag{3.8'}$$

characteristics: flat-spacetime rays

Here $t^{\alpha\beta}_{LL}$ is the Landau-Lifshitz pseudotensor (Landau and Lifshitz 1962, eq. 100.7; MTW eq. 20.22) which, in de Donder gauge, can be written as

$$\begin{aligned} 16\pi(-g)t^{\alpha\beta}_{LL} = {} & \tfrac{1}{2}\, \mathfrak{g}^{\alpha\beta} \mathfrak{g}_{\lambda\mu}\, \bar{h}^{\lambda\nu}{}_{,\rho} \bar{h}^{\rho\mu}{}_{,\nu} + \mathfrak{g}_{\lambda\mu} \mathfrak{g}^{\nu\rho} \bar{h}^{\alpha\lambda}{}_{,\nu} \bar{h}^{\beta\mu}{}_{,\rho} \\ & - (\mathfrak{g}^{\alpha\lambda} \mathfrak{g}_{\mu\nu} \bar{h}^{\beta\nu}{}_{,\rho} \bar{h}^{\mu\rho}{}_{,\lambda} + \mathfrak{g}^{\beta\lambda} \mathfrak{g}_{\mu\nu} \bar{h}^{\alpha\nu}{}_{,\rho} \bar{h}^{\mu\rho}{}_{,\lambda}) \\ & + \tfrac{1}{8}\, (2\mathfrak{g}^{\alpha\lambda} \mathfrak{g}^{\beta\mu} - \mathfrak{g}^{\alpha\beta} \mathfrak{g}^{\lambda\mu})(2\mathfrak{g}_{\nu\rho} \mathfrak{g}_{\sigma\tau} - \mathfrak{g}_{\rho\sigma} \mathfrak{g}_{\nu\tau}) \bar{h}^{\nu\tau}{}_{,\lambda} \bar{h}^{\rho\sigma}{}_{,\mu} \end{aligned} \tag{3.9}$$

where $\mathfrak{g}_{\alpha\beta} = (-g)^{-\frac{1}{2}} g_{\alpha\beta}$ is the inverse of $\mathfrak{g}^{\alpha\beta}$. The law of local conservation of energy and momentum $T^{\alpha\beta}{}_{;\beta} = 0$ can be written in terms of partial derivations as

$$\left[(-g)(T^{\alpha\beta} + t^{\alpha\beta}_{LL})\right]_{,\beta} = 0 \tag{3.10}$$

(Landau and Lifshitz 1964, eq. 100.8; MTW eq. 20.23b).

The field equations (3.8) and (3.8') can be thought of as wave equations for $\bar{h}^{\alpha\beta}$ with source terms that include "gravitational stress-energy" (nonlinear terms in $\bar{h}^{\mu\nu}$). In the form (3.8) the wave operator is that of curved spacetime; its characteristics are the null rays of the curved spacetime metric $g_{\alpha\beta}$, and none of the source terms involve second derivatives of $\bar{h}^{\mu\nu}$. By contrast the form (3.8') involves a flat-spacetime wave operator; it is obtained from (3.8) by moving the second derivative term $\bar{h}^{\alpha\beta}{}_{,\mu\nu}\bar{h}^{\mu\nu}$ out of the wave operator and into the source.

The form (3.8'), with its flat-spacetime wave operator $\Box \equiv \eta^{\mu\nu}\partial_\mu\partial_\nu$, has great computational advantages over (3.8): It can be solved (formally) for $\bar{h}^{\alpha\beta}$

using a flat-spacetime Green's function, whereas the (formal) solution of (3.8) requires a far more complicated curved-spacetime Green's function (cf. DeWitt and Brehme 1960); and its solution is naturally decomposed into spherical harmonics because spherical harmonics are eigenfunctions of the flat operator $\Box$ but not of the curve-spacetime wave operator (3.8).

On the other hand, the flat operator $\Box$ entails serious dangers: (i) It propagates gravitational waves with the wrong speed, thereby losing at linear order the "Coulomb" phase shift produced by the M/r field of the source, and then trying to correct for this loss at quadratic order with a term that diverges logarithmically in r far from the source. I avoid this danger by restricting my use of $\Box$ to the "wave generation problem", which is formulated entirely at radii $r < r_0$, and by using the correct curved-spacetime wave operator when studying "wave propagation" at radii $r > r_0$ [cf. the paragraph preceding eq. (1.8)]. (ii) The flat-operator field equations (3.8') produce divergences, due to the second-derivative source terms $\bar{h}^{\alpha\beta}{}_{,\mu\nu}\bar{h}^{\mu\nu}$, in calculations of the gravitational interactions of (idealized) point particles; see, e.g., Crowley and Thorne (1977). I avoid this danger in these lectures and in RMP by not using point-particle idealizations.

I believe, and hope, that <u>all</u> of my calculations with the flat-operator field equations (3.8') have been so designed as to avoid these and other pitfalls.

3.1.4 Multipole moments of a fully relativistic, stationary system

The de Donder formulation (3.8') of the Einstein field equations can be used to extend the linearized multipole analysis of §3.1.1 to fully relativistic, stationary systems. Full details are given in §X of RMP. Here I shall sketch the methods and summarize the results.

The key idea of the analysis is to construct, in de Donder gauge, the <u>general</u> external gravitational field of a fully relativistic, stationary (time-independent) system surrounded by vacuum. The de Donder coordinates are chosen to be stationary and asymptotically flat – i.e., to satisfy, in addition to equations (3.6)-(3.10), also

$$\bar{h}^{\alpha\beta}{}_{,0} = 0; \qquad \bar{h}^{\alpha\beta} \propto 1/r \quad \text{as} \quad r \equiv (\delta_{ij}x^i x^j)^{\frac{1}{2}} \to \infty . \tag{3.11}$$

For such a system the gauge conditions (3.7) and vacuum field equations (3.8') are

$$\bar{h}^{\alpha j}{}_{,j} = 0; \; \bar{h}^{\alpha\beta}{}_{,jj} = W^{\alpha\beta} = \left(\begin{array}{l}\text{expression of quadratic order and higher in}\\ \bar{h}^{\mu\nu} \text{ and its spatial derivatives, each term}\\ \text{containing precisely two spatial derivatives}\end{array}\right). \tag{3.12}$$

Here and throughout this section I use the notation of flat-space Cartesian coordinates in which the location of spatial indices, up or down, is of no importance. Equations (3.12) can be solved by a "nonlinearity expansion" in which terms of first order are linear in $\bar{h}^{\alpha\beta}$ (or, equivalently, linear in the gravitation constant $G = 1$), terms of second order are quadratic, etc. The first-order part of $\bar{h}^{\alpha\beta}$, denoted ${}_1\bar{h}^{\alpha\beta}$, satisfies the linearized equations ${}_1\bar{h}^{\alpha j}{}_{,j} = 0$ and ${}_1\bar{h}^{\alpha\beta}{}_{,jj} = 0$ and thus, with specialization of gauge and mass centering of coordinates, has the general linearized-theory form (3.2):

$$\begin{aligned}{}_1\bar{h}^{00} &= \frac{4M}{r} + \sum_{\ell=2}^{\infty} \frac{4(2\ell-1)!!}{\ell!\,r^{\ell+1}} \mathscr{I}_{A_\ell} N_{A_\ell} , \\ {}_1\bar{h}^{0j} &= \sum_{\ell=1}^{\infty} \frac{4\ell(2\ell-1)!!}{(\ell+1)!\,r^{\ell+1}} \epsilon_{jka_\ell} \mathscr{S}_{kA_{\ell-1}} N_{A_{\ell-1}} , \qquad \bar{h}^{ij} = 0.\end{aligned} \tag{3.13}$$

The quadratic-order part ${}_2\bar{h}^{\alpha\beta}$ satisfies

$$ {}_2\bar{h}^{\alpha j}{}_{,j} = 0, \qquad {}_2\bar{h}^{\alpha\beta}{}_{,jj} = \begin{pmatrix} \text{quadratic part of } W^{\alpha\beta} \\ \text{constructed from } {}_1\bar{h}^{\mu\nu} \end{pmatrix} . \tag{3.14} $$

It is straightforward, though tedious, to solve these equations for ${}_2\bar{h}^{\alpha\beta}$ and for higher-order corrections — the kind of task ideally suited for symbolic-manipulation software on a computer; cf. Appendix of Gürsel (1982). The full details are not of interest here, but the spherical-harmonic structure of the solution is of interest. That structure is dictated by the following properties of spherical harmonics: (i) Taking gradients and inverting Laplacians does not change the spherical-harmonic order of a term; and (ii) the product of two harmonics of order ℓ and ℓ' contains pieces of orders $\ell+\ell'$, $\ell+\ell'-1$, ..., $|\ell-\ell'|$. These properties plus the quadratic-order equations (3.14) and linear-order solutions (3.13) imply that the generic term in ${}_2\bar{h}^{\alpha\beta}$ has the form

$$ {}_2\bar{h}^{\alpha\beta} \sim \frac{\mathcal{M}_{A_\ell}}{r^{\ell+1}} \cdot \frac{\mathcal{M}_{B_{\ell'}}}{r^{\ell'+1}} \sim \frac{S_{\ell+\ell'} + S_{\ell+\ell'-1} + \dots + S_{|\ell-\ell'|}}{r^{\ell+\ell'+2}} . \tag{3.15} $$

Here $\mathcal{M}_{A_\ell} = (\mathcal{I}_{A_\ell} \text{ or } \mathcal{S}_{A_\ell})$, $\mathcal{M}_{B_{\ell'}} = (\mathcal{I}_{B_{\ell'}} \text{ or } \mathcal{S}_{B_{\ell'}})$, and $S_\ell \equiv$ (something unspecified that has harmonic order ℓ and is independent of r). The key feature of this generic term is that the power $\ell+\ell'+2$ of its radial dependence is larger by a factor 2 than the order of any of its harmonics. By an extension of this argument one sees that in ${}_n\bar{h}^{\alpha\beta}$ the generic term of order $1/r^k$ has harmonics of order k-n and smaller. Thus, the nonlinear parts of the solution add up to give

$$ {}_2\bar{h}^{\alpha\beta} + {}_3\bar{h}^{\alpha\beta} + \dots = \sum_{\ell=1}^{\infty} \frac{1}{r^{\ell+1}} (S_{\ell-1} + S_{\ell-2} + \dots + S_0). \tag{3.16} $$

By adding these to ${}_1\bar{h}^{\alpha\beta}$ and then computing the corresponding metric from (3.6) one obtains

$$ g_{00} = -1 + 2\frac{M}{r} - 2\frac{M^2}{r^2} + \sum_{\ell=2}^{\infty} \frac{1}{r^{\ell+1}} \left[\frac{2(2\ell-1)!!}{\ell!} \mathcal{I}_{A_\ell} N_{A_\ell} + S_{\ell-1} + \dots + S_0 \right], \tag{3.17a} $$

$$ g_{0j} = \sum_{\ell=1}^{\infty} \frac{1}{r^{\ell+1}} \left[-\frac{4\ell(2\ell-1)!!}{(\ell+1)!} \epsilon_{jka_\ell} \mathcal{S}_{kA_{\ell-1}} N_{A_\ell} + S_{\ell-1} + \dots + S_0 \right], \tag{3.17b} $$

$$ \begin{aligned} g_{ij} = {} & \delta_{ij}\left(1 + 2\frac{M}{r}\right) + \frac{M^2}{r^2}(\delta_{ij} + n_i n_j) \\ & + \sum_{\ell=2}^{\infty} \frac{1}{r^{\ell+1}} \left[\frac{2(2\ell-1)!!}{\ell!} \mathcal{I}_{A_\ell} N_{A_\ell} \delta_{ij} + S_{\ell-1} + \dots + S_0 \right] . \end{aligned} \tag{3.17c} $$

Note the following features of this general, asymptotically flat, stationary, vacuum metric: (i) As in linearized theory, so also here, the metric is determined fully by two families of moments: the mass moments M, $\mathcal{I}_{ij}$, $\mathcal{I}_{ijk}$,...; and the current moments $\mathcal{S}_i$, $\mathcal{S}_{ij}$, $\mathcal{S}_{ijk}$,... . (ii) The mass dipole moment vanishes because I have insisted that the coordinates be mass centered. (iii) The moments are constant STF tensors that reside in the asymptotically flat region of spacetime (i.e., rigorously speaking, at spacelike infinity). (iv) In de Donder coordinates the mass ℓ-pole moment $\mathcal{I}_{A_\ell}$ can be "read off" the metric as the $1/r^{\ell+1}$, ℓ-harmonic-order part of g_{00}; and the current ℓ-pole moment $\mathcal{S}_{A_\ell}$ can similarly be read off g_{0j}.

It would be very unpleasant if one had to transform a metric to de Donder coordinates in order to compute its multipole moments. Fortunately, there are other ways of computing them. If one only wants to know the moments of order $\ell = 0, 1, 2, \ldots, \ell_{max}$, it is adequate to find coordinates where the metric has the form

$$g_{\alpha\beta} = \eta_{\alpha\beta} + \sum_{\ell=0}^{\ell_{max}-1} r^{-(\ell+1)} \left[S_\ell + S_{\ell-1} + \ldots + S_0\right] + O\left[r^{-(\ell_{max}+1)}\right], \tag{3.18}$$

with the $1/r^2$ dipole of g_{00} vanishing. Such coordinates are called "Asymptotically Cartesian and Mass Centered to order ℓ_{max}-1" [ACMC – (ℓ_{max}-1)]. In them one can read off the first ℓ_{max} moments (both mass and current) by the same prescription as in de Donder coordinates, and one will obtain the same answers as one would in de Donder coordinates (RMP §XI). Alternatively, one can compute the moments by elegant techniques at spacelike infinity, due to Geroch (1970) and Hansen (1974). As Gürsel (1982) has shown, the Geroch-Hansen prescription gives the same moments as the above, aside from normalization:

$$\mathcal{I}_{A_\ell} = \frac{1}{(2\ell-1)!!} \mathcal{M}_{A_\ell}, \quad \mathcal{S}_{A_\ell} = \frac{(\ell+1)}{2\ell(2\ell-1)!!} \mathcal{J}_{A_\ell}, \tag{3.19}$$

where $\mathcal{M}_{A_\ell}$ and $\mathcal{J}_{A_\ell}$ are the Geroch-Hansen moments.

3.2 Gravitational wave generation by slow-motion sources: $\lambda\!\!\!^{-} \gg L \gtrsim M$

3.2.1 Metric in the weak-field near zone

Turn attention now from stationary systems to a system with slowly changing gravitational field:

$$\lambda\!\!\!^{-} \equiv \begin{pmatrix}\text{timescale} \\ \text{of changes}\end{pmatrix} \gg L \equiv \begin{pmatrix}\text{size of} \\ \text{system}\end{pmatrix} \gtrsim M \equiv \begin{pmatrix}\text{mass of} \\ \text{system}\end{pmatrix}. \tag{3.20}$$

Such a "slow-motion" system possesses a weak-field near zone (WFNZ)

$$(10M \text{ and } L) < r < \lambda\!\!\!^{-}/10 \tag{3.21}$$

(Fig. 2 and associated discussion). In that WFNZ and in de Donder gauge I have developed an algorithm for computing the general "gravitational field" $\bar{h}^{\alpha\beta}$ and the spacetime metric $g_{\alpha\beta}$; see §IX of RMP. That algorithm is based on a simultaneous "nonlinearity expansion" like that used above for stationary systems, and "slow-motion expansion" – i.e., expansion of the time evolution of the metric in powers of $r/\lambda\!\!\!^{-}$.

At lowest order in $r/\lambda\!\!\!^{-}$, $\bar{h}^{\alpha\beta}$ and $g_{\alpha\beta}$ are identical to the general stationary solution (eqs. 3.13, 3.16, 3.17); except that now the multipole moments of order $\ell \geq 2$ are slowly changing functions of time t rather than constants. [The $\ell = 0$ and $\ell = 1$ moments, M = (mass) and $\mathcal{S}_j$ = (angular momentum) are forced, by the field equations, to be constant at lowest order in $r/\lambda\!\!\!^{-}$; but they change due to radiation reaction at orders $(r/\lambda\!\!\!^{-})^5$ and higher.] The slow time changes of $\mathcal{I}_{A_\ell}(t)$ and $\mathcal{S}_{A_\ell}(t)$ produce, through the field equations (3.8') and gauge conditions (3.7) and through matching to outgoing waves at $r \gtrsim \lambda\!\!\!^{-}$, the "motional" corrections of order $r/\lambda\!\!\!^{-}$, $(r/\lambda\!\!\!^{-})^2, \ldots$ to $\bar{h}^{\alpha\beta}$ and $g_{\alpha\beta}$.

3.2.2 Metric in the induction zone and local wave zone

In the inner parts $r \ll \lambda\!\!\!^{-}$ of the WFNZ the motional corrections are very small but the nonlinear corrections may be large; and $\bar{h}^{\alpha\beta}$, $g_{\alpha\beta}$ are essentially those of a stationary system (eqs. 3.13, 3.16, 3.17) with slowly changing moments. In the outer parts $r \gg L \gtrsim M$ of the WFNZ the nonlinear corrections are very small but as r nears $\lambda\!\!\!^{-}$ the motional corrections become large. This allows us to ignore nonlinearities when extending the $\bar{h}^{\alpha\beta}$ of the outer part of the WFNZ into the induction zone and local wave zone. In other words, we can compute $\bar{h}^{\alpha\beta}$ in the induction zone and local wave zone by constructing the general outgoing-wave solution of the linearized, time-dependent, vacuum field equations and gauge conditions

$$\eta^{\mu\nu}\,\bar{h}^{\alpha\beta}{}_{,\mu\nu} = 0, \qquad \bar{h}^{\alpha\beta}{}_{,\beta} = 0; \tag{3.22}$$

and by matching that solution onto the $O([r/\lambda\!\!\!^{-}]^0)$ solution (3.13), (3.16) in the WFNZ. The result is

$$\bar{h}^{00} = \frac{4M}{r} + \sum_{\ell=2}^{\infty} (-1)^{\ell}\,\frac{4}{\ell!}\left[\frac{1}{r}\,\mathcal{I}_{A_\ell}(t-r)\right]_{,A_\ell} + \begin{pmatrix}\text{small nonlinear}\\ \text{terms}\end{pmatrix}, \tag{3.23a}$$

$$\begin{aligned}\bar{h}^{0j} = {} & \frac{2\epsilon_{jpq}\mathcal{S}_p n_q}{r^2} + \sum_{\ell=2}^{\infty} (-1)^{\ell}\,\frac{4\ell}{(\ell+1)!}\left[\frac{1}{r}\,\epsilon_{jpq}\mathcal{S}_{pA_{\ell-1}}(t-r)\right]_{,qA_{\ell-1}} \\ & - \sum_{\ell=2}^{\infty} (-1)^{\ell}\,\frac{4}{\ell!}\left[\frac{1}{r}\,\dot{\mathcal{I}}_{jA_{\ell-1}}(t-r)\right]_{,A_{\ell-1}} + \begin{pmatrix}\text{small nonlinear}\\ \text{terms}\end{pmatrix},\end{aligned} \tag{3.23b}$$

$$\begin{aligned}\bar{h}^{jk} = \sum_{\ell=2}^{\infty} \Bigg\{ & (-1)^{\ell}\,\frac{4}{\ell!}\left[\frac{1}{r}\,\ddot{\mathcal{I}}_{jkA_{\ell-2}}(t-r)\right]_{,A_{\ell-2}} + (-1)^{\ell+1}\,\frac{8\ell}{(\ell+1)!}\,\times \\ & \times\left[\frac{1}{r}\,\epsilon_{pq(j}\dot{\mathcal{S}}_{k)pA_{\ell-2}}(t-r)\right]_{,qA_{\ell-2}}\Bigg\} + (\text{small nonlinear terms}).\end{aligned} \tag{3.23c}$$

Here dots denote $\partial/\partial t$, and as indicated the moments with $\ell \geq 2$ are to be regarded as functions of t-r. The dominant nonlinear corrections to this solution are discussed in §IX of RMP; see also equation (3.25) below. The metric can be computed from (3.23) via equations (3.6), which reduce to

$$g_{\alpha\beta} = \eta_{\alpha\beta} + h_{\alpha\beta} + \text{nonlinearities}, \qquad h_{\alpha\beta} = \bar{h}_{\alpha\beta} - \tfrac{1}{2}\,\bar{h}\eta_{\alpha\beta}\,, \tag{3.24}$$

where indices on $\bar{h}^{\alpha\beta}$ are lowered (as usual) using $\eta_{\mu\nu}$.

The matching of the solution (3.23) onto that of the WFNZ can be done either by elementary techniques, which require care and thought, or by the sophisticated technique of "matched asymptotic expansions" (see the lecture by Kates in this volume; also those of Damour), which do the job with less danger of error.

* * * * *

Exercise 19. Show that (3.23) without nonlinear terms is an exact solution of the linearized field equations and gauge conditions (3.22). Then, at radii $r \ll \lambda\!\!\!^{-}$, expand (3.23) in powers of $r/\lambda\!\!\!^{-}$ and show that the leading terms, of

$O([r/\lambda\!\!\!^{-}]^0)$, is identical to the linear part (3.13) of the WFNZ field.

3.2.3 Gravitational-wave field in local wave zone

The gravitational-wave field h^{TT}_{jk} of the local wave zone can be computed from expression (3.23c) by letting the spatial derivatives all act on $\mathcal{I}$ and $\mathcal{S}$ (so as to keep only the $1/r$ part of the field); and by then taking the TT part. The result is

$$h^{TT}_{jk} = \left\{ \sum_{\ell=2}^{\infty} \frac{1}{r}\frac{4}{\ell!}\, {}^{(\ell)}\mathcal{I}_{jkA_{\ell-2}}(t-r)\, N_{A_{\ell-2}} + \sum_{\ell=2}^{\infty} \frac{1}{r}\frac{8\ell}{(\ell+1)!}\, \epsilon_{pq(j}\, {}^{(\ell)}\mathcal{S}_{k)pA_{\ell-2}}(t-r)\, n_q N_{A_{\ell-2}} \right\}^{TT} \left\{ 1 + O\!\left(\frac{M}{\lambda\!\!\!^{-}} \ln \frac{\lambda\!\!\!^{-}}{L}\right) \right\} \tag{3.25}$$

effects of nonlinearities (the $O(\ldots)$ term).

Here a prefix superscript (ℓ) means "take ℓ time derivatives"

$${}^{(\ell)}\mathcal{I} \equiv (\partial/\partial t)^{\ell}\mathcal{I} ; \tag{3.26}$$

and I have indicated the magnitude of the cumulative effects of nonlinearities, integrated up from the inner part of the WFNZ into the local wave zone, which in effect cause the multipole moments of the radiation field to differ slightly from those one would measure in the inner part of the weak-field near zone; see §IX.H of RMP.

Note that the mass quadrupole part of the radiation field (3.25) has the familiar form first derived (in different notation) by Einstein (1918):

$$h^{TT}_{jk} = \frac{2}{r}\, \ddot{\mathcal{I}}^{TT}_{jk}(t-r). \tag{3.27}$$

For most slow-motion systems these mass quadrupole waves will dominate; but when quadrupole motions are suppressed by special symmetries (e.g., in torsional oscillations of neutron stars, §3.2.7 below), other moments may dominate. Note that, in the absence of suppression due to symmetries, the magnitudes of the various multipole components of the waves are

$$\left(h^{TT}_{jk}\right)_{\text{mass } \ell\text{-pole}} \sim \frac{M}{r}\left(\frac{L}{\lambda\!\!\!^{-}}\right)^{\ell}, \quad \left(h^{TT}_{jk}\right)_{\text{current } \ell\text{-pole}} \sim \frac{M}{r}\, v \left(\frac{L}{\lambda\!\!\!^{-}}\right)^{\ell} \tag{3.28}$$

(cf. eq. 3.4). Typically the internal velocity v will be of order $L/\lambda\!\!\!^{-}$, so

$$\begin{gathered}(\text{current quadrupole waves}) \sim (\text{mass octupole waves}),\\ (\text{current } \ell\text{-pole waves}) \sim (\text{mass } [\ell+1]\text{-pole waves}).\end{gathered} \tag{3.29}$$

This is the same pattern as one sees in electromagnetism, for which "electric" multipoles are the analogs of "mass" multipoles and "magnetic" multipoles are the analogs of "current" multipoles.

3.2.4 Slow-motion method of computing wave generation

Equations (3.17) and (3.25) are the foundation for the slow-motion method of computing gravitational-wave generation (RMP §XII): (i) Analyze the near-zone structure and evolution of any slow-motion ($\lambda\!\!\!^{-} \gg L \gtrsim M$) system in any convenient coordinate system and by any approximation scheme that gives, with reasonable fractional accuracy, the time evolution of the system's asymmetries. [One attractive approximation scheme is the "instantaneous gravity" method, in which one sets to zero all time derivatives of the metric (but not of the matter variables) when solving the near-zone Einstein field equations; see, e.g., Thorne (1983) and Schumaker and Thorne (1983).] (ii) From the near-zone analysis obtain an approximation to the system's external gravitational field which, at any moment, satisfies the time-independent, vacuum Einstein equations. (iii) Compute the dominant multipole moments of that quasistationary field (moments with largest values of ${}^{(\ell)}\mathcal{I}_{A_\ell}$ or ${}^{(\ell)}\mathcal{S}_{A_\ell}$) either by transforming to de Donder or ACMC coordinates and comparing with equations (3.17), or by the methods of Geroch (1970) and Hansen (1974) plus equation (3.19). (iv) Insert those moments into equation (3.25) to obtain the radiation field in the local wave zone.

3.2.5 Example: Rigidly rotating neutron star

As an example, consider the gravitational waves produced by a slowly rotating neutron star (pulsar) idealized as a non-axisymmetric, fully relativistic body which rotates rigidly. Full details are given in Gürsel and Thorne (1983); the main ideas will be sketched here.

The star can rotate rigidly (distance between every pair of neighboring "material particles" forever fixed) only to first order in the angular velocity Ω. At order $(\Omega L)^2$ there is a Lorentz contraction of distances; and as the star's angular velocity precesses that Lorentz contraction changes. Thus, the Gürsel-Thorne analysis, which assumes rigid rotation and works to first order in Ω, has fractional errors of order ΩL.

Gürsel and Thorne show, by a de Donder-gauge analysis of the star's interior [step (i) of "slow-motion wave-generation method"] that to first order in Ω the star's angular momentum $\mathcal{S}_j$ and its angular velocity Ω_j (which are both spatial vectors residing in the nearly flat, weak-field near zone) are proportional to each other

$$\mathcal{S}_j = I_{jk}\Omega_k; \tag{3.30a}$$

and that their ratio, the moment of inertia tensor, is symmetric and rotates with angular velocity Ω_j

$$I_{jk} = I_{kj}, \quad \dot{I}_{jk} = \epsilon_{jpq}\Omega_p I_{qk} + \epsilon_{kpq}\Omega_p I_{qj}. \tag{3.30b}$$

Of course, the angular momentum is conserved (aside from negligible radiation-reaction changes)

$$\dot{\mathcal{S}}_j = 0. \tag{3.30c}$$

Equations (3.30) are identical to the classical Euler equations which govern the precession of a rigidly rotating, nongravitating body (Goldstein 1980). Thus, any fully relativistic, slowly ($\Omega L \ll 1$) and rigidly rotating body undergoes a free precession which is identical to that of a nongravitating body with the same moment of inertia I_{jk} and the same angular momentum $\mathcal{S}_j$. The only influence of relativistic gravity will be through its influence on the values of the components of the moment of inertia tensor I_{jk}; cf. Hartle (1973). Gürsel and Thorne go on to show that the mass moments $\mathcal{I}_{A_\ell}$, which characterize g_{00} in the weak-field near zone, like I_{jk} rotate with angular velocity Ω_j:

$$\dot{\mathcal{I}}_{jk} = \epsilon_{jpq}\Omega_p\mathcal{I}_{qk} + \epsilon_{kpq}\Omega_p\mathcal{I}_{jq}, \quad \text{and similarly for } \mathcal{I}_{A_\ell}. \tag{3.31}$$

The mass quadrupole $\mathscr{I}_{jk}$ will be the dominant source of gravitational waves unless the star has very unexpected symmetries. The waves that it produces are described by the standard quadrupole-moment formula

$$h^{TT}_{jk} = (2/r)\, \ddot{\mathscr{I}}^{TT}_{jk}(t-r). \tag{3.32}$$

Because the precessional equations (3.30) are identical to those of Euler and the waves are given by the same standard quadrupole moment formula (3.32) as one often uses for weakly gravitating systems, one might expect the waves from a fully relativistic, rigidly and slowly rotating body to be the same as those from a weakly gravitating body with the same moment of inertia. However, I doubt that this is so, because I suspect that relativistic gravity destroys the classical relationship

$$\mathscr{I}_{jk} = I_{jk} - \frac{1}{3} I_{ii}\, \delta_{jk} \tag{3.33}$$

between the quadrupole moment and the moment of inertia.

Zimmermann and Szedenitz (1979) and Zimmermann (1980) have computed in detail the quadrupole waves from a rigidly and slowly rotating body under the assumption that the classical relationship (3.33) is preserved. They show that the spectrum of the waves is rather rich and contains much detailed information about the star's angular momentum vector and moment of inertia tensor. Future theoretical studies should probe the possible breakdown of the classical relation (3.33) and should quantify deviations from rigid-body rotation due to the finiteness of the shear modulus and bulk modulus of neutron-star matter.

3.2.6 Example: compact binary system

Consider a binary system with stars sufficiently compact that tidal distortions of each other can be ignored (this is frequently true), and with separation between stars that is large compared to gravitational radii. Then general relativistic "near-zone" analyses (e.g., Damour in this volume; or, for the case of two black holes, D'Eath 1975) show that the orbital motions are Keplerian, aside from post-Newtonian corrections of size (gravitational radii)/(separation of stars); and this is true no matter how strong the stars' internal gravity may be. Moreover, the quadrupole moment which one reads off the weak-field, near-zone metric in de Donder gauge (eq. 3.17; Damour in this volume) is the same and evolves the same as that which one would compute for the Kepler problem using Newtonian techniques; and thus the gravitational waves obtained by inserting that quadrupole moment into $h^{TT}_{jk} = (2/r)\ddot{\mathscr{I}}^{TT}_{jk}$ are the same as one would compute for a nearly Newtonian system with the same masses and semimajor axis. For details of those waves see Peters and Mathews (1963).

3.2.7 Example: torsional oscillations of a neutron star

"Glitches" observed in the timing of pulsars are thought to be due to starquakes, i.e., due to ruptures in the crystalline crust of the neutron star. Such ruptures may trigger torsional oscillations of the star with a restoring force, due to the crystal's shear modulus, which is sufficiently small that the oscillations are slow ($\lambda\!\!\!{}^{-} \gg L$). In such oscillations its mass-energy density T^{00} remains constant while the momentum density T^{0j} oscillates; and, as a result, the star's mass quadrupole moment $\mathscr{I}_{jk}$ is constant but its current quadrupole moment $\mathscr{S}_{jk}$ oscillates. The resulting gravitational waves are thus current quadrupole rather than mass quadrupole

$$h^{TT}_{jk} = \left[\frac{8}{3r}\, \epsilon_{pq(j}\ddot{\mathscr{S}}_{k)p}(t-r)\, n_q\right]^{TT}. \tag{3.34}$$

Schumaker and Thorne (1983) have analyzed such torsional oscillations in detail using perturbation theory and have derived, in the "instantaneous gravity approximation", an eigenequation that governs the oscillations and determines the current quadrupole moment $\mathcal{S}_{jk}(t)$ for insertion into the gravity-wave formula (3.34).

3.3 Multipole decomposition of arbitrary waves in the local wave zone

3.3.1 The radiation field

The gravitational waves from any source — slow-motion or fast, weak-gravity or strong — can be decomposed into multipole components in the local wave zone. The multipole moments can be computed as surface integrals of the radiation field (RMP eq. 4.11):

$$^{(\ell)}\mathcal{I}_{A_\ell} = \left[\frac{\ell(\ell-1)(2\ell+1)!!}{2(\ell+1)(\ell+2)} \frac{r}{4\pi} \int h^{TT}_{a_1 a_2} n_{a_3} \ldots n_{a_\ell} \, d\Omega\right]^{STF} , \tag{3.35a}$$

$$^{(\ell)}\mathcal{S}_{A_\ell} = \left[\frac{(\ell-1)(2\ell+1)!!}{4(\ell+2)} \frac{r}{4\pi} \int \epsilon_{a_1 jk} n_j h^{TT}_{ka_2} n_{a_3} \ldots n_{a_\ell} \, d\Omega\right]^{STF} ; \tag{3.35b}$$

and the field can be reconstructed as a sum over the multipole moments — the same sum as we encountered in the theory of slow-motion sources (eq. 3.25)

$$h^{TT}_{jk} = \sum_{\ell=2}^{\infty} \left\{ \frac{1}{r} \frac{4}{\ell!} \, {}^{(\ell)}\mathcal{I}_{jkA_{\ell-2}}(t-r) N_{A_{\ell-2}} + \frac{1}{r} \frac{8\ell}{(\ell+1)!} \epsilon_{pq(j} \, {}^{(\ell)}\mathcal{S}_{k)pA_{\ell-2}}(t-r) n_q N_{A_{\ell-2}} \right\}^{TT} . \tag{3.36}$$

For slow-motion sources the lowest few moments will dominate; but for fast-motion sources the radiation may be highly directional and many moments may contribute. See, e.g., Kovács and Thorne (1978) for the example of "gravitational bremsstrahlung radiation", in which the radiation from one particle flying past another at a speed $v \simeq 1$ is beamed forward into a cone of half angle $\sim \gamma^{-1} = (1-v^2)^{1/2} \ll 1$, and moments $\ell = 2, 3, 4, \ldots, \gamma$ all contribute significantly to the waves. In such cases multipole expansions are not very useful.

3.3.2 The energy, momentum, and angular momentum carried by the waves

In the local wave zone the gravitational waves, which have $\ell \geq 2$, coexist with the (nearly) time-independent $\ell = 0$ (mass) and $\ell = 1$ (angular momentum) parts of the source's gravitational field; in TT gauge and neglecting nonlinearities and induction terms the total spacetime metric is

$$\underbrace{g_{00} = -1 + 2M/r}_{\ell=0} , \quad \underbrace{g_{0j} = (-2/r^2)\epsilon_{jk\ell}\mathcal{S}_k n_\ell}_{\ell=1} , \quad g_{jk} = \underbrace{(1 + 2M/r)\delta_{jk}}_{\ell=0} + \underbrace{h^{TT}_{jk}}_{\ell\geq 2} . \tag{3.37}$$

This metric is written in coordinates that coincide with the asymptotic rest frame of the source; in this frame the source's linear momentum P_j vanishes; i.e., the 4-momentum (a 4-vector residing in the asymptotically flat region) is $\vec{P} = M\partial/\partial t$.

The gravitational waves carry 4-momentum and angular momentum away from the source, thereby causing changes in the asymptotic rest frame, in M, and in S_j. A detailed analysis of those changes is given in chapters 19 and 20 of MTW; here I shall sketch only one variant of the main ideas.

The foundation for the analysis is the quantity

$$H^{\mu\alpha\nu\beta} \equiv \mathfrak{g}^{\mu\nu}\mathfrak{g}^{\alpha\beta} - \mathfrak{g}^{\alpha\nu}\mathfrak{g}^{\mu\beta}, \tag{3.38}$$

where $\mathfrak{g}^{\alpha\beta}$ is the metric density of equations (3.6) and Lorentz gauge is not being imposed. In the asymptotic rest frame of the source, where the metric is (3.37) plus nonlinearities and induction terms, the surface integral of $H^{\mu\alpha0j}{}_{,\alpha}$ plucks out the $1/r$ $\ell = 0$ and $\ell = 1$ parts of $g_{\alpha\beta}$ (which have zero contribution from nonlinearities and induction terms); i.e., it gives the 4-momentum of the source:

$$P^{\mu} = \frac{1}{16\pi}\oint H^{\mu\alpha0j}{}_{,\alpha}\, d^2S_j = \begin{cases} 0 \text{ for } P^j \\ M \text{ for } P^0, \end{cases} \tag{3.39}$$

where d^2S_j is the surface element computed as though spacetime were flat. The rate of change of the 4-momentum is computed, with the help of Einstein's vacuum field equations in the form $H^{\mu\alpha\nu\beta}{}_{,\alpha\beta} = -H^{\mu\alpha\beta\nu}{}_{,\alpha\beta} = 16\pi(-g)t^{\alpha\beta}_{LL}$ (MTW eq. 20.21):

$$\begin{aligned}\frac{dP^{\mu}}{dt} &= \frac{1}{16\pi}\oint H^{\mu\alpha0j}{}_{,\alpha0}\, d^2S_j = \frac{1}{16\pi}\oint \left[H^{\mu\alpha\beta j}{}_{,\alpha\beta} - H^{\mu\alpha ij}{}_{,\alpha i}\right] d^2S_j \\ &= -\oint(-g)t^{\mu j}_{LL}\, d^2S_j - \frac{1}{16\pi}\underbrace{\int H^{\mu\alpha ij}{}_{,\alpha ij}\, dx^1dx^2dx^3}_{0}.\end{aligned} \tag{3.40}$$

The volume integral vanishes by symmetry; and the conversion from surface integral to volume integral requires the topology of the space slices to be Euclidean — which it always can be for astrophysically realistic systems, including those with black holes (see Fig. 5). By averaging equation (3.40) over Δt = (several $\lambda\!\!\!{}^{-}$) and noting that the average of the Landau-Lifshitz pseudotensor is equal to the Isaacson stress-energy tensor for the gravitational waves (MTW exercise 35.19), we obtain

$$\langle dM/dt\rangle = -\oint T^{0r}_{(W)}\, r^2 d\Omega, \quad \langle dP^j/dt\rangle = -\oint T^{jr}_{(W)}\, r^2 d\Omega. \tag{3.41}$$

When the waves are decomposed into multipoles (eq. 3.36) these integrals give (RMP eqs. 4.16' and 4.20'):

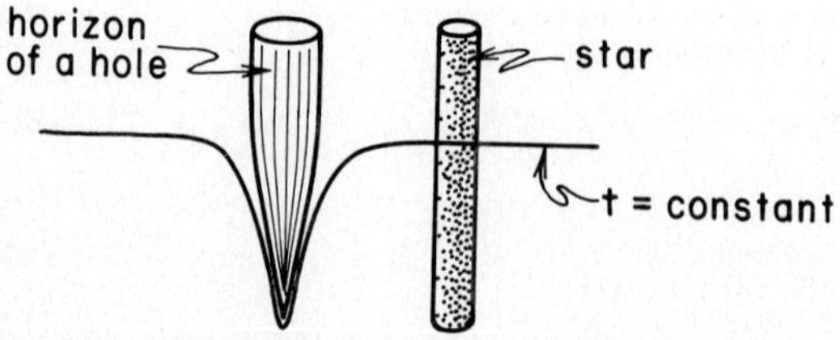

Fig. 5. Spacetime diagram showing how the slices of constant time can be chosen everywhere spacelike and have Euclidean topology even in the presence of a black hole.

$$\left\langle \frac{dM}{dt} \right\rangle = -\sum_{\ell=2}^{\infty} \left\{ \frac{(\ell+1)(\ell+2)}{(\ell-1)\ell\cdot\ell!(2\ell+1)!!} \left\langle {}^{(\ell+1)}\mathcal{I}_{A_\ell} \; {}^{(\ell+1)}\mathcal{I}_{A_\ell} \right\rangle \right.$$

$$\left. + \frac{4\ell(\ell+2)}{(\ell-1)\cdot(\ell+1)!(2\ell+1)!!} \left\langle {}^{(\ell+1)}\mathcal{S}_{A_\ell} \; {}^{(\ell+1)}\mathcal{S}_{A_\ell} \right\rangle \right\} , \tag{3.42}$$

$$\left\langle \frac{dP_j}{dt} \right\rangle = -\sum_{\ell=2}^{\infty} \left\{ \frac{2(\ell+2)(\ell+3)}{\ell(\ell+1)!(2\ell+3)!!} \left\langle {}^{(\ell+2)}\mathcal{I}_{jA_\ell} \; {}^{(\ell+1)}\mathcal{I}_{A_\ell} \right\rangle \right.$$

$$+ \frac{8(\ell+3)}{(\ell+1)!(2\ell+3)!!} \left\langle {}^{(\ell+2)}\mathcal{S}_{jA_\ell} \; {}^{(\ell+1)}\mathcal{S}_{A_\ell} \right\rangle \tag{3.43}$$

$$\left. + \frac{8(\ell+2)}{(\ell-1)(\ell+1)!(2\ell+1)!!} \epsilon_{jpq} \left\langle {}^{(\ell+1)}\mathcal{I}_{pA_{\ell-1}} \; {}^{(\ell+1)}\mathcal{S}_{qA_{\ell-1}} \right\rangle \right\} .$$

Note that for typical slow-motion sources, with moments of order (3.4) and $v \sim L/\lambda\!\!\!^{-}$, the mass loss is predominantly due to the mass quadrupole moment beating against itself

$$\langle dM/dt \rangle = -(1/5) \langle \dddot{\mathcal{I}}_{jk} \dddot{\mathcal{I}}_{jk} \rangle \sim M^2 L^4/\lambda\!\!\!^{-6} ; \tag{3.44}$$

and the momentum change is due to the mass quadrupole beating against the mass octupole <u>and</u> against the current quadrupole:

$$\left\langle \frac{dP_j}{dt} \right\rangle = -\frac{2}{63} \langle \dddot{\mathcal{I}}_{ab} \ddddot{\mathcal{I}}_{abj} \rangle - \frac{16}{45} \epsilon_{jpq} \langle \dddot{\mathcal{I}}_{pa} \dddot{\mathcal{S}}_{qa} \rangle \sim \frac{M^2 L^5}{\lambda\!\!\!^{-7}} . \tag{3.45}$$

As the momentum of the source changes, its asymptotic rest frame changes. Since I have formulated my discussion of the external fields of slow-motion sources in mass-centered de Donder coordinates which coincide with the asymptotic rest frame, in applying my equations one must continually readjust the coordinates as time passes.

The intrinsic angular momentum of the source can be computed by a surface integral analogous to (3.39), which picks out the $1/r^2$ dipole part of the metric (3.37):

$$\mathcal{S}_j = \frac{1}{16\pi} \oint \epsilon_{jpq} (x^p H^{q\alpha 0i}{}_{,\alpha} + H^{pi0q}) d^2S_i . \tag{3.46}$$

By manipulations analogous to (3.40) one can show that

$$d\mathcal{S}_j/dt = -\oint \epsilon_{jpq} x^p (-g) t^{qr}_{LL} r^2 d\Omega . \tag{3.47}$$

By computing the Landau-Lifshitz pseudotensor (MTW eq. 20.22) for the local-wave-zone metric (3.37), inserting it into (3.47), and then averaging over Δt = (several $\lambda\!\!\!^{-}$), we obtain (RMP eq. 4.22)

$$\left\langle \frac{d\mathcal{S}_j}{dt} \right\rangle = \frac{1}{16\pi} \oint \epsilon_{jpq} x^p \langle -(h^{TT}_{qa} \dot{h}^{TT}_{ab})_{,b} + \tfrac{1}{2} h^{TT}_{ab,q} \dot{h}^{TT}_{ab} \rangle r^2 d\Omega . \tag{3.48}$$

When the multipole expansion (3.36) is inserted this becomes (RMP eq. 4.23'):

$$\left\langle\frac{d\mathcal{S}_j}{dt}\right\rangle = -\sum_{\ell=2}^{\infty}\left\{\frac{(\ell+1)(\ell+2)}{(\ell-1)\ell!(2\ell+1)!!}\,\epsilon_{jpq}\left\langle{}^{(\ell)}\mathcal{I}_{pA_{\ell-1}}\;{}^{(\ell+1)}\mathcal{I}_{qA_{\ell-1}}\right\rangle + \frac{4\ell^2(\ell+2)}{(\ell-1)(\ell+1)!(2\ell+1)!!}\,\epsilon_{jpq}\left\langle{}^{(\ell)}\mathcal{S}_{pA_{\ell-1}}\;{}^{(\ell+1)}\mathcal{S}_{qA_{\ell-1}}\right\rangle\right\} . \tag{3.49}$$

For typical slow-motion sources the dominant term is mass quadrupole beating against mass quadrupole:

$$\left\langle\frac{d\mathcal{S}_j}{dt}\right\rangle = \frac{2}{5}\,\epsilon_{jpq}\left\langle\ddot{\mathcal{I}}_{pa}\,\dddot{\mathcal{I}}_{qa}\right\rangle \sim \frac{M^2L^4}{\lambda\!\!\!^{-5}} . \tag{3.50}$$

The above analysis encounters serious difficulties for a source which changes its asymptotic rest frame significantly in a few gravity-wave periods, i.e., for which $|(dP_j/dt)\lambda\!\!\!^-| \sim M$. Because the local wave zone, where one constructs the above surface integrals, must have a size $\Delta r \gg \lambda\!\!\!^-$, the momentum of such a source is not well defined there (it is changing too fast); and thus there is no clean prescription for constructing the source's asymptotic rest frame or for "mass centering" the coordinates in it. As a result, the instantaneous mass M and linear momentum P_j of the source (which depend on the choice of time t) are somewhat ill defined; and the instantaneous angular momentum $\mathcal{S}_j$ is even more ill defined because it is sensitive to the mass centering (factor of x^p in eqs. 3.47, 3.48). This difficulty is discussed, using the Bondi-Sachs formulation of gravitational waves at "future null infinity", in a lecture by Ashtekar in this volume.

Fortunately for theorists (unfortunately for experimenters) all realistic astrophysical sources are believed to radiate momentum only weakly

$$|dP_j/dt| \ll M/\lambda\!\!\!^- \tag{3.51}$$

(see the lectures by Eardley) and thus have asymptotic rest frames that are well enough defined for the above analysis to be well founded.

3.3.3 Order-of-magnitude formulas

For typical slow-motion sources the gravitational-wave amplitude at earth (eq. 3.27 propagated on out to earth through a nearly flat universe) will be

$$h^{TT}_{jk} \simeq \frac{2}{r}\ddot{\mathcal{I}}^{TT}_{jk} \sim \frac{M}{r}\left(\frac{L}{\lambda\!\!\!^-}\right)^2 \sim \frac{G}{c^4}\,\frac{(\text{internal kinetic energy of source})}{r}$$

$$\sim (\text{Newtonian potential at earth produced by internal kinetic energy of source})$$

$$\sim 10^{-17} \times \frac{(\text{internal kinetic energy})}{(\text{total mass-energy of Sun})} \times \frac{(\text{distance to galactic center})}{(\text{distance to source})} . \tag{3.}$$

In using this formula one must include only the internal kinetic energy associatec with quadrupolar-type (nonspherical) motions. The total power carried by such sources is expressed most conveniently in terms of the "universal power unit"

$$\mathcal{L}_o = c^5/G = 1 = 3.63 \times 10^{59}\ \text{erg/sec} = 2.03 \times 10^5\ M_\odot c^2/\text{sec} \tag{3.53}$$

and the source's internal power flow $\mathcal{L}_{int}$ = (internal kinetic energy)/$\lambdabar$:

$$\mathcal{L}_{GW} \simeq \frac{1}{5} \langle \dddot{\mathcal{I}}_{jk} \dddot{\mathcal{I}}_{jk} \rangle \sim \left(\frac{ML^2}{\lambdabar^3}\right)^2 \sim \left(\frac{\mathcal{L}_{int}}{\mathcal{L}_o}\right)^2 \mathcal{L}_o \, . \tag{3.54}$$

Realistic astrophysical sources — even those with fast, large-amplitude motions and strong internal gravity — are not expected to deviate strongly from these order-of-magnitude formulas; see the lectures of Eardley. Moreover, all calculations to date suggest that no realistic source can radiate away a substantial fraction of its mass more quickly than the light travel time across its gravitational radius; i.e.,

$$\mathcal{L}_{GW} \lesssim M/M = 1 = \mathcal{L}_o \qquad \text{for all sources} \tag{3.55a}$$

(a limit first suggested, so far as I know, by Dyson 1963); and, correspondingly, that the gravity-wave amplitude will always be smaller than

$$h^{TT}_{jk} \lesssim \lambdabar/r \qquad \text{for all sources.} \tag{3.55b}$$

3.4 Radiation reaction in slow-motion sources

There are three approaches to the theory of gravitational radiation reaction in slow-motion sources, each of which is sufficiently rigorous to make me happy; but none of which is sufficiently rigorous to make the most mathematically careful of my colleagues happy (see, e.g., Ehlers, Rosenblum, Goldberg, and Havas 1976). I shall discuss each of these approaches in turn.

3.4.1 Method of conservation laws

The method of conservation laws is based on equations (3.41) and (3.48), which express the rates of change of the source's mass M, momentum P_j, and angular momentum $\mathcal{S}_j$ in terms of integrals over its gravitational waves, and thence is based on expressions (3.42)-(3.45) and (3.49)-(3.50) for $\dot{M}$ and $\dot{P}_j$ in terms of multipole moments that are computable by "instantaneous-gravity", near-zone analyses. These formulas for $\dot{M}$, $\dot{P}_j$, and $\dot{\mathcal{S}}_j$ ("conservation laws") rely, ultimately, on the vacuum Einstein equations (e.g., through the third equality of equation 3.40).

It is crucial for radiation-reaction theory that the M, P_j, and $\mathcal{S}_j$ of these conservation laws are physically measurable (e.g., by Kepler's laws and the precession of gyroscopes) in the weak-field near zone or the local wave zone, and correspondingly that they are computable in terms of the physical near-zone properties of the gravitating system. For example, in the case of a compact binary system (e.g., the binary pulsar), near-zone analyses give

$$M = m_1 + m_2 - \frac{m_1 m_2}{2a} + M_{pN} + M_{p^2N}$$
$$\mathcal{S} \equiv |\underset{\sim}{\mathcal{S}}| = \left[\frac{m_1^2 m_2^2}{m_1 + m_2} a(1-e^2)\right]^{1/2} + \mathcal{S}_{pN} + \mathcal{S}_{p^2N} \, . \tag{3.56}$$

Here m_1 and m_2 are the masses of each of the stars as measured by Kepler's laws and as manifest in the stars' external metrics; a and e are the semimajor axis and eccentricity of the orbits at Newtonian order; and M_{pN}, M_{p^2N}, $\mathcal{S}_{pN}$, $\mathcal{S}_{p^2N}$ are post-

Newtonian and post-post Newtonian contributions. Moreover, for such a binary the conservation laws (3.44) and (3.50) reduce to

$$\left\langle \frac{dM}{dt} \right\rangle = -\frac{32}{5} \frac{m_1^2 m_2^2 (m_1+m_2)}{a^5(1-e^2)^{7/2}} \left(1 + \frac{73}{24} e^2 + \frac{37}{96} e^4\right) ,$$

$$\left\langle \frac{d\mathcal{S}}{dt} \right\rangle = -\frac{32}{5} \frac{m_1^2 m_2^2 (m_1+m_2)^{\frac{1}{2}}}{a^{7/2}(1-e^2)^2} \left(1 + \frac{7}{8} e^2\right) \tag{3.57}$$

(Peters and Mathews 1963, Peters 1964).

Consider the evolution of such a binary over time scales $\Delta t \gg M_{pN}/\langle dM/dt\rangle \simeq$ (10^3 years for the binary pulsar). It is "physically obvious" (or one can show by a careful analysis such as that in Damour's lectures) that m_1 and m_2 are unaffected by the gravity-wave emission. Moreover, over these long time scales the changes of M_{pN}, M_{p^2N}, $\mathcal{S}_{pN}$, and $\mathcal{S}_{p^2N}$ are negligible compared to the much larger M and $\mathcal{S}$ carried off in the radiation. Thus, the changes of M and $\mathcal{S}$ must be fully accounted for by changes of a and e — changes that are fully determined by equations (3.56) and (3.57). And from those changes one can compute the change of orbital period $P = 2\pi[a^3/(m_1+m_2)]^{1/2}$, the most directly measurable quantity.

For evolution of the binary pulsar on time scales P = 7.75 hours $\ll \Delta t \ll$ 1000 years (corresponding to current measurements), the same argument gives the same result (which agrees with the measurements), if one makes a "highly plausible" assumption: that $M_{pN} + M_{p^2N}$ and $\mathcal{S}_{pN} + \mathcal{S}_{p^2N}$ are not sharply changing functions of the (nearly conserved) orbital parameters such as a and e, and thus cannot account for any significant piece of the changes in M and $\mathcal{S}$. Of course, one can only feel fully comfortable about this conclusion after detailed pN and p^2N calculations have verified this assumption; see the lectures of Damour.

3.4.2 Radiation reaction potential

For systems which, unlike the binary pulsar, have weak internal gravity as well as slow motions, one can compute radiation reaction using Newtonian gravity augmented by Burke's (1969) radiation-reaction potential:

$$\underset{\sim}{F}_{grav} = -m\underset{\sim}{\nabla}\Phi; \qquad \Phi = \Phi_{Newton} + \Phi_{react};$$

$$\Phi_{react} = \frac{1}{5}\, {}^{(5)}\mathcal{I}_{jk}\, x^j x^k . \tag{3.58}$$

Here $\underset{\sim}{F}_{grav}$ is the gravitational force that acts on a material element of mass m.

Physically Φ_{react} results from matching the near-zone gravitational field onto outgoing gravitational waves. If the near-zone field were matched onto standing waves Φ_{react} would be zero; if it were matched onto ingoing waves Φ_{react} would change sign. Mathematically one derives the equation of motion (3.58) by constructing the outgoing-wave solution of the Einstein equations in any convenient gauge, matching it onto the near-zone solution, identifying the largest terms in the near-zone metric which are sensitive to outgoing waves versus ingoing waves, and discarding all terms except these sensitive ones and the terms of Newton. By an appropriate change of gauge one then obtains equations of motion of the form (3.58).

I have a confession to make: The derivation along these lines given in §36.11 of MTW is flawed. As Walker and Will (1980) point out, when one works in de Donder gauge (as I did in writing §36.11), one obtains reaction terms of magnitude ${}^{(3)}\mathcal{I}_{jk}$ in the near-zone metric when one matches onto outgoing waves. Although these terms are "pure gauge", i.e., have no direct physical consequences, they produce nonlinear corrections in the final gauge change, corrections which I mistakenly ignored in MTW but which are cancelled by a nonlinear iteration of the Einstein equations that I also mistakenly ignored. The reason for my sloppiness in writing MTW is that I had previously derived the radiation-reaction potential (3.58) working not in de Donder gauge but in "Regge-Wheeler gauge" (Thorne 1969); and in that gauge ${}^{(3)}\mathcal{I}_{jk}$ terms never arise and a final gauge change and nonlinear iteration are not needed. Having been very careful in my Regge-Wheeler-type derivation, I was highly confident of the final result — and, buoyed by this confidence, I became careless when constructing the de Donder-gauge proof in MTW.

Historically, Peres (1960) gave the first correct analysis of gravitational radiation reaction by the technique of identifying the dominant terms sensitive to the outgoing-wave boundary condition. However, Peres did not write his answer in terms of a Newton-type radiation-reaction potential Φ_{react}; that was first done by Burke (1969).

3.4.3 pN, p^2N, and $p^{2.5}$N iteration of the field equations

The method (3.58) of the radiation reaction potential discards all post-Newtonian and post-post-Newtonian effects in the evolution of the system — even though radiation reaction is a somewhat smaller, post$^{2.5}$-Newtonian phenomenon over times of order $\lambdabar$. The justification is that radiation reaction, unlike pN and p^2N effects, produces secular changes of such quantities as the period of a binary system; and those secular changes can build up over long times $\Delta t \gg \lambdabar$, becoming ultimately much larger than post-Newtonian order. However, over shorter timescales ($\Delta t \lesssim 1000$ years in the case of the binary pulsar) the cumulative effects do not exceed post-Newtonian order; and thus for full confidence in one's results one should augment the Newtonian forces and $p^{2.5}$N radiation-reaction forces by a full pN and p^2N analysis of the system.

Damour, in his lectures in this volume, describes the history of attempts at such full analyses and presents a beautiful, full analysis of his own for the special case of binary systems with compact (white-dwarf, neutron-star, and black-hole) members.

3.5 Gravitational-wave generation by fast-motion sources: $\lambdabar \lesssim L$

Elsewhere (Thorne 1977) I have reviewed methods for computing gravitational waves from fast-motion sources. Here I shall give only a brief classification of the various methods and a few recent references where each method is used.

There are three ways to classify methods for computing wave generation: by strength of the source's internal gravity ("weak" if a Newtonian analysis gives $|\Phi| \ll 1$ everywhere; "strong" if $|\Phi| \gtrsim 1$ somewhere); by speed of the source's internal motions ("slow" if $\lambdabar \gg L$; "fast" if $\lambdabar \lesssim L$); and by the fractional amount that the source deviates from a nonradiating spacetime ("large deviations" or "small deviations"). Here is a list of frequently used methods of computing wave generation, classified in these three ways:

1. Slow-Motion Method
   - Arbitrary gravity, slow speed, arbitrary deviations.
   - § 3.2 above.

2. Post-Newtonian and Post-Post-Newtonian Wave-Generation Methods
   - Moderate gravity, moderate speed, arbitrary deviations.
   - Epstein and Wagoner (1975); Wagoner and Will (1976); RMP §§V.D,E.

3. Post-Linear (≡ Post-Minkowski) Wave-Generation Method

- Weak gravity, arbitrary speed, arbitrary deviations.
- Kovács and Thorne (1978).

4. First-Order Perturbations of Nonradiating Solutions

- Arbitrary gravity, arbitrary speed, small deviations.
- Cunningham, Price, and Moncrief (1978); Schumaker and Thorne (1983); Detweiler (1980); lecture by Nakamura in this volume; eq. (2.29) above.

5. Numerical Relativity

- Arbitrary gravity, arbitrary speed, arbitrary deviations.
- Lectures by York, Piran, Nakamura, and Isaacson in this volume.

The strongest radiators of gravity waves will be those with strong gravity, fast motions, and large deviations (e.g., collisions between two black holes); and such systems can be analyzed quantitively by only one technique: numerical relativity.

The results of wave-generation calculations for various astrophysical sources are reviewed in the lectures of Eardley in this volume.

4 THE DETECTION OF GRAVITATIONAL WAVES

Turn attention now from methods of analyzing the generation of gravitational waves to methods of analyzing their detection. If the size of the detector is small compared to a reduced wavelength, $L \ll \lambda\!\!\!^{-}$, it can be analyzed in the "proper reference frame" of the detector's center of mass (§4.1). If $L \gtrsim \lambda\!\!\!^{-}$, the proper reference frame is not a useful concept; and the detector is usually analyzed, instead, using "post-linear" (≡ "post-Minkowski") techniques and some carefully chosen gauge (§4.2).

4.1 Detectors with size $L \ll \lambda\!\!\!^{-}$

4.1.1 The proper reference frame of an accelerated, rotating laboratory

Most gravity-wave detectors reside in earth-bound laboratories whose walls and floor accelerate relative to local inertial frames ("acceleration of gravity") and rotate relative to local gyroscopes ("Foucault pendulum effect"). In such laboratories the mathematical analog of a LIF is a "proper reference frame" (PRF). A PRF is constructed by choosing a fiducial world line which is usually attached to the detector's center of mass and thus accelerates, by next constructing spatial slices of simultaneity, $t = \text{const}$, which are orthogonal to the fiducial world line and are as flat as the spacetime curvature permits; and by then constructing in each slice of simultaneity a spatial coordinate grid which is as Cartesian as the spacetime curvature permits and is attached to the laboratory walls and thus rotates. The origin of the spatial grid is on the fiducial world line, and the time coordinate t of the slices of simultaneity is equal to proper time along the fiducial world line. Such a PRF is a mathematical realization of the type of coordinate system that a very careful experimental physicist who knows little relativity theory would likely set up in his earth-bound laboratory.

One version of such a PRF is the rotating, accelerating analog of a Fermi normal coordinate system (eq. 2.15); its spacetime metric is (Ni and Zimmermann 1978)

$$ds^2 = -dt^2 \Big[1 + \underbrace{2\underset{\sim}{a}\cdot\underset{\sim}{x} + (\underset{\sim}{a}\cdot\underset{\sim}{x})^2}_{\text{grav'l redshift}} - \underbrace{(\underset{\sim}{\Omega}\times\underset{\sim}{x})^2}_{\text{Lorentz time dilation}} + R_{0\ell 0m}x^\ell x^m \Big]$$

$$+ 2dtdx^i \Big[\underbrace{\epsilon_{ijk}\Omega^j x^k}_{\text{Sagnac effect}} - \tfrac{2}{3} R_{0\ell im}x^\ell x^m \Big] + dx^i dx^j \Big[\delta_{ij} - \tfrac{1}{3} R_{i\ell jm} x^\ell x^m \Big]$$

$$+ O(r^3\, dx^\alpha dx^\beta). \tag{4.1}$$

Here $\underset{\sim}{a}$ is the acceleration of the fiducial world line (minus the local "acceleration of gravity") and $\underset{\sim}{\Omega}$ is the angular velocity of the spatial grid, i.e., of the laboratory walls, relative to local gyroscopes. Other versions of a PRF have spatial grids and slices of simultaneity that are bent from those of (4.1) by amounts of the order of the bending enforced by the spacetime curvature: $x^{j'} = x^j + O(r^3/\mathcal{R}^2)$, $t' = t + O(r^3/\mathcal{R}^2)$ where $\mathcal{R} \sim (R_{\alpha\beta\gamma\delta})^{-1/2}$; cf. eq. (2.16). In them g_{00} will be the same as (4.1), but g_{0i} and g_{jk} may be different by amounts of $O(r^2/\mathcal{R}^2)$.

In the PRF (4.1) a test particle acted on by an external force acquires a coordinate acceleration (obtained from the geodesic equation with a force term added)

$$\frac{d^2x^i}{dt^2} = \underbrace{-a^i}_{\text{"acceleration of gravity"}} \underbrace{-2(\underset{\sim}{\Omega}\times\underset{\sim}{v})^i}_{\text{Coriolis acceleration}} \underbrace{-[\underset{\sim}{\Omega}\times(\underset{\sim}{\Omega}\times\underset{\sim}{x})]^i}_{\text{centrifugal acceleration}} \underbrace{-(\dot{\underset{\sim}{\Omega}}\times x)^i}_{\text{effect of changing }\underset{\sim}{\Omega}} \underbrace{+f^i/m}_{\text{external force}}$$

$$+ \Big[\begin{array}{c}\text{special relativistic corrections to these inertial effects,}\\ \text{equation (20) of Ni and Zimmermann (1978)}\end{array} \Big]$$

$$\underbrace{- R_{0i0\ell}x^\ell}_{\text{geodesic deviation}} + \underbrace{2R_{ij0\ell}v^j x^\ell}_{\text{source of "spin-curvature coupling"}} + \tfrac{2}{3} R_{ijk\ell}v^j v^k x^\ell \tag{4.2}$$

$$+ 2v^i R_{0j0\ell}v^j x^\ell + \tfrac{2}{3} v^i R_{0jk\ell}v^j v^k x^\ell .$$

Here v^j is the coordinate velocity of the particle. The terms on the first line are far bigger than those on the last three lines; they are familiar from nonrelativistic mechanics in a uniform, Newtonian gravitational field.

4.1.2 Examples of detectors

Figure 6 shows three types of gravitational-wave detectors with $L \ll \lambda\!\!\!^{-}$ that are now under construction or look favorable for future construction.

"Weber-type resonant-bar detectors" have been under development for twenty years and are discussed in detail in the lectures of Blair, Braginsky, Hamilton, Michelson, and Pallotino. In such a detector the waves couple to and drive normal modes of oscillation of a mechanical system ("antenna"), usually a solid bar made

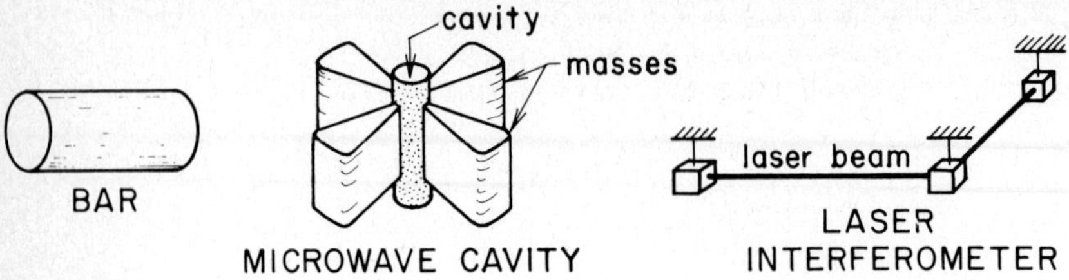

Fig. 6 Examples of gravitational-wave detectors with size $L \ll \lambda\!\!\!^{-}$.

of aluminum, and those oscillations are monitored by a transducer which is attached to the ends or sides of the bar.

In a "microwave-cavity detector" with $L \ll \lambda\!\!\!^{-}$ the gravitational waves drive oscillatory deformations of the walls of a microwave cavity; and those wall motions pump microwave quanta from one normal mode of the cavity into another. To enhance the wall deformations, big masses may be attached to the walls at strategic locations. (See, e.g., Braginsky et al. (1974), Caves (1979), Pegoraro and Radicati (1980), Grishchuk and Polnarev (1981), and references therein.) Although the design sensitivities of such detectors are comparable to those of bars, no serious efforts are now under way to develop them.

"Laser interferometer detectors" have been under development for about a decade and are discussed in detail in the lectures of Drever and Brillet. In such a detector three (or more) masses are suspended as pendula from overhead supports and swing back and forth in response to gravitational waves; and their relative motions are monitored by laser interferometry.

4.1.3 Method of analyzing detectors

For me the conceptually clearest way to analyze these three detectors, and any other with $L \ll \lambda\!\!\!^{-}$, is using the PRF of the detector's center of mass. The gravitational waves enter such an analysis entirely through the Riemann curvature terms of the metric (4.1), which have sizes

$$g^{(W)}_{\alpha\beta} \sim R^{(W)}_{\alpha\beta\gamma\delta}\, L^2 \sim h^{TT}_{jk}\,(L/\lambda\!\!\!^{-})^2 \ll h^{TT}_{jk} \quad \text{in PRF.} \tag{4.3}$$

By contrast, in TT gauge the waves would contribute $g^{(W)}_{\alpha\beta} \sim h^{TT}_{jk}$ to the metric. An important consequence is this: In the PRF analysis the direct coupling of the gravitational waves to the detector's electromagnetic field can be ignored; and this is true whether the EM field is in a transducer on the bar, or in a microwave cavity, or in a laser beam. The direct coupling produces terms in Maxwell's equations for the vector potential with size $\delta A/A \sim g^{(W)}_{\mu\nu} \sim h^{TT}_{jk}\,(L/\lambda\!\!\!^{-})^2$, which are smaller by $(L/\lambda\!\!\!^{-})^2$ than the "indirect" coupling effects

$$\begin{pmatrix}\text{gravity waves deform}\\ \text{or move masses}\end{pmatrix} \rightarrow \frac{\delta L}{L} \sim h^{TT}_{jk} \rightarrow \begin{pmatrix}\text{changes of boundaries}\\ \text{for Maxwell equations}\end{pmatrix} \rightarrow \frac{\delta A}{A} \gtrsim h^{TT}_{jk}. \tag{4.4}$$

By contrast, in TT gauge the direct coupling is not negligible, and one must consider the direct interaction of the gravitational waves with both the electromagnetic field and the mechanical parts of the detector.

For all three detectors in Figure 6 and all other promising ones, the velocities of the mechanical parts of the system relative to the center of mass are $|v^j| \ll 1$. Consequently, in the mechanical equation of motion (4.2) all Riemann curvature terms except $-R_{0i0\ell}x^\ell$ can be ignored. Because $R^{(W)}_{0i0\ell} = -\frac{1}{2}\ddot{h}^{TT}_{i\ell}$ (where a dot means $\partial/\partial t$), the equation of motion for each mass element in the detector becomes

$$\ddot{x}^i = \frac{1}{2}\ddot{h}^{TT}_{ij}x^j + \left(\begin{array}{c}\text{all acceleration terms associated with}\\ \text{non-gravitational-wave effects}\end{array}\right). \tag{4.5}$$

In summary, if one knows how to analyze the detector in the absence of gravitational waves, one can take account of the waves by simply adding the driving acceleration $\frac{1}{2}\ddot{h}^{TT}_{jk}x^j$ to the equation of motion of the detector's mass elements and by ignoring direct coupling of the waves to the detector's electromagnetic field.

This conclusion is valid even if the detector is large compared to inhomogeneities in the Newtonian gravity of the earth or solar system — e.g., if the detector is a normal mode of the earth itself. Then one cannot use the proper reference frame (4.1), so far as Newtonian-gravity effects are concerned; but one can still use (4.1) so far as gravitational-wave effects are concerned ($g^{(W)}_{\alpha\beta} \sim \ddot{h}^{TT}_{jk} L^2$). In other words, one can graft the waves onto a Newtonian analysis by means of

$$g^{(W)}_{00} = -R^{(W)}_{0\ell 0m}x^\ell x^m,$$

$$|g^{(W)}_{0i}| \sim |g^{(W)}_{ij}| \sim R^{(W)}_{\alpha\beta\gamma\delta}L^2 \left(\begin{array}{c}\text{details depend on specific variant of PRF}\\ \text{and are unimportant because } |v^j| \ll 1\end{array}\right), \tag{4.6}$$

and by means of the resulting equation of motion (4.5).

The gravitational-wave driving acceleration $\frac{1}{2}\ddot{h}^{TT}_{jk}x^j$ can be described by a quadrupole-shaped "line-of-force" diagram (Fig. 7; MTW Box 37.2).

4.1.4 Resonant-bar detectors

Consider, as an example, the analysis of a Weber-type resonant-bar gravitational-wave detector (MTW Box 37.4). One begins by computing the normal-mode eigenfrequencies ω_n and eigenfunctions $\underset{\sim}{u}^{(n)}$ of the antenna ignoring the weak frictional and fluctuational coupling between modes and ignoring external forces (e.g., gravity waves). The resulting eigenfunctions, which are real (not complex) are normalized so that

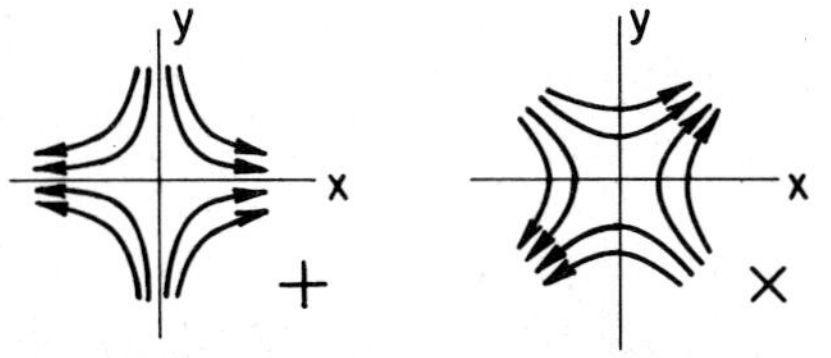

Fig. 7 "Lines of force" for the gravitational-wave acceleration (4.5) in the PRF of a detector. The two drawings correspond to waves with + polarization and with × polarization.

$$\int \rho \underset{\sim}{u}^{(n)} \cdot \underset{\sim}{u}^{(m)} d^3x = M\delta_{nm}; \qquad \rho = \text{density}, \quad M = \text{antenna mass}. \tag{4.7}$$

One then expands the vibrational displacement of the bar's material in terms of normal modes

$$\delta \underset{\sim}{x} = \sum_n X^{(n)} \underset{\sim}{u}^{(n)}(\underset{\sim}{x})\, e^{-i\omega_n t}; \qquad X^{(n)} \equiv \text{"complex amplitude of mode n"}. \tag{4.8}$$

Next one writes down the equation of motion for $\delta \underset{\sim}{x}$ in the presence of gravity waves [force per unit volume equal to $\frac{1}{2}\rho \ddot{h}^{TT}_{jk} x^j$], internal friction, Nyquist forces [i.e., weak fluctuational couplings between normal modes], and coupling to the transducer. When one resolves that full equation of motion into normal modes one obtains

$$\dot{X}^{(n)} = -(2/\tau_n)X^{(n)} + \frac{ie^{i\omega_n t}}{M\omega_n} \int \underset{\sim}{f} \cdot \underset{\sim}{u}^{(n)} d^3x\,, \tag{4.9}$$

where τ_n is the (very long) frictional damping time for mode n and $\underset{\sim}{f}$ is the force per unit volume in the antenna including gravity-wave force, Nyquist forces, and "back-action forces" of the transducer on the antenna. The gravity-wave force, when integrated over the normal mode, $\underset{\sim}{u}^{(n)}$, gives

$$\int \underset{\sim}{f}^{(W)} \cdot \underset{\sim}{u}^{(n)} d^3x = \frac{1}{4} \ddot{h}^{TT}_{jk} \mathscr{I}^{(n)}_{jk}, \tag{4.10a}$$

$$\begin{aligned} \mathscr{I}^{(n)}_{jk} &= \int \rho (u^j_{(n)} x^k + u^k_{(n)} x^j - \tfrac{2}{3} \delta_{jk} \underset{\sim}{u}_{(n)} \cdot \underset{\sim}{x})\, d^3x \\ &= \left[X^{(n)} e^{-i\omega_n t}\right]^{-1} \times \begin{pmatrix}\text{contribution of mode n to antenna's} \\ \text{quadrupole moment}\end{pmatrix}. \end{aligned} \tag{4.10b}$$

Thus, the same quadrupole moment as would govern emission of gravitational waves by mode n also governs their reception; this is an aspect of the principle of detailed balance (MTW §37.7).

If the antenna is hit by a broad-band burst of gravitational waves with spectral energy flux $\mathscr{F}_\nu$ (ergs cm^{-2} Hz^{-1}) and polarization e_{jk} (normalized so $e_{jk}e_{jk} = 2$)

$$h^{TT}_{jk} = A(t)e_{jk}, \qquad \mathscr{F}_\nu = \frac{\omega^2}{4} \left| \frac{1}{\sqrt{2\pi}} \int_{-\infty}^{+\infty} A(t)\, e^{i\omega t} dt \right|^2, \qquad \omega = 2\pi\nu > 0, \tag{4.11}$$

then equations (4.9) and (4.10) give for the wave-induced change of complex amplitude $\delta X^{(n)}$

$$\begin{aligned} \frac{1}{2} M\omega_n^2 |\delta X^{(n)}|^2 &= \begin{pmatrix}\text{energy that would be absorbed by antenna mode n} \\ \text{if } X^{(n)} \text{ were zero when the wave burst hit}\end{pmatrix} \\ &= \mathscr{F}_\nu(\omega = \omega_n) \int \sigma_n d\nu. \end{aligned} \tag{4.12}$$

Here $\int \sigma_n d\nu$ is the antenna cross section integrated over frequency

$$\int \sigma_n d\nu = \frac{\pi}{4} \frac{\omega_n^2}{M} \left(\mathcal{I}_{jk}^{(n)} e_{jk} \right)^2$$
$$\sim 10^{-21}\ \mathrm{cm}^2\ \mathrm{Hz} \text{ for typical antennas with } M \sim 1 \text{ ton, } \omega_n/2\pi \sim 1 \text{ kHz.} \qquad (4.13)$$

For further details and discussion see MTW, chapter 37; also the lectures by Blair, Braginsky, Hamilton, Michelson, and Pallotino in this volume.

* * * * *

Exercise 20. Derive equation (4.9) by resolving the equation of motion for δx into normal modes. Show that the driving term due to gravity waves has the form (4.10) and show that $\mathcal{I}_{jk}^{(n)}$ has the claimed relationship to the quadrupole moment.

Exercise 21. Show that (eq. 4.11) correctly represents the spectral energy flux of a gravity wave in the sense that $\int \mathcal{F}_\nu d\nu$ is the energy per unit area that passes the detector. Show that the broad-band burst of gravity waves (4.11) produces the change (4.12) of the antenna's complex amplitude. Show that for typical antennas the frequency-integrated cross section is $\sim 10^{-21}$ cm^2 Hz as claimed.

Exercise 22. Show that for a homogeneous, spherical antenna whose quadrupolar oscillations are being driven by gravity waves, the quadrupole moment $\mathcal{I}_{jk}$ obeys the equation of motion (2.39a).

4.2 Detectors with size $L \gtrsim ƛ$

Examples of gravitational-wave detectors with $L \gtrsim ƛ$ include the Doppler tracking of spacecraft (lectures by Hellings in this volume), and microwave-cavity detectors in which the gravity waves pump microwave quanta from one normal mode to another via direct interaction with the electromagnetic field as well as via deformation of the walls or wave guides which confine the field (Braginsky et al. (1974), Caves (1979), Pegoraro and Radicati (1980), Grishchuk and Polnarev (1981) and references therein).

Because the Riemann tensor of the waves varies significantly over the volume of such a detector, the "proper reference frame" is not a useful tool in analyzing it. Instead, analyses are based on the linearized approximation to general relativity (MTW chapter 18), with the metric $g_{\alpha\beta} = \eta_{\alpha\beta} + h_{\alpha\beta}$ including both Newtonian gravitational potentials Φ and gravitational waves; and the waves are usually treated in TT gauge:

$$g_{00} = -1 - 2\Phi, \qquad g_{0j} = 0, \qquad g_{jk} = \delta_{jk}(1-2\Phi) + h_{jk}^{TT}.$$

The analysis is actually "post-linear" (or "post-Minkowski") in that the "equations of motion" for the matter (sun, planets, detector) are not taken to be $T^{\alpha\beta}{}_{,\beta} = 0$, but rather $T^{\alpha\beta}{}_{;\beta} = 0$ with connection coefficients linear in $h_{\mu\nu}$ and Φ. See, e.g., §2 of Thorne (1977) for a careful discussion of the differences between linear theory and post-linear theory.

For an example of such an analysis see Hellings' treatment, in this volume, of the interaction of gravitational waves with NASA's doppler tracking system. As in that analysis, so in most analyses of detectors with $L \gtrsim ƛ$, direct interaction of the gravitational waves with the electromagnetic field is as important as interaction with the mechanical parts of the detector.

A mathematical trick that sometimes simplifies calculations of the interaction of gravity waves with electromagnetic fields is to write the curved-spacetime

Maxwell equations in a form identical to those for flat spacetime in a moving, anisotropic dielectric medium (e.g., Volkov, Izmest'ev, and Skrotskii 1970). Caves (unpublished) has combined this technique with gauge changes that attach the spatial coordinates onto the cavity walls even when the walls are wiggling, and has thereby produced an elegant and powerful formalism for analyzing microwave cavity detectors with $L \gtrsim \lambda\!\!\!^{-}$.

5 CONCLUSION

Most of my own research on gravitational-wave theory is motivated by the need to prepare for the day when gravitational waves are detected and astronomers confront the task of extracting astrophysical information from them. The task of preparing for that day is nontrivial. The ideas described in these lectures are a foundation for those preparations, but much further theoretical research is needed — especially the computation of gravitational wave forms $h_{jk}^{TT}(t-r; \theta, \varphi)$ from fast-motion, strong-gravity sources such as black-hole collisions.

We theorists often pay great lip service to a second motivation for our research: to give guidance to experimenters who are designing and constructing gravitational-wave detectors; and experimenters often follow with avid interest and thumping hearts the fluctuations in theoretical predictions of the waves bathing the earth. However, we theorists are far more ignorant than most experimenters imagine. For those strong sources whose wave characteristics are fairly well known (e.g., collisions between black holes), the event rate is uncertain by many orders of magnitude; and for those whose event rates are fairly well known (e.g., supernovae), the wave strengths are uncertain by many orders. Our ignorance has a simple cause: The information carried by electromagnetic waves, which is the foundation of today's theories, is nearly "orthogonal" to the information carried by gravitational waves. As a corollary, when they are ultimately detected, gravitational waves will likely give us a revolutionary new view of the universe; but until they are detected, we theorists can offer little precious advice to our experimental colleagues, and our colleagues should turn a half-deaf ear to our most confident remarks about the characteristics of the waves for which they search.

REFERENCES

Aichelburg, P. C., Ecker, G., and Sexl, R. U. 1971, Nuovo Cimento B, 2, 63.

Bontz, R. J. and Haugan, M. P. 1981, Astrophys. Space Sci., 78, 204.

Bondi, H., van der Burg, M. G. J., and Metzner, A. W. K. 1962, Proc. Roy. Soc., A269, 21.

Braginsky, V. B., Caves, C. M., and Thorne, K. S. 1977, Phys. Rev. D, 15, 2047.

Braginsky, V. B., Grishchuk, L. P., Doroshkevich, A. G., Zel'dovich, Ya. B., Novikov, I. D., and Sazhin, M. V. 1974, Sov. Phys.—JETP, 38, 865.

Burke, W. L. 1969, unpublished Ph.D. thesis, Caltech; see also Phys. Rev. A, 2, 1501 (1970).

Caves, C. M. 1979, Phys. Lett., 80B, 323.

Caves, C. M. 1980, Ann. Phys. (USA), 125, 35.

Crowley, R. J. and Thorne, K. S. 1977, Astrophys. J., 215, 624.

Cunningham, C. T., Price, R. H., and Moncrief, V. 1978, Astrophys. J., 224, 643.

Cyranski, J. F. and Lubkin, E. 1974, Ann. Phys. (USA), 87, 205.

Davis, M., Ruffini, R., Press, W. H., and Price, R. H. 1971, Phys. Rev. Lett., 27, 1466.

D'Eath, P. 1975, Phys. Rev. D, 12, 2183.

Detweiler, S. 1980, Astrophys. J., 239, 292.

DeWitt, B. S. and Brehme, R. W. 1960, Ann. Phys. (USA), 9, 220.

Dicke, R. H. 1964, in Relativity, Groups, and Topology, ed. B. and C. DeWitt (Gordon & Breach, New York).

Dyson, F. 1963, in Interstellar Communication, ed. A. G. W. Cameron (Benjamin, New York).

ELLWW: See Eardley, Lee, Lightman, Wagoner, and Will (1973).

Eardley, D. M., Lee, D. L., and Lightman, A. P. 1973, Phys. Rev. D, 8, 3308.

Eardley, D. M., Lee, D. L., Lightman, A. P., Wagoner, R. V., and Will, C. M. 1973, Phys. Rev. Lett., 30, 884; cited in text as ELLWW.

Ehlers, J., Rosenblum, A., Goldberg, J. N., and Havas, P. 1976, Astrophys. J. (Letters), 208, L77.

Einstein, A. 1918, Preuss. Akad. Wiss. Berlin, Sitzber. 1918, 154.

Epstein, R. and Wagoner, R. V. 1975, Astrophys. J., 197, 717.

Geroch, R. 1970, J. Math. Phys., 11, 2580.

Geroch, R., Held, A., and Penrose, R. 1973, J. Math. Phys., 14, 874.

Goldstein, H. 1980, Classical Mechanics, second edition (Addison Wesley, Reading, Mass.), §5-6.

Grishchuk, L. P. and Polnarev, A. G. 1981, chapter 10 of General Relativity and Gravitation, Vol. 2, ed. A. Held (Plenum Press, N.Y.).

Gürsel, Y. 1982, J. Gen. Rel. Grav., submitted.

Gürsel, Y. and Thorne, K. S. 1983, Mon. Not. Roy. Astron. Soc., submitted.

Hansen, R. O. 1974, J. Math. Phys., 15, 46.

Hartle, J. B. 1973, Astrophys. Space Sci., 24, 385.

Hartle, J. B. and Thorne, K. S. 1983, paper in preparation.

Hobson, E. W. 1931, The Theory of Spherical and Ellipsoidal Harmonics (Cambridge U. Press, Cambridge), p. 119. Republished in 1955 by Chelsea Publishing Co., New York.

Isaacson, R. A. 1968, Phys. Rev., 166, 1263 and 1272.

Kelvin, Lord (Sir William Thomson) and Tate, P. G. 1879, Treatise on Natural Philosophy, Appendix B of Chapter 1 of Volume 1 (Cambridge U. Press, Cambridge).

Kovàcs, S. J. and Thorne, K. S. 1978, Astrophys. J., 224, 62.

MTW: see Misner, Thorne, and Wheeler (1973).

Mashhoon, B. 1973, Astrophys. J. (Letters), 181, L65.

Misner, C. W., Thorne, K. S., and Wheeler, J. A. 1973, Gravitation (Freeman, San Francisco); cited in text as MTW.

Ni, W.-T. and Zimmermann, M. 1978, Phys. Rev. D, 17, 1473.

Pegoraro, F. and Radicati, L. A. 1980, J. Phys. A, 13, 2411.

Peres, A. 1960, Nuovo Cimento, 15, 351.

Peters, P. C. 1964, Phys. Rev., 136, B1224.

Peters, P. C. and Mathews, J. 1963, Phys. Rev., 131, 435.

Pirani, F. A. E. 1964, in Lectures on General Relativity, ed. A. Trautman, F. A. E. Pirani, and H. Bondi (Prentice Hall, Englewood Cliffs, N.J.).

Press, W. H. 1979, J. Gen. Rel. Grav., 11, 105.

Price, R. H. 1972, Phys. Rev. D, 5, 2419.

RMP: see Thorne (1980a).

Rosen, N. 1973, J. Gen. Rel. Grav., 4, 435; see also N. Rosen, Ann. Phys. (USA), 84, 455 (1974).

Sachs, R. K. 1962, Proc. Roy. Soc., A270, 103.

Schumaker, B. L. and Thorne, K. S. 1983, Mon. Not. Roy. Astron. Soc., in press.

Sonnabend, D. 1979, To the Solar Foci, JPL Publication 79-18 (Jet Propulsion Laboratory, Pasadena).

Szekeres, P. 1971, Ann. Phys., 64, 599.

Thorne, K. S. 1969, Astrophys. J., 158, 997.

Thorne, K. S. 1977, in Topics in Theoretical and Experimental Gravitation Physics, ed. V. De Sabbata and J. Weber (Plenum Press, London).

Thorne, K. S. 1980a, Rev. Mod. Phys., 52, 299; cited in text as RMP.

Thorne, K. S. 1981, Mon. Not. Roy. Astron. Soc., 194, 439.

Thorne, K. S. 1983, Astrophys. J., in preparation.

Thorne, K. S. and Campolattaro, A. 1967, Astrophys. J., 149, 591.

Turner, M. 1977, Astrophys. J., 216, 914.

Volkov, A. M., Izmest'ev, A. A., and Skrotskii, G. V. 1970, Zh. Eksp. Teor. Fiz., 59, 1254 [Sov. Phys.-JETP, 32, 636 (1971)].

Wagoner, R. V. and Will, C. M. 1976, Astrophys. J., 210, 764.

Walker, M. and Will, C. M. 1980, Astrophys. J. (Letters), 242, L129.

Will, C. M. 1982, Theory and Experimentation in Gravitational Physics (Cambridge University Press, New York).

Zimmermann, M. 1980, Phys. Rev. D, 21, 891.

Zimmermann, M. and Szedenits, E. 1979, Phys. Rev. D, 20, 351.

GRAVITATIONAL RADIATION AND THE MOTION OF COMPACT BODIES

Thibaut Damour

Groupe d'Astrophysique Relativiste
Equipe de Recherche du C.N.R.S. n° 176
Observatoire de Paris-Meudon
92190 Meudon (France)

Using a post-Minkowskian approximation method supplemented by a technique of asymptotic matching, we obtain the general relativistic gravitational field outside two compact bodies (neutron stars or black holes). The equations of orbital motion of the compact bodies are deduced from the vacuum field equations by an Einstein-Infeld-Hoffmann-Kerr type approach simplified by the use of complex analytic continuation. The same process of analytic continuation allows one to push the accuracy of the calculations up to the third order: gravitational field containing cubic non-linearities and equations of motion deduced from the quartically non-linear vacuum Einstein equations. The equations of motion are explicitly written in Newtonian-like form as an expansion in powers of the inverse velocity of light up to the fifth order inclusively. The equations of motion up to c^{-4} are deduced from a generalized Lagrangian. The construction of Noetherian quantities conserved up to c^{-4} allows one to separate and investigate the c^{-5} secular kinematical effects caused by the finite velocity of propagation of gravity (Laplace-Eddington effect or "radiation damping"). These results agree with the phenomena observed in the Hulse-Taylor pulsar PSR 1913 + 16.

1. MOTIVATION

Two of the most remarkable features of Einstein's gravitational equations are:

1) their "hyperbolicity" (presence of propagation effects at a finite velocity),
2) their (infinite) non-linearity ("gravity generates gravity and influences its propagation").

It was soon realized (Einstein 1916) that the first feature implied the existence of wave-like solutions of the "linearized" vacuum field equations. Later these "linearized" waves were shown to be associated with an outgoing "energy flux" far from the system given, in the case of slow sources, by the famous "quadrupole formula" (Einstein 1918, see the lectures of K.S. Thorne and M. Walker in these proceedings):

$$\text{Energy flux} = -\frac{1}{5Gc^5}(d^3Q_{ik}/dt^3)^2, \tag{1}$$

where Q_{ik} is the quadrupole moment of the radiating source:

$$Q_{ik} = G\int d^3x\,\rho\,(x^i x^k - \frac{1}{3}x^2 f^{ik}), \tag{2}$$

G being Newton's constant, c the velocity of light, ρ the mass density and f^{ik} the Kronecker symbol (in these lectures we shall denote the Minkowski metric by f^{ab} with $f^{00} = -1$ and $f^{ik} = +$ (Kronecker)^{ik}).

It was first realized by Weyl (1921) and Eddington (1924) that the second feature, non-linearity, together with the very special structure of Einstein's equations implied that, not only was the gravitational field determined by the sources, but the equations of motion of the sources could also be deduced from the field equations (see section 3 below). Consequently Eddington (1924) pointed out that the existing derivations of (1) and of a correlated "energy loss" in the source could not be automatically applied to a binary star where non-linear effects are essential because they provide the binding of the system. He even pointed out that one should take into account the cubic non-linearity of Einstein's equations in any radiation damping calculation (though the situation is somewhat simpler for an "energy flux" calculation where, as shown by Landau and Lifshitz (1941), only quadratic non-linearities need to be considered and where a simple argument leads back to (1-2)). Subsequently many authors, starting with the pioneering work of Hu (1947), tried to include the effects due to the propagation of gravity in the equations of motion of gravitationally bound matter, hoping to get some kind of radiation reaction on the motion of the sources of the gravitational field. However the sought-for effect is so small that one must include many highly non-linear contributions before being sure that the result is complete. Many conflicting results were obtained but, in the early seventies, an agreement was reached between some detailed, albeit incomplete, calculations, valid only for systems where the gravitational field is weak everywhere, and a heuristic argument ("balance" between the "energy flux" (1) lost in the "wave zone" and a loss of the "near zone" "Newtonian energy" of the system) (see section 3 and the criticisms in section 15).

Although in the meantime, the search for gravitational waves had begun with the pioneering work of J. Weber (see the lectures of D. Blair, V. Braginsky and R. Drever), nevertheless the successful detection on Earth of gravitational wave signals seems still far ahead of us. In 1979, however, Taylor, Fowler and McCulloch (1979) reported the observations of a secular acceleration of the mean orbital longitude of the binary pulsar PSR 1913 + 16 : i.e., in other words, a secular diminution of the time of return to the periastron (see the lectures of D. Eardley).

While this effect had been qualitatively and quantitatively predicted on the basis of the above-mentioned heuristic argument (Esposito and Harrisson 1975, Wagoner 1975), it had not been validly demonstrated to be a consequence of Einstein's theory: on one hand because the detailed calculations were not complete enough to control all the terms of the equations of motion and were plagued by mathematical inconsistencies, and, on the other hand, because the methods of calculation did not apply to a system, like the binary pulsar, containing "compact" objects, i.e. objects with a radius $\sim G(\text{mass})/c^2$ and therefore with very strong self gravitational fields (the inconclusiveness of these calculations, as well as of other derivations, is further discussed in Sections 3 and 15). It was therefore necessary to re-examine afresh the problem of motion of two bodies in General Relativity by a method able:

1) to deal with the interaction of compact objects,
2) to include all the propagation effects of gravity without running into mathematical inconsistencies at higher orders,
3) to push the calculations up to the inclusion of all the non-linear terms which are greater than or equal to the "radiation damping" effects.

The aim of these lectures is to present a new method which fulfils all these requirements and to describe the results that have been obtained from it. Our final result justifies the conclusions obtained from the earlier heuristic arguments, and hence, in conjunction with Taylor's observations of the binary pulsar, provides a profound confirmation of the non-linear hyperbolic structure of Einstein's theory. Hence it provides also an indirect confirmation of the existence of gravitational waves.

2. OUTLINE OF THESE LECTURES

Section 3 reviews the history of the problem of motion with special emphasis on the birth and evolution of the concepts that will be useful in these lectures: asymptotic matching, radiation damping, Post-Minkowskian Approximation schemes, deduction of the equations of motion from the vacuum field equations. It contains also a brief discussion of the Post-Newtonian Approximation schemes. A short history of the other useful concepts: analytic continuation and action principles will be found in sections 7 and 13 respectively. Section 13 contains also a brief discussion of the clarifying -- though perhaps deceptively simple -- analogy between the electromagnetic and gravitational interactions ("radiation reaction", "least action principles," "conservation laws").

Section 4 presents a new strategy for analyzing and solving the problem of the motion of two compact objects. The first step of this strategy, which deals with the tidal effects on a compact object, is presented in Section 5. Section 6 uses the information from the tidal distortion of the gravitational field outside (but "near") each compact object to provide necessary boundary conditions for the gravitational field in the empty region of space-time which is outside two world tubes containing the two compact objects.

Section 7 presents a brief introduction to a mathematical tool which will be extremely useful in the following: the analytic continuation of certain integrals.

Section 8 shows how to get a particular solution for the external ("harmonically relaxed") gravitational field (outside the two world tubes of section 6) by means of a well-defined algorithm based on analytic continuation. This solution takes into account the cubic non-linearity of the "harmonic" Einstein equations.

Section 9 deduces the equations of motion from the vacuum field equations by demanding that the "harmonicity conditions" be satisfied. These "integrability conditions" applied to the quartically non-linear Einstein equations provide the third order equations of motion. These equations of motion are calculated thanks to analytic continuation, from the cubically non-linear external field only.

Section 10 shows that the particular solution of the external problem constructed in Sections 8--9, because it fulfils the necessary boundary conditions of Section 6, is the unique solution of Einstein's equations which matches two compact objects.

Section 11 describes the transformation of "retarded" equations of motion into predictive Poincaré invariant ones.

Section 12 deduces the Newtonian-like equations of motion of two compact objects, complete up to terms of order $(v/c)^5$ ($2^{1/2}$Post-Newtonian level).

Section 13 describes the deduction of the second post-Newtonian equations of motion from a "generalized" Lagrangian.

Section 14 deduces from the preceding "generalized" Lagrangian some quantities which are constant at the $(v/c)^4$ level.

Section 15 uses the preceding "conserved quantities" as a tool for studying secular kinematical effects in a binary system. The Laplace-Eddington effect is obtained in complete agreement with the observations of PSR 1913 + 16.

The Appendix contains some technical details. The references are listed by alphabetical order at the end: for instance: M. ABRAHAM (1903) Ann.d. Phys. 10, 156...

Nota Bene: pay attention to a peculiarity of notation introduced for typographical reasons: I tried to avoid as far as possible all Greek, Gothic,... letters. Therefore the space-time indices: 0,1,2,3 will be denoted by a,b,c,d,e,f,g,h, the space indices: 1,2,3 by i,j,k,...and the Gothic metric by $\underline{g}^{ab}$.

3. DIGEST OF THE HISTORY OF THE PROBLEM OF MOTION

In 1687, I. Newton showed how the orbital motion of approximately spherical extended objects could be well-approximated by the motion of point masses. This is a very important result of Newtonian physics whose extension to General Relativity is highly non-trivial, as was pointed out by M. Brillouin (1922). M. Brillouin called this schematization of an extended body by a point mass with disappearance of all internal structure: "le principe d'effacement" ("effacing principle;" perhaps a more picturesque name would be: "the Cheshire cat principle"). In Newtonian physics the proof of this "effacing principle" makes an essential use of:

1) the linearity of the gravitational field as a function of the matter distribution (which allows one to define and separate the self-field and the external field);
2) the Action and Reaction principle (which allows one to define the center of mass and to ignore the contribution of the self-field to its motion);
3) Newton's theorem on the attraction of spherical bodies.

More specifically, for a binary system constituted of non-rotating nearly spherical bodies of masses m and m', one deduces from 1) that the main correction to the point mass idealization will come from the tidal field $Gm'd^{-3}r$ (where G is Newton's constant, r is the distance away from the center of mass of the first object m, and d is the distance between the two objects). If b denotes the radius of the first object, the tidal field will deform slightly its shape: $\delta b/b = h(m'/d^3)(b^3/m)$, where h, the first Love (1909) number, is a dimensionless quantity of order unity. This deformation induces in turn a small quadrupole moment: $Q = k\, m'b^5d^{-3}$, where k, the second Love number, is a dimensionless quantity of order unity ($h = 3/5$ and $k = 4/15$ for the Earth). Finally this tidally induced quadrupole moment will create a small correction to Newton's law for point masses: $\delta F/F \sim k\,(b/d)^5$. Therefore as long as the radii of the objects are much smaller than their mutual distances, their internal structure (if they are not rotating) will be utterly negligible. We shall show in Section 5 how this result of "effacing" can be extended to Einstein's theory even, and in fact most accurately, in the case of compact objects, i.e. when the radius $b \sim Gm/c^2$. But as we shall not be able to use 1) and 2) above, we shall need a completely different approach to show that the very strong "self field" of the compact object does not contribute to its orbital motion.

From 1798 to 1825, P.S. Laplace published his "Traité de Mécanique Céleste" which contains at least two ideas which will be of importance for the following. (Incidentally, it is interesting to note that during the preparation of his famous treatise Laplace was greatly helped, especially for numerical calculations, by a collaborator: Alexis Bouvard. According to Arago, Bouvard was born "in an obscure village in a valley of the Alps, not very far from Saint-Gervais;" in fact this village was Les Houches!). The first idea introduced by Laplace is now called "asymptotic matching". Laplace was investigating the shape of a large drop of mercury resting on a plane. The basic partial differential equation that must be satisifed by the height $z = z(x,y)$ of the drop is (as first determined by Laplace):

$$(1 + (z,_x)^2 + (z,_y)^2)^{-3/2}((1 + (z,_y)^2)z,_{xx} + (1 + (z,_x)^2)z,_{yy} - \\ - 2z,_x z,_y z,_{xy}) - a.z = 0. \qquad (1)$$

(a being a positive constant: 2g/A).

(1) is a highly non-linear partial differential equation and therefore there is little hope of solving it exactly. But the idea of Laplace is that there are two regimes where (1) is amenable to a perturbative treatment:

a) when the slope is small $(z,_x)^2+(z,_y)^2 << 1$, (1) reduces to:

$$z,_{xx} + z,_{yy} - a.z = (\text{non-linear terms}), \qquad (2)$$

which can be solved iteratively because the leading terms are linear.

b) at the boundary of the drop the slope is not necessarily small (it even becomes infinite) but the fact that the radius of the drop is large allows one to approximate the two-dimensional problem (1) by a one-dimensional problem ($z,_Y = 0$ for a local choice of coordinates X,Y at the boundary):

$$(1 + (z,_X)^2)^{-3/2} z,_{XX} - a.z = 0, \qquad (3)$$

which can be further transformed by posing: $z,_X = \tan(u(X))$ which allows one to treat the infinite slope points. Then one can look for approximations better than (3). Finally Laplace writes that the solutions of (2) and (3) must match asymptotically, that is to say, that they must approximately coincide in an open domain which is near the boundary but where the slope is small. This determines completely the unknown constants that appear in the solutions of (2) and (3). In the following sections we shall use a similar method and get similar results when dealing with Einstein's equations for two compact objects instead of (1).

The second idea introduced by Laplace is that if gravity propagates with a finite velocity c, then there should exist corrections to Newton's law for the motion of a planet which:

A) are of order v/c where v is the velocity of a planet.

B) are of a "damping" type $(-k\, v^i)$

C) will cause a shrinkage and a circularization of the orbit together with a secular acceleration of the mean orbital longitude.

Moreover, Laplace pointed out that only the last effect would be observable. The "known" secular acceleration of the moon led him to conclude that the velocity of propagation of gravity is at least seven million times the velocity of light! As we shall see explicitly in Section 12, the conclusion A) is not correct, the first order effect is compensated and the corrections due to the velocity of propagation of gravity are an expansion of the type: $(v/c)^2 + (v/c)^4 + (v/c)^5 + \ldots$ (the fact that it starts at order 2, therefore making a value of c equal to the velocity of light compatible with the astronomical observations was proved very generally by H. Poincaré in June 1905 in his attempt to describe a general Lorentz invariant gravitational interaction). However, we shall prove in Section 15 that conclusion B) is essentially correct for the $(v/c)^5$ term (the conclusion that the "residual Laplace effect" was contained in the $(v/c)^5$ term was first reached by Eddington (1924, see below) in his study of the radiation damping of a spinning rod). Finally, we shall prove that conclusion C) is not modified by the $(v/c)^2 + (v/c)^4$ terms but that it leads precisely to the observed secular orbital acceleration of the binary pulsar. Therefore from this point of view, this acceleration, that we shall call the "Laplace-Eddington effect," is a direct confirmation that gravity propagates with the speed of light and therefore an indirect confirmation of the existence of gravitational waves.

The concept of a "damping" force associated with an interaction which propagates with a finite velocity was to find its first full elaboration in electromagnetic theory. Apparently H.A. Lorentz was the first to mention, in 1892, the existence of such a "résistance." What is very interesting for the following, and premonitory of what was going to happen much later in the gravitational case is that:

1) Lorentz obtained this result by a direct calculation of the resultant force on a small extended accelerated particle due to its self field;
2) His result:

$$F^i = e^2 c^{-3} \ddot{v}^i , \tag{4}$$

was wrong by a factor 3/2!

This illustrates the difficulty of any direct calculation of a self force even in a linear theory. In fact it seems that the correct result was first obtained by a heuristic argument based on energy conservation due, not too unexpectedly, to M. Planck in 1897:

$$F^i = \frac{2}{3} e^2 c^{-3} \ddot{v}^i. \tag{5}$$

Lorentz corrected his first result (4) in 1902 and published the first complete direct calculation in 1903 (see also his book in 1909). The relativistic generalization of this celebrated "radiation reaction" force was first obtained by a heuristic argument based on energy and linear momentum conservation by M. Abraham (1903, 1904):

$$F^a = \frac{2}{3} e^2 (\ddot{u}^a - \dot{u}^2 u^a). \tag{6}$$

Then G.A. Schott (1912, 1915) obtained (6) by a direct relativistic self-field calculation.

In 1916 Einstein's theory of gravitation started its brilliant career. It was immediately clear that one would often have to resort to approximation schemes in order to draw physical conclusions from this theory. Indeed, in this same year the two main types of approximation schemes that were going to be used from then on were first clearly expounded. Einstein (1916) introduced an iterative method for solving his equations whose zeroth approximation is a flat Minkowski metric (denoted here and in the following by f_{ab}:-,+,+,+). In order to get a first approximation, Einstein transforms his equations into a diagonal hyperbolic partial differential system by using the celebrated "harmonic" coordinate condition in linearized form (this condition, sometimes named after De Donder, Lanczos, or even Lorentz, was apparently first suggested to Einstein in a private communication by W. De Sitter, see Einstein (1916)):

$$g_{ab} = f_{ab} + \underset{1}{g}_{ab} + \dots, \tag{7}$$

$$f^{bc}(\underset{1}{g}_{ab,c} - \tfrac{1}{2}\underset{1}{g}_{bc,a}) = 0. \tag{8}$$

$$\Box\, \underset{1}{g}_{ab} = -16\pi G c^{-2}(T_{ab} - \tfrac{1}{2} f_{ab} f^{cd} T_{cd}) + \underset{2}{N}_{ab}, \tag{9}$$

where: g_{ab} is the sought-for metric of space-time, $\Box$ is the usual d'Alembertian, or wave operator: $\Delta - c^{-2}\partial_t^2$, T_{ab} is the stress-energy tensor (divided by c^2 so that it has the dimension of a mass density), the indices a,b,c,d = 0,1,2,3 and where all the non-linear and higher order terms are hidden in $\underset{2}{N}_{ab}$ and were neglected by Einstein (as well as by most other authors until fairly recently!). Equations (7-9) do not constitute an iterative algorithm because a partial differential equation has many solutions. One needs some extra conditions. Einstein augmented the algorithm by the prescription that one should solve (9) by means of the flat space retarded Green function (Lorentz's "retarded potentials"); this amounts essentially to imposing the Kirchhoff-Sommerfeld "no-incoming-radiation" boundary conditions to $\underset{1}{g}_{ab}$ (see e.g. Fock (1959) section 92). These conditions are, more generally, for $h_{ab} = g_{ab} - f_{ab} = \underset{1}{g}_{ab} + \dots$, that rh_{ab} and $rh_{ab,c}$ be bounded and that:

$$\lim_{\substack{r\to+\infty \\ t+r/c=\text{const.}}} \left((rh_{ab})_{,r} + \frac{1}{c}(rh_{ab})_{,t} \right) = 0. \tag{10}$$

Note that this condition is imposed in the infinite past at infinite distances, such that $t + r/c = \text{const}$. This limiting process: $r \to +\infty$, $t \to -\infty$ with $t + r/c = \text{const}$. is often referred to as: going to (Minkowski) $\mathcal{I}^-$: scri minus. This condition should not be imposed, as is often mistakenly believed, at infinite distances but at constant time or even worse in the infinite future: $t - r/c = \text{const}$. ("wrong" outgoing wave condition instead of the "correct" no-incoming radiation condition (10)). In the following I shall refer to the complete algorithm (7,8,9,10) as a Post-Minkowskian Approximation scheme(sometimes abbreviated to PMA scheme). This terminology is, in my opinion, much better than the often used "Fast Motion Approximation" because, as is clear from the preceding discussion, the magnitude of the velocities of the sources of the gravitational field does not play any role; what is important is the constant use of the geometry of the Minkowski space-time and above all of its causality properties (use of "retarded" potentials versus the use of "instantaneous" potentials in the Post-Newtonian, sometimes called "Slow Motion," Approximation scheme to be described next). We emphasize this point here because we shall later use a Post-Minkowsian Approach together, at some point, with the simplifying assumption of "slow relative motion" (a Minkowski invariant concept) when treating the highest (cubic) non-linearities of Einstein's equations.

Simultaneously with Einstein, J. Droste (1916) and W. DeSitter (1916), motivated by the (urgent) necessity of working out the main astronomical consequences of Einstein's theory, which meant in particular estimating the first relativistic corrections in the solar system (and not just the perihelion precession of a planet around a fixed center) introduced an alternative iterative method for solving Einstein's equations which tried to keep as close as possible to Newtonian concepts. In particular they introduced from the start the assumption not only that the velocities were small: $v/c \ll 1$, but,most importantly, that the time derivatives of the gravitational field were smaller, by a factor of order v, than the space derivatives. They formalized this assumption by saying: "$g_{ij} - f_{ij}$ $(i,j = 1,2,3)$ and $g_{00} - f_{00}$ will be of the first order, g_{0i} will be of order 3/2... The velocities $\dot{x}_i = dx_i/cdt$ are of the order 1/2..., a differentiation with respect to $x_0 = ct$ increases the order of smallness by 1/2, and such a term as , e.g., $g_{00,00}$ is of the second order..." (De Sitter 1916, p. 155-156):a very modern way of defining what is now called a Post-Newtonian Approximation scheme (abbreviation: PNA scheme). In contrast with Einstein they did not introduce a clearly defined coordinate condition right from the beginning, but they introduced coordinate conditions progressively. However the main distinction is that their assumption about the smallness of time derivatives led them to perturbative equations of the following type:

$$\Delta \underset{n\text{th order}}{g_{ab}} = \text{source terms} + \text{terms known from preceding approximations.} \quad (11)$$

Now one should beware of the fact that, contrary to what is often believed, the appearance of a Laplacian in (11) does not mean that (11) is essentially non-equivalent to (9) where a D'Alembertian appeared. In fact, the two partial differential systems (11) and (9) are, in a perturbative sense, equivalent. Nevertheless, the physical results that one will deduce from them will be different if one supplements the Post-Newtonian Approximation scheme by a prescription for solving (11) which is not equivalent to the preceding use of "retarded potentials" i.e. to the satisfaction of the Kirchhoff-Sommerfeld conditions (10). Droste and DeSitter solved (11) by using the usual inverse of the Laplacian: the familiar "instantaneous potentials." Then they checked explicitly that their (Post-Newtonian) result was equivalent, at the order they considered, to the corresponding Post-Minkowskian one. It was realized only much later that this equivalence does not persist at higher approximations and, worse, that the reiterated use of "instantaneous potentials" (even somewhat corrected for taking into account odd-time retardation) leads always to divergent integrals at some order of approximation. This means that it is an intrinsically inconsistent method of solving Einstein's equations. On the other hand, however, there are hints that "retarded potentials" can be indefinitely reiterated. The reason why "instantaneous potentials" necessarily lead to divergent integrals when used in a non-linear theory is that they correspond to expanding in powers of the retardation time r/c where r is the distance between the source point and the field point. But even the simplest retarded field: $\Phi = S(t - r/c)/r$ yields, when so expanded:

$$\frac{S(t - r/c)}{r} = \frac{S(t)}{r} - \frac{1}{c}\dot{S}(t) + \frac{1}{c^2}\frac{\ddot{S}(t)r}{2} - \frac{1}{c^3}\frac{\dddot{S}(t)r^2}{6} + \ldots \tag{11'}$$

Therefore terms which grow like positive powers of r will appear and will generate similar terms in the right hand side of (11) which in turn cause (infrared) divergent integrals. A possible cure for this is to realize that (11') is valid only in the near zone ($r \ll \lambda$) and that the solutions of (11) can only be meaningful in the near zone. Then one must somehow match the general solution of (11) to a wave zone solution (see "Asymptotic Matching" below).

The next important step in the history of the problem of motion was the realization that the equations of motion of a body as a whole could be deduced from the vacuum field equations together with some knowledge of the structure of the gravitational field around the body under consideration. This was first understood by H. Weyl (1921) but his method, as well as the one used by Einstein and Grommer (1927), can only be applied to the test particle case (in the sense that the object considered has a negligible influence on the "external field," though such a "test" object is permitted to have a strong self field). In 1938, Einstein, Infeld and Hoffman, in a celebrated paper, succeeded in implementing this idea in the case of comparable masses. Taking advantage of the freedom of choice of the coordinate system, they imposed the following conditions on the "gothic metric" perturbation:

$$\underline{h}^{ab} := g^{1/2} g^{ab} - f^{ab} \,, \tag{12}$$

$$\underline{h}^{oi}{}_{,i} + \underline{h}^{00}{}_{,0} = 0, \tag{13a}$$

$$\underline{h}^{ik}{}_{,k} = 0. \tag{13b}$$

Then they introduced a Post-Newtonian scheme:

$$\underline{h}^{ab}(x) = (1/c^2)\,{}^{2}\underline{h}^{ab}(x) + (1/c^3)\,{}^{3}\underline{h}^{ab}(x) + \ldots, \tag{14a}$$

$${}^{n}\underline{h}^{ab}{}_{,0} \sim {}^{n+1}\underline{h}^{ab} \,. \tag{14b}$$

(14b) is formalized by writing time as: $x^0 = ct$. Basically the expansion parameter used by them, here denoted $1/c$, is the square root of the expansion parameter implicitly used by Droste and De Sitter. Introducing the nth reiterated field, i.e. the sum of the first n approximations:

$${}^{(n)}\underline{h}^{ab} = (1/c^2)\,{}^{2}\underline{h}^{ab} + \ldots + (1/c^n)\,{}^{n}\underline{h}^{ab}, \tag{15}$$

the Einstein vacuum field equations gave:

$${}^{(n+2)}\underline{h}^{00}{}_{,ss} = {}^{(n+2)}N^{00}(\ldots), \tag{16a}$$

$${}^{(n+1)}\underline{h}^{oi}{}_{,ss} = {}^{(n+1)}N^{oi}(\ldots), \tag{16b}$$

$${}^{(n+2)}\underline{h}^{ik}{}_{,ss} = {}^{(n+2)}N^{ik}({}^{(n+1)}\underline{h}^{oi}, \ldots), \tag{16c}$$

where the dots in the right hand sides denote the lower approximations. Now the basic idea of their method is that if we calculated somehow the preceding approximation: ${}^{(n)}\underline{h}^{oo}$, ${}^{(n-1)}h^{oi}$, ${}^{(n)}\underline{h}^{ik}$ then we would have now 14 equations constraining the 10 unknowns of the next approximation: the 10 (Poisson) field equations (16) and the 4 coordinate conditions (13). The system is "overdetermined". They showed that this "overdetermination" implied some further constraints on the preceding approximation. If the preceding approximation was expressed as a functional of the motion of the "particles" which are the sources of the field then these new constraints coming from the next approximation provide precisely the equations of motion of the "particles." Einstein, Infeld and Hoffmann found a very beautiful way of extracting from the overdetermined system (13) and (16), necessary constraints on the preceding approximation (which appears in the right hand sides of (16)). Using (13), they transformed (16b) and (16c) so as to exhibit some "curls" in the left hand sides: for instance (15b) became:

$$\left({}^{(n+1)}\underline{h}^{oi}{}_{,s} - {}^{(n+1)}\underline{h}^{os}{}_{,i} \right)_{,s} = {}^{(n+1)}N^{oi} + {}^{(n)}\underline{h}^{oo}{}_{,oi}. \tag{15b'}$$

The left hand side of (15b') is the "curl" of the "curl" of the vector $A^i = {}^{(n+1)}\underline{h}^{oi}$. Then they used the well-known fact that the "flux" integral of a curl over any closed 2-surface is identically zero (even if the vector A becomes singular at some points within the surface) to write necessary constraints on the preceding approximation in the form of 2-surface integrals:

$$\int \left({}^{(n+1)}N^{oi} + {}^{(n)}h^{oo}{}_{,oi} \right) dS_i = 0, \tag{17a}$$

$$\int {}^{(n+2)}N^{ik} dS_k = 0. \tag{17b}$$

The beauty of this result is that the equations of motion of a "particle" are given by some integrals over any two-surface enclosing the "particle." This means that we do not need to know precisely the internal structure of the "particle": it could be endowed with a very strong self gravitational field, it could be a black hole or a naked singularity; even in the most singular case the equations of motion are given by finite two surface integrals. This means also that we are replacing a knowledge of the precise internal structure by a knowledge of the structure of the gravitational field around the "particle" as is evident from the fact that we need to know ${}^{(n)}\underline{h}^{oo}$,... in order to compute the surface integrals (17). Einstein, Infeld and Hoffmann achieved this by prescribing a partly implicit set of rules for solving the preceding approximations: ${}^{(n)}\underline{h}^{oo}$,..., so that it was not clear to what kind of objects their results could be applied. Later, in Sections 5-6, we shall use a technique of asymptotic matching to transform the knowledge of the internal structure of the source "particles" (tidally distorted compact objects) into some knowledge of the behaviour of the gravitational field around the "particle," and we shall show that the latter partial knowledge is in fact sufficient to determine the gravitational field and the equations of motion of the objects. On the other hand, the theoretical beauty of the surface integral formulation of the equations of motion as well as its usefulness when dealing with strong field sources (no need to deal with the strong fields inside the object) are plagued by a very serious technical drawback: the surface integrals (17) are very complicated to compute explicitly. Einstein, Infeld and Hoffmann worked out "only" the first relativistic correction (v^2/c^2) to the (Newtonian) equations of motion and this entailed calculations so long that they could not publish them and that they deposited a detailed manuscript at the Institute for Advanced Study. Now the reader should remember that we need to push the calculation up to the order v^5/c^5

in order to try to explain the observed kinematical behaviour of PSR 1913 + 16! Later, in section 9, we shall see how the use of a mathematical trick (analytic continuation) allows one to tremendously simplify the calculations while still essentially respecting the spirit of the Einstein-Infeld-Hoffmann method, that is, deducing the nth approximated equations of motion from the integrability conditions of the (n+1) approximated vacuum field equations.

Now that we have described, in statu nascendi, the concepts that are going to be important for the following sections (except for two of them that are dealt with in sections 7 and 13) let us briefly sketch their evolution in time:

DEDUCTION of the equations of MOTION from VACUUM field equations was further investigated by Einstein and Infeld (1940, 1949) and Infeld and Schild (1949). A great clarification of the structure of the method, a correction of several flaws in the original method, as well as its extension to the Post-Minkowskian Approximation case is due to the excellent work of Kerr (1959, 1960). Infeld (1954, 1957) and Infeld and Plebanski (1960) discovered "experimentally," so to speak, that the calculations could be greatly simplified by the formal use of "good delta functions" playing the role of effective sources of the gravitational field. But they could never give any sound theoretical basis to their use of these "delta functions," even on a formal level where only consistency is required. Their only justification, and this is true for all the other works using "delta functions" until very recently, rested on the "experimental" agreement with the Einstein-Infeld-Hoffmann results at order $1/c^2$. However in the last two years, the constraints coming from the structure of Einstein's equations when one requires formal consistency of the use of "delta functions" have been investigated by Bel, Damour, Deruelle, Ibañez and Martin (1981). Moreover, one possible sound theoretical justification for their use in computing the gravitational field, together with a proof that the equations of motion deduced from them were effectively the integrability conditions of the next approximation, has been given by Damour (1980) (see also section 9 below). Other methods using only vacuum field equations to get the equations of motion and which are the descendants of the Weyl (1921) approach are quoted in the next paragraph.

ASYMPTOTIC MATCHING was introduced in General Relativity by V. Fock (1959), section 87), who matched a Post-Newtonian near zone expansion to a wave zone expansion. It was first applied to the problem of motion by F.K. Manasse and J.A. Wheeler (Manasse 1963) in a study of the tidal distortion and the radial infall of a small black hole into a large one. In 1969 Burke and Thorne proposed the use of asymptotic matching to the wave zone as a way of getting boundary conditions for the Post-Newtonian near zone expansions. This is a nice way of supplementing the PNA schemes by a prescription for solving the Poisson equations (11) which extends the validity of the PNA schemes beyond their usual limits: non-asymptotic flatness and divergencies due to the systematic use of "instantaneous potentials." But there remain problems associated with this method: the use of an outgoing-wave condition instead of a no-incoming radiation one, and the possibility of having higher order terms matching back to a low order. Moreover, Walker and Will (1980) pointed out a flaw in Burke's (1971) paper as well as in the corresponding section of Misner, Thorne and Wheeler (1973). Work aimed at meeting this criticism has been undertaken by Kates (1980a, 1980b). However the consistency of the whole scheme has never been checked and little attention, if any, has been given to time-even post-Newtonian terms, as well as to the role of non-linearities. In 1974 Demianski and Grishchuk applied a technique of asymptotic matching to the problem of the motion of a black hole around an object of comparable mass. Nearly at the same time D'Eath (1975a,b) treated with a similar technique but with more completeness the problems of a test-rotating black hole in a background space time and of a binary black hole system (PNA order $1/c^2$). More recently Kates gave a general discussion of the use of asymptotic matching techniques in General Relativity (Kates 1981) and devised a combination of Burke's and D'Eath's types of approaches when dealing with the motion of a binary system containing possibly compact objects (Kates 1980a,b). (see also Vilenkin and Fomin 1978).

THE POST-MINKOWSKIAN APPROXIMATION stayed dormant for a long while and was revived by Bertotti (1956) (first approximation). The second approximation was first tackled by Bertotti and Plebanski (1960). Other developments are due to Havas (1957), Kerr (1959), Lavas and Goldberg (1962), Kühnel (1963), Stephani (1964), and Schmutzer (1966). Then a new approach to the post-linear formalism was devised by Thorne and Kovács (1975), Crowley and Thorne (1977), Kovács and Thorne (1977) and applied by them to the calculation of bremsstrahlung during (possibly fast) small angle gravitational scattering. More recently a pioneering work of Rosenblum (1978, 1981) has spurred a detailed investigation of the Post-Minkowskian method beyond the linear order: Westpfahl and Göller (1979) have computed some post-linear (second Post-Minkowskian: 2PMA) equations of motion after using some ad hoc regularization (later these equations of motion have been applied by them to the small angle gravitational scattering case: work reported by K. Westpfahl at the Ringberg workshop, 1981, of which I know no published reference). Bel, Damour, Deruelle, Ibañez and Martin (1981) have investigated the formal consistency of the use of point masses and the constraints on the regularization procedures, calculated <u>explicitly</u> a 2PMA gravitational field as well as 2PMA equations of motion and transformed these equations into an ordinary differential system (see section 11). The behaviour at infinity of this 2PMA gravitational field has been worked out by Deruelle (1982). Finally Damour (1982) has investigated the 3PMA and worked out explicitly the 3 PMA equations of motion in Newtonian-like form neglecting terms of order c^{-6} (see section 12) (the necessity of including the contribution from the 3 PMA in a radiation reaction calculation had been first pointed out by Eddington (1924)).

THE POST-NEWTONIAN APPROXIMATION was further investigated in a remarkable work of Lorentz and Droste (1917). (This work seems to have been completely forgotten and is never qoted. I found it serendipitously in Lorentz's Collected Papers while writing up these lectures. A great historical surprise, expounded in Section 13, was contained in this work, like a genie in a bottle.) The work of Levi Civita (1937a, 1937b, 1950) clarified the hypotheses used in the PNAs and stressed the importance of proving the "effacing principle" (or "Cheshire cat principle"). Then came the classical papers of Einstein, Infeld and Hoffmann (1938), Fock (1939) and his school (Fock, 1959), and Papetrou (1951). Further, more complete (and/or more accurate),investigations are due to: the Polish school (see Infeld and Plebanski 1960), Peres (1959, 1960), Carmeli (1964, 1965), Chandrasekhar and his collaborators (see Chandrasekhar 1965 as well as many subsequent papers in the Astrophysical Journal), to Synge (1970), the Japanese school (Ohta et. al. 1973, 1974; Okamura et. al. 1973), Spyrou (1975) and Anderson and Decanio (1975). More recent works are quoted in the next paragraph.

RADIATION DAMPING in General Relativity was first investigated by Eddington (1924). In his supplementary note n° 8, he derived the loss of energy of a spinning rod by a direct near-zone radiation damping approach and not, as Einstein (1918), by a wave-zone energy flux computation (the two results agree though). He pointed out that the physical mechanism responsible for this damping was the effect discussed by Laplace: "If gravitation is not propagated instantaneously, the lag may cause tangential components of the force to occur, so that there will be a couple presumably opposing the rotation...We now know that the first order effect which Laplace expected is compensated; but the loss of energy (1)(the "quadrupole formula") is actually the residual Laplace effect...". However, he concluded that the agreement with the quadrupole <u>flux</u> formula (1.1) was validly demonstrated only for systems which are not gravitationally bound ("linearized theory") and that <u>cubically non-linear terms</u> should be taken into account in the study of gravitationally bound systems, so that in "the problem of the double star...we cannot be sure that even the sign of (1) is correct." This last doubt was increased by many later works: Hu (1947, see also 1982) found an energy gain. Infeld and Scheidegger believed in the absence of any damping (Infeld and Scheidegger 1953, 1955). This view was criticized by Goldberg (1955). In 1957 Havas discussed the contribution to radiation damping coming from the first Post-Minkowskian approximation. The result of a more complete investigation, of an improved Post-Newtonian type, by Peres (1959 a,b,1960) was, in the case of circular orbits, a damping (energy loss) in agreement with the "quadrupole formula" (however, and contrary to what Walker and Will (1980) seem to believe, this agreement is partly fortuitous; a scrutiny of the results of Peres (1960) shows that they are not entirely correct and would not agree with the "quadrupole formula" for elliptic orbits). The first attempt, and the only one until the work presented in these lectures, to work out complete equations of motion up to and including radiation reaction is due to the remarkable work of Carmeli (1964, 1965). The results however are not in agreement with the results presented below. Neither is the "quadrupole" energy loss recovered even for circular orbits. A scrutiny of the work of Carmeli shows that this disagreement is due both: to problems linked with the occurrence of divergent integrals (of infrared and ultraviolet type)and other meaningless quantities which are "regularized," and, to problems linked with the method used for solving Einstein's equations. In 1965 Smith and Havas found antidamping, which is not surprising because they were using only a first Post-Minkowskian approximation whereas three iterations (as done in the works of Peres and Carmeli) were necessary. In 1969 appeared the work of Infeld and Michalska-Trautman which investigated only time-odd effects: they obtained a result which agrees with the "quadrupole formula" for circular orbits, but this agreement would not be preserved in the elliptic case (contrary to what is generally believed). In the same year, Burke, using a matching technique described above, introduced a resistive potential and its associated radiation damping force acting on the mass m located at z:

$$F^i = -\frac{2}{5}c^{-5}mz^kQ^{(5)}_{ik} \quad , \tag{18}$$

where Q_{ik} is the quadrupole moment of the system:

$$Q_{ik} = \Sigma \ Gm(z^i z^k - \frac{1}{3} z^2 f^{ik}) \ . \tag{19}$$

The validity of (18) was proved by Thorne (1969) in the special case of slight perturbations of a spherical star. The proof by Burke (1971) for the general case was flawed (Walker and Will 1980). Therefore, as in the case of Planck's heuristic derivation of the electromagnetic damping force (5) (which came after the partly incorrect direct calculation by Lorentz), the main reason that can be invoked in favour of the general validity of (18) is its ability, if one assumes the existence of "good" conservation laws at lower orders, to cause secular losses of the energy and of the angular momentum in the near-zone that agree with the corresponding (quadrupole) fluxes in the wave zone. However it is interesting to note that our final result (section 15) will contain a damping force different from (18) but still in agreement with the "quadrupole" secular losses. In fact the coordinate freedom of General Relativity not only prevents one from comparing directly two partial results (like two "damping forces") but, in fact, makes meaningless any partial result: only a complete determination of all the terms of the equations of motion together with a knowledge of the gravitational field has any operational meaning in General Relativity.

The first direct calculation, "à la Lorentz," of a radiation reaction force which obtained a result in agreement with the "quadrupole" losses is due to Chandrasekhar and Esposito (1970). This work was, however,as was pointed out by Ehlers, Rosenblum, Goldberg and Havas (1976), blemished by some mathematical inconsistencies (divergent integrals). This type of approach (extended fluid sources, weak field everywhere, Post-Newtonian Approximation) has been clarified, systematized and made more rigorous by the works of Papapetrou and Linet (1981), McCrea (1981), Kerlick (1980),and Breuer and Rudolph (1981). The last two works use an improved PNA scheme due to Ehlers (1980) which postpones (but does not prevent) the appearance of divergencies. In fact, all the preceding works become mathematically inconsistent at some approximation level (divergent integrals due to the post-Newtonian near zone expansions (11')). On the

other hand, the work of Kates (1980) is aimed: at curing these divergencies (by using a Burke-Thorne approach) and at extending the validity of the approach to binary systems containing possibly compact objects (by using asymptotic matching to the "body zone"). However, neither has the overall consistency of Kates' approach ever been checked, nor has the role of time-even post Newtonian terms been clarified. A different approach to the problem of radiation reaction has been introduced by Schutz (1980). This approach has been extended recently to the gravitationally bound case by B. Schutz and Futamase.
Starting from the work of Bel,et.al. (1981), Damour and Deruelle (1981a) computed the Newtonian-like equations of motion of two slowly-moving point masses during a small-angle gravitational scattering (this restriction of validity is due to the lack of the cubically non-linear terms). Their equations of motion include "radiation reaction forces" which imply a net mechanical angular momentum loss which agrees with the quadrupole formula in the small angle scattering limit (the energy loss which depends on terms of order G^3 could not be computed). When neglecting these "radiation reaction forces", they showed (Damour and Deruelle 1981b) that these equations of motion could be deduced from a generalized Lagrangian (for the meaning of this, see Section 13). They studied the symmetries of this generalized Lagrangian and deduced therefrom 10 conservation laws (Damour and Deruelle 1981c) (see Section 14). On the other hand, Linet (1981), starting from the work of Papapetrou and Linet (1981) valid for everywhere-weak field gravitationally bound systems, calculated the time-odd part of the relative acceleration of two extended objects and showed that it could be gauge transformed into Burke's expression (18). However, as said above, the meaning of such a comparison between partial results ("time-odd" only) is a priori unclear because any part of the acceleration can be transformed at will (even into zero) by a suitable coordinate transformation.

As the preceding review has been certainly incomplete and perhaps biased by the author's point of view, the reader is urged to consult: the reviews of Goldberg (1962); Ehlers, Rosenblum, Goldberg and Havas (1976); Ehlers (1980); Walker and Will (1980); Thorne (1980); Cooperstock and Hobill (1982); as well as the proceedings of the third Gregynog relativity workshop (Walker 1979), of the 67th Enrico Fermi School (Ehlers

1979), and the account of the Round Table on the equations of motion (moderator: A. Ashtekar) in these proceedings.

In conclusion, up to 1981:

1) there existed no complete calculations of the equations of motion (and of the gravitational field) of a binary system up to the radiation reaction terms.
2) all the detailed calculations (generally complete only for time-odd terms) were inconsistent at higher orders of approximation, or, even their consistency at low orders had not been checked.
3) most of the detailed calculations were valid only for non-compact objects (weak self fields). The other ones were in want of a firmer footing.

4. "DISCOURS DE LA METHODE"

Before embarking on any details of the method of approximation that will be used, I would like to comment briefly on its connection, or the lack thereof, with what is rigorously known, in a "French mathematical sense", about Einstein's theory. At this point the reader should have a look at the patch-work picture of space-time, which is reproduced in this book. This drawing represents the different domains of validity (or, sometimes, what one thinks or hopes they are) of some of the main approaches used to deal with Einstein's theory and discussed in these proceedings. The best proofs of existence and uniqueness of solutions of Einstein's equations have been obtained in the study of the Cauchy problem (Choquet-Bruhat 1952, see the lectures of J. York in these proceedings) and their domain of validity covers the violin-shaped region in the middle of the drawing: the Cauchy development of initial data given on a space-like hypersurface. However we shall use in the following global harmonic coordinates, boundary conditions in the infinite past (3·10), and we shall solve Einstein's equations by reiterating a flat space Green function (instead of the sucesively improved curved space Green functions used in the existence proofs). For the moment only partial mathematical results are known which can give us confidence that we are on a right track: Choquet-Bruhat, Christodoulou and Francaviglia 1979,

Choquet-Bruhat and Christodoulou (1980), Friedrich (1981, 1982) (see also the contribution of H. Friedrich to these proceedings), and Christodoulou and Schmidt (1980). Nevertheless let us proceed: "Es muss sein!" (Beethoven 1826).

In order to try to meet the requirements listed at the end of Section 1 we shall adopt the following strategy (similar to the one used by Laplace in his study of the shape of a large drop of mercury, see Section 3): to split the problem of the gravitational interaction of two compact bodies in two parts:

a) the internal perturbation schemes (one for each body) where one studies the small perturbation of the internal structure and of the gravitational field inside and outside each body due to the (tidal) influence of its faraway companion,

b) the external perturbation scheme (one for the system) where one studies the (post-post-linear) perturbations of flat space, due to the presence of the two bodies, in a vacuum region outside two 2-surfaces enclosing the bodies.

To fix one's imagination in the case of PSR 1913 + 16 which is very probably constituted of two neutron stars of radii $\sim$ ten kilometers, a million kilometers apart, one can think of the internal regions as extending up to two hundred kilometers away from each pulsar and of the external region as staying at least a hundred kilometers away from each pulsar.

After having so analyzed the problem, we shall take up the following <u>method</u>:

1) Studying, by means of an internal perturbation scheme, the distortion of the gravitational field <u>outside</u> a compact object caused by the influence of its far-away companion (Section 5).

2) Converting, by means of a very general coordinate transformation linking internal and external variables, the information acquired in step 1) into information about the behaviour of the gravitational field in the external region (expressed as a function of the external coordinates and as a functional of a "central worldline" defined by the transformation between internal and external coordinates). This information on the external gravitational field will play the role of <u>boundary conditions</u> for the external perturbation scheme (section 6).

3) Finding a particular solution of the "harmonically relaxed" vacuum external perturbation scheme by means of a well-defined algorithm based on analytic continuation (introduced in Section 7): this solution is a functional of two free worldlines in Minkowski space-time and takes into account the cubic non-linearity of the "harmonic" Einstein equations (Section 8).

4) Showing that this particular solution will be a solution of the complete (non-relaxed) vacuum Einstein equations if and only if the "central" world lines satisfy some equations of motion. This result can be generalized to the quartically non-linear relaxed Einstein equations and yields the required cubically non-linear equations of motion (Section 9). This method of getting the equations of motion, only from the vacuum field equations and the external gravitational field, is a generalization (to higher orders and to a PMA) and a simplification (thanks to analytic continuation) of the approach of Einstein-Infeld-Hoffmann and Kerr sketched in Section 3.

5) Checking that the particular solution of the vacuum Einstein equations now constructed (by implicitly replacing the free world lines of step 3) by solutions of the equations of motion of step 4)) is the unique solution of the cubically non-linear external perturbation scheme which satisfies the boundary conditions of step 2) near each compact object and the Kirchoff "no incoming radiation" conditions (Section 10).

These five steps are therefore sufficient to prove (under several plausible technical assumptions and one plausible physical assumption) that the gravitational field and the equations of motion obtained are effectively the gravitational field outside and the equations of motion of two compact objects. The plausible physical assumption is the set of hypotheses used in step 1). However it is desirable to check explicitly all these plausible assumptions by perfecting the preceding method by a sixth step (that I shall leave to future work):

6) Checking that one can fit an explicit model of a compact object into the previously constructed external gravitational field.

Similarly, we shall leave to future work: the important task of estimating the errors entailed by the approximation method (the method used seems to guarantee that they are finite but one must check their smallness); to check the technical assumptions used (for instance regarding the existence and behaviour of solutions of the equations of motion); to study the behaviour of the gravitational field, constructed in steps 3) and 4), at "infinity."

5. INTERNAL PERTURBATION SCHEME

Assuming the knowledge of the internal structure $T_{ab}^{(0)}$ and of the gravitational field $g_{ab}^{(0)}$ of one isolated body the internal scheme consists in studying the small perturbations thereof caused by the presence of a faraway companion. For simplicity we shall make the following physical hypotheses about the body one considers:

1) the body is compact, i.e., either it is a black hole or its radius = b $\sim$ G(mass)/c^2 (this hypothesis can be relaxed to: $(b/d)^5 \ll (v/c)^5$ where d is the distance to the companion and v the orbital velocity (Damour 1981)),

2) the body is non-rotating and spherically symmetric before the interaction (this hypothesis can be relaxed to slow rotation: spin velocity << c (Damour 1982)),

3) the internal perturbations must tend to zero when either m' (the mass of the companion) or d^{-1} tends to zero, and must vary on the same time scale as d, which is much slower than the internal time scale of a compact body: Gm/c^3 (this means physically that we consider only the (tidal) perturbations caused by the companion and exclude the perturbations due to some internal mechanism which could trigger for instance some fast vibrations. Moreover, it must be noted that this "slow internal motion " hypothesis is in no way incompatible with the Post-Minkowskian Approximation scheme which will be used for the external field).

Technically one introduces some internal coordinates X^a with:

$$\begin{aligned} X^0 &= T \\ X^1 &= R\sin\theta\cos\phi \\ X^2 &= R\sin\theta\sin\phi \\ X^3 &= R\cos\theta \quad . \end{aligned} \tag{1}$$

(Beware of notations: in this section R denotes $(X^iX^i)^{1/2}$ and d the distance to the companion, in later sections R will denote the distance to the companion). One looks for a perturbed metric:

$$g_{ab}(X^c) = g^{(o)}_{ab}(X^i,0) + h_{ab}(X^c) + \ldots, \tag{2}$$

with:

$$g^{(o)}_{ab}dX^a dX^b = - A(c^2R/Gm)dT^2 + B(c^2R/Gm)\, dR^2 + + C(c^2R/Gm)R^2(d\theta^2 + \sin^2\theta d\phi^2). \tag{3}$$

where outside the object (Birkhoff's theorem):

$$A = B^{-1} = 1 - 2Gm/c^2R\ , \quad \text{and } C = 1. \tag{4}$$

We have denoted by m the Schwarzchild mass of the isolated object (a constant). Via the matching of the next section the same constant m will appear in the "boundary conditions" for the external field and, therefore, via the uniqueness result of section 10 the same constant m will appear in the external field and in the equations of motion. The perturbed metric must satisfy Einstein's equations:

$$E_{ab}(g^{(o)} + h + \ldots) = 8\pi\ Gc^{-2}(T^{(o)}_{ab} + s_{ab} + \ldots\ ), \tag{5}$$

where E_{ab} is the Einstein tensor $(R_{ab} - \frac{1}{2}Rg_{ab})$ and s_{ab} the first order perturbation of the stress-energy tensor · The dots in (2) and (5) mean that we start looking at the first order perturbation only. However, we do need to consider higher order perturbations in order to be consistent with the external scheme. Our strategy consists in studying first the linearized perturbation h_{ab} and to deduce therefrom the functional form of the general non-linear perturbation (eqn (17) below). The information contained in this functional form will be sufficient for our purposes.

A natural tool for studying the first order metric perturbation h_{ab} is the Regge-Wheeler formalism (Regge and Wheeler 1957, Campolattaro and Thorne 1970, Zerilli 1970). It consists in expanding h_{ab} in tensorial spherical harmonics:

$$h_{ab}(X^c) = \sum_{L=0}^{\infty} \sum_{M=-L}^{+L} \sum_{A=1}^{10} H^L_{M(A)}(\hat{R},\ T)\ Y^{M(A)}_{Lab}(\theta,\phi), \tag{6}$$

where we have introduced the radial variable in units of the small length scale:

$$\hat{R} \equiv \frac{c^2R}{Gm}\ . \tag{7}$$

A L = 0 term in (6) would correspond to a radial vibration of the body with no change of the gravitational field outside the body (apart from a constant change of the mass which can be incorporated in (4)). Hence such a term would not be caused by the influence of the companion but only by some internal mechanism and therefore by the hypothesis 3) ; we shall not include any L = 0 term in (6). Similarly a L = 1 term in (6) would correspond to a dipolar vibration of the body with no physical change of the gravitational field outside the body (apart from a constant small Lense-Thirring term which is not present by hypothesis 2)). This has been shown by Campolattaro and Thorne (1970) and Zerilli (1970), who interpreted the coordinate system where the mathematical change of the gravitational field outside the body is zero as a Center of Mass system. As before, in this Center of Mass system the remaining internal perturbations can only be due to some internal mechanism and should be discarded. Therefore, with our hypotheses, there exists a coordinate system such that the series (6) starts only at L = 2. We shall in the following use such an internal "Mass Centered" coordinate system.

When $L \geqslant 2$ we can simplify (6) by using a Regge-Wheeler gauge. In this coordinate system only 6 independent functions of R and T are left for each L, M (instead of 10 in general). Then the L,M part of h_{ab} can be written as:

$$h_{ab}^{LM} = \begin{pmatrix} \frac{\hat{R}-2}{\hat{R}} H_o & H_1 & -h_o \frac{1}{\sin\theta}\frac{\partial}{\partial\phi} & +h_o \sin\theta \frac{\partial}{\partial\theta} \\ \text{sym.} & \frac{\hat{R}}{\hat{R}-2} H_2 & -h_1 \frac{1}{\sin\theta}\frac{\partial}{\partial\phi} & +h_1 \sin\theta \frac{\partial}{\partial\theta} \\ \text{sym.} & \text{sym.} & \hat{R}^2 K & 0 \\ \text{sym.} & \text{sym.} & \text{sym.} & \hat{R}^2 \sin^2\theta K \end{pmatrix} Y_L^M(\theta,\phi) \tag{8}$$

where we have suppressed the indices L, M on the 6 functions $H_0, H_1, H_2, K, h_0, h_1$. These functions satisfy a partial differential system whose right hand side is given by the L,M projection of the perturbed stress-energy tensor s_{ab} and therefore depends explicitly on the internal structure of the body. This differential system is greatly simplified by using our hypothesis 3) which implies that we can in first approximation neglect the time derivatives compared to the space derivatives (this can be checked a posteriori because we shall see that effectively we shall obtain some functions H_0, ... whose length scale is $G\,m/c^2$ but whose time scale is the external time scale). Then we need only to consider stationary perturbations (quasi-stationary tides) (Manasse 1963). It has been shown by Regge-Wheeler (1957) that for vacuum stationary perturbations:

$$\begin{aligned} H_0 &= H_2 \quad (=H \text{ say}) \\ H_1 &= 0 \\ h_1 &= 0 \end{aligned} \tag{9}$$

Then one can find in vacuum a decoupled second order differential equation for $H = H_0 = H_2$ for instance (Edelstein and Vishveshwara 1970, Demianski and Grishchuk 1974):

$$\hat{R}(\hat{R}-2)d^2(H/\hat{R}(\hat{R}-2))/d\hat{R}^2 + 3(2\hat{R}-2)d(H/\hat{R}(\hat{R}-2))/d\hat{R} - \\ - (L-2)(L+3)\ H/\hat{R}(\hat{R}-2) = 0. \tag{10}$$

The general solution of this second order differential equation contains 2 arbitrary constants. For instance, when $L = 2$, one finds for the general quadrupolar H perturbation in vacuum, i.e. outside the body:

$$H = D(\hat{R}(\hat{R}-2) + k\ \hat{R}(\hat{R}-2) \int_{\hat{R}}^{\infty} 5dx/(x^3(x-2)^3)\ ). \tag{11}$$

The dimensionless constant k is a relativistic generalization (Damour 1981) of the second Love number (Love 1909) which was introduced in Section 3. It is, in a sense, a dimensionless measure of the yielding of the object to an external tidal solicitation. It depends on the internal structure of the body (equations of state,...) and can be determined for an ordinary body (not a black hole) by imposing the regularity of the metric perturbation H, K, h_0 at the center of the body and when crossing the surface of the body (see e.g., Thorne and Campolattaro 1967). By our hypothesis 1) we have $\hat{R} \sim 1$ at the radius of the object, therefore as there are no other scales in the problem, k must be of order unity (like the non-relativistic one):

$$k \sim 1 \tag{12}$$

(More generally for non-necessarily compact objects of dimensionless radius $\hat{b}$, one will have $k \sim \hat{b}^5$ which allows one to justify the remark after hypothesis 1)). In the case of a black hole, k is determined by imposing the regularity of metric perturbation on the future horizon: in this case one finds $k = 0$ (in agreement with D'Eath 1975a). Incidently, one should not conclude from this result that there are no tidal responses of a black hole to an external solicitation: such a non-zero response is contained in the first term of the righthand side of (11): $\hat{R}\ (\hat{R} - 2)$ which differs from the usual term (in absence of any object): $\hat{R}^2$.

On the other hand the second constant D cannot be determined by internal considerations only but must be obtained by somehow matching out (11) to the yet to be determined "external field." (Manasse 1963, D'Eath 1975). When $\hat{R} >> 1$, but still $R << d$, I.E. in the outer part of the region where we use the internal scheme, (11) becomes:

$$H \sim D\ (\hat{R}^2 - 2\hat{R} + k/\hat{R}^3 + O(1/\hat{R}^4)). \tag{13}$$

To such a metric perturbation $\sim D\hat{R}^2$ corresponds when $\hat{R} >> 1$ a curvature $\sim Dc^4/G^2m^2$. It is fairly obvious that this must correspond to the curvature of the far field of the companion $\sim Gm'/c^2d^3$, m' being the mass of the companion and d the distance between the two bodies; hence:

$$D \sim \frac{G^3}{c^6}\ \frac{m^2m'}{d^3} \quad \text{(at lowest order)} \tag{14}$$

(In fact one does not need to appeal to any "obviousness": by imposing only the finiteness of the preceding curvature as $G \to 0$ and by using the results of section 6 and 10 at the lowest order in G one can prove that this curvature is effectively given, in lowest order, by the linearized far field of the companion.). A similar argument for $L > 2$ leads to the introduction of higher orders Love numbers k, and overall coefficients D (for each L there are several of these, corresponding to the different independent metric perturbation functions) with the result that:

$$k_L \sim 1, \tag{15a}$$

$$D_L \sim \left(\frac{G}{c^2}\right)^{L+1} \frac{m^L m'}{d^{L+1}} \quad \text{(at lowest order)}. \tag{15b}$$

At first sight it would seem that the information that we have obtained about internal perturbations: (12) (14)(15) is much too vague to be of any use in the problem of transforming the knowledge of the internal structure of the bodies (now coded in the generalized Love numbers k_L) into a knowledge of the behaviour of the gravitational field "near" but outside the objects in the external approximation scheme (remember from section 3 that it is precisely this kind of knowledge that we need in order to get the equations of motion of the objects by an approach à la Einstein-Infeld-Hoffmann). Moreover we have considered up to now only the lowest order internal perturbations (linearized in h_{ab}, lowest order in the coupling to the companion, neglect of some time derivatives). However, we are going to show that the knowledge so acquired about the functional form of the lowest order internal perturbation can be extended to higher orders (including all kind of non-linearities and inclusion of time derivatives) and, as we said earlier, we shall see later that this information will be sufficient for our purposes.

For convenience let us put c = 1 and denote a product of the type:

$$G^p m^{p-q} (m')^q \text{ with } \underline{\underline{q \geqslant 1}} \text{ by } G'^p, \tag{16}$$

up to now we considered mainly the case $q = 1$, but later we shall include $q > 1$.

Then we can summarize our results (2-15) by:

$$g_{ab}(X^i,T) = g_{ab}^{(0)}(\frac{X^i}{G^m}, 0) + \sum_{p\geqslant 3} G'^p g_{ab}^{(p)}(\frac{X^i}{Gm}, d(T), k) \quad (+...) \tag{17}$$

where the dots denote the higher order terms that we still have to include, and where, as indicated by the somewhat symbolic notation, the functions $g_{ab}^{(p)}$ depend:

- on space only through the "reduced" spatial coordinates: X^i/Gm
- on time only through variables linked with the companion: distance, velocity...
- and, apart from that, depend only on dimensionless numbers of order unity:

pure numbers (2,5,...as they appeared in (11))and various Love numbers $k \sim 1$. It is interesting to note at this point that the appearance of the pure numbers is due essentially to Birkhoff's theorem (universality of the functional form of the unperturbed metric outside the body when expressed in reduced variables) and that the appearance of the other numbers of order unity (k) is due to the hypothesis of compactness.

Now we can compute the higher order terms by iteration: we plug (17) in the Einstein equations (5) and "grind", keeping now non-linear terms and time derivatives. Because of the functional form (17) we can now check effectively, a posteriori, that time derivatives generate only higher order terms. All these higher order terms can be considered, together with terms coming from the right hand side of (5), as effective sources for the higher order metric perturbations (the dots in (17)). But as the functional form of (17) is preserved by the"grinding" we can look for higher order metric perturbations with the same functional form as (17). Moreover these source terms are, by construction, multiplied by G'^4 at least. Note that now G'^p can contain m' more than once. The most general higher order metric perturbation will be, at each iteration step, the sum of a particular solution of the inhomogeneous equation of order G'^4 at least, and of the general solution of the homogeneous equation which is the same as the one considered before when dealing with the lowest order perturbations. Therefore the same reasoning as before will allow us to conclude that this general homogeneous solution is of the form (17) in a suitable coordinate system. Finally we end up with the interesting result that the most general fully non-linear internal metric perturbation can be written as (17) where now we can discard the dots.

Before deducing from (17) the general behaviour of the gravitational field outside the body let us comment on one of the most restricted formulations of what was introduced in section 3, without being precisely formulated, under the name of the "principle of effacing internal structure" or "Cheshire cat principle."

The lowest order term, in the metric outside the body, where the internal structure begins to show up, is in the second term of the right hand side of (11) (and in similar terms for the other metric functions): the term which is multiplied by the Love number k whose value depends on the details of the internal structure. As we see from (11) this term can be expanded in inverse powers of $\hat{R}$ when $\hat{R} >> 1$:

$$H^{\text{structure}}_{\text{dependent}} \sim Dk\,(\hat{R}^{-3} + O\,(\hat{R}^{-4})) \tag{18}$$

Replacing D by (14) and $\hat{R}$ by (7) we get:

$$H^{\text{structure}}_{\text{dependent}} \sim \frac{G^6}{c^{12}}\, k\, \frac{m^5 m'}{d^3 R^3}\,. \tag{19}$$

Therefore when viewed in the external scheme (next section) this term is of extremely high order (G^6). As we shall compute the equations of motion only from the external field we see that the internal structure will show up in the equations of motion of each body as a whole only at the negligible order G^6. Before this order the compact bodies appear, in the external scheme, only through (one central world-line, see next section, and through) one constant parameter (the "grin" of the cat): the mass m. In other words it means that up to and including order G^5 one could replace any two compact bodies (neutron stars with any kind of equation of state,...) by two black holes (Damour 1981). As indicated at the beginning of this section this result can be somewhat generalized by relaxing the hypotheses that were needed to prove it: for instance instead of supposing compactness it is sufficient to require that the radius b of each body is such that $(b/d)^5$ is negligible compared to what we wish to compute (in the case at hand where we are looking for high order radiative effects it means $(b/d)^5 << (v/c)^5$ where v is the orbital velocity). However the reader should note that, although the final result about the order of magnitude of the tidal effects would have been the same had we used the Newtonian formulae of section 3, it was necessary to use the preceding relativistic machinery in order to give meaning to and to prove these formulae in the strongly relativistic case of compact objects. The generalization to rotating compact objects is less easy, because if they are very rapidly rotating they will be no longer spherical and their shape, and their quadrupole moment (even at zeroth order) will depend on their internal structure. This is why it has been possible to generalize the preceding results (and the entire approach of the next sections) only in the case of slowly spinning objects (Damour 1982).

At this point, it is convenient, for facilitating the use of our result (17) in the next sections, to change, outside the body, the coordinates X^i, T that we have been using in this section to X'^i, T' with:

$$T' = T$$

$$X'^i = \frac{R - Gm}{R}\, X^i \tag{20}$$

This transformation leaves invariant the functional form of (17), the main difference being now that the zeroth approximation $g^{(0)}_{ab}$ will be, outside the body, the Schwarzchild metric expressed in harmonic coordinates (Fock 1959)(for simplicity we drop the primes):

$$g^{(0)}_{ab}\, dX^a dX^b = -\frac{R - Gm}{R + Gm}\, dT^2 + \frac{R+Gm}{R-Gm}\, dR^2 + (R+Gm)^2\, (d\theta^2 + \sin^2\theta\, d\phi^2). \tag{21}$$

In the following we shall find it more convenient to use the "gothic" contravariant metric:

$$\underline{g}^{ab} = g^{1/2} g^{ab} \tag{22}$$

where g is the negative of the determinant of g_{ab}. We have in the quasi-Cartesian coordinates (20):

$$\underline{g}^{ab}_{(0)} = f^{ab} - G^2 m^2 \frac{N^a N^b}{R^2} + \left(1 - \frac{(1+Gm/R)^3}{1-Gm/R}\right) U^a U^b \tag{23}$$

where $N^o = 0$, $N^i = X^i/R$ and $U^o = 1$, $U^i = 0$. (23) can be expanded in powers of Gm/R (when $Gm/R < 1$):

$$\underline{g}^{ab}_{(0)} = f^{ab} - 4\frac{Gm}{R} U^a U^b - \frac{G^2 m^2}{R^2} (7U^a U^b + N^a N^b) - \\ - 8\,\frac{G^3 m^3}{R^3} U^a U^b - 8\,\frac{G^4 m^4}{R^4} U^a U^b - \text{and so on.} \tag{24}$$

For later convenience we denote by $S^{ab}_n(U,N)$ the coefficient of $(Gm/R)^n$:

$$S^{ab}_1(U,N) = -4U^a U^b,$$
$$S_2{}^{ab}(U, N) = -7U^a U^b - N^a N^b,$$
$$n \geq 3 : \quad S_n{}^{ab}(U,N) = -8U^a U^b, \tag{25}$$

$$\underline{g}^{ab}_{(0)} = f^{ab} + \sum_{n \geq 1} \frac{G^n m^n}{R^n} S^{ab}_n(U,N) \tag{26}$$

We have seen above (see eqn (11)) that the lowest order correction $G'^3 g^{(3)}_{ab}(X^i/Gm, d(T))$ to $g^{(0)}_{ab}$ could be expanded in a series of positive and negative powers of $\hat{R}$. This result can be extended iteratively to all the $g^{(p)}_{ab}$ $(p \geq 3)$ of (17) and therefore also to all the $\underline{g}^{ab}_{(p)}$ $(p \geq 3)$ of the expansion for $\underline{g}^{ab}$ corresponding to (17) in the new coordinate system (20), hence:

$$p \geq 3, \; G'^p \underline{g}^{ab}_{(p)} = \sum_{n,q} G^p m^{p-q} m'^q \, T^{ab}_{n,p,q}(d(T),k) \left(\frac{Gm}{R}\right)^n \tag{27}$$

Therefore, putting together (17), (26), and (27), we reach the final conclusion that: the coefficient of $1/R^n$ ($n \geq 0$) in the expansion of $\underline{g}^{ab}(X^i, T)$ outside a compact body is:

$$G^n m^n S_n^{ab}(U,N) + \sum_{p \geq 3} \sum_{q \geq 1} G^{n+p} m^{n+p-q} m'^q T^{ab}_{n,p,q}(d(T),k) \; . \tag{28}$$

More simply put: the coefficient of $1/R^n$ ($n \geq 0$) is the same as for an isolated Schwarzchild solution plus corrections due to the tidal interaction of the companion which are smaller by a factor G'^3 at least (i.e. $\sim G^3 m' m^2/d^3$ or $G^3 m'^2 m/d^3$, a very small correction indeed $\sim (v/c)^6$).

In the next section we shall convert this knowledge of the magnitude of the tidal distortion of the gravitational field outside the body in internal coordinates into a similar, but more useful, knowledge in external coordinates.

6. EXTERNAL PERTURBATION SCHEME

In the exterior region, i.e. everywhere except inside two 2-surfaces (two space-time tubes), enclosing each body and of "diameter" much smaller than the distance between the two bodies constituting the binary system, the "gothic" gravitational field:

$$\underline{g}^{ab}(x) = g^{1/2} g^{ab}, \quad (g = -\det g_{ab}), \tag{1}$$

expressed in external coordinates x^a, must satisfy the Einstein (-Grossmann) vacuum field equations:

$$2gE^{ab} = 0 \tag{2a}$$

that is, explicitly:

$$\begin{aligned}(2gE^{ab} \equiv)\; & \underline{g}^{cd}\underline{g}^{ab}{}_{,cd} + \underline{g}^{ab}\underline{g}^{cd}{}_{,cd} - \underline{g}^{ac}\underline{g}^{bd}{}_{,cd} - \underline{g}^{bc}\underline{g}^{ad}{}_{,cd} + \underline{g}^{ab}{}_{,c}\underline{g}^{cd}{}_{,d} - \underline{g}^{ac}{}_{,d}\underline{g}^{bd}{}_{,c} + \\ & + \underline{g}_{cd}\underline{g}^{ce}{}_{,f}(\underline{g}^{af}\underline{g}^{bd}{}_{,e} + \underline{g}^{bf}\underline{g}^{ad}{}_{,e}) - \underline{g}_{cd}\underline{g}^{ef}\underline{g}^{ac}{}_{,e}\underline{g}^{bd}{}_{,f} - \frac{1}{2}\underline{g}^{ab}\underline{g}_{cd}\underline{g}^{ce}{}_{,f}\underline{g}^{df}{}_{,e} - \\ & - \frac{1}{8}(2\underline{g}^{ac}\underline{g}^{bd} - \underline{g}^{ab}\underline{g}^{cd})(2\underline{g}_{eg}\underline{g}_{fh} - \underline{g}_{ef}\underline{g}_{gh})\underline{g}^{ef}{}_{,c}\underline{g}^{gh}{}_{,d} = 0,\end{aligned} \tag{2b}$$

where $\underline{g}_{ab}$ is the matrix inverse of $\underline{g}^{ab}$ (i.e. $g^{-1/2} g_{ab}$). (2) constitutes a system of non-linear, nonhyperbolic, partial differential equations. De Donder and Lanczos found a way of "relaxing" (2) into a diagonal system of non-linear <u>hyperbolic</u> partial differential equations which is better suited to a perturbative treatment (as well as being nearly indispensable for mathematical investigations about the existence and uniqueness of the solutions of (2), see however the contribution of Y. Choquet to these proceedings). This "relaxing" consists in introducing, as auxiliary equations, the harmonic coordinate conditions:

$$\underline{g}^{ab}{}_{,b} = 0 \tag{3}$$

which, when plugged into (2), yield the "harmonically relaxed" Einstein vacuum equations:

$$\underline{g}^{cd}\underline{g}^{ab}{}_{,cd} + Q^{ab}(\partial\underline{g}, \partial\underline{g}) = 0 \tag{4}$$

where Q^{ab}, which is quadratic in the derivatives of $\underline{g}^{ab}$, is obtained from (2b) by ignoring the 2^{d}, 3^{d}, 4th and 5th terms. We shall assume the global existence of harmonic coordinates so that the "external" gravitational field can be considered as fulfilling both eqn (3) and eqn (4) in the exterior region. (4) being a partial differential system we expect to be able to characterize one of its solutions by means of some kind of boundary conditions. More precisely (4) being hyperbolic, one should give, in fact, "initial conditions" (Cauchy data on a space-like hypersurface). However, the exterior region being pierced by two space-time tubes we shall be led to try to characterize a solution of (4) by two kinds of "boundary conditions":

1) some Kirchoff-type boundary conditions at infinite distances in the infinite past (see eqn (3 · 10)),

2) some "boundary conditions" "on" the space-time tubes enclosing the bodies (see below).

Concerning the first type of boundary conditions one should probably, in view of the structure of (4), impose boundary conditions at infinite past (affine) distances along the characteristics of (4), i.e., along the null geodesics of the exact (but unknown!) metric g. However, in our Post-Minkowskian Approximation treatment, we shall introduce an auxiliary flat metric f^{ab} (which at this level means only a diagonal matrix (-1, +1, +1, +1)) and the "gothic"metric"perturbations":

$$h^{ab} = \underline{g}^{ab} - f^{ab} . \tag{5}$$

(Beware that, for the ease of notation, we did not put a bar below h^{ab}, so that our future convention for moving indices with the flat metric will yield a "covariant" h_{ab} which is different from the one used in preceding sections: eqn (3.10), (5.2)).

Now we shall assume that the metric that we are looking for satisfies the Kirchoff "no-incoming-radiation" conditions at infinite past (affine) distances along the null geodesics of the auxiliary flat metric. This means that, in the harmonic external coordinate system x^{a} (introducing auxiliary polar variables $x^{o}= t, r,\theta,\phi$

constructed in the usual way), rh^{ab} and $rh^{ab}{}_{,c}$ are supposed to be bounded and that:

$$\lim_{\substack{r \to \infty \\ \theta,\phi,\ t + r/c = \text{const.}}} \left((rh^{ab})_{,r} + (rh^{ab})_{,t} \right) = 0 \,. \tag{6}$$

Concerning the second type of boundary conditions we shall deduce them from the results of the preceding section by transforming internal coordinates X^a of, say, the first body, into external coordinates x^a. In order to deduce necessary conditions on the external field $\underline{g}^{ab}(x)$, we must investigate the most general coordinate transformation $X^a \to x^a$ compatible with the hypotheses 1), 2), and 3) of the beginning of Section 5. We need to further assume that: 4) in the overlap region between the internal and the external scheme the functions $x^a(T, X^i)$ can be expanded in (positive or negative) powers of $R = (X^i X^i)^{1/2}$ as well as in positive powers of the masses and of the small interaction parameter $\sim Gm'/d$, and that: 5) the transformation $X \to x$ reduces to a Poincaré transformation when the interaction vanishes. (These last two assumptions seem very plausible and can probably be justified by some more work as done for proving eqn (5.17)). Then it can be shown that the most general coordinate transformation compatible with these hypotheses is of the type:

$$x^a(T,X^i) = z^a(T) + e^a_i(T)X^i + O(G')\,O(R^2) + O(G'^3)O(1/R) + O(G'^4) \tag{7}$$

where the functions $z^a(T)$ and $e^a_i(T)$ must be such that dz^a/dT, $e_1{}^a$, $e_2{}^a$, $e_3{}^a$ constitute a Minkowski orthonormal tetrad when the interaction vanishes (i.e. formally $G' \to 0$). (For the meaning of G' see (5.16)). As we see from eqn (7) the meaning of the function $z^a(T)$ is just, at order G'^3, the image in the external coordinate system of the "center" of the internal coordinates: $X^i = 0$. We have seen in Section 5 that the X coordinate system could be considered as "Mass Centered" (this convention can be, evidently, maintained after the transformation (5.20)). In fact, by the way it was defined, it might be better to call it "Field Centered." Therefore the "point": $X^i = 0$ can be called the "Center of Mass" or the "Center of Field." Note that this "point" is defined only by the symmetry of the gravitational field just outside the object and does not need to, and even cannot, in the black hole case, coincide with any material particle. Thence the function $z^a(T)$ defines, in the external coordinate system, a world-line which can be called the "central world-line" of the (first) compact object. From now on, it will be convenient to choose as parameter along this central world-line the Minkowski proper time: s. Let us introduce the Minkoswkian 4-velocity of this "central world line":

$$u^a(s) = \frac{dz^a(s)}{ds} \tag{8}$$

With any x^a we can associate a "contemporary" point: $z^a_C = z^a(s_C)$ such that:

$$f_{ab}\,(x^a - z^a(s_c))\,u^b(s_c) := 0\ . \tag{9}$$

Let r_C be:

$$r_c := (f_{ab}(x^a - z^a_c)(x^b - z^b_c))^{1/2}, \tag{10}$$

and n^a_C be:

$$n^a_c := (x^a - z^a{}_c)/r_c . \tag{11}$$

Applying the general coordinate transformation (7) to the final result of the preceding section: eqn (5.28), we conclude that: there exist two constant parameters m, m' and two world-lines $z^a(s)$, $z'^a(s')$ in R^4 (the external coordinate chart) such that the external "gothic" metric corresponding to two compact objects has <u>necessarily</u> the following behaviour near each world-line:

$$\underline{g}^{ab} = -4Gm\left(\frac{u^a u^b}{r}\right)_C - G^2 m^2\left(\frac{7u^a u^b + n^a n^b}{r^2}\right)_C - 8G^3 m^3\left(\frac{u^a u^b}{r^3}\right)_C + O(G'^2)O\left(\frac{1}{r_c}\right) +$$
$$O(G'^3)O\left(\frac{1}{r_c^2}\right) + O(r_c^0) + O(G^4), \tag{12}$$

and the corresponding "primed" equation near $z'(s')$. ($(u^a u^b/r)_C$ means $u^a_C u^b_C/r_C \ldots$).

In simpler terms: up to the order G^3 inclusively, the <u>singular behaviour</u> of the metric near the world-line is <u>dominated,</u> at each order G^n, by a <u>Schwarzschild-like</u> behaviour.

This result is another form of what we called before the "Cheshire cat principle": only the mass m appears in (12) for characterizing the behaviour of the external field near the world-line. Although this result is less precise than our preceding statement, eqn (5.19), about the internal field, however it will be very useful later for characterizing uniquely the external field.

To conclude this section, let us gather the necessary conditions that the "gothic metric perturbation" h^{ab} have to satisfy. If we define an effective non-linear source N^{ab} as:

$$N^{ab} = -h^{cd}h^{ab}{}_{,cd} - Q^{ab} \tag{13}$$

(where Q^{ab} was defined in eqn (4)), then we get:

$$f^{cd}h^{ab}{}_{,cd} \; (= \Box h^{ab}) = N^{ab}(h) \tag{14a}$$

$$h^{ab}{}_{,b} = 0 \tag{14b}$$

together with the following "boundary conditions":

1) The Kirchoff conditions at Minkowski past null infinity: eqn (6)

2) The third order "Dominant Schwarzschild" condition near each central world-line: eqn (12) and a similar one for $z'(s')$ and m'.

7. INTRODUCTION TO ANALYTIC CONTINUATION

Marcel Riesz (1938, 1949) introduced a very powerful method for solving the wave equation in a flat or curved space-time of any dimension. The basic tool of this method was the process of analytic continuation of functions of a complex variable. This continuation process allowed Riesz to define, to use in rigorous demonstrations and to compute some, otherwise divergent and therefore meaningless, integrals. The technical utility of this method was quickly realized: Gustafson (1945, 1946) applied it in Quantum Field Theory in order to define meaningless integrals; Fremberg (1946) and Riesz (1949) applied it to the Classical Theories of the interaction between electromagnetic or mesonic fields and point particles, again this allowed them to define, and to compute some a priori meaningless quantities: like the self-force of a point electron: Ma (1947) proved the agreement between Riesz's method and another formal regularization process, due to Dirac, Bhabha and Harish-Chandra in giving a meaning to the derivatives of the self electromagnetic field at the position of a point electron: Schwartz (1950) showed that the Riesz kernels could be interpreted as "distributions" depending holomorphically on a parameter; this point of view has been amplified and used systematically, by Guelfand and Chilov (1962), to define new "distributions" by Riesz's method; Havas and Goldberg (1962) pointed out that Riesz's method might be useful in a Post-Minkowskian Approximation to General Relativity, with formal (a priori meaningless) point-like sources, however they used, instead of it, the formal regularization method of Dirac, Bhabha and Harish-Chandra in their study of the first Post-Minkowskian Approximation (1 PMA or linear approximation); later, because of the mathematical difficulties posed by the second Post-Minkowskian Approximation, Schieve, Rosenblum and Havas (1972) considered the simpler case of the interaction between point particles and electromagnetic and mesonic fields, they used "Riesz potentials" to define a formal post-linear approximation but they could not carry out the integrations completely even with the simplifying assumptions of small velocities and small oscillatory spatial motion; at the same time, Riesz's idea found renewed applications to Quantum Field Theory under the form of "dimensional regularization"; however, let us point out that even in Quantum Field Theory where one looks for a method to give a meaning to undefined divergent quantities, one still has to check the consistency of the method when it is used in proving renormalizability or in computing renormalized quantities (this point, which is frequently overlooked in formal calculations, has been stressed, in the context of Classical Renormalization Theory, by Damour (1974, 1975), and, in the context of Quantum Renormalization Theory by Breitenlohner and Maison (1977)); moreover the great technical usefulness of Riesz's method has been further shown by Damour (1974, 1975) who reduced the computation of (linear) self-action terms to mere inspection; more recently a well-defined algorithm, using Riesz's ideas, has been set up, has been checked to <u>define</u> a post-post-linear 3 PMA relaxed gravitational field outside two "point masses" and has been <u>proved</u> to satisfy the complete vacuum Einstein equations (outside two world-lines) if and only if the two world lines satisfied some "equations of motion," themselves <u>computable</u> by means of analytic continuation (Damour 1980).

Let us stress that in all the preceding works analytic continuation has been employed only as a trick for <u>defining</u> a priori meaningless concepts (self-field of a point electron, locally interacting quantum fields, general relativistic point mass) however we are dealing in these lectures with a physically and mathematically <u>well-defined</u> concept (gravitational interaction of two neutron stars of supposedly known internal structure), in other words we do not have the freedom of playing with formal concepts even if we check the consistency of our game. On the contrary, our strategy is going to be the following:

1) We first make use of analytic continuation to <u>define</u> a post-post-post linear (4PMA) "harmonically relaxed" gravitational field which is a functional of two world-lines in R^4 (Section 8) (contrary to what has been asserted by Havas and Goldberg (1962) the possibility of this quartically non-linear definition is far from being a trivial consequence of Riesz's linear method: one must <u>prove</u> already in this first step that the non-linearities do not generate poles at the point of the complex plane where we want to continue the integrals).

2) We have recourse again to analytic continuation to <u>prove</u> that the precedingly constructed "relaxed" gravitational field will fulfill the complete vacuum Einstein equations outside the two world-lines if and only if these world-lines satisfy some "equations of motion" which are, in turn, <u>defined</u> by analytic continuation (section 9).

3) We have recourse again to analytic continuation to <u>compute</u> explicitly these "equations of motion" which contain integrals which seem to be very difficult to calculate by usual methods (Section 12).

4) We <u>check</u> that the precedingly defined solution of the complete vacuum Einstein equations satisfy the "boundary conditions" of Section 6.

5) Finally we prove (modulo some technical assumptions) that there is a unique solution of the vacuum Einstein equations which satisfy these "boundary conditions" (section 10). As we have shown in sections 5 and 6 that these conditions are necessarily satisfied by the gravitational field outside two compact objects, we shall have thereby proved that the precedingly analytic-continuation-defined gravitational field and equations of motion are necessarily the gravitational field outside and the equattions of motion of two compact objects.

Before setting up our algorithm let us briefly describe how analytic continuation works and what are the properties that make it such a powerful computational technique. Let a smooth (C^∞) function of a real variable, with compact support, be given: F(x) (the preceding conditions could be relaxed to sufficient differentiability and proper fall off at infinity at the expense of some changes and restrictions in the following results; this is in fact the case in actual use but for simplicity we present the idea in its simplest form). Let A be a complex number. Let us define the following function of A:

$$I_F(A) := \int_0^\infty x^A F(x)\, dx \tag{1}$$

As is well known, the integral (1), i.e. $I_F(A)$, is a priori convergent and therefore defined only when the real part of A satisfies:

$$\mathrm{Re}\,(A) > -1 \tag{2}$$

In other words the complex function I_F of the complex variable A is defined only in half the complex plane. Now we see by formal differentiation of (1) with respect to A that:

$$\frac{dI_F(A)}{dA} = \int_0^\infty x^A \log x\; F(x)\, dx \tag{3}$$

whose right-hand side is convergent, and thus equal to its left-hand side, under the same restriction (2). For the sake of conciseness let us call D_{-1} the domain of the complex A plane defined by eqn (2). We conclude that eqn (1) defines an analytic function I_F of the complex variable in the domain D_{-1}. We are going to show that, although the original definition of I_F was meaningful only in D_{-1}, it is possible to define I_F in a much larger domain. We first write (1) as:

$$I_F(A) = \int_0^1 x^A F(x)\, dx + \int_1^\infty x^A F(x)\, dx. \tag{4}$$

The reason for doing this is that the problems of divergence come from the neighbourhood of the origin. Because of the assumed smoothness of F(x), it is possible to define, for any integer n, a smooth function $G_n(x)$ such that:

$$F(x) = F(0) + x\,F'(0) + \frac{x^2}{2!}F''(0) + \ldots + \frac{x^n}{n!}F^{(n)}(0) + x^{n+1}G_n(x). \tag{5}$$

Plugging (5) into (4) and explicitating the integrals of $x^P \cdot (p \leq n)$ from 0 to 1 we find:

$$I_F(A) = \frac{F(0)}{A+1} + \frac{F'(0)}{A+2} + \frac{F''(0)}{2!(A+3)} + \frac{F^{(n)}(0)}{n!(A+n+1)} + \\ + \int_0^1 x^{A+n+1}G_n(x)dx + \int_1^\infty x^A F(x)dx. \tag{6}$$

Eqn (6) has up to now only a meaning in D_{-1}, but we see that the right hand side is an analytic function of A in the larger domain:

$$D^{\odot}_{-n-2} = D_{-n-2} - \{-1, -2, \ldots, -n-1\}, \tag{7}$$

in words: $D^{\odot}_{-n-2}$ is the half of the complex plane at the right of $-n-2$ with the exclusion of the points: $-1, -2, \ldots, -n-1$. So that we can now define $I_F(A)$ in the domain $D^{\odot}_{-n-2}$, and in fact because of the smoothness of F, in the domain:

$$D^{\odot} = D^{\odot}_{-\infty} = C - \{-1,-2,\ldots,-n,\ldots\}, \tag{8}$$

by the formula (6). Moreover we see from the definition (6) that this extended I_F is still an analytic function of the complex variable A with only single poles at $-1, -2, \ldots$. So, in this particular way, we can now give a meaning to the integral (1) even when it is divergent (except for $A = -1, -2, \ldots$): for instance we would find in this way:

$$\int_0^\infty x^{-3/2}e^{-x}dx := -2\,\pi^{1/2} \tag{9}$$

However, this way of defining (1) seems to be very particular and a priori one would expect to get a different result if one had used a different trick, e.g. integrating (1) by parts. That this is not so is one of the main advantages of the complex variable approach. Analytic continuation is unique in the following sense: had we used a different trick for extending the definition of I_F, to an analytic function $\tilde{I}_F(A)$ in a domain $\tilde{D}$ larger than D_{-1}, then, necessarily $\tilde{D} \subseteq D^{\odot}$ and $\tilde{I}_F(A) = I_F(A)$, as defined by (6) in $\tilde{D}$. This uniqueness follows from the theorem of "continuation of identity" for (single-valued) analytic functions: Let each of two functions f(A) and g(A) be analytic in a common connected domain D. Let f(A) and g(A) coincide in some portion D' of D (D' may be a subdomain, a segment of a curve, or even only an infinite set of points having a limit point in D). Then f(A) and g(A) coincide throughout D.

Therefore any procedure which allows one to define an analytic function which coincides with (1) even only for a small interval of real values of A, e.g. $0.33 < A < 0.34$ will coincide with (6) in all its domain of definition (it is clear that (6), with variable n, defines the "maximal" analytic continuation of I_F). The preceding "continuation of identity" theorem is also extremely useful (and in fact of constant use in practical calculations) for proving that one can recur to familiar integration techniques even when dealing with "divergent" integrals (e.g. (1) for $\mathrm{Re}(A) < -1$). For instance we know that when $\mathrm{Re}(A) > -1$ we can integrate (1) by parts, which yields:

$$\int_0^\infty x^A F(x)dx = \left[\frac{x^{A+1}F(x)}{A+1}\right]_0^\infty - \frac{1}{A+1}\int_0^\infty x^{A+1}F'(x)dx. \quad (10)$$

But the "integrated part" or "surface term" vanishes for $\mathrm{Re}(A) > -1$, hence:

$$\int_0^\infty x^A F(x)dx = -\frac{1}{A+1}\int_0^\infty x^{A+1}F'(x)dx. \quad (11)$$

We have already seen how the left hand side of (11) could be analytically continued in $D^\odot$ by eqn (6), by the same method we can analytically continue $I_{F'}(A+1)$, and therefore the right hand side of (11), in $D^\odot$. As these two analytic functions coincide for $\mathrm{Re}(A) > -1$, they are identical all over $D^\odot$, which means that we can always integrate (1) by parts in discarding the "surface terms." Moreover we have considered here for simplicity a one-dimensional integral but the whole approach can be, and actually is, generalized to multiple integrals. Then one can extend to analytically continued "divergent" integrals the familiar integration techniques: linear decomposition of the integrand, decomposition of the domain of integration, integration by parts, differentiation with respect to a parameter under the integration symbol, change of variable... (however all these operations should not be done blindly, but one should always check, from the "continuation of identity" theorem, that they can be freely performed).

In spite of the preceding "uniqueness" of the analytic continuation, the reader should be warned that this does not mean that there is a unique way of regularizing any divergent integral. For instance, if one considers eqn (1) only on the real A axis there is no unique way to find explicit real expressions which extend (1) below -1. Moreover if one was to start with the integral:

$$\int_0^\infty x^{-3/2}F(x)dx, \quad (12)$$

there would be infinitely many unequivalent ways of giving a meaning to (12). However, the basic advantage of Riesz' method of analytic continuation is that it allows one to use all the familiar integration techniques when handling "divergent" integrals and it is this fact which allows one not only to define an otherwise meaningless quantity but to prove the consistency of the definition and to prove that the analytic continuation defined-quantity satisfies some extra conditions (which in general are not guaranteed by the use of arbitrary "regularization" techniques applied to the formal "divergent" definition of the quantity). There will be many instances of that in the following.

To conclude this section let us define Riesz basic kernel in flat space. Let us consider, on a n dimensional Minkowski space (signature −++...), the following function which depends parametrically on a complex number A:

$$Z_A(x) = \frac{(-f_{ab}x^a x^b)^{\frac{A-n}{2}}}{H_n(A)}, \tag{13a}$$

when x is future directed ($x^0 > 0$, $-f_{ab}x^a x^b > 0$), and, otherwise:

$$Z_A(x) = 0, \tag{13b}$$

with the coefficient $H_n(A)$ being:

$$H_n(A) = \pi^{\frac{n-2}{2}} . 2^{A-1} . \Gamma(\tfrac{A}{2}) . \Gamma(\tfrac{A+2-n}{2}). \tag{13c}$$

(Γ denoting the usual Eulerian gamma function).

$H_n(A)$ is infinite for A = 0, −2, −4,... and A = n−2, n−4,..., therefore for these values the function $Z_A(x)$ is zero.

The main properties of Z_A are:

$$\Box Z_{A+2} = -Z_A , \tag{14}$$

$$Z_A * Z_B = Z_{A+B} \tag{15}$$

where $*$ denotes the convolution. If Z_A is considered not as a function but as a distribution then it is an "entire function" of A (i.e. analytic without singularities all over the complex plane) and the value of the distribution Z_A when A = 0 is the n-dimensional Dirac distribution:

$$Z_0 = \delta_{(n)} \tag{16}$$

From (16) and (14), one deduces that the distribution Z_2 (which can be computed as the analytic continuation in A = 2 of the function (13) is (minus) the retarded "Green function" ("elementary kernel") of the n-dimensional space-time. When n =4 one finds:

$$Z_2(x) = + \frac{1}{4\pi} \frac{\delta(x^o - /x/)}{/x/} \tag{17a}$$

$$\Box Z_2 = - \delta_{(4)} \tag{17b}$$

In the following we shall not consider Z_A as a distribution (except Z_2, see below) because we wish, contrary to Riesz and Schwartz, to perform non-linear operations on Z_A (remember that it is impossible in general to define the product of distributions). Therefore we shall consider $Z_A(x)$ as a function over Minkowski space depending analytically on a complex parameter A. This will allow us to consider the integral of some products of some Z_A's and if we can prove that the integral converges for some values of A and can be analytically continued then we shall be able to extend the meaning of the integral beyond its convergence range. At the end of the process we shall try to continue A down to the value zero (so that because of (16) we shall have simple equations satisfied by our A dependent integrals); however, we shall have to prove that this is possible because the non-linearities could create pole singularities in zero. All this will be done only for n = 4 (usual space-time), yet it has been checked by Damour (1980) that one could formally use Z_0 from the beginning, but work in a space-time of dimension:

$$n = 4 - A, \tag{18}$$

and that would yield the same final result (at least at the 3PMA order) as the physical approach: n = 4, Z_A, A ≠ 0. However, I wish to stress that such a formal "dimensionally regularized" calculation has no mathematical meaning and therefore cannot be used to prove anything about the quantities so calculated, contrary to the physical n = 4, A ≠ 0 appraoch.

8. A PARTICULAR SOLUTION OF THE RELAXED EXTERNAL SCHEME

We have seen in section 6, eqn (6.14), that the external "gothic gravitational field" $h^{ab} = \underline{g}^{ab} - f^{ab}$ had to satisfy, in harmonic coordinates, two equations:

$$f^{cd} h^{ab}{}_{,cd} = N^{ab}(h), \tag{1}$$

$$h^{ab}{}_{,b} = 0 \tag{2}$$

and two types of boundary conditions: "Kirchoff" (6.6) and "Dominant Schwarzschild" (6.12). In this section we shall set up an algorithm which will generate a partic-

ular solution of the "relaxed" vacuum field equation (1) satisfying the two preceding boundary conditions. We shall consider eqn (2) in the next section.
We shall try to incorporate the second type of boundary conditions by introducing a fictitious stress-energy tensor (more precisely a contravariant tensor density of weight + 2 corresponding to $16\Pi g$ times the usual tensor):

$T_A^{ab}(x, m, m'; z(s), z'(s'), \underline{g}(y))$ which is:

- a <u>function</u> of a point $\underline{x}$ in Minkowski space,
- a <u>function</u> of <u>two</u> constant parameters: m, m',
- a <u>functional</u> of <u>two arbitrary</u> time-like <u>world-lines</u> z(s) and z'(s') in Minkowski space,
- a <u>functional</u> of the, yet to be defined, "gothic metric" $\underline{g}^{cd}(y) = f^{cd} + h^{cd}(y)$
- an <u>analytic function</u> of a complex <u>parameter A</u>.

Moreover, $T_A^{ab}(x)$ is such that it vanishes when A = 0 and x is not on any of the world-lines. At the end of the process, we shall analytically continue A down to zero, m and m' will appear as the "Schwarzschild" masses of two compact objects, and, z and z' will appear as the "central world-lines" of two compact objects (see section 6 for the meaning of these concepts).

We define T_A^{ab} as:

$$T_A^{ab} := \Sigma 16\pi m \int_{-\infty}^{+\infty} ds\; Z_A(x-z)\, u^a u^b\, (\underline{g}(z))^{1/4} (\underline{g}_{cd}(z) u^c u^d)^{-1/2}, \tag{3}$$

where: Σ denotes a summation on the two worldlines z and z' (endowed with their respective parameters m and m'), s is the Minkowski proper-time along z(s), u is the Minkowski 4-velocity: dz/ds ($f_{ab}u^a u^b = -1$), $\underline{g}$ is minus the determinant of the contravariant gothic metric $\underline{g}^{ab}$(it is equal to the usual g), $\underline{g}_{ab}$ is the inverse matrix of $\underline{g}^{ab}$ (or $g^{-1/2} g_{ab}$), and Z_A is the Riesz kernel defined in eqn (7.13) (with n = 4). T_A^{ab} must be multiplied by G/c^2: the Newton-Einstein coupling constant between mass and gravitational field. In the sections 8-11 we shall take c = 1 but we shall keep G as the "small" coupling constant which will allow us to define a perturbative solution of Einstein's vacuum equations.

We now consider, instead of (1), the following equation:

$$f^{cd} h^{ab}_{,cd} = G T_A^{ab}(f+h) + N^{ab}(h) \tag{4}$$

Then we incorporate the Kirchoff "no-incoming-radiation" condition (6.6) by using the flat space retarded Green function $-Z_2$ (section 7) for transforming (4b) in an integro-differential equation:

$$h^{ab} = -Z_2 * (GT_A^{ab}(f+h) + N^{ab}(h)). \tag{5}$$

In eqn (5) the star $*$ denotes a space-time convolution and $-Z_2$ denotes the retarded "Green function" (7.17) that is: a distribution. In other words $4\Pi Z_2\, T$ is just the usual retarded integral of T. On the other hand $Z_A(x)$ which appears in T_A^{ab} is to be considered as a plain function of x which depends analytically on the complex parameter A. N^{ab} is at least quadratic in h. More precisely we deduce from (6.13) (6.4) and (6.2), in expanding $\underline{g}_{ab} = (f^{ab}+h^{ab})^{-1}$ in "powers of the matrix h":

$$N^{ab}(h) = II^{ab}(h,h) + III^{ab}(h,h,h) + IV^{ab}(h,h,h,h) + O(h^5), \tag{6}$$

where II, III, IV are respectively quadratically, cubically and quartically non-linear in h. By this we mean for instance: II $\sim h\partial^2 h + \partial h \partial h$ (10 terms), III $\sim h\partial h\partial h$ (21 terms),... The explicit expressions of II and III can be found in the appendix A of Bel, Damour, Deruelle, Ibañez and Martin (1981). By similarly expanding $T^{ab}(f + h)$ in "powers of the matrix h" we can write:

$$T^{ab}(f+h) = T^{ab}(f) + \overline{II}^{ab}(h) + \overline{III}^{ab}(h,h) + \overline{IIII}^{ab}(h,h,h) + O(h^4). \tag{7}$$

Because of this structure of the right hand side of (5) we can now define our iterative Post-Minkowskian Algorithm:

$$h^{ab}_{A(0)} := 0 \qquad (\text{i.e. } \underline{g}^{ab}_{A(0)} = f^{ab} \tag{8a}$$

$$h^{ab}_{A(n+1)} := -Z_2 * ((GT_A{}^{ab}(f+h_{(n)}))_{(n+1)} + (N^{ab}(h_{(n)}))_{(n+1)}) \tag{8b}$$

where the suffix (n + 1) in the right hand side of (8b) means the following:

- take the preceding iteration, which is a truncated expansion in powers of G of a function-functional:

$$h_{A(n)}(x;z) = Gh_{A1}(x;z) + G^2 h_{A2}(x;z) + \ldots + G^n h_{An}(x;z) \tag{9}$$

- plug it into the non-linearity expansions (6) and (7), and
- keep only the powers of G up to G^{n+1} (included).

In this way $h_{(n+1)}$ is a truncated expansion: (9) + one extra term $O(G^{n+1})$.

Explicitating the algorithm we find for the first coefficients of G^P in (9):

$$h_{A1} = -Z_2 * T(f) \tag{10a}$$

$$h_{A2} = -Z_2 * (II(h_{A1}) + II(h_{A1}, h_{A1}) \tag{10b}$$

$$h_{A3} = -Z_2 * (II(h_{A2}) + III(h_{A1}, h_{A1}) + II(h_{A1}, h_{A2}) + III(h_{A1}, h_{A1}, h_{A1})). \tag{10c}$$

For the explicit computation of the "equations of motion" of the binary pulsar it will be necessary and sufficient to compute h_1, h_2 and h_3 (cubic non-linearities). However in order to prove that these "equations of motion" are consequences of the vacuum field equations (Einstein-Infeld-Hoffmann approach) we shall need to consider also h_4 (quartic non-linearities), that is why we have included in (6) and (7) the corresponding terms.

Up to here we have only formally defined an algorithm: (8), we have now to prove that this definition makes sense, that is that the integrals appearing in (8) and (10) are meaningful. In order to see how the algorithm works, and why analytic continuation is so useful, let us first consider the one-body problem (m' =0). Moreover we shall assume from the start that the world-line z(s) is a straight-line in Minkowski space: the justification for this assumption is that, as can be deduced from the arguments of section 9, the "harmonicity condition" eqn (2) implies at each order G^n that the acceleration of the world-line is zero (when m' = 0), therefore in a perturbative sense at least, this acceleration must be taken to be exactly zero if we wish to satisfy the complete Einstein vacuum equations (1) and (2).

In order to be able to consider even the first step of the algorithm (8), i.e. the equation (10a), we must first inquire about the meaning of the fictitious source $T_A(f)$. According to eqn (3) we have, when m' = 0, $\underline{g} = \underline{f}$, and z is a straight line:

$$T_A^{ab}(f) := 16\pi m u^a u^b \int_{-\infty}^{+\infty} ds\ Z_A(x-z)\ ? \tag{11}$$

Using a coordinate system, centered at the point x, with time axis parallel to the straight world line so that $x^\circ - z^\circ = -t = -s$ and $/x^i - z^i/ = \text{const.} = r$ say (the distance between the point x and the world-line) the integral appearing in (11) is of the form:

$$\int_{-\infty}^{-r} dt \quad (t^2 - r^2)^{\frac{A-4}{2}} \quad . \tag{12}$$

This integral converges, and therefore is a priori defined, only if:

$$2 < \text{Re}(A) < 3. \tag{13}$$

The lower bound is due to the behaviour of the integrand near $t = -r$ and the upper bound to its behaviour near $t = -\infty$. However after computing (12) and plugging it in (11) with the denominator (7.13c) one finds:

$$T_A^{ab}(f) = 16mu^a u^b \frac{\Gamma(\frac{3-A}{2})}{\pi 2^A \Gamma(\frac{A}{2})} r^{A-3} \quad . \tag{14}$$

We see from the explicit expression (14) that although T_A was originally defined only in the vertical strip (13) of the complex plane it can be analytically continued to a meromorphic function defined everywhere apart from simple poles at $A = 3,5,7, \ldots$ As we have seen in section 7, the process of analytic continuation is unique when possible. Therefore we shall, in fact, define T_A as the maximal analytic continuation of (11) which must necessarily be equal to (14).

Now that the "source" T_A is defined nearly all over the complex plane we can inquire about the meaning of the first step of our algorithm. Plugging (7.17) and (8.14) in (8.10a) we find an integral which is convergent, and therefore a priori defined, only if:

$$0 < \mathrm{Re}(A) < 1. \tag{15}$$

However, an explicit computation yields:

$$h_{A1}^{ab} = -4mu^a u^b C_1(A) r^{A-1}, \tag{16}$$

with:

$$C_1(A) = \frac{\Gamma(\frac{1-A}{2})}{\pi^{1/2} 2^A \Gamma(\frac{A+2}{2})} \quad . \tag{17}$$

Therefore h_A can be analytically continued everywhere except for simple poles in $A = 1, 3, 5, \ldots$.Now we can consider the second iteration (10b). We must first inquire about the meaning of $\Pi_A(h_{A1})$ which contains $h_{A1}(z)$. A look at (16) tells us that $h_{A1}(z)$ is defined for $\mathrm{Re}(A) > 1$ and $A \neq 3, 5, \ldots$. It is then equal to zero (because $r = 0$ when $x = z$) and can therefore be analytically continued everywhere. Then we must consider the quadratically non-linear "source terms." We find:

$$\Pi(h_{A1}, h_{A1}) \sim (\partial h_{A1})^2 + h_{A1} \partial^2 h_{A1} \sim r^{2A-4} \tag{18}$$

Plugging (18) into (10b) we find an integral which is convergen when:

$$1/2 < \mathrm{Re}(A) < 1. \tag{19}$$

The result of the integration can however be analytically continued everywhere except for (possibly multiple) poles in 1/2, 1, 3, 5,.... This result can be written as:

$$h^{ab}_{A2} = -m^2(7C_2(A)u^a u^b + C_2'(A)n^a n^b)\ r^{2A-2}\ , \tag{20}$$

where n^a denotes the unit radial vector, defined by eqn (6·11) and where the coefficients C_2 and C_2' are, like C_1 in eqn (17), equal to 1 when $A = 0$. In this simple one-body case it is possible to push the iteration ad infinitum. One finds: that the fictitious source $T_A(f + h)$ is nothing but $T_A(f)$, eqn (14), that the non-linear effective source N_n of the nth iteration leads to convergent integrals if: $1 - 1/n < \mathrm{Re}(A) < 1$ but that the result of the integration can be analytically continued everywhere except for (multiple) poles at: 1/2, 2/3,..., (n-1)/n; 1, 3, 5, ... The nth iterated gravitational field can be written as:

$$h^{ab}_{A(n)} = -4Gmu^a u^b C_1(A) r^{A-1} - G^2m^2(7C_2(A)u^a u^b + C_2'(A)n^a n^b)r^{2A-2} - \\ - \sum_{p=3}^{n} G^p m^p (8C_p(A)u^a u^b + AC_p'(A)n^a n^b + AC_p''(A)f^{ab})r^{pA-p}, \tag{21}$$

where all the coefficients C, C', or C" are equal to 1 when A = 0. It is therefore possible to analytically continue down to A = 0 the nth iterated gravitational field; this yields:

$$h^{ab}_{0(n)} = -4Gmu^a u^b r^{-1} - G^2m^2(7u^a u^b + n^a n^b)r^{-2} - \sum_{p=3}^{n} 8G^p m^p u^a u^b r^{-p}\ . \tag{22}$$

We recognize in eqn (22) the nth truncated expansion in powers of G of the exact Schwarzchild metric in usual harmonic coordinates: eqns (5.23) and (5.24).

Before proceeding to the much more interesting two-body case let us draw some conclusions from the one-body case:

1) We must supplement our algorithm (8) by the rule of "maximal analytic continuation," that is: any A-dependent quantity which is initially defined only for a small range of the parameter A must be understood as being analytically continued all over the complex plane except for some isolated pole singularities (this rule makes sense because the types of operations involved in (8) generate only poles and no branch points, so that the analytic continuation is unique over C).

2) Although we started with an entire analytic function of A: Z_A, both the linear (integrations) and non-linear operations included in the algorithm have a tendency to generate multiple poles on the real axis. This fact has been sometimes overlooked because of too much confidence in the regularizing power of Riesz' method

(remember that the framework in which Z_A is proved to be regular is the theory of distributions where only certain types of linear operations are considered). Therefore we must check the regularity of the result of our non-linear algorithm near A = 0 which is the value that we wish to consider at the end of the algorithm (we do not need to care about pole singularities elsewhere).

3) The last result eqn(22) shows that it is possible, in a perturbative sense at least, to consider the Schwarzschild metric as being "generated" by a (Minkowski) time-like world line. It also shows the fictitious source (3) has the effect that we wanted: to incorporate in the solution of the vacuum equations (1) the "Dominant Schwarzschild" conditions (6.12).

4) If we had tried to set up an algorithm with A = 0 from the beginning ("delta-function-source," "point mass"), then already the second step of the algorithm: (10b) would have been meaningless: both because of $\infty\cdot\delta$-type terms in $\Pi(h_1)$ and because of the appearance of divergent integrals due to the non-linear source $\Pi\,(h_1)$: $\int d^3x r^{-4}$. However, Bel, Damour, Deruelle, Ibañez and Martin (1981) showed that the use of a set of regularizing prescriptions (based on Hadamard's "partie finie" instead of Riesz's analytic continuation) yielded the same result (22) in the one-body case. On the other hand they showed that in the two-body case (at order G^2) the structure of the theory itself demanded to reconsider this set of regularization prescriptions. We shall show below that our analytic continuation approach (which has the further advantage of dealing uniformly with the $\infty.\delta$ and with the divergent integrals problems) not only yields the same G^2 metric as Bel et.al. (1981) but can be extended to the G^3 and the G^4 metric. Moreover the G^2 equations of motion of Westpfahl and Göller (1979) and Bel et. al. (1981) will be proved to be the integrability conditions of the G^3 field equations, and we shall obtain G^3 equations of motion from the integrability conditions of the G^4 field equations.

In the <u>two-body case</u> we must start all over again. Let us consider two sufficiently smooth time-like world-lines z (s) and z'(s') in Minkowski space, and two constant parameters m and m'. According to our algorithm, augmented by the conclusion 1) above, we must first consider the maximal analytic continuation in A of the lowest order fictitious source:

$$T_A{}^{ab}(f) := \sum_{m,m'} 16\pi m \int_{-\infty}^{+\infty} ds\; u^a(s) u^b(s)\; Z_A(x - z(s)), \tag{23}$$

where the unit tangent vector $u^a = dz^a/ds$ is no longer constant. Let us however assume that $u^a(s)$ (and $u'^a(s')$) has a limit when s(s') tends to minus infinity and, more precisely, that du^a/ds tends to zero as s^{-2}. In other words we assume that the system was unbound in the infinite past. This assumption is not necessary at this stage of our iteration (because one could slightly modify the algorithm so that, in the first iteration, only a finite segment of the world-lines matters), however it is needed for ensuring that the whole sequence of highly non-linear effective sources N^{ab} always lead to infra-red (i.e. at large distances) convergent integrals. On the other hand this assumption seems very plausible on intuitive grounds (a system staying bound for an infinite time would radiate an infinite amount of energy). Moreover it should be possible to check a posteriori this assumption by studying, in the manner of Walker and Will (1979), the infinite past behaviour of the solutions of our final equations of motion which contain "radiation damping" type terms. Granted

this assumption the integral (23) converges for $2 < \mathrm{Re}(A) < 3$. Moreover, even if contrary to the one-body case, (eqn (14), we cannot compute explicitly (23) in order to analytically continue it, we can nevertheless use the type of reasonings employed in section 7 about similar integrals: (7.1) to prove that (23) can be analytically continued everywhere apart from simple poles at $A = 3,5,\ldots$ (in the following we shall cease to precise the positions and multiplicities of all the poles to concentrate on the possible appearance of a pole at $A = 0$). Plugging (23) into (10a) leads to an integral which is convergent for $0 < \mathrm{Re}(A) < 1$. Moreover , using eqn (7.15) we find the following expression of h_1:

$$h^{ab}_{A1} = -\Sigma\ 16\pi m \int ds\ u^a u^b Z_{A+2}(x-z). \tag{24}$$

Exploiting again the type of arguments used in Section 7 we can prove that h_{A1} can be continued "everywhere"(except some poles but none at $A = 0$). We now have to face the difficult problem of handling non-linearities: we must plug (24) into (10b) and investigate the existence of the resulting integral and the possibility of continuing it, with respect to A, outside its range of convergence. A way of achieving this has been indicated by Damour (1980). It consists first in generaliaing the formula (16) to <u>curved</u> world-lines. This is achieved by combining some expansion techniques studied in Damour (1974, 1975) with the analytic continuation method. Because of the lack of space the method cannot be explicitated here (full details about this as well as about many other technical results of the following sections will be contained in a paper by myself to be submitted to the Proceedings of the Royal Society, London). The useful result, though, is that h_{A1} admits the following expression <u>near each world-line</u> (here the first for instance):

$$h_{A1} = r_C^{\,A-1} \cdot F_0(x,A) + F'_0(x,A), \tag{25}$$

where r_c was defined in (6.10) (Minkowski orthogonal distance between the field point x and the first world-line z(s)) and where F_o and F'_o are two functions which are smooth in x (if the world-line is smooth) and analytic in A (no poles at $A = 0$).

Moreover, the index zero in F_0 and F'_0 means that these functions are of order one when x is on the world-line. For simplicity we shall denote by F_n any function (sometimes we do not even put primes for distinguishing different functions) which is analytic in A (no poles at A = 0), smooth in x, and of order r_c^n when x approaches the first world-line. Plugging (25) into the quadratically non-linear terms leads to a non-linear effective source which behaves near each world-line as:

$$II(h_{A1},h_{A1}) = r_c^{2A-6} \cdot F_2 + \underline{\underline{r_c^{A-5} \cdot F'_2}} + F_0 \; . \tag{26}$$

According to (10b) we must now compute the retarded integral of II. As explained in section 7 we can decompose this integral in two integrals near the two world-lines and one over the exterior region of space-time and continue separately these three integrals. Because of our assumption about the behaviour of the world lines in the infinite past the integral over the exterior region is convergent and analytic in A as soon as Re(A) <1. Therefore possible singularities at A = 0 can come only from the integrals near the world-lines. For studying the analytic behaviour of these integrals it is then sufficient to plug the expression (26) in the retarded integral (10b) and to look for possible singularities in A near A = 0 linked with the singular behaviour in r_c near $r_c = 0$. Using for instance as local space-time coordinates near the first world-line: $x^a \to (s_c, r_c, \Theta_c, \phi_c)$ where where Θ_c and ϕ_c are usual polar coordinates parametrizing the direction n_c^a in the 3-space orthogonal to the world-line, the retarded integral of $II(h_{A1}, h_{A1})$ takes the form:

$$\int (r_c^{2A-6} \cdot \hat{F}_2 + r_c^{A-5} \cdot \hat{F}'_2 + \hat{F}_0) \, r_c^2 dr_c \, \sin\theta_c \, d\theta_c \, d\phi_c \quad , \tag{27}$$

where, after having made a new expansion over the time variable s_c, the arguments of the new smooth functions $\hat{F}_2$, $\hat{F}'_2$, $\hat{F}_0$ are: a fixed s_c, r_c, Θ_c, ϕ_c . This integral is convergent when Re(A) > 1/2. We can then perform the integration over the angles which gives as possibly singular integrals:

$$4\pi \int_0^R (r_c^{\;2A-2}((\hat{F}_2/r_c^2)) + r_c^{A-1}((\hat{F}_2'/r_c^2)) \,) \, dr_c \; , \tag{28}$$

R being a finite radius defining a tube around the world-line and the double parentheses denoting an average over the angles. The expression (28) is of the form (7.1) (with $x = r_c$), therefore it can be analytically continued everywhere except for simple poles on the real axis. We must inquire about the location of these poles because we worry about a pole at A = 0. Using the fact that the angle average of a smooth function of $X^a = r_c n_c^a$ is a smooth function of r_c^2 (because odd powers of X^a average to zero) we can now take $x = r_c^2$ as variable, so that (28) is transformed into:

$$\int_0^{R^2} x^{A-3/2} F(x)dx + \int_0^{R^2} x^{(A/2)-1} F'(x)dx. \tag{29}$$

Now it is clear using the results of section 7 (for (7.1) with $x = r_c^2$) that the first integral in (29) may have simple poles at A = 1/2, -1/2, -3/2,... (but none at A = 0, and that the second integral may have simple poles at A = 0, -2, -4, ... Therefore there may be a pole at A = 0, the residue of this pole is 2F'(0) (see section 7) which is proportional to $((\hat{F}'_2))$ and thence to the angle average of the underlined second term of the right hand side of eqn (26): $r_c^{A-5} \cdot F'_2$. However, by looking more precisely at the structure of this non-linear term it is easily checked that $((F'_2)) = 0$, which means that in fact there is no pole at A = 0. In conclusion: the part of h_{A2}(10b) which is the retarded integral of the quadratically non-linear terms is convergent for 1/2 <Re(A)< 1 and can be analytically continued everywhere except for some poles but there is no pole at A = 0. The stress-energy part of h_{A2} (10b) is simpler to handle because according to our conclusion 1) above $h_{A1}(z)$ which appears in $\Pi(h_{A1})$ is to be understood as the maximal analytical continuation of $h_{A1}(z)$. According to eqn (25) $h_{A1}(z)$ is well-defined when Re(A)> 1 and is then equal to $F'_0(z, A)$, this last quantity is analytic in A (no poles at A = 0) and must be replaced in $\Pi(h_1)$. Then the integral over s converges when 2< Re(A)< 3 and, as before, can be continued so as to define its retarded integral. Finally $h_{A2}(x)$ is well-defined as a function of x, a functional of z(s) and z'(s') and as an analytic function of A (no poles at A = 0). In order to proceed to the next iteration we must have some knowledge of the "singular behaviour" of h_{A2} near each world-line. A close scrutiny of the retarded integral (10b) of $\Pi(h_{A1})$ and $II(h_{A1}, h_{A1})$ (see eqn (26): full details will be given elsewhere) allows one to conclude that near the first world-line:

$$h_{A2} = r_c^{2A-4} . F_2 + r_c^{A-3} . F'_2 + F_0 \ . \text{ (no poles at A=0)}. \tag{30}$$

We must now plug (25) and (30) in (10c). As before the first two terms of the right hand side of (10c) (stress-energy terms) are easily dealt with: from (30) $h_{A2}(z) = F_0(z, A)$, from (25) $h^2_{A1}(z) = F^2_0(z,A)$, and the integrations are done as before. On the other hand the cubically non-linear effective sources $II(h_{A1}, h_{A2})$ and $III(h_{A1}, h_{A1}, h_{A1})$ are much more complicated. Many "dangerous" terms appear (liable to generate poles at A = 0) but a close scrutiny shows that most of these terms give rise only to false poles (zero residue, as the underlined term in (26)), still a few dangerous terms are left which create real poles of the following type:

$$G^3 h_{A3} \sim \frac{G^3 m^3}{A} (\dot{u}\, F(x) + \ddot{u} G(x)), \tag{31}$$

where $\dot{u}$ is the acceleration (or curvature of the world-line) $\dot{u} = du/ds$ and where $\ddot{u}$ is d^2u/ds^2. However we are going to show in the next section that the harmonicity condition (2) will impose as constraints on the world-lines some equations of motion of the type:

$$\dot{u}^a = GW_1{}^a(z(s);z'(s')) + G^2W_2{}^a(z;z') + G^3W_3{}^a(z;z') + O(G^4), \tag{32}$$

which imply that a term like (31), although coming from the third iteration, is in fact of order G^4. Therefore these terms will create no problems for the G^3 gravitational field and their influence, if any, will show up in the analysis of the G^3 equations of motion which are deduced from the G^4 gravitational field (see next section). Finally, we get a thrice iterated field:

$$h_{A3} = r_c^{3A-7}\cdot F_4 + r_c^{2A-6}\cdot F_4 + r_c^{A-5}\cdot F_4 + F_0 + A^{-1}O(G^3\dot{u}) + A^{-1}O(G^3\ddot{u}). \tag{33}$$

In conclusion the process of analytic continuation allowed us to construct a solution of eqn (4), accurate to order G^3 inclusively:

$$h^{ab}_{A(3)}(x;z;z') = Gh^{ab}_{A1}(x;z;z') + G^2h^{ab}_{A2}(x;z;z') + G^3h^{ab}_{A3}(x;z;z'). \tag{34}$$

Due to lack of space we cannot write down here the semi-explicit expression of $h_{A(3)}$ (which is still partly in integral form) which has been used in actual calculations. The solution (34) is a function of the field point x in Minkowski space, a functional of two world-lines (unrestricted apart from $\dot{u} = O(G)$)and is analytic in a complex parameter A except for (usually simple) poles located at some rational points on the real axis but none in a neighbourhood of the origin A = 0. On the other hand we know that the source T_A, when considered as a function of x and not as a distribution over Minkowski space, vanishes when A = 0 (see section 7 particularly eqn (7.16)). Therefore replacing A by zero in (34) generates a solution of eqn (1). Moreover, it appears from eqns (25), (30) and (33) that the most singular terms near the first worldline when A = 0 are, when A ≠ 0 of the type $O(r_c^{nA-n})$ for each order G^n(n = 1,2,3). It is easily checked that these terms contain the nth power of the mass m only (no explicit dependence on m'). Therefore these terms are the same as for the one-body case except that now the world-line is curved. This curvature though can be shown to introduce only less singular terms when $r_c \to 0$. Hence, our preceding result (22) for the straight-line-one-body case shows that for each order G^n the most singular terms in h^{ab}_{On}, near each world-line, are Schwarschild-like: $G^n(m/r_c)^n S^{ab}_n(u_c,n_c)$ (see (5.25-26)). Therefore $h^{ab}_{O(3)}$ satisfies the "Dominant Schwarzschild" conditions (6.12). On the other hand it seems clear that $h^{ab}_{A(3)}$, being constructed with the retarded Green function Z_2, $h^{ab}_{O(3)}$ will satisfy the Kirchoff "no incoming radiation" conditions (6.6) (we leave to future work an explicit check of this property).

In conclusion to this section: by means of an analytic continuation process, we have constructed a particular solution, $h^{ab}_{0(3)}$, of the cubically non-linear relaxed vacuum field equations (1) which satisifes both the "Dominant Schwarschild" conditions near each world-line and the Kirchoff "no-incoming radiation" conditions at past null infinity. In the next section we shall address ourselves to the "stand by" equation (2).

9. EQUATIONS OF MOTION AS INTEGRABILITY CONDITIONS OF THE EXTERNAL SCHEME

In section 8 we constructed a particular solution of:

$$f^{cd}h^{ab}_{\ \ ,cd} = N^{ab}(h), \tag{1}$$

at least up to the order G^3 inclusively. That solution was a functional of two arbitrary world-lines:

$$h^{ab}(x) = h^{ab}(x;\ z(s),\ z'(s')) \tag{2}$$

Let us define the "harmonicity" of h^{ab} as the following quantity:

$$H^a(x) := h^{ab}{}_{,b} \equiv \underline{g}^{ab}{}_{,b} \tag{3}$$

Our aim is to construct a solution of the complete vacuum Einstein equations (6.2). These equations reduce to the "relaxed" form (1) in harmonic coordinates, that is to say when the "harmonicity" vanishes. Therefore we must investigate when our particular solution h^{ab} satisfy the "harmonicity condition":

$$H^a\ (x;z(s),z'(s')) = 0. \tag{4}$$

As is clear from eqn (4) this condition will in general restrict the still arbitrary world-lines used in the construction of h^{ab}. In fact, we shall see that eqn (4) implies the equations of motion of the two world-lines. An important tool in showing this is the use of the Bianchi identities:

$$E^{ab}{}_{;b} := E^{ab}{}_{,b} + E^{bc}\ \Gamma^{\ a}_{bc} + E^{ab}\Gamma^{c}_{bc} \equiv 0\ . \tag{5}$$

These identities can also be written in function of the covariant derivative of the tensor density of weight +2, $\underline{E}^{ab}: =gE^{ab}$: $\underline{E}^{ab}{}_{;b} := \underline{E}^{ab}{}_{,b} + \underline{E}^{bc}\Gamma_{bc}^{\ \ a} - \underline{E}^{ab}\Gamma_{bc}^{\ \ c} \underline{=} 0.$ (6)

(Note the minus sign of the last term). Using eqn (6) and the definition of N^{ab} ((6.2), (6.4) and (6.13)) we get the following identity satisfied by N:

$$N^{ab}{}_{,b} \equiv (\Box h^{bc} - N^{bc})\Gamma^{a}_{bc} - (\Box h^{ab} - N^{ab})\,\Gamma^{c}_{bc} + O(Hh)\ , \tag{7}$$

where the abbreviation O(Hh) denotes some terms which are linear combinations of H and its derivatives with coefficients which are at least linear in h and its derivatives. If we knew only that eqn (1) were fulfilled, we would deduce from (1), (3), and (7) that:

$$f^{cd}H^{a}{}_{,cd} = O(Hh). \tag{8}$$

Eqn (8) is very important in the study of the Cauchy problem, because its consideration is sufficient for proving that if H and $H_{,0}$ vanish on the initial hypersurface (which implies that 4 initial constraint equations must be satisfied by h) then H vanishes everywhere and therefore h is a solution of the full Einstein equations. However in our treatment, which is not of the "initial value" type, eqn (8) is of little help for finding further constraints on h in a useful form. Therfore at this point it is very convenient to recur again to the process of analytic continuation and to remember that the particular solution of (1) was obtained from a perturbative solution of:

$$h^{ab}_{A} = -Z_2 * (GT_A{}^{ab} + N^{ab}(h_A)) \tag{9}$$

where $T_A(h_A)$ was defined in eqn (8.3), by analytically continuing A in zero. Because of the nice properties of the analytic continuation, which allows one to treat "divergent" integrals as if they were convergent (as we said in section 7 this should not be done blindly but here it works) one can differentiate the right hand side of (9) under the integration symbol hidden in the convolution symbol:

$$Z_2 * F = \int d^4y\ Z_2(x-y)F(y) = \int d^4y Z_2(y)\ F(x-y). \tag{10}$$

Therefore a derivative of h can be expressed as a convolution with the derivative of the source: GT + N. In particular the definition (3) implies:

$$H^{a}_{A} = -Z_2 * (GT^{ab}_{A\ ,b} + N^{ab}{}_{,b}) \tag{11}$$

Using the identity (7) and the eqn (9) we get:

$$H^{a}_{A} = -Z_2 * (GT^{ab}_{A\ ;b} + O(H_A h_A)\ ), \tag{12}$$

where the semi-colon denotes the covariant derivative appropriate to tensor densities of weight + 2 (see eqn (6)) with Christoffel symbols corresponding to the metric h_A. Eqn (12) is much more useful than eqn (8) specially in a perturbative approach because of the appearance of the coupling constant G. Indeed we should have worked, from the beginning of this section, only with truncated G expansions. This has the effect of replacing (12) by its truncated form:

$$H^a_{A(n)} = -Z_2 * ((GT_A^{ab};_b)_{(n)} + (O(H_A h_A))_{(n)}) .$$

(13)

Now the right hand side of (13) depends at most on $h_{A(n-1)}$. Therefore, imposing the complete solving of the nth iteration ("complete" means including the harmonicity condition: $H_{(n)} = 0$) provides some constraints which depend only on the (n-1)th iterated metric. In order to derive these constraints let us study more precisely $T^{ab};_b$. From its definition (8.3) T_A^{ab} can be written as:

$$T_A^{ab} = \Sigma \ 16\pi \int ds \ M_A(s) u^a u^b Z_A(x-z) ,$$

(14)

where $M_A(s)$ is an "effective" variable mass which reduces to m in absence of interaction and whose value can be read off (8.3) and (8.7). From (14) one deduces by integration by parts:

$$T_A^{ab},_b = \Sigma \ 16\pi \int \ ds \frac{d}{ds}(M_A u^a) \ Z_A(x-z) .$$

(15)

Moreover we have seen in the preceding section that, near each world-line, $h_{A(n)}$ ($n \leq 3$) could be written as:

$$h^{ab}_{A(n)}(x) = (\sum_{p,q,r} r_c^{pA-q} \cdot F_r^{ab}(x,A)) + F_0^{ab}(x,A) ,$$

(16)

where p,q and r are integers and where $F_r^{ab}(x,A)$ and $F_0^{ab}(x,A)$ are smooth in x and analytic in A (poles at A = 0 appear only at order G^4 or are multiplied at least by a factor $G^3\dot{u}$ or $G^3\ddot{u}$ which will be shown below to be of the same order as G^4.) We call the first term of the right hand side of (16): the "singular part" of $h_{A(n)}$ (denoted sing($h_{A(n)}$)) and the second term (F_0): the "regular part" of $h_{A(n)}$ (denoted reg($h_{A(n)}$)). When computing from (16) the Christoffel symbols of the metric f + $h_{A(n)}$ and truncating at order n we find a similar form:

$$\Gamma_{A(n)} = sing(\Gamma_{A(n)}) + reg(\Gamma_{A(n)}) .$$

(17)

Moreover it can be checked that:

$$reg(\Gamma_{A(n)}) := reg((\Gamma(h_{A(n)}))_{(n)}) = (\Gamma(reg(h_{A(n)})))_{(n)} .$$

(18)

Taking into account the fact that when $A = 0$ the function $T_A(x)$ vanishes everywhere except maybe on the world-lines but that when $A \neq 0$ $T_A(x)$ is singular near each world-line so that the distribution T_A tends to a Dirac distribution on each world-line, we see that the first term of the right hand side of (13) will contribute terms $O(A)$ (i.e. vanishing with A) except for the parts of the Z_2 integral coming from an arbitrary small neighbourhood of the world-lines. Hence it will be sufficient to use the near-world-line behaviour (17). Writing (13) for the order $n + 1$ we get:

$$H^a_{A(n+1)} = \Sigma -GZ_2 * (T^{ab}_{A(n),b} + T^{bc}_{A(n)} \mathrm{reg}(\Gamma^a_{A(n)bc}) - T^{ab}_{A(n)} \mathrm{reg}(\Gamma^c_{A(n)bc})) +$$
$$+ \Sigma - GZ_2 * (T^{bc}_{A(n)} \mathrm{sing}(\Gamma^a_{A(n)bc}) - T^{ab}_{A(n)} \mathrm{sing}(\Gamma^c_{A(n)bc})) -$$
$$- Z_2 * (O(H_{A(n)} h_{A(n)})) + O(A) + O(G^{n+2}) \quad . \tag{19}$$

Here we have replaced, for simplicity, the "truncation suffix" $(n + 1)$ which should be added to the right hand side of (19) by an extra $O(G^{n+2})$. The first three terms of (19) can be dealt with in the framework of distribution theory because reg (Γ) is a smooth function of x and T_A becomes a Dirac distribution when $A = 0$. Using eqn (15), replacing $M(\dot{s})$ by its definition (8.3) and (8.7), and taking into account eqn (18) it can be shown that the first three terms of (19) give the following contribution to $H^a_{A(n+1)}$:

$$\Sigma -16\pi G \int ds\, M\, (B^a_{(n)} - u^a\, \mathrm{reg}(g_{bc})_{(n)} B^b_{(n)} u^c (\mathrm{reg}(g_{de})_{(n)} u^d u^e)^{-1})\, Z_2(x-z) +$$
$$O(A) + O(G^{n+2}) \tag{20}$$

where $B^a_{(n)}$ is an abbreviation for:

$$B^a_{(n)} := \frac{du^a}{ds} + (f^a_b + f_{bc} u^a u^c)\, u^d u^e \mathrm{reg}\, (\Gamma^b_{0(n)de})(z). \tag{21}$$

Because of eqn (18) and because by definition (eqn (16)) a "singular term," together with its derivatives, vanishes on the world-line when the real part of A is large enough we can write for any function $G_A(x)$ of the type (16):

$$\mathrm{reg}\,(G_0)(z) = \underset{A = 0}{\text{Analytic Continuation}}\ (G_A(z)). \tag{22}$$

Therefore $B_{(n)}^{\ a}$ can be written as:

$$B^a_{(n)} = \underset{A = 0}{\text{An.Cont.}}\ (\dot{u}^a + (f^a_b + u^a u_b)\, u^c u^d\, \Gamma^b_{cd}\, (h_{A(n)})(z)), \tag{23}$$

where, for simplicity, u_b denotes $f_{bc}u^c$ and not $g_{bc}u^c$.

On the other hand the fourth and the fifth terms of eqn (19) are much more complicated to handle. The mathematical reason for this complication is that they cannot be treated in the framework of distribution theory (where they would yield meaningless quantities of the type: $\infty \cdot \delta$). The physical reason for this complication is that these terms "correspond" to the "self-action" of a compact body. I use the word "correspond" and not "represent" because in the approach taken here, the equations of motion are deduced from the vacuum field equations and the vacuum field in an improved Einstein-Infel-Hoffmann's way. The improvement consists in that, instead of dealing with the surface integral of a very complicated non-linear expression (which would be proportional to $N^{ab}(h_{(n)})_{(n+1)}$) we are now dealing with the retarded volume integral of a much simpler expression (19). This drastic simplification comes from the fact that the divergence of $N^{ab}_{(n+1)}$ is much simpler than $N^{ab}_{(n+1)}$ itself ("Bianchi" identity (7)). However it has been possible to take advantage of this simplification only because of our mathematically well-defined use of analytic continuation (intuitively we are somehow using Gauss' theorem, but it would be meaningless to use it directly on the surface integrals because of the singular behaviour in $r_c = 0$). At the same time our use of a "fictitious" stress energy tensor makes the calculations, which deal in fact only with quantities in vacuum, similar to the familiar extended body calculations, and in this sense the incriminated terms correspond somehow with the "self-action" of the body (we put quotation marks because this concept is not defined in general, and, a fortiori in the case of compact bodies).

In order to analyze these terms we must work out explicitly the expression for the "singular" behaviour of $\Gamma_{A(n)}$ near the first world-line, as well as a similar expression for the behaviour of T_A and we must investigate the resulting integrals. Using arguments similar to the one used in the preceding section we end up with integrals of the following type:

$$A\int_0^R x^{pA-q}F(x)dx \;. \tag{24}$$

Pay attention to the fact that the appearance of a factor A does not mean necessarily that these terms are O(A) in the sense used above. Indeed as was discussed in Section 7 the integral contained in eqn (24) is defined by analytic continuation and can have a simple pole in $A = 0$, in which case (24) gives a non zero contribution to (19) when $A = 0$ (and this case is not at all exceptional because the first three terms of (19) can be written as (24) and have been shown to contribute (20)). At this point, in order to include also the contribution of the sixth and last term of (19): O(Hh), it is simpler to proceed iteratively.

When n = 0, which means considering the "harmonicity" up to first order: $H_{(1)}$, only the first term of (19) is left and we reach the result:

$$H^a_{O(1)} = \Sigma - 16\pi G \int ds\ m\ B^a_{(0)} Z_2(x-z) \ , \tag{25}$$

where $B^a_{(0)}$ is nothing but the Minkowski acceleration: du^a/ds. Therefore the first order metric $h_{O(1)}$ will satisfy the harmonicity condition (4), and thence the first order complete vacuum field equations, exactly if and only if each world-line is such that:

$$B^a_{(0)} = \dot{u}^a = 0. \tag{26}$$

However as we are solving Einstein equations in a perturbative manner in any case, there is no need to satisfy the harmonicity condition exactly (which would force the world-lines to be straight because of (26)). It is sufficient to require that the harmonicity condition is satisfied at the same order as the field equations:

$$H^a_{O(1)} = O(G^2), \tag{27}$$

so that the world-lines are only required to satisfy:

$$B^a_{(0)} = \dot{u}^a = O(G). \tag{28}$$

As discussed in Bel, Damour, Deruelle, Ibañez and Martin (1981), eqn (28) does not mean that the world-lines have to be globally close to straight-lines but only that they are solutions of a system of equation of the type written in eqn (8.32).

Assuming that, what we shall call the zeroth order equations of motion (28) are satisfied, we can now consider n = 1 i.e. the harmonicity condition up to second order: $H_{(2)}$. In this case the last term of eqn (19) is $O(H_{(1)}h_{(1)})$ which is, by (27), $O(G^3)$ and therefore negligible at this order. Moreover in this case it is not difficult to prove that the 4th and 5th terms of (19) contribute terms of the type (24) where the integral has no pole in A = 0 which means that these self-action terms vanish when A = 0. Then we are left with:

$$H^a_{O(2)} = \Sigma - 16\pi G \int ds M_{(1)} (B^a_{(1)} - u^a \mathrm{reg}(g_{(1)bc}) B^b_{(1)} u^c (\mathrm{reg}(g_{(1)de}) u^d u^e)^{-1})\, x$$
$$x Z_2(x-z) \tag{29}$$

However, by its definition (21) $f_{bc} B^b_{(1)} u^c = 0$, thence the second term of (29) is at least $O(G^2 B_{(1)})$, i.e., because of (28), $O(G^3)$ which is negligible. For the same reason $M_{(1)}$ can be replaced by $M_{(0)} = m$ in the first term of (29). So that we are left with:

$$H^{a}_{O(2)} = \Sigma -16\pi G \int ds\ m\ B^{a}_{(1)}\ Z_2(x-z) + O(G^3) \ . \tag{30}$$

Hence the second order metric $h_{O(2)}$ will satisfy the harmonicity conditions, and therefore the full Einstein equations, at third order if and only if each world-line satisfies the "first order equations of motion":

$$B^{a}_{(1)} = O(G^2). \tag{31}$$

A result equivalent to (31) has been first obtained by Bel et.al.(1981) by direct computation of $H_{(2)}$.

Assuming that the first order equations of motion (31) are satisfied we can now consider n = 2,i.e. the harmonicity condition up to third order. For the same reason as before the last term of (19): O(Hh) is negligible. On the other hand the 4th and 5th terms contribute terms of the type (24) where the integrals do have a pole in A = 0. However the residue of this pole is easily shown to be at least O(G) and therefore the "self-action terms" contribute still negligibly at this order. Now one should beware of the fact that: "self-action terms" means just: "the 4th and 5th terms in eqn (19)". In eqn (16) the "regular" term contains in fact the gravitational analogue of the Lorentz-Schott-Dirac self-electromagnetic field responsible for the "radiation reaction" force (3.6). Therefore our "self-action terms" correspond only to the Newtonian-like self forces which vanish because of the Action and Reaction principle. Then we are left with (20) for n = 2. As before it can be simplified so that we can write:

$$H^{a}_{O(3)} = \Sigma -16\pi G \int ds\ m\ B^{a}_{(2)} Z_2(x-z) + O(G^4). \tag{32}$$

Hence, the third order metric $h_{O(3)}$ which was constructed in the preceding section, will satisfy the harmonicity conditions, and therefore the full vacuum Einstein equations, at fourth order, if and only if each world-line satisfies the "second order equations of motion":

$$B^{a}_{(2)} = O(G^3). \tag{33}$$

This result was first obtained by Damour (1980) and used to prove that the equations of motion of Westpfahl and Göller (1979) and of Bel et.al. (1981), obtained by formal regularization of meaningless quantities, were effectively the correct integrability conditions of the third order vacuum field equations. Let us emphasize once more that the process of analytic continuation, as employed here, is not another formal regularization procedure but only a tool for finding and computing well-defined quantities. A look back at eqn (21) or at eqn (23) shows that a knowledge of the analytically continued second order metric $h_{A(2)}$ is sufficient to compute the second order equations of motion (33). On the other hand simple dimensional considerations (dating back to Eddington (1924)) show that we need to include terms of order G^3 in the equations of motion in order to get all the terms up to the "radiation reaction" terms inclusively. We can then hope that the precedingly constructed third order metric $h_{A(3)}$ will be sufficient to compute the third order equations of motion. That this is so can be proven by a generalization of the preceding arguments. Starting from the third order metric $h_{0(3)}$ which is an approximate solution of the Einstein vacuum equations if (33) is satisfied we ask the following question: is it possible to find a fourth order metric $h_{(4)}$ which fulfills both eqn (1) with the quartically non-linear terms of eqn (8.6) and eqn (4)? The answer is: this is possible if and only if the world-lines appearing in $h_{(4)}$ satisfy some third order equations of motion (therefore the third order equations of motion can be considered as the integrability conditions of the fourth order vacuum field equations). Because of the appearance of poles at A = 0 of order $G^3\dot{u} \sim G^4$ coming from the third iteration as well as other poles coming from the fourth iteration we must modify our method for constructing $h_{(4)}$. When this is done we find that we must still consider eqn (19). The "self-action" terms are now becoming really intricate and liable to contribute to the final equations of motion. However a scrutiny of these "self action" terms show that their contribution to the third order equations of motion is $O(G^3v_r^2)$ where v_r^2 denotes the square of the relative velocity of the two world-lines (or geometrically the square of the space-time angle between the world-lines). v_r^2 is a Poincaré invariant quantity ($\sim f_{ab}(u^a-u'^a)(u^b-u'^b)$) which we shall assume to be always small. An example, among the simplest, of such a $G^3v_r^2$ term is: $G^2m^2d^3u^a/ds^3$ (where $du^a/ds = O(G)$ can be replaced by its value deduced from the equation of motion (31)). Note that we are here making a Slow-Motion hypothesis without abandoning the Poincaré invariance of our Post-Minkowskian Approach.

The other terms of (19) are dealt with as before and we are left with the following third order equations of motion:

$$B^a_{(3)} = O(G^3v_r^2) + O(G^4). \tag{34}$$

(As we said already, the full proofs of our results will be spelled out in an article to be submitted to the Proceedings of the Royal Society (London)).

We shall see below that the accuracy of these equations of motion is sufficient for getting all the terms smaller than or equal to the "radiation reaction" which will be shown to be $O(G^2v_r^3 + G^3v_r)$.

The physical content of eqn (34) will be analyzed in sections 11 - 15; let us just remark here that, because of eqns (18), (21) and (23), eqn (34) means that, with the accuracy indicated, each world-line is a geodesic of the A = 0 analytically continued metric g_A or, equivalently, a geodesic of each (world-line dependent) metric reg (g_0) (the unfamiliar $f_{bc}u^a u^c$ term in eqns (21) and (23) is due to the use of the Minkowski parametrization: z(s)). On the other hand, in the case of slowly spinning compact bodies, Damour (1982) has deduced from the fourth order harmonicity condition two types of integrability conditions:

1) some orbital equations of motion which are a Papapetrou (1951) - like generalization of the preceding equations (34),
2) some spin propagation equations which had been obtained previously by a formal use of Infeld-Plebanski "good delta functions" (Damour 1978, equivalent spin propagation equations had also been obtained by other quantum or classical heuristic arguments: Barker and O'Connel (1975), Hari Dass and Radhakrishnan(1975,)Börner, Ehlers and Rudolph(1975).)

10. UNIQUENESS OF THE SOLUTION

In section 8 we constructed a particular solution, up to third order, of the "relaxed" vacuum field equations. This solution was a functional of two arbitrary world lines:

$$h^{ab}_{0(3)}(x;z(s),z'(s')) = \underset{A=0}{\text{Anal.cont.}}\ h^{ab}_{A(3)}\ (x;\ z(s),z'(s')). \tag{1}$$

In section 9 we showed that $h^{ab}_{0(3)}$ was a solution of the full vacuum field equations if the world-lines were restricted to satisfy the second order equations of motion:

$$B^a_{(2)} := \frac{du^a}{ds} - W^a_{(2)}(z(s),z'(s')) = O(G^3),\ (2) \tag{2}$$

where $W_{(2)}$ denotes (see (9.23) with $u_b := f_{bc}u^c$):

$$W^a_{(2)} := -\underset{A=0}{\text{An.cont.}}\ (f^a_b+u^a u_b)u^c u^d\ \Gamma^b_{cd}(h_{A(2)})(z). \tag{3}$$

Hence (1) together with (2) determines one particular solution of the full vacuum field equations up to third order: $h_{0(3)}$. On the other hand what we want is the solution of the full vacuum field equations which is the gravitational field outside two compact objects: h_c. We have proved in section 6 that h_c satisfies necessarily two types of boundary conditions:

- "3DS": the "third order Dominant Schwarzschild" conditions (6.12)
- "K": the "Kirchoff no-incoming-radiation" conditions (6.6)

We have checked in section 8 that the particular solution $h_{O(3)}$ satisfied both types of boundary conditions: "3DS" and "K". Therefore if we prove that there is a, geometrically and physically, unique solution of the vacuum Einstein equations, up to third order inclusively, which satisfies both 3DS and K, it will follow that $h_{O(3)} = h_c + O(G^4)$ (modulo a diffeomorphism), i.e. that $h_{O(3)}$ is the gravitational field outside two compact objects (truncated at order G^4). For simplicity, and by lack of space, we shall prove this result of uniqueness only at second order. The result, though, is valid at third order but its demonstration is more involved. As usual we proceed by iteration and start immediately at second order (the uniqueness of the first order being proved along the same line).

Given a uniquely determined first order gravitational field $h_{(1)}$ let us look for the most general second order field $h_{(2)}$ which satisfies:

- the vacuum Einstein equations, which can always be written in harmonic coordinates:

$$\Box\, h^{ab}_{(2)} = N^{ab}_{(2)}(h_{(1)}) \tag{4}$$

$$h^{ab}_{(2)},_b = 0 \ (\text{ or } O(G^3)) \tag{5}$$

- the second order Dominant Schwarzschild conditions: i.e. there exist two world-lines z(s) and z'(s') such that, near each world-line:

$$h^{ab}_{(2)} = -4Gm\left(\frac{u^a u^b}{r}\right)_c - G^2m^2\left(\frac{7u^a u^b + n^a n^b}{r^2}\right)_c + O(r_c^0) + O(G'^2)O\left(\frac{1}{r_c}\right) + O(G^3)\ , \tag{6}$$

- and the Kirchoff conditions : $rh^{ab}_{(2)}$ and $rh^{ab}_{(2),c}$ are bounded and:

$$\lim_{\substack{r\to\infty \\ \theta,\phi,t+r/c=\text{ const.}}} \left((rh^{ab}_{(2)}),_r + (rh^{ab}_{(2)}),_t \right) = 0\ . \tag{7}$$

In section 8 we have constructed a particular solution $h_{O(2)}$ of (4). Therefore the most general solution of (4) (where $h_{(1)}$ is known from the preceding iteration) is:

$$h^{ab}_{(2)} = h^{ab}_{O(2)} + k^{ab}, \tag{8}$$

where k^{ab} satisfies:

$$\Box\, k^{ab} = 0. \tag{9}$$

Moreover, as $h_{0(2)}$ satisfied the Kirchoff conditions, k must satisfy them as well:

$$\lim_{\substack{r\to\infty \\ t+rc^{-1}=\text{const.}}} \left((rk^{ab})_{,r} + (rk^{ab})_{,t} \right) = 0. \tag{10}$$

and, as $h_{0(2)}$ was constructed so as to satisfy the second order Dominant Schwarzchild conditions (6) (see section 8), k must satisfy near each world-line:

$$k^{ab} = O(G'^2)O(1/r_c) + O(r_c^0) + O(G^3) . \tag{11}$$

Let us write down what was called by Hadamard the Fundamental Identity (valid for two arbitrary functions):

$$Z(x)\,\square\, k^{ab}(x) - k^{ab}(x)\,\square Z(x) \equiv (f^{cd}(Zk^{ab}{}_{,d} - k^{ab}Z_{,d}))_{,c} . \tag{12}$$

Let us replace $Z(x)$ by $Z_2(x_0 - x)$, for a given x_0 (see (7.17) for the definition of Z_2) and let us integrate both sides of the identity (12) on a region of space-time which is outside two (thin) tubes containing the two world-lines and inside one (thick) tube whose diameter will be allowed to go to infinity. By (9), the first term of the left hand side of (12) vanishes and by (7.17) the second term is equal to $k^{ab}(x_0)$ (assuming that x_0 is in the region of integration). Using Gauss' theorem the right hand side of (12) is reduced to three surface integrals. To start with they are 3-surface integrals but, because $Z_2(x_0 - x)$ is zero everywhere except on the <u>past</u> Minkowski light cone with vertex x_0, they are in fact 2 - surface integrals. On one hand the Kirchoff condition (10) is precisely the condition which ensures that the integral over the thick tube (in fact over a large 2-surface on the past light cone of x_0) tends to zero when the radius of the thick tube tends to infinity. On the other hand the other boundary conditions (11) ensure that the integral over each thin tube tends to a world-line integral of $Z_2(x_0 - z(s))$ when the radius of the tube tends to zero. Hence, suppressing now the index zero to x, we get the following necessary expression for k:

$$k^{ab}(x) = \Sigma -16\pi G^2 \int ds\; K^{ab}(s)\; Z_2(x-z(s)), \tag{13}$$

where $K^{ab} = K^{ba}$ is an undetermined function of s. However we must still fulfill eqn (5). Using the fact that, by construction, $h^{ab}_{0(2)}$ satisfies eqn (9.30), we conclude that k^{ab} must satisfy:

$$k^{ab}{}_{,b} + \Sigma\; -16\pi G \int dsm(\dot{u}^a - GW_1^a)Z_2(x-z) = O(G^3). \tag{14}$$

Eqn (14) together with eqn (13) is very constraining for k^{ab}. One finds that K^{ab} must be of the form:

$$K^{ab}(s) \;=\; Ku^a u^a + O(G), \tag{15}$$

where K must be constant. Therefore k^{ab} represents only a small $(O(G^2))$ constant readjustment of the monopole term: $h^{ab}_{O(1)}$ (eqn(8.24)). However the symbol $O(G'^2)$ in (11), (6) (and (6.12)) meant in fact that this term was not only $O(G^2)$ but also caused by the interaction and therefore was to vanish in the case of vanishing interaction, thence the constant K must in fact vanish and we are left with:

$$k^{ab} = O(G^3), \tag{16}$$

or, in other words, that the most general solution of (4-7) is necessarily equal to the particular solution $h_{O(2)}$ (modulo G^3). A direct consequence of this uniqueness is that the second order metric of Bel et.al. (1981), which has been obtained by some formal regularizing rules,as the field due to two "point masses",and which can be checked to be a solution of the complete vacuum Einstein equations satisfying "K" and "2DS," is necessarily equal to $h_{O(2)}$ and therefore to the metric (up to second order) outside two compact objects.

It is possible, with more work, to generalize this uniqueness to the third order metric, although several new features show up. On one hand the uniqueness is true only in a geometrical sense, that is to say modulo a coordinate transformation (leaving invariant the harmonicity). On the other hand the "3DS" conditions (6.12) leave the possibility of a $O(G'^2)$ shift of the world-lines which however changes only the functional form of $h_{(3)}(x;z(s))$ but not its numerical value. Therefore the physical content both of the third order metric and of the second order equations of motion is uniquely determined. Moreover it is always possible to normalize the functional form of $h_{(3)}(x;z)$ to $h_{O(3)}(x;z)$ which amounts only to a choice of the "central world-line" in the external scheme (see section 6).

In consequence the physical content of the third order equations of motion, which, as shown in the preceding section are the integrability conditions of the fourth order metric but which can be expressed only in function of the third order metric, is uniquely determined.

In conclusion, the particular solution $h_{O(3)}$ is necessarily equal to the metric outside two compact objects (modulo G^4) and the third order equations of motion (9.34) are the equations of a particular image in the external coordinates of the "central world-line" defined in the internal coordinates in sections 5 and 6.

11. PREDICTIVE POINCARE INVARIANT EQUATIONS OF MOTION

The equations of motion obtained in section 9 do not constitute a system of ordinary differential equations because the acceleration du/ds of each world-line is given as a complicated functional of the two worldlines. More precisely, because of our systematic use of "retarded potentials," this functional depends only on the parts of the two world-lines which are in the (Minkowski) past of the point Z whose acceleration $du/ds = d^2z/ds^2$ one computes. This kind of equation is known in the literature as "retarded-functional differential system." Up to the very recent work of Eder (1982) there were no theorems of existence and uniqueness for the solutions of these systems. Under certain technical conditions, on the structure of the system and using "initial data" for the two world-lines in the infinite past, Eder proves the existence and uniqueness of the solution up to a finite time. This result increases our confidence in the framework of "predictive relativistic mechanics" (for a review see Bel and Fustero (1976) and references therein). In this approach it is assumed (see however the recent result of Bel (1982) on "spontaneous predictivisation") that one can describe the evolution of two world-lines satisfying a retarded functional-system:

$$\frac{dz^a}{ds} = u^a \ , \ \frac{du^a}{ds} = W^a \ (s;z(r);z'(r')) \ ,$$

$$\frac{dz'^a}{ds'} = u'^a \ , \ \frac{du'^a}{ds'} = W'^a \ (s';z'(r');z(r)) \ , \qquad (1)$$

(where, in the first line, r is restricted to be smaller than s and r' smaller than $\hat{s}'$ the proper time of the intersection of z'(s') with the past light cone of z(s)), by an ordinary differential system of the type:

$$\frac{dz^a(p)}{dp} = u^a \ , \ \frac{du^a(p)}{dp} = X^a \ (z(p),u(p),z'(p),u'(p))$$

$$\frac{dz'^a(p)}{dp} = u'^a \ , \ \frac{du'^a(p)}{dp} = X'^a \ (z'(p),u'(p),z(p),u(p)). \qquad (2)$$

The functions X^a must fulfill the following requirements:

1) covariance under the Poincaré group (Poincaré 1905),
2) orthogonality: $f_{ab}X^a u^b = 0$,
3) invariance under world-line "sliding" (Droz-Vincent 1969, 1970):

$$u'^b X^a_{,z'b} + X'^b X^a_{,u'b} = 0. \qquad (3)$$

Under these conditions the system (2) can be changed in each frame of reference into a Newtonian type system (12 equations using $t = z^o = z'^o$ as parame ter instead of the 16 equations (2)) while still preserving the invariance under the Poincaré group (Bel 1970, 1971). Such a system (2) is called a predictive Poincaré invariant system (its general solution depends only on 12 essential parameters). The consideration of such a system is especially useful in setting up an Hamiltonian formalism for the dynamics of two particles (see Bel and Fustero 1976, Bel and Martin 1980).

When the functionals W are in fact functions of z(s), u(s) and of $\hat{z}' = z'(\hat{s}')$, where $\hat{s}'$is the proper time of the intersection of the second world-line with the past directed light cone of vertex z(s),

$$W^a(s \ ; z(r); z'(r'), r<s, r'<\hat{s}') = W^a(z(s),u(s), z'(\hat{s}'), u'(\hat{s}')), \tag{4}$$

it is possible to set up an iterative algorithm for explicitly constructing the functions X^a, given the W^a (Bel, Salas and Sanchez 1973) (Bel et.al. 1981). This algorithm is most easily obtained by solving perturbatively the following integro-functional equation (Hirondel 1974):

$$X^a(z,u,z',u') = R'(\hat{p}')W^a(z,u,z',u') - \int_{\hat{p}'}^{0} dp'R'(p')(X'^b X^a_{,u'b}) \ , \tag{5}$$

where $\hat{p}' = -(z-z').u' - (((z-z').u')^2 + (z-z')^2)^{1/2}$ (Minkowski products and squares), and where R'(p') is a "shift" operator which acts on a function of z,u,z', u' by replacing z' by z' + p'u'. In practical applications W is always multiplied by a "small" coupling constant, G in our case:

$$W^a = GW^a_1 + G^2W^a_2 + O(G^3), \tag{6}$$

therefore eqn (5) can be, and has been, used to generate W^a as a truncated expansion in powers of G:

$$X^a = GX^a_1 + G^2X^a_2 + O(G^3). \tag{7}$$

In the gravitational case, X_1 has been first obtained by Portilla (1979), together with a corresponding first order Hamiltonian formalism.

X_2 has been worked out by Bel, Damour, Deruelle, Ibañez and Martin (1981). We refer to the latter article for the setting up of the algorithm and for the explicit computation of X_2 starting from the W_2 which is derived in the same article (that W_2 being equivalent to the equations of motion of Westpfahl and Göller (1979).

In equation (6) we did not write the third order term G^3W_3, derived in section 9 because, contrary to the first two approximations, it does not seem easy (maybe it is not even possible) to obtain for W_3 an expression having the simplified functional form of eqn (4), and thence to construct X_3 by the algorithm deduced from eqn (5). In the next section we shall resort to a different approach for transforming retarded-functional equations of motion (1) into ordinary differential equations.

12. NEWTONIAN-LIKE EQUATIONS OF MOTION

In order to compare theory and observations one must extract some explicit physical predictions from the equations of orbital motion of two compact objects derived in section 9. One possible way of achieving this is to transform them into a predictive Poincaré invariant system (see section 11). This approach has many theoretical advantages: manifest Poincaré invariance, applicability to fast objects ($v \sim c$), possibility of defining an associated Hamiltonian formulation (references in section 11). However it has several practical drawbacks: it may not be applicable in its usual form to the third order equations of motion and it leads quickly to heavy calculations. Therefore in this section we shall restrict ourselves to the case of slowly moving objects ($v \ll c$). This assumption, on one hand will simplify very much the calculations by allowing us to use truncated expansions in powers of c^{-1} (while the Poincaré invariant approach is somewhat equivalent to resuming infinite power series of c^{-1}), and on the other hand will be sufficient for dealing with the kind of binary systems we have in mind (like the Hulse-Taylor pulsar PSR 1913 + 16).

By Newtonian-like equations of motion up to order c^{-n} (also called (n/2) Post-Newtonian equations of motion) we mean the following: in a given Lorentz coordinate system $x^a = (x^o = ct, x^i)$ $(i = 1,2,3)$, using $t = c^{-1}z^o = c^{-1}z'^o$ as parameter for each world-line one can write:

$$\frac{dz^i(t)}{dt} = v^i \;, \quad \frac{dv^i(t)}{dt} = \sum_{p=0}^{n} c^{-p} A_p^i(z(t),v(t),z'(t),v'(t)). \tag{1}$$

Because the Einstein coupling constant between mass and gravity is in fact Gc^{-2} and because the acceleration contains two differentiations with respect to $x^o = ct$, a "retarded equation of motion up to order G^n" (as considered in sections 9 and 11) neglects terms or order G^{n+1}, which means in the preceding Newtonian sense, that it neglects terms of order c^{-2n} (nth Post-Newtonian terms). This formal rule for playing with the orders in G and c^{-1} is especially useful when dealing with gravitationally bound systems where the virial theorem: $Gc^{-2}m/R \sim c^{-2}v^2$ allows us to replace the Einstein coupling constant Gc^{-2} by c^{-2} when counting the Post-Newtonian order.

Consequently we see that the cubically non-linear equations of motion of section 9 (n = 3) neglect terms of order c^{-6} (3 Post-Newtonian terms) that is why it was consistent to neglect terms of order $G^3 v_r^2/c^2$ in section 9 and that it will be sufficient in this section to truncate all the c^{-1} expansions at order c^{-6} so that our final equations of motion will be accurate up to order c^{-5} inclusively ($2^1/2$ Post-Newtonian accuracy).

There are at least three different methods for obtaining Newtonian-like equations of motion up to order c^{-n}:

1) to compute, when possible, the predictive Poincaré invariant equations of motion. To write them down in a given Lorentz frame in their 3 + 1 form which yields: $dv/dt = F(z(t), c^{-1}v(t), z'(t), c^{-1}v'(t))$. At last to expand all the velocity dependent quantities up to order c^{-n}.

2) to start from the retarded system: $\dot{u} = W$, and to use, when possible, the formula of Lagrange (1770) for expanding all the functions of retarded quantities: $\hat{z}'$, $\hat{u}'$, ... in powers of c^{-1}. However Lagrange's expansion formula introduces successive derivatives of z(t), but an iterative use of the lower order Newtonian-like equations of motion allows one to reduce the order of differentiation to one, in the right hand side (Kerner 1965).

3) to start from eqn (9.34) (together with 9.23)) which means that, when neglecting $O(G^4) + O(G^3 v_r^2)$ each world-line is a geodesic of the analytically continued metric g^A_{ab} for A = 0. To expand $g^A_{ab}(x)$ in powers of c^{-1} (near zone expansion). To plug this near zone expansion in the geodesic equation and to truncate the result at order c^{-n} inclusively.

When starting from the G^2 retarded equations of motion all three methods are possible and the first and the third have been used, and checked to be equivalent, by Damour and Deruelle (1981a). On the other hand the G^3 retarded equations of motion have a more intricate functional dependence on the world-lines and it has been possible to use only the third method (Damour 1982).

Despite the frightfully complicated structure of the third Post-Minkowskian metric (8.10) it has been found possible to separate many contributions to the equations of motion (9.34) which are, in their exact form, already of order $G^3 v_r^2$ (where v_r^2 is a Lorentz invariant squared relative velocity, see section 9), and which therefore can only contribute terms of order c^{-6}, at least, to the Post-Newtonian equations of motion. Even after this drastic simplification we are still left with many complicated expressions. Although some of them are still in (analytic continuation defined) integral form it is remarkable that all the integrals appearing in the final c^{-1} expanded expression can be carried out. By lack of space, it is impossible to even outline the calculation; I woud like to stress however, that the integrals coming from the cubic non-linearities in the metric were computed thanks to a "new" process of analytic continuation. By "new" I mean here that this process is theoretically independent from the ("old") process used above for defining the metric (section 8) and deriving the retarded equations of motion (section 9). Here analytic continuation is employed only as a technical tool for carrying out complicated integrals (which are convergent or are defined by the "old" process of analytic continuation). Finally, owing to the use of this "new" process, all the integrals can be calculated in function of the following formula defined by the "new" process of analytic continuation with respect to two complex parameters B and C :

$$\frac{1}{4\pi}\int d^3x/x-z/^B/x-z'/^C = \frac{\pi^{1/2}}{4}\,\frac{\Gamma(\frac{B+3}{2})\Gamma(\frac{C+3}{2})\Gamma(-\frac{B+C+3}{2})}{\Gamma(-\frac{B}{2})\Gamma(-\frac{C}{2})\Gamma(\frac{B+C+6}{2})}\,/z-z'/^{B+C+3}. \tag{2}$$

Denoting the velocity dz^i/dt by v^i and the <u>acceleration</u> dv^i/dt by a^i, the final result is of the following form:

$$a^i = A_0^i(z-z') + c^{-2}A_2^i(z-z',v,v') + c^{-4}A_4^i(z-z',v,v',S,S') + \\ + c^{-5}A_5^i(z-z',v-v') + O(c^{-6}), \tag{3}$$

where all the quantities appearing in the right hand side are to be taken at the same time t (in a given Lorentz frame) as the lefthand side a(t). This feature is compatible, though not in a manifest way, with the c^{-6} approximate Poincaré invariance of eqn(3), see Currie (1966), Hill (1967), Bel (1970) and the references in section 11. Note however that all the terms of (3) are manifestly invariant under time translations and space translations. The last term, which embodies, as we shall prove below, the "Laplace-Eddington effect" (or "radiation reaction effect"), is moreover invariant under Galileo transformations (Galilei 1638). All the terms of (3) are also invariant under space rotations. Note that A_4, but not A_5, depends on the <u>spins</u> S_{ik} and S'_{ik} of the two objects (Damour 1982). For the sake of simplicity we shall not consider here these spin dependent terms (see Damour 1978, 1982) which do not modify the final results.

Let us denote the instantaneous coordinate distance between the two worldlines by:

$$R := /z^i(t)-z'^i(t)/ := (\,(z-z')^2\,)^{1/2}\ , \tag{4}$$

where, for simplicity, we denote an Euclidean square: $f_{ik}b^ib^k(i,k = 1,2,3)$ by b^2 and a Euclidean scalar product: $f_{ik}a^ib^k$ by (ab). Let us denote the instantaneous unit radial vector from the second to the first world-line by:

$$N^i := R^{-1}(z^i(t) - z'^i(t)), \tag{5}$$

and the instantaneous relative velocity by:

$$V^i := v^i(t) - v'^i(t). \tag{6}$$

Then we can write down the following explicit expressions for the different terms in eqn(3) (m and m' being respectively the two masses):

$$A^i_o = -Gm'R^{-2}N^i \ , \tag{7}$$

$$A^i_2 = Gm'R^{-2}(\ N^i(-v^2-2v'^2+4(vv')+\tfrac{3}{2}(Nv')^2+5(Gm/R)+4(Gm'/R))+(v^i-v'^i)(4(Nv)-3(Nv'))), \tag{8}$$

$$A^i_4 = B^i_4 + C^i_4 \ , \tag{9}$$

with :

$$\begin{aligned} B^i_4 = Gm'R^{-2}(N^i(&-2v'^4+4v'^2(vv')-2(vv')^2+\tfrac{3}{2}v^2(Nv')^2+\tfrac{9}{2}v'^2(Nv')^2-6(vv')(Nv')^2-\tfrac{15}{8}(Nv')^4+ \\ &+(Gm/R)(-\tfrac{15}{4}v^2+\tfrac{5}{4}v'^2-\tfrac{5}{2}(vv')+\tfrac{39}{2}(Nv)^2-39(Nv)(Nv')+\tfrac{17}{2}(Nv')^2)+ \\ &+(Gm'/R)(4v'^2-8(vv')+2(Nv)^2-4(Nv)(Nv')-6(Nv')^2))+ \\ &+(v^i-v'^i)(v^2(Nv')+4v'^2(Nv)-5v'^2(Nv')-4(vv')(Nv)+ \\ &\qquad +4(vv')(Nv')-6(Nv)(Nv')^2+\tfrac{9}{2}(Nv')^3+ \\ &\qquad +(Gm/R)(-\tfrac{63}{4}(Nv)+\tfrac{55}{4}(Nv'))+(Gm'/R)(-2(Nv)-2(Nv')))), \end{aligned} \tag{10}$$

$$C^i_4 = G^3m'R^{-4}\ N^i\ (-\tfrac{57}{4}\ m^2 - 9\ m'^2 - \tfrac{69}{2}\ mm'), \tag{11}$$

$$\begin{aligned} A^i_5 = \tfrac{4}{5}\ G^2\ mm'R^{-3}(\ &V^i(-V^2 + 2(Gm/R) - 8(Gm'/R)) + \\ &+N^i(NV)(3V^2 - 6(Gm/R) + \tfrac{52}{3}(Gm'/R))). \end{aligned} \tag{12}$$

A_o was first obtained by Newton (1687), A_2 was first obtained by Lorentz and Droste (1917) (weak field extended sources, see next section) and by Einstein, Infeld and Hoffmann(1938), B_4 and the G^2 part of A_5 were first obtained by Damour and Deruelle (1981a), a result equivalent to $A_5 - A'_5$ was obtained by Linet (1981) (weak field extended sources), finally C_4 and the complete A_5 were first obtained by Damour (1982). The remainder $0(c^{-6})$ of eqn (3) has contributions coming from the 1 PMA, 2 PMA, and 3 PMA (after an expansion in 1/c) and from the 4 PMA and $G^3\ v_r^2$ terms which are already of order c^{-6}. We leave to future work a more rigorous study of these errors.

13. ELECTROMAGNETIC ANALOGY AND POST-POST-NEWTONIAN GENERALIZED LAGRANGIAN

The well-known (time dependent) least action principle of classical point mechanics:

$$\delta \int_{t_1}^{t_2} dt L(z(t), v(t)) = 0 , \tag{0a}$$

where the "Lagrangian" L is given by

$$L(z,v) = \Sigma \left(\frac{1}{2} mv^2 \right) - U , \tag{0b}$$

(U= potential energy) was in fact discovered by Hamilton (1835). (On the other hand "Hamilton's equations" were first written down by Lagrange! Moreover Euler and Lagrange knew the time independent least action principle, named after Maupertuis). This "Lagrangian" formalism (0a)(0b) has undergone, after the discovery of relativistic interactions, an interesting evolution which is generally ignored and which has caused many mistakes. In order to clarify our later use of a "generalized" gravitational Lagrangian we shall first discuss the case of the retarded electromagnetic interaction between point charges which provides a simple analogue to the gravitational case.

As we have seen in section 3, Lorentz (1892) and Planck (1897) discovered the existence of a "radiation reaction" "self-force" (eqn (3.5)) acting on a charge e (with position z^i, velocity v^i, acceleration a^i):

$$F^i = \frac{2}{3} \frac{e^2}{c^3} \frac{da^i}{dt} + O\left(\frac{1}{c^5} \right) \tag{1}$$

However the expression (1) is just a small piece of the total force acting on the charge. The main part of the total force comes from the retarded field of the companion charge (e', for simplicity's sake we restrict our attention to a binary electric system). Expanding, by means of Lagrange's formula (see section 12), the retarded action of the companion, using the lower order equations of motion for reducing the order of differentiation (Kerner 1965) and adding the expression (1) (augmented with its relativistic corrections see eqn (3.6)) one obtains the equations of motion of the first charge in the following form:

$$\begin{aligned} ma^i = {} & F_0^i(z-z') + c^{-2} F_2^i(z-z', v, v') + c^{-3} F_3^i(z-z', v-v') + \\ & + c^{-4} F_4^i(z-z', v, v') + c^{-5} F_5^i(z-z', v, v') + O(c^{-6}). \end{aligned} \tag{2}$$

The first term in the right hand side of eqn (2) is the familiar "instantaneous" Coulomb force:

$$F_0^i = ee'R^{-2}N^i, \tag{3}$$

where we use the notations of the preceding section. The third term is equal to:

$$F_3^i = \frac{2}{3}e^2e'\left(\frac{e}{m} - \frac{e'}{m'}\right) R^{-3}\left(V^i - 3N^i(NV)\right). \tag{4}$$

It can also be written as (Darwin 1920):

$$F_3^i = \frac{2}{3}\, e\, \frac{d}{dt}\left(\frac{e}{m}F_0^i + \frac{e'}{m'}F_0'^{\,i}\right). \tag{5}$$

The expression in the right hand side of eqn (5) contains two terms: the first one is easily recognized as the contribution due to the Lorentz-Planck force (1) and the second one comes from the c^{-3} term in the Lagrange expansion of the retarded force due to the companion. If one computes the power "dissipated" by $c^{-3}F_3$, the result is:

$$F_3^i v^i + F_3'^{\,i} v'^{\,i} = -\frac{2}{3c^3}(ea^i + e'a'^{\,i})^2 + \frac{1}{c^3}\frac{d}{dt}Q_3 + O\left(\frac{1}{c^5}\right), \tag{6}$$

where dQ_3/dt is an "exact time derivative." The first term in the right hand side of eqn (6) is identical with the familiar "dipole" energy loss calculated from the Poynting flux in the wave zone. It is often believed that this fact alone (appearance of the "dipole" energy loss) is sufficient: 1) for considering $c^{-3}F_3$ as the "total radiation reaction" force (modulo errors $O(c^{-5})$), 2) for concluding that the Coulombian energy of the system will be dissipated, in an average sense at least, according to the "dipole formula" and, 3) for deriving, from the usual conservation laws of mechanics (energy, linear momentum, angular momentum), the secular kinematical effects (shrinkage of the binary orbit,..)due to this "radiation reaction." However these conclusions can be reached only if one proves two lemmas:

Lemma 1: there exist well defined conservation laws at the post-Coulombian level ($F_0 + c^{-2}F_2$) which guarantee the absence of any secular effects similar to or interfering with the ones caused by the "radiation reaction" $c^{-3}F_3$,

Lemma 2: the quantity Q_3, whose "exact time derivative" appears in eqn (6) is a univalued function of the instantaneous state (positions and velocities) of the system.

In the present case it is easy to check directly the validity of Lemma 2 from eqn (5) but we have mentioned it explicitly because in some derivations Q_3 (or its analogue) is only obtained as an integral over the whole 3-space of some "field energy". This makes the corresponding "balance" equation (6) useless because such an integral is in general a functional of the entire past history of the two particles and could contain contributions of the type $\int_{-\infty}^{t}(ea^i + e'a'^i)^2 dt$ which would modify completely the meaning of eqn (6). It is also essential to prove the validity of Lemma 1 because the often quoted argument that $F_0 + c^{-2}F_2$ is "time-even" is completely insufficient for ensuring the existence of "good" post-Coulombian conservation laws which are needed for separating the effects due to the "radiation reaction."

The first proof of Lemma 1, when neglecting terms $O(c^{-4})$ in eqn (2), is due to Darwin (1920). His proof was based on the discovery that the post-Coulombian equations of motion ($ma = F_0 + c^{-2}F_2$) could be deduced from a Lagrangian:

$$L(z,v) = L_0(z,v) + c^{-2}L_2(z,v) \tag{7}$$

where L_0 is the usual Lagrangian:

$$L_0 = \Sigma \left(\frac{1}{2}mv^2 - \frac{1}{2}\frac{ee'}{R} \right) , \tag{8}$$

(Σ denotes a summation over the two particles) and where:

$$L_2 = \Sigma \left(\frac{1}{8}mv^4 + \frac{ee'}{4R}((vv') + (Nv)(Nv')) \right). \tag{9}$$

Because the Lagrangian (7) is manifestly invariant under time translations, space translations and space rotations, Darwin deduced from it some post-Coulombian conservation laws corresponding to the familiar conservation laws of energy, linear momentum and angular momentum. These conservation laws are violated by the term $c^{-3}F_3$. These results allow one to separate from lower order corrections and therefore to investigate meaningfully the effects due to the term $c^{-3}F_3$ which is seen now, and only now, to merit its name of "radiation reaction" (when neglecting terms of order c^{-4}).

However, when the two charges are alike or more generally when:

$$\frac{e}{m} = \frac{e'}{m'} , \tag{10}$$

the "radiation reaction" $c^{-3}F_3$ (eqn 4) vanishes. The condition (10) implies also the vanishing of the electric "dipole" energy flux (in the wave zone) and of the "magnetic dipole" energy flux. Therefore the first non zero contribution to the wave zone energy flux is the "quadrupole" one:

$$\text{Energy flux} = -\frac{1}{20}c^{-5}(\dddot{Q}_{ik})^2, \tag{11}$$

where $Q_{ik} = \Sigma\, e(z^i z^k - \frac{1}{3} z^2 f^{ik})$. This situation is especially interesting for us because it is analogue to the gravitational case. When condition (10) is satisfied, and because of the result (11), one is led to conjecture that the role of "radiation reaction" will be played by the term $c^{-5}F_5$ in eqn (2). However in order to prove this conjecture, we must prove Lemma 1 at the post-post Coulombian level. We can try to do so by extending the result of Darwin to the next order.

Indeed it has been argued (Landau and Lifshitz 1976, §65) that the possibility of having a Lagrangian description of a system of charges is directly related to the non-existence (at some approximation) of radiation of electromagnetic waves because these waves represent the true degrees of freedom of the electromagnetic field (which cannot be accounted for by the usual degrees of freedom of a mechanical system). Landau and Lifshitz argued therefore that when condition (10) is satisfied there should exist a post-post-Coulombian Lagrangian and they even computed this Lagrangian, from the work of Smorodinski and Golubenkov (1956), in the Problem 2 of §75. However this result cannot be correct because it has been proven, on general grounds, by Martin and Sanz (1979) that the dynamics of a system of particles interacting via any of the usual classical fields (electromagnetic, gravitational,...) could never admit a Lagrangian description when terms of order c^{-4} are included in the equations of motion. The solution of this dilemma is that the Lagrangian of Smorodinski and Golubenkov is effectively incorrect but that there exists a "generalized" Lagrangian, or "higher order Lagrangian", namely a function $L(z,v,a)$ of the instantaneous positions, velocities and <u>accelerations</u> of the two particles such that the solutions of the post-post-Coulombian equations of motion ($ma = F_0 + c^{-2}F_2 + c^{-4}F_4$) extremize, when working up to order c^{-4} inclusively, the following action:

$$S = \int_{t_1}^{t_2} dt L(z(t), \frac{dz(t)}{dt}, \frac{d^2z(t)}{dt}, z'(t), \frac{dz'(t)}{dt}, \frac{d^2z'(t)}{dt}) , \tag{12}$$

with given values of z, dz/dt, z', dz'/dt in t_1 and t_2. The correct generalized Lagrangian is easily obtained by proceeding as in §65 of Landau and Lifschitz (1976). One starts from the Lagrangian of one charge in an external electromagnetic potential $A^a = (V, A^i)$:

$$L_1 = -mc^2(1 - v^2/c^2)^{1/2} - eV + c^{-1}eA^iv^i. \tag{13}$$

Then one replaces V and A^i by the Lagrange expansions of the retarded potentials of the second charge. One introduces separate notations for the time differentiation when it acts on the kinematical variables of the first particle only (leaving aside the variables of the second particle) and vice versa (for instance:

$Q(z(t), z'(t)),_1 = v^i Q,_{z^i}$, $Q(z,z'),_2 = v'^i Q,_{z'^i}$, $dQ/dt \equiv Q,_1 + Q,_2$). Then by discarding some total time derivative one can transform L_1 into an expression L'_1 which is symmetrical under the exchange of the two particles. From this last expression it is trivial to guess a generalized Lagrangian for the <u>system</u> of the two particles : $L(z,v,a) = L_0 + c^{-2}L_2 + c^{-4}L_4$, (14)

where L_0 and L_2 are the same as before and where :

$$L_4(z,v,a) = mv^6/16 + m'v'^6/16 - \frac{ee'}{8}(R^{-1}(v^2v'^2 - 2(vv')^2 + 3(Nv)^2(Nv')^2 - (Nv)^2v'^2 - (Nv')^2v^2) + 2(Nv)(va') - 2(Nv')(v'a) + (Na)(v'^2 - (Nv')^2) - (Na')(v^2 - (Nv)^2) + 3R(aa') - R(Na)(Na')) . \tag{15}$$

(The interaction terms in L_4 come from: $-ee'(\frac{1}{2}(R(vv')),_{12} + \frac{1}{24}(R^3),_{1122})$).
Then one can, a posteriori, see that the "Lagrangian" of Smorodinski and Golubenkov is obtained from (15) by replacing the accelerations by their Coulombian values. Such a replacement is incorrect in a generalized Lagrangian because in the action principle (12) z(t) must be freely varied. Indeed the Euler-Lagrange equations of (12) with (14-15) are:

$$L,_z - \frac{d}{dt}L,_v + \frac{d^2}{dt^2}L,_a = 0, \tag{16}$$

and are not equivalent to the Euler-Lagrange equations of $L(z,v,m^{-1}F_0(z))$. The eqn (16) leads a priori to a fourth order differential system, however the coefficients of $\ddot{a}$ and $\ddot{a}'$ are of order c^{-4} and, now that we have varied z(t), we can correctly replace the accelerations in the equations of motion by their Coulombian (or, when necessary, post-Coulombian) values. This gives the post-post Coulombian equations of motion of eqn (2) (with (10) and the neglecting of $O(c^{-5})$). Now that we have succeeded in deducing the post-post-Coulombian dynamics from a generalized Lagrangian which is manifestly invariant under time and space translations and space rotations, we can make use of Noether's theorem (see next section) to obtain some "good" post-post Coulombian conservation laws which allow us to prove the validity of Lemma 1 (at order c^{-4}) and therefore to prove that $c^{-5}F_5$ can be rightly called "the radiation reaction" (the existence of a "balance" equation of type (6) at order c^{-5}, and Lemma 2 are straightforwardly checked; see Deruelle 1982). In the case of half retarded - half advanced electromagnetic interaction there are no "time-odd" terms and the Lagrangian approach can be generalized to any order of approximation (Kerner 1965).

Going back now to the gravitational case, we come, as announced in section 3, to the very remarkable work of Lorentz and Droste (1917). Indeed it is well known that the post-Newtonian equations of motion derived by Droste and DeSitter (DeSitter 1916) are incorrect, as well as the later result of Levi-Civita (1937); however,

I found serendipitously that Lorentz and Droste (1917) not only derived correctly the post-Newtonian equations of motion (generally thought of as having been obtained in 1938 by Einstein, Infeld and Hoffmann, and by Eddington and Clark), but also have proved that these equations could be deduced from a post-Newtonian Lagrangian (generally attributed to Fichtenholz 1950):

$$L(z,v) = L_0(z,v) + c^{-2}L_2(z,v), \tag{17}$$

with:

$$L_0 = \Sigma\left(\frac{1}{2}mv^2 + \frac{1}{2}\frac{Gmm'}{R}\right), \tag{18}$$

$$L_2 = \Sigma\left(\frac{1}{8}mv^4 + \frac{Gmm'}{R}\left(\frac{3}{2}v^2 - \frac{7}{4}(vv') - \frac{1}{4}(Nv)(Nv') - \frac{1}{2}\frac{Gm}{R}\right)\right). \tag{19}$$

On the other hand we have seen in the preceding section that the equations of motion of two non-rotating compact objects were of the form:

$$a^i = A_0^i(z-z') + c^{-2}A_2^i(z-z',v,v') + c^{-4}A_4^i(z-z',v,v') + \\ + c^{-5}A_5^i(z-z',v-v') + O(c^{-6}). \tag{20}$$

Therefore, although the Lorentz-Droste-Fichtenholz Lagrangian (17) allows us to define post-Newtonian conservation laws, these laws are not sufficient for proving the preceding Lemma 1 at the post-post-Newtonian level, that is, for proving, as expected from the analogy with the electromagnetic case when (10) is satisfied, that $c^{-5}A_5{}^i$ is "the radiation reaction." In 1974, Ohta, Okamura, Kimura and Hiida, computed a post-post-Newtonian Lagrangian $\hat{L}(z,v) = L_0 + c^{-2}L_2 + c^{-4}L_4$. However, according to the precedingly quoted work of Martin and Sauz, this result cannot be correct. Effectively it has been proved by Damour and Deruelle (1981b), that when neglecting in the equations of motion (20) the terms of order G^3 and/or the terms of order c^{-5} (see eqns (12.7)(12.8)(12.10)) the resulting equations could be deduced from a generalized Lagrangian:

$$L(z,v,a) = L_0(z,v)+c^{-2}L_2(z,v)+c^{-4}L_4(z,v,a). \tag{21}$$

This result has been extended by Damour (1982) to the complete post-post Newtonian equations of motion (including order G^3, neglecting order c^{-5}), even with the inclusion of the spin-orbit interaction (for slowly spinning compact objects). For simplicity we shall not discuss here the spin dependent terms which bring in new subtleties, but we shall give the explicit expression of $L_4(z,v,a)$ (L_o and L_2 being the same as before: (18) and (19)):

$$L_4(z,v,a) = M_4 + N_4 , \tag{22}$$

$$\begin{aligned} M_4(z,v,a) = & \Sigma \left(\frac{1}{16}mv^6\right) + \\ & + \Sigma\, Gmm'R^{-1}\left(\frac{7}{8}v^4 + \frac{15}{16}v^2v'^2 - 2v^2(vv') + \frac{1}{8}(vv')^2 - \frac{7}{8}(Nv)^2v'^2 + \right. \\ & \left. + \frac{3}{4}(Nv)(Nv')(vv') + \frac{3}{16}(Nv)^2(Nv')^2 \right) + \\ & + \Sigma\, G^2m^2m'R^{-2}\left(\frac{1}{4}v^2 + \frac{7}{4}v'^2 - \frac{7}{4}(vv') + \frac{7}{2}(Nv)^2 + \frac{1}{2}(Nv')^2 - \frac{7}{2}(Nv)(Nv')\right) + \\ & + \Sigma\, Gmm'\left((Na)\left(\frac{7}{8}v'^2 - \frac{1}{8}(Nv')^2\right) - \frac{7}{4}(v'a)(Nv')\right) , \end{aligned} \tag{23}$$

$$N_4(z) = \frac{G^3mm'}{R^3}\left(\frac{1}{2}m^2 + \frac{1}{2}m'^2 + \frac{19}{4}mm'\right). \tag{24}$$

The generalized Lagrangian (21-24) has been obtained by guess-work contrary to the preceding generalized electromagnetic Lagrangian (14-15) which was nearly straightforwardly derived from (13)(there is though some amount of guesswork in the last steps leading to (14)). On the other hand the fact that one succeeded in deriving the complicated equations of motion (20)(neglecting $O(c^{-5})$)(see eqns (12.7) to (12.11)) from a variational principle is a very stringent check on the correctness of these equations of motion: indeed one wrong coefficient in these equations is often sufficient for ruling out the existence of a Lagrangian (generalized or not). There is though a remarkable exception to this rule: the coefficient of the last term of eqn (12.11): -69/2 could have any numerical value and would still allow a Lagrangian deduction. In fact, having obtained -69/2 after a very long calculation divided into sixteen simpler contributions, I was worried because Damour and Deruelle (1981b) had conjectured a different coefficient: -36. However this conjecture was based on the assumption that the only incorrectness in the Lagrangian of Ohta et.al. (1974) was, as in the case of Smorodinski and Golubenkov, due to the replacing of the accelerations by their Newtonian values. However a close scrutiny of their work revealed that the preceding coefficient was related to their U^{TT} (see their §5) itself expressed as the sum of three integrals. A reevaluation of these three integrals I_1, I_2, I_3 by means of the "new" process of analytic continuation (section 12) showed that I_2:

$$I_2 = \frac{G^3}{2\pi} m^2m'^2 \int d^3x\, r^{-1}_{,i}\, r'^{-1}_{,k}(\log(r+r'+R))_{,z^k z'^i} \tag{25}$$

was equal to $-1G^3m^2m'^2/R^3$ instead of their result: $-(3/2)G^3m^2m'^2/R^3$. Taking into account this correction, the preceding conjecture, with some more work due to the use of different coordinate systems, then provided a confirmation of the litigious coefficien -69/2 and thereby of the last coefficient of eqn (24): 19/4.

The post-post-Newtonian conservation laws implicitly contained in the generalized Lagrangian (21-24) are derived in the next section.

14. POST-POST-NEWTONIAN CONSERVED QUANTITIES

We have seen in the preceding section that in order to meaningfully identify the term $c^{-5}A_5$ with a "radiation reaction", one had to prove the "Lemma 1," namely that the post-post-Newtonian (2 PN in brief) equations of motion ($a = A_0 + c^{-2}A_2 + c^{-4}A_4$) admitted some "good" conservation laws. We use the word "prove" because, on one hand the "time-even" character of these equations is not sufficient to imply the existence of such conservation laws (counter-examples can be constructed) and, on the other hand, the fact that the complete system, matter plus gravitational field, admits some global conservation laws in integral form is not sufficient to imply that the field-functional conserved quantities are functions of the instantaneous state of the matter only (see the comments after Lemma 2 in the preceding section). However we have seen in section 13 that the 2 PN equations of motion could be deduced from the generalized Lagrangian L(z,v,a) (13.21-24). Therefore if L(z,v,a) admits some symmetries we shall be able to construct some corresponding conserved quantities by using the general theorem of Noether (1918). In fact L(z,v,a) is manifestly invariant under time translations, space translations and space rotations. From these symmetries, Damour and Deruelle (1981c) have constructed quantities (7 integrals of the motion):

$$E(z,v,a) := -L + \Sigma\,(p_i v^i + q_i a^i)\,, \tag{1}$$

$$P_i(z,v,a) := \Sigma\, p_i\,, \tag{2}$$

$$J_{ik}(z,v,a) := \Sigma\,(z_i p_k - z_k p_i + v_i q_k - v_k q_i)\,, \tag{3}$$

where p and q denote:

$$p_i := L,_{v^i} - \frac{d}{dt} L,_{a^i}\,, \qquad q_i := L,_{a^i}\,. \tag{4}$$

For the details of the proof of the constancy of (1 - 3) see Damour and Deruelle (1981c)(note that in their notations one should take $\alpha = 0$ and $\beta = -1/2$ in order to recover exactly L(z,v,a)).

On the other hand L(z,v,a) admits a further symmetry which is not manifest (indeed it is quite hidden!) and which is only approximate. This symmetry is linked to the pure Lorentz transformations (boosts) and I would like to comment more on this symmetry because the literature is nearly nonexistent (and sometimes incorrect) on this subject. Let us first go back to the usual Lagrangian of classical mechanics:

$$L(z,v) = \Sigma\,(\tfrac{1}{2}\,mv^2) - U(z-z') \tag{5}$$

Let us consider an infinitesimal Galileo transformation acting on space-time (b^i being an infinitesimal velocity):

$$\delta x^i = b^i t \quad , \quad \delta t = 0 \tag{6}$$

This transformation acts on the motions z(t) in the following way:

$$\delta z^i = b^i t \quad , \quad \delta v^i = b^i \tag{7}$$

Hence we find the variation of the Lagrangian:

$$\delta L \equiv \Sigma\, m v^i \delta v^i \equiv \frac{d}{dt}(b^i\, \Sigma\, m z^i). \tag{8}$$

The Lagrangian is changed only by an exact time derivative and this result constitutes a symmetry of the Lagrangian which implies both a symmetry of the dynamics (Galilean relativity) and the existence of a new vectorial integral of the motion. Indeed the general "integration by parts" identity:

$$\delta L(z,v) = \frac{d}{dt}\,(\Sigma\, L_{,v^i}\delta z^i) + \Sigma\,(L_{,z^i} - \frac{d}{dt}\, L_{,v^i})\,\delta z^i, \tag{9}$$

implies, when the Euler-Lagrange equations are satisfied, an equation for δL, which, when (7) is satisfied, can be reapproached from the identity (8). This leads to the famous "center of mass integral".

$$K^i = \Sigma\,(m z^i) - t\,\Sigma\,(m v^i). \tag{10}$$

A similar, though more complicated, result is valid in the case of interest: generalized Lagrangian L(z,v,a) and Lorentz boosts:

$$\delta x^i = b^i t \quad , \quad \delta t = c^{-2} b^i x^i. \tag{11}$$

A first technical delicacy lies in the action of the boosts (11) on the motions z(t) because of the joint change in space and time. Then the main difficulty lies in proving that there exists a univalued function of z,v,a, whose time derivative is identically equal to δL (modulo O(c-6)). This is done in the precedingly quoted work. From this result one deduces, on one hand a check on the approximate Poincaré invariance of the 2PN equations of motion and on the other hand the existence of a vectorial integral:

$$K^i(z,v,a) := G^i - t.P^i \tag{12}$$

where P^i is (2) and where:

$$G^i(z,v) := \Sigma\,(Mz^i) - \frac{7}{4}\,\frac{Gmm'}{c^4}\,((Nv)+(Nv'))(v^i - v'^i), \tag{13a}$$

$$M := m + c^{-2}\left(\frac{1}{2}\,mv^2 - \frac{1}{2}\,\frac{Gmm'}{R}\right) + c^{-4}\,\frac{3}{8}\,mv^4 +$$

$$+\, c^{-4}\,\frac{Gmm'}{R}\left(\frac{19}{8}v^2 - \frac{7}{8}v'^2 - \frac{7}{4}(vv') - \frac{1}{8}(Nv)^2 - \frac{1}{4}(Nv)(Nv') + \frac{1}{8}(Nv')^2 -\right.$$

$$\left. - \frac{5}{4}\,\frac{Gm}{R} + \frac{7}{4}\,\frac{Gm'}{R}\right). \tag{13b}$$

We have stressed the deduction of this further 2 PN integral from the boost-symmetry of the Lagrangian because usually, even for the simpler 1 PN case, K is obtained by a direct calculation starting from the constancy of P and not from a Noetherian approach.

Let us add that the preceding 2 PN integrals E,P,J,K have been defined as functions of z,v, and a, but that once they have been constructed one can correctly replace a by its Newtonian value thereby defining some integrals E^{2PN}, P^{2PN}, J^{2PN}, K^{2PN} functions of z and v only. Finally we wish to point out that we have refrained from calling these ten integrals: energy, linear momentum, angular momentum and center of mass integrals respectively. The reason is that we shall need in the next section the conservation laws associated with these integrals in order to separate the kinematical effects caused by the "radiation reaction", the dynamical meaning of E,P,J,K will be of no interest to us. Similarly the link, if any, of E for instance with the A.D.M. or the Bondi mass is not at all relevant.

15. THE LAPLACE-EDDINGTON EFFECT AND THE BINARY PULSAR

In section 12 we obtained the "second and a half post-Newtonian" (in brief "2 1/2 PN") equations of motion of two non-rotating compact bodies (for slowly rotating compact bodies see Damour 1982):

$$a^i := \frac{d^2z^i}{dt^2} = A_0^i(z-z') + c^{-2}A_2^i(z-z',v,v') + c^{-4}A_4^i(z-z',v,v') +$$

$$+ c^{-5}A_5^i(z-z',v-v') + O(c^{-6}). \tag{1}$$

The first term in the right hand side of (1) is the familiar Newtonian acceleration and all the other terms are relativistic corrections due to the non-linear hyperbolic structure of Einstein's equations. However, we have proved in section 14 the validity of the "Lemma 1" of section 13, namely the existence of ten conservation laws at the 2PN level. We can therefore take advantage of the corresponding 2 PN integrals for investigating the secular effects caused by the $c^{-5}A_5$ term in (1). Let us denote any of the precedingly defined "integral of the 2 PN notion," that is a function of the instantaneous kinematical state of the binary system by: $C^{2PN}(z(t), v(t), z'(t), v'(t))$ (we have seen that we can always, in a perturbative sense at least, remove the dependence on the instantaneous accelerations). Then the time derivative of $C^{2PN}(z,v)$ during the actual motion (including now the c^{-5} correction) is:

$$\frac{dC^{2PN}(z,v)}{dt} = \Sigma\ (C^{2PN}_{,zi}v^i + C^{2PN}_{,vi}(A^i_0+c^{-2}A^i_2+c^{-4}A^i_4+c^{-5}A^i_5+O(c^{-6}))) \quad (2)$$

Now, because C^{2PN} is constant during a 2PN motion all the terms of the right hand side of eqn (2), except the c^{-5} term, reduce to $O(c^{-6})$ (they do not reduce exactly to zero on one hand because the replacement of the accelerations by their Newtonian values introduce errors of order c^{-6}, and on the other hand because the constancy of the integral K is, like the corresponding boost symmetry of the generalized Lagrangian, valid only modulo errors of order c^{-6}). Then we are left with:

$$\frac{dC^{2PN}(z,v)}{dt} = \Sigma c^{-5}\ A^i_5\ C^{2PN}_{,vi} + O(c^{-6}) \quad (3)$$

An equivalent result can also be obtained directly from the Noetherian approach of the preceding section (Damour and Deruelle 1981c). Eqn (3) can be further simplified by taking into account the fact that the function of z,v: $C^{2PN}(z,v)$ is easily seen, from its definition (14.1), (14.2), (14.3) or (14.12), to be given by a truncated expansion in powers of c^{-1}:

$$C^{2PN}(z,v) = C^N(z,v)+c^{-2}C_2(z,v)+c^{-4}C_4(z,v)+O(c^{-6}) \quad (4)$$

where the first term $C^N(z,v)$ is in fact the familiar Newtonian Noetherian integral corresponding to the space-time symmetry used for deriving C^{2PN} from L(z,v,a) (Newtonian integrals of "energy", "linear momentum," "angular momentum" and "center of mass motion": eqn (14.10)). Plugging eqn (4) into eqn (3) leads to the simplified expression:

$$\frac{dC^{2PN}(z,v)}{dt} = \Sigma c^{-5}\ A^i_5\ C^N_{,vi} + O(c^{-6}) \quad (5)$$

We can further transform eqn (5) by taking into account that the explicit expression given for A_5 in eqn (12.12):

$$A^i_5 = \frac{4}{5}G^2 mm' R^{-3}(V^i(-V^2+2(Gm/R)-8(Gm'/R)) + N^i(NV)(3V^2-6(Gm/R)+\frac{52}{3}(Gm'/R))), \quad (6)$$

where $V^i = v^i - v'^i$, $RN^i = z^i - z'^i$, $N^2 = 1$) can also be written as (Damour 1982):

$$A_5^i = \frac{3}{5} z^k Q_{ik}^{(5)} + 2v^k I_{ik}^{(4)} + \frac{10}{3} a^i I^{(3)} + \frac{1}{5} I_{iss}^{(5)} - J_{iss}^{(4)} + O(c^{-2}) , \tag{7}$$

with:

$$I_{ik} := \Sigma\, Gmz^i z^k , \quad I := I_{ss} , \quad Q_{ik} := I_{ik} - \frac{1}{3} I f_{ik} ,$$

$$I_{iss} := \Sigma\, Gmz^2 z^i , \quad J_{iss} := \Sigma\, Gmz^2 v^i , \quad Q^{(n)} := d^n Q/dt^n. \tag{8}$$

Replacing eqn (7) into eqn (5) leads to the following results for the time derivative of the 2PN integrals E^{2PN}, P_i^{2PN}, J_{ik}^{2PN}, $K_i^{2PN} = G_i^{2PN} - tP_i^{2PN}$ defined in section 14:

$$\frac{dE^{2PN}(z,v)}{dt} = -c^{-5} \frac{dE^5(z,v)}{dt} - \frac{1}{5Gc^5} Q_{ik}^{(3)} Q_{ik}^{(3)} + O(c^{-6}) , \tag{9}$$

$$\frac{dP_i^{2PN}(z,v)}{dt} = -c^{-5} \frac{dP_i^5(z,v)}{dt} + 0 + O(c^{-6}) , \tag{10}$$

$$\frac{dJ_{ik}^{2PN}(z,v)}{dt} = -c^{-5} \frac{dJ_{ik}^5(z,v)}{dt} - \frac{2}{5Gc^5} (Q_{is}^{(2)} Q_{ks}^{(3)} - Q_{ks}^{(2)} Q_{is}^{(3)}) + O(c^{-6}) , \tag{11}$$

$$\frac{d(G_i^{2PN}(z,v) - tP_i^{2PN}(z,v))}{dt} = -c^{-5} \frac{d(G_i^5(z,v) - tP_i^5(z,v))}{dt} + 0 + O(c^{-6}) \tag{12}$$

As indicated by the notation the quantities E^5, P^5, J^5, and G^5 appearing in the right hand side of the preceding equations are some univalued functions of the instantaneous state of the binary system: $z(t)$, $z'(t)$, $v(t)$, $v'(t)$ (higher derivatives having been reduced to z and v only). These functions are straightforwardly obtained from (5) and (7), and their explicit expression is not important; what is important is their existence. The equations (9-12) are the gravitational analogues of the electromagnetic "balance" equation (13.6) supplemented by the consequences of Lemma 1 and Lemma 2 of the same section (remember that Lemma 1 was dealing with the existence of pre-radiation reaction conserved quantities (C^{2PN} here) and Lemma 2 with the functional nature of the balance-violating quantities ($-dC^5/dt$ here)). We can further simplify eqn (9-12) by introducing some new functions of the instantaneous state of the system:

$$C^{2\ 1/2PN}(z,v) := C^{2PN}(z,v) + c^{-5} C^5(z,v). \tag{13}$$

Then $P^{2\frac{1}{2}PN}$ and $K^{2\frac{1}{2}PN}$ are constant (modulo c^{-6}) and, $dE^{2\frac{1}{2}PN}/dt$ and $dJ^{2\frac{1}{2}PN}/dt$ precisely balance the "quadrupole" fluxes of energy and angular momentum in the wave zone (the second terms in the right hand sides of eqns (9) and (11), see the lectures of K. Thorne. Such an agreement between the decrease of a well-defined function of the instantaneous state of the system and a loss due to an outward flux in the wave zone is a result which had never been proved before. All the previous "proofs" of this "balance" were incomplete mainly because they could never control the functional nature of the "energy of the system," for instance. This requirement regarding the functional nature of the energy is generally overlooked; however it is essential because if the "energy" is not a function of the instantaneous kinematical state of the binary system but contains some terms, even of the small order c^{-5}, which are functionals of the past history of the system, then the "energy balance" equation is meaningless and says nothing about the secular kinematical behaviour of the system (see the comments after Lemma 2 of section 13). Moreover the precise knowledge of the variables appearing in $C^{2^1/_2 PN}$ is essential in the case of rotating objects, because we need a "balance" between the orbital energy and the gravitational energy flux, when many previous derivations could only give a "balance" between the "total" energy of the system (including the kinetic spin energy of the bodies) and the "total" energy flux in the wave zone (including the fluxes of electromagnetic waves, relativistic particles,...). Such a "total balance" is useless in the case of the Hulse-Taylor pulsar where the losses of orbital and spin energy are of the same order of magnitude. However it has been possible to extend the preceding method to the case of slowly rotating compact bodies (slowly, meaning for instance $v_{spin} \sim v_{orbit}$, a relation satisfied by the Hulse-Taylor pulsar) with, as result, "balance" equations of the same form as above: (eqn (9-12)), but where the quantities C^{2PN} have only a very small (c^{-4}) and extremely slowly variable (c^{-6}) spin-dependent contribution (Damour 1982). This last "mainly orbital balance" can then be meaningfully applied to the Hulse-Taylor system.

However the result (9-13) is not quite sufficient for reaching our goal which is to investigate the secular kinematical effects implied by the relativistic corrections up to order c^{-5}. One must start from the $2^1/2$ PN equations of motion (1) and study directly their solutions. This study can be carried out by, first investigating the solutions of the 2PN equations of motion (with the help of the 2PN integrals) and then by applying to these solutions Lagrange's method of "variation of arbitrary constants" (which means more than the preceding eqns (9 - 12)). The detailed calculations and results will be published elsewhere, we shall only give here the formula for the time of the Nth periastron passage:

$$t_N = t_0 + PN + \frac{1}{2}P\dot{P}N^2, \tag{14}$$

with,

$$\dot{P} = -\frac{3}{2}\,P(E^{2PN})^{-1}\left(\left(\frac{dE^{2PN}}{dt}\right)\right), \tag{15}$$

where P is a parameter obtained by fitting (14) to the observations and where the double parentheses denote a time average. From eqn (9) it is seen that eqn(15) can be expressed in function of the time average of the "quadrupole" energy loss (1.1). Replacing the explicit expression of this time average (Peters and Mathews 1963) leads to the formula proposed previously by Esposito and Harrison (1975) and Wagoner (1975) (see also Blandford and Teukolsky (1976) for a clarification of the observational meaning of a "period derivative"). Thanks to the superb work of Taylor and his collaborators this formula, which embodies the Laplace-Eddington effect (see section 3) has been compared with the observed secular acceleration of the binary pulsar PSR 1913 + 16 (Taylor, Fowler and McCulloch (1979), Taylor and Weisberg (1982) and Taylor (May 1982, private communication)):

$$\dot{P}_{\text{observed}} = (-2.40 \pm 0.20) \times 10^{-12}. \tag{16}$$

Assuming that the binary pulsar is constituted of two neutron stars and that the system is "clean" (for discussions of the high plausibility of these assumptions see Srinivasan and van den Heuvel (1982), and Taylor and Weisberg(1982)) one can use the equations of motion and the metric of two compact objects at PN order for analyzing the pulse arrival times (see the lectures of D. Eardley). This leads to a determination of the parameters of the system and thereby, using formula (15), to a predicted value of the secular acceleration:

$$\dot{P}_{\text{predicted}} = (-2.403 \pm 0.005) \times 10^{-12} . \tag{17}$$

The 8% agreement between (16) and (17) provides an impressive confirmation of the existence of the Laplace-Eddington effect. Remembering that we derived formulae (14-15) after a long theoretical path where we made an essential use of the following features of Einstein's equations: 1)their hyperbolicity ("retarded potentials"), 2) the quartic non-linearity of the weak-field expansion of the vacuum equations, 3) the infinite non-linearity of these equations (when dealing with the strong field regions), and knowing that investigations of alternative theories of gravity (Will and Eardley 1977, Will 1977, Weisberg and Taylor 1981) have led to quantitatively and qualitatively very different predictions, we conclude that the work reported in these lectures, in conjunction with Taylor's observations, provides the most sensitive available confirmation of the non-linear hyperbolic structure of Einstein's theory (and therefore, also an indirect confirmation of the existence of gravitational radiation).

ACKNOWLEDGEMENTS

It is a pleasure to acknowledge helpful discussions with: L. Bel, B. Carter, Y. Choquet-Bruhat, D. Christodoulou, N. Deruelle, B. Jones, A. Jourdanney, A. Lichnerowicz, D. Maison, A. Papapetrou, B. Schmidt, K.S. Thorne, and J. York.

I would like to thank C.H. Liebow for her suggestions on wording and her courage in typing a difficult manuscript.

REFERENCES

Abraham, M. (1903) Ann.d.Phys. 10, 105 and 156.
Abraham, M. (1904) Ann;d;Phys. 14, 236.
Anderson, J.L. and Decanio, T.C. (1975) Gen. Rel.Grav. 6, 197.
Arago, F.D., Oeuvres, t II, P. 596, quoted by R. Barthalot: "L'Observatoire de Paris," Thèse de 3ème cycle, 21 avril 1982, Paris I.
Beethoven, L. van (1826) Heading to the last movement of his last composition (16th Quartet, op. 135): "The resolution made with great difficulty. Must it be? It must be! It must be! (Es muss sein!)".
Bel, L. (1970) Ann.I.H.P. 12,307.
Bel, L. (1971) Ann.I.H.P. 14, 189.
Bel, L. (1982) C.R.Acad. Sci. Paris, série I. 294, 463.
Bel, L., Damour, T., Deruelle, N., Ibañez, J., and Martin, J. (1981) Gen.Rel. Grav. 13, 963.
Bel, L. and Fustero, X. (1976) Ann.I.H.P., A25, 411, and references therein.
Bel, L. and Martin, J. (1980) Ann.I.H.P., A33, 409 and (1981) A34, 231.
Bel, L.,Salas, A., and Sanchez, J.M. (1973) Phys. Rev.D7, 1099.
Bertotti, B. (1956) Nuov.Cim. 4, 898.
Bertotti, B., and Plebanski, J. (1960) Ann. Phys. (N.Y.), 11, 169.
Blandford, R., and Teukolsky, S. (1976) Ap.J. 205, 580.
Breitenlohner, P. and Maison, D.(1977)Commun.math.Phys. 52, 11, 39, and 55.
Breuer, R. and Rudolph, E. (1981) Gen. Rel. Grav. 13, 777.
Brillouin, M. (1922) CR.R.Acad.Sci.Paris 175, 1008.
Burke, W.L. (1969) unpublished Ph.D.thesis, California Institute of Technology.
Burke, W.L. (1971) J.Math.Phys.12, 401.
Campolattaro, A., and Thorne, K.S. (1970) Ap.J. 159, 847.
Carmeli, M. (1964) Phys.Lett.11, 24.
Carmeli, M. (1965) Nuov.Cim. 37, 842.
Chandrasekhar, S. (1965)Ap.J. 142, 1488.
Chandrasekhar, S., and Esposito, F.P. (1970) Ap.J. 160, 153.
Choquet-Bruhat, Y. (1952) Acta Matematica 88, 141.
Choquet-Bruhat, Y., and Christodoulou, D. (1980) "Cauchy problem at past infinity" to appear in the issue of "Advances in Mathematics," proceedings of the Symposium in honor of I.E.Segal.
Choquet-Bruhat, Y., Christodoulou, D. and Francaviglia, M. (1979) ANN.I.H.P. A31,399.
Christodoulou, D., and Schmidt, B. (1979) Commun. Math. Phys. 68, 275.
Cooperstock, F.I. and Hobill, D.W. (1982) Gen.Rel.Grav.14, 361.
Crowley, R.J., and Thorne, K.S. (1977) Ap.J. 215, 624.
Currie, D.G.(1966) Phys.Rev.142, 817.
Damour,T. (1974) "Théorie classique de la renormalisation," Thèse de 3ème cycle, Paris (unpublished).
Damour, T. (1975) Nuov.Cim. 26B, 157.

Damour, T. (1978) "Note on the Spin Precession Effect in a Relativistic Binary System," p.547 in "Physics and Astrophysics of Neutron Stars and Black Holes," Varenna (1975), course 45, R. Giacconi and R. Ruffini ed., North Holland, Amsterdam.

Damour, T. (1980) C.R.Acad.Sci.Paris, 291, série A, 227.

Damour, T. (1981) "Le problème des N corps en relativité générale" in "Comptes rendus des journées relativistes 1981, Institut Fourier, Grenoble.

Damour, T. (1982) C.R.Acad.Sci.Paris, 294, série II, 1355.

Damour, T., and Deruelle, N. (1981a)Phys.Lett.87A, 81.

Damour, T. and Deruelle, N. (1981b) C.R.Acad.Sci.Paris 293, série II, 537.

Damour, T., and Deruelle, N. (1981c)C.R.Acad.Sci.Paris 293, série II, 877.

Darwin, C.G. (1920) Phil.Mag. 39, 537.

D'Eath, P.D. (1975a) Phys.Rev.D11, 1387.

D'Eath, P.D. (1975b) Phys.Rev.D12, 2183.

Demianski, M., and Grishchuk, L.P. (1974) Gen.Rel.Grav. 5, 673.

Deruelle, N. (1982) "Sur les équations du mouvement et le rayonnement gravitationnel d'un système binaire en relativité générale." Thèse de doctorat d'Etat, Paris (unpublished).

DeSitter, W. (1916) Mon.Not.R.A.S. 76, 699 and 77, 155.

Droste, J. (1916) Versl.K.Akad.Wet.Amsterdam 25, 460.

Droz-Vincent, P. (1969) Lett.Nuov.Cim. 1, 839.

Droz-Vincent, P. (1970) Phys.Scripta 2, 129.

Eddington, A.S. (1924) "The Mathematical Theory of Relativity," Cambridge at the University Press (second edition).

Eddington, A.S., and Clark, G.L. (1938) Proc. Roy. Soc. London, A166, 465.

Edelstein, L.A. and Vishveshwara, C.V. (1970) Phys.Rev.D1, 3514.

Eder, E. (1982) "Existence, uniqueness and iterative construction of motions of charged particles with retarded interactions" preprint Max Planck Institut, April 1982, submitted to Commun. Math. Phys.

Ehlers, J. (1979) Editor: "Isolated Gravitating Systems in General Relativity," Varenna 1976, course 67, North Holland, Amsterdam.

Ehlers, J. (1980) Ann.N.Y.Acad.Sci. 336, 279.

Ehlers, J., Rosenblum, A., Goldberg, J.N. and Havas, P. (1976), Ap.J. 208, L77.

Einstein, A. (1916) Sitzber.PReuss.Akad.Wiss.(Berlin), 688.

Einstein, A. (1918) Sitzber.Preuss.Akad.Wiss.(Berlin), 154.

Einstein, A., and Grommer, J., (1927) Sitzber.Preuss.Akad.Wiss(Berlin) 2 and 235.

Einstein, A., Infeld,L.(1940) Ann.Math. 41, 455.

Einstein,A., Infeld, L. (1949) Can.J.Math.1, 209.

Einstein, A., Infeld,L., and Hoffmann(1938) Ann.Math.39, 65.

Esposito, L.W. and Harrison, E.R. (1975) Ap.J.(Letters), 196, L1.

Fichtenholz, I.G.(1950) Zh.Eksp.Teor.Fiz.20 824.

Fock, V.A. (1939) J.Phys. (Moscow) 1, 81.

Fock, V.A. (1959) "Theory of Space, Time and Gravitation," Pergamon, London.

Fremberg, N.E. (1946) Proc.Roy.Soc. (London) A 188, 18.

Friedrich, H.(1981) Proc.Roy.Soc.Lond. A375, 169 and 378, 401.

Friedrich, H. (1982) Proc.Roy.Soc.Lond.A381, 361.

Galilei, G. (1638) "Discorsi e dimostrazioni matematiche intorno a due nove scienze attenanti alla meccanica e i movimenti locali", Leyde.

Goldberg, J.N.(1955) Phys.Rev.99, 1873.

Goldberg, J.N.(1962) "The Equations of Motion" in "Gravitation: an introduction to current research," L.Witten ed., Wiley, New York.

Guelfand, I.M., and Chilov, G.E. (1962) "Les Distributions," Dunod, Paris.

Gustafson, T. (1945) Kgl.Fys. Sallsk. i Lund Forhandl., 15, n° 28.

Gustafson, T. (1946) Kgl.Fys.Sallsk.i Lund. Forhandl., 16, n° 2.

Hamilton, R.W.(1835)Phil.Trans.Roy.Soc.London, part I, 95.

Havas, P. (1957) Phys.Rev.108, 1351.

Havas, P., and Goldberg, J.N.(1962) Phys.Rev.128, 398.

Hill, R.N.(1967) J.Math.Phys. 8, 201.

Hirondel, D. (1974) J.Math.Phys.15, 1689.

Hu,N. (1947) Proc.Roy.Irish Acad. 51A, 87.

Hu,N.(1982), p.717 in "Proceedings of the Second Marcel Grossmann Meeting on General Relativity," R.Ruffini ed., North Holland, Amsterdam.

Infeld,L. (1954) Acta Phys.Polon. 13, 187.
Infeld, L. (1957) Rev.Mod.Phys. 29, 398.
Infeld,L., and Michalska-Trautman, R. (1969) Ann.Phys.(N.Y.) 55, 561.
Infeld,L., and Plebanski,J. (1960) "Motion and Relativity," Pergamon, London.
Infeld,L., and Scheidegger, A.E.(1951) Can.J.Math. 3, 195.
Infeld,L., and Schild,A., (1949) Rev.Mod.Phys.21, 408.
Kates,R.E.(1980a) Phys.Rev.D22,1853.
Kates,R.E.(1980b) Phys.Rev.D22, 1871.
Kates,R.E.(1981) Ann.Phys.(N.Y.) 132, 1.
Kerlick, G.D.(1980) Gen.Rel.Grav.12,467 and 521.
Kerner, E.H.(1965) J.Math Phys. 6, 1218.
Kerr, R.P. (1959) Nuov.Cim. 13, 469, 492 and 673.
Kerr, R.P. (1960) Nuov. Cim. 16, 26.
Kovács,S. and Thorne, K.S. (1977) Ap.J. 217, 252.
Kühnel, A. (1963) Acta Phys.Polon. 24, 399.
Lagrange, L. (1770). "Nouvelle méthode pour résoudre les équations littérales par le moyen des séries," Mémoires de l'Académie Royale des Sciences et Belles Lettres de Berlin, tome 24. See also E.T. Whittaker and G.N Watson, "A course of modern analysis," 4th ed., Cambridge U.P. (1978), p.132.
Landau,L.D., and Lifshitz,E.M. (1941) "Teoriya Polya," Nauka,Moscow.
Landau,L.D., and Lifshitz,E.M. (1976) "Teoria dei Campi," Editori Riuniti, Roma.
Laplace,P.S.(1798-1825) "Mécanique Céleste," Courcier,Paris. Second part: book 10, chapter 7 ("Laplace effect"), and, second supplement to the book 10 ("Asymptotic matching").
Levi-Civita, T. (1937) Am.J.Math.59, 9 and 225.
Levi-Civita, T. (1950) "Le problème des N corps en relativité générale," Mémorial des Sciences Mathématiques 116, Gauthier-Villars, Paris.
Linet, B. (1981) C.R.Acad. Sci. Paris 292,série II, 1425.
Lorentz,H.A.(1892) Arch.néerl. 25, 363 (see §120). Reprinted in the Collected Papers of H.A.Lorentz, vol.2, p.164, The Hague, Nijhoff (1936).
Lorentz,H.A. (1902) Arch. néerl. 7, 299 (see §3). Reprinted in: Collected Papers, vol. 3, p. 73. and (1903) Encycl.d.math.wiss.V,14,§ 20.
Lorentz, H.A. (1909) "The Theory of Electrons;" Teubner, Leipzig.
Lorentz, H.A., and Droste, J. (1917) Versl.K.Akad.Wet.Amsterdam, 26, 392 and 649. Reprinted in the Collected Papers of H.A.Lorentz, vol. 5, p.330, The Hague, Nijhoff (1937).
Love, A.E.H. (1909) Proc.Roy.Soc.London A82, 73.
Ma, S.T. (1947) Phys.Rev. 71, 787.
Manasse, F.K. (1963) J.Math.Phys. 4, 746.
Martin, J., and Sanz, J.L.(1979) J.Math.Phys. 20, 26.
McCrea, J.D.(1981) Gen.Rel.Grav.13, 397.
Misner, C.W., Thorne, K.S., and Wheeler, J.A.(1973), "Gravitation," Freeman, San Francisco.
Newton, I. (1687) "Philosophiae Naturalis Principia Mathematica", Streater, London.
Noether, E. (1918) Nachr. Ges. Wiss. Göttingen, Math.Phys.Kl., p.235.
Ohta, T., Okamura, H., Kimura, T., and Hiida, K. (1973) Prog.Theor.Phys. 50, 492.
Ohta, T., Okamura, H., Kimura, T., and Hiida, K. (1974) Prog.Theor.Phys. 51, 1220.
Okamura, H., Ohta, T., Kimura, T., and Hiida, K. (1973) Prog. Theor.Phys. 50, 2066.
Papapetrou, A. (1951), Proc.Phys.Soc.Lond. A 64, 57.
Papapetrou, A. (1951)' Proc.Roy.Soc.Lond. A 209, 248.
Papapetrou, A., and Linet, B. (1981) Gen.Rel.Grav. 13, 335.
Peres, A. (1959) Nuov.Cim. 11, 617 and 644, and 13, 437.
Peres, A. (1960) Nuov.Cim. 15, 351.
Peters, P.C., and Mathews, J. (1963) Phys.Rev. 131, 435.
Planck, M. (1897) Ann.d.Phys.60, 577.
Poincaré, H. (1905) C.R.Acad.Sci.Paris, 140, 1504, 5 June 1905.
Portilla,M. (1979) J.Phys.A 12, 1075.
Regge, T., and Wheeler, J.A. (1957) Phys.Rev. 108, 1063.
Riesz,M.(1938) Bull.Société Math.France, 66.
Riesz,M. (1949) Acta Mathematica 81, 1.
Rosenblum, A. (1978) Phys.Rev.Lett.41, 1003.

Rosenblum, A. (1981) Phys.Lett.81A, 1.
Scheidegger, A.E. (1953) Rev.Mod.Phys. 25, 451.
Scheidegger, A.E. (1955) Phys.Rev. 99, 1883.
Schieve, W.C., Rosenblum, A., and Havas, P. (1972) Phys.Rev.D 6, 1501.
Schmutzer, E., (1966) Ann.d.Phys. 17, 107.
Schott, G.A. (1912) "Electromagnetic Radiation," Cambridge U.P.
Schott, G.A. (1915) Phil. Mag. 29, 49.
Schutz, B.F. (1980) Phys.Rev.D 22, 249.
Schwartz, L. (1950) "Théorie des Distributions" Publications de l'Institut de Mathématique de l'Université de Strasbourg.
Smith, S.F., and Havas, P. (1965) Phys.Rev. 138, B495.
Smorodinsky, Ya.A., and Golubenkov, V.N. (1956), Zh. Eksp. Teor.Fiz., 31, 330.
Spyrou, N., (1975) Ap.J. 197, 725.
Srinivasan, G., and van den Heuvel, E.P.J. (1982) Astron. Astrophys. 108, 143.
Stephani, H., (1964) Acta Phys.Polon. 26, 1045.
Synge, J.L., (1970) Proc.Roy.Irish Acad. A 69, 11.
Taylor, J.H., Fowler, L.A., and McCulloch, P.M. (1979) Nature 277, 437.
Taylor, J.H., and Weisberg, J.M. (1982) Ap.J.253, 908.
Thorne, K.S.(1969) AP.J. 158, 997.
Thorne, K.S. (1980) Rev.Mod.Phys. 52, 285 and 299.
Thorne, K.S., and Campolattaro,A(1967)ApJ.149, 591 and errata, Ap.J. 152, 673.
Thorne, K.S. and Kovács, S. (1975) Ap.J. 200, 245.
Vilenkin, A.V., and Fomin, P.I. (1978) Nuov. Cim. 45, 59.
Wagoner, R. (1975) Ap.J.(Letters), 196, L63.
Walker, M. (1979) Editor: "Proceedings of the Third Gregynog Relativity Workshop on Gravitational Radiation Rheory," Max Planck Institute publication, Munich.
Walker, M., and Will, C.M. (1979) Phys.Rev. D 19, 3483 and 3495.
Walker, M., and Will, C.M. (1980) Ap.J. (Letters) 242, L129.
Weisberg, J.M., and Taylor, J.H. (1981) Gen. Rel. Grav.13, 1.
Westpfahl, K., and Göller, M. (1979) Lett. Nuov. Cim. 26, 573.
Weyl, H. (1921) "Raum, Zeit, Materie," 4th edition, §36, Berlin.
Will, C.M. (1977) Ap.J. 214, 826.
Will, C.M., and Eardley, D.M. (1977) Ap.J.(Letters) 212, L91.
Zerilli, F.J. (1970) Phys.Rev.D 2, 2141.

ON THE POSITIVITY OF TOTAL GRAVITATIONAL ENERGY AT RETARDED TIMES

Martin Walker

Max-Planck-Institut für Astrophysik
Karl-Schwarzschild-Str. 1
D-8046 Garching, FRG

Contents

I. Introduction

Gravitational waves from a spatially isolated matter distribution propagate mainly along future-directed outgoing null geodesics in space-time. The investigation of gravitational waves far from their material sources therefore requires an investigation of the structure of space-time asymptotically along such null geodesics. The first successful investigations of this kind were made just over twenty years ago by Bondi, van der Burg and Metzner (1962) for axially symmetric fields, and by Sachs (1962a) in the general case. These authors introduce a "retarded time" function u, whose level surfaces are null hypersurfaces opening into the future, and a luminosity distance parameter r along the generators of {u = const}, together with suitable angular coordinates. The coefficient of r^{-1} in the uu component of the metric with respect to these coordinates is called the "mass aspect" of the system. The average of the mass aspect over a sphere at infinity in {u = const} is identified, by analogy with stationary solutions, with the mass at retarded time u. The central result of their work is that the mass at retarded times decreases monotonically in the presence of radiation, as a consequence of the vacuum gravitational field equations. The mass is constant if and only if no radiation is present.

Transformations of coordinates preserving the asymptotic form of the metric define an asymptotic symmetry group, the BMS (Bondi-Metzner-Sachs) group, which is the semi-direct product of the homogeneous Lorentz group with an infinite parameter abelian normal subgroup, called the supertranslation subgroup. The BMS group contains exactly one four dimensional normal subgroup, called the translation group (Sachs,1962b). Lorentz transformations, and in particular rotations, do not commute with supertranslations. This means that two asymptotic frames which are non-trivially supertranslated with respect to one another differ by more than just the shift of origins familiar from special relativity.

The translation subgroup is well-defined, however, and this leads to a definition of an energy-momentum covector for isolated gravitational systems (Sachs, 1963, Tamburino and Winicour 1966, Ashtekar and Streubel 1981). The Bondi-Sachs mass loss generalizes to an energy-momentum loss in the presence of gravitational radiation (Penrose 1964, 1967).

What appeared to be a very difficult and vitally important result, that in an asymptotically flat spacetime containing matter satisfying a positive energy condition, the Bondi-Sachs energy-momentum at retarded times is timelike and future directed, has recently yielded to a beautiful and elegant proof based on a spinorial argument originally used by Witten (1981) to prove positivity of energy measured at spacelike infinity (Horowitz and Perry 1982, Ludvigsen and Vickers 1982). A positivity proof using methods of functional analysis has been given by Schoen and Yau (1982). This result is more fundamental than that at spatial infinity (Schoen and Yau 1979a,b; Witten 1981) because the latter covector measures the total energy momentum content of matter plus all radiation, and is therefore unchanging with time. For a system having no incoming radiation, it can be thought of as the total energy momentum present in the infinite past. The Bondi-Sachs energy-momentum, however, decreases in time when a system radiates, and it is important to know that it remains future directed and timelike. Otherwise one would be confronted with the discomforting possibility of being able to radiate more energy than had been present originally, or even of being able to extract an infinite amount of energy from an isolated system.

The proof of the positivity of total gravitational energy in fact establishes a relation between the energy-momentum content of the material sources and the asymptotically measured energy-momentum of the gravitational field. It may well be that the spinorial identity establishing this relation will prove susceptible to an iterative approximation procedure, and therefore provide the long sought-after rigorous relationship between the far field and the sources in gravitational theory. This attractive possibility is being vigorously pursued. For gravitational wave astronomy, of course, it is of the utmost importance to be able to deduce properties of the structure and evolution of the material sources from the asymptotically measured wave-forms and their time dependence. To be able to do this with rigorous error estimates was until recently a distant hope; this hope has now become appreciably nearer to achieving concrete fruition.

The purpose of these notes is to describe a proof that the energy-momentum measured asymptotically at retarded times is future directed and timelike. This will be done in as complete and self-contained a manner as possible, given the limitations of time and space available. The proof described here is a slight modification of that of Ludvigsen and Vickers (1982). It will be taken for granted that the reader is familiar with the following: Penrose's (1963,1965) conformal approach to infinity, together with the consequences of Penrose's definition of asymptotic flatness at future null infinity for the asymptotic behaviour of the metric, connection, and curvature along outgoing null hypersurfaces, as described by Newman and Penrose (1962), Newman and Unti (1962), and Exton et al. (1969); the use of two-component spinors in gravitational theory as described, e.g., by Pirani (1965), or Penrose (1968). That part of the structure of the BMS group and its Lie algebra required in the proof will be described. The energy-momentum covector will be defined using Geroch and Winicour's (1981) version of Tamburino and Winicour's "linkages". The complementary approach of Ashtekar and Streubel (1981) will, despite its importance, only be mentioned briefly. Finally, the proof of a theorem required, asserting existence and uniqueness of solutions of a certain elliptic boundary value problem, will not be described.

Notation: the "Battelle conventions" (Penrose 1968) for tensor and spinor indices will be used. Thus the latin indices ocurring are abstract labels, bookkeeping devices to keep track of symmetries, valence, contractions, etc., and do not denote components with respect to a basis. A tensor index, a, therefore corresponds to a pair of spinor indices, AA', and both types of index can (and will) occur in the same equation, e.g. $g_{ab} = \varepsilon_{AB}\varepsilon_{A'B'}$, $K^a = \lambda^A\bar{\lambda}^{A'}$, etc., without use of the van der Waerden connection symbols $\sigma^a{}_{AA'}$ used by Pirani (1965). When components with respect to a basis are introduced, they will be labelled by bold face indices, $\underline{a}$, to distinguish them from the abstract tensorial indices. The metric, curvature, and Einstein conventions are exactly opposite to those of Misner, Thorne and Wheeler (1973), and latin rather than greek indices will be used. These conventions are:

metric signature (+ ---)

curvature $$2\nabla_{[a}\nabla_{b]}\, t_c = -R_{abcd}\, t^d,$$

$$R_{ab} = R^c{}_{acb}\,,\quad G_{ab} = R_{ab} - \frac{1}{2}Rg_{ab} = -8\pi T_{ab}.$$

The reason for adopting these conventions is that they avoid a plethora of minus-signs when using spinors, and that almost all of the literature on and using spinors utilizes them. Since no functional analysis occurs here, all manifolds and tensor and spinor fields will be assumed to be of differentiability class C^∞.

All spacetimes are orientable, globally hyperbolic and strongly causal (see, e.g. Hawking and Ellis 1973), unless otherwise stated.

II Asymptotic flatness at future null infinity

Penrose's (1963, 1965; see also Geroch 1976) conformal approach to the asymptotic structure of fields and spacetimes provides a geometrical formulation of the asymptotic flatness condition given in local charts by Bondi et al and Sachs. The idea is to multiply the metric by a positive factor, which vanishes sufficiently quickly far from the sources, that points which were infinitely far away with respect to the original metric sit at a finite distance with respect to the rescaled metric. This conformal rescaling has the effect of adding an idealized "endpoint at infinity" to each outgoing null geodesic in spacetime. The requirement that the collection of these future end points form a hypersurface ($\mathscr{I}^+$, "scri"), having the same features as that for flat spacetime, then becomes the definition of asymptotic flatness at future null infinity. There is a variety of precise definitions in the literature (see, e.g. Geroch and Horowitz, 1978, for some critical remarks). The definition given here is adequate for our purposes.

Definition:

A (strongly causal, orientable, globally hyperbolic) spacetime (M, g_{ab}) is asymptotically flat at future null infinity if

AF1 there exists a new ("unphysical") spacetime $(\hat{M}, \hat{g}_{ab})$ with boundary $\mathscr{I}^+$; the interior $\hat{M} \setminus \mathscr{I}^+$ of $\hat{M}$ is conformal with M : $\hat{g}_{ab} = \Omega^2 g_{ab}$, and $\Omega > 0$ on M.

AF2 $(\hat{M}, \hat{g}_{ab})$ is C^∞.

AF3 Ω is C^∞ on $\hat{M}$, $\Omega = 0$ on $\mathscr{I}^+$.

AF4 g_{ab} satisfies the vacuum gravitational field equations in a neighbourhood (in M) of $\mathscr{I}^+$.

AF5 $\mathscr{I}^+$ has the topology $\mathbb{R} \times S^2$.

Remarks:

It is not necessary in AF3 to require that $\nabla_a \Omega \neq 0$ on $\mathscr{I}^+$. One of the vacuum field equations requires that a certain second order ordinary differential equation for Ω along outgoing null geodesics be satisfied. By uniqueness of solutions, and from the form of this equation, the only solution for which Ω and its derivative vanish on $\mathscr{I}^+$ is the zero solution. Since $\Omega > 0$ in M, this cannot happen (Penrose, 1965). Therefore $\nabla_a \Omega \neq 0$ on $\mathscr{I}^+$. Condition AF4 can be generalized to spacetimes in which the Ricci tensor falls off sufficiently quickly along outgoing null rays, e.g. to the vacuum Einstein-Maxwell equations (cf. Ludwig, 1976). The intuitive content of AF5 is that, at least for a finite interval of retarded time, as many future directed null geodesics escape to infinity as in Minkowski space.

Although the spacetimes of Bondi et al and Sachs, proposed as candidates for radiating isolated systems, satisfy Penrose's conditions in the future, it was unclear for a long time to what extent the definition was compatible with the gravitational field equations. There are few exact, nonstationary examples (Bicâk, 1968; Schmidt, 1980; Ashtekar and Dray, 1981), and no physically realistic ones. The question of compatibility has recently been answered in the affirmative by Friedrich (1981), at least for analytic data. A perhaps more important problem, whether asymptotically flat initial data on a spacelike Cauchy hypersurface produces a spacetime which is asymptotically flat at future null infinity, remains open.

From the definition, the following results can be proved:

1) $\nabla_a\Omega \neq 0$, $g^{ab}(\nabla_a\Omega)(\nabla_b\Omega) = 0$ on $\mathcal{I}^+$; $\mathcal{I}^+$ is a null hypersurface in M.

2) The Weyl tensor of g_{ab} vanishes on $\mathcal{I}^+$.

3) The peeling theorem holds (Sachs 1964); see below.

Proofs can be readily constructed from results of Penrose (1965), Geroch (1971), and Geroch (1976).

Remarks:

Since the Weyl tensor is invariant under conformal rescalings, $\hat{C}^a{}_{bcd} = C^a{}_{bcd}$, and is equal to the curvature tensor in vacuum, result 2) says that the curvature of the physical spacetime vanishes asymptotically. Since $\mathcal{I}^+$ is a null hypersurface in the spacetime with conformally rescaled metric, with topology $\mathbb{R} \times S^2$, $\mathcal{I}^+$ for curved asymptotically flat spacetimes has the same properties as $\mathcal{I}^+$ for Minkowski space.

The peeling theorem describes both the rate of approach to flatness along outgoing null geodesics and the relation of the tangent vector to these geodesics to principal null directions of zero rest mass fields. The latter will not be of interest here, but the asymptotic behaviour of certain components of the metric, connection and curvature will be required. Both to describe this behaviour and in the proof of the theorem of section V it will be convenient to introduce a particular chart and particular frames for tensor and spinor fields in the asymptotic region. This is done as follows.

Choose a one-parameter family of outgoing null hypersurfaces {u = const} in M which intersect $\mathcal{I}^+$, when extended in $\hat{M}$, in a family of non-intersecting spherical sections. Denote by r an affine parameter along the outgoing null geodesic generators of the hypersurfaces {u = const} . Choose a conformal factor so that the metric on $\{u = \text{const}\} \cap \mathcal{I}^+$ induced from $\hat{g}_{ab}$ is (minus) that of a unit sphere. Choose spherical coordinates (θ,ϕ) on one such sphere. Then define θ and ϕ in a neighbourhood of $\mathcal{I}^+$ to be constant along generators of $\mathcal{I}^+$ and along generators of {u = const} . The four functions (u,r,θ,ϕ) define a Bondi chart in a neighbourhood of $\mathcal{I}^+$.

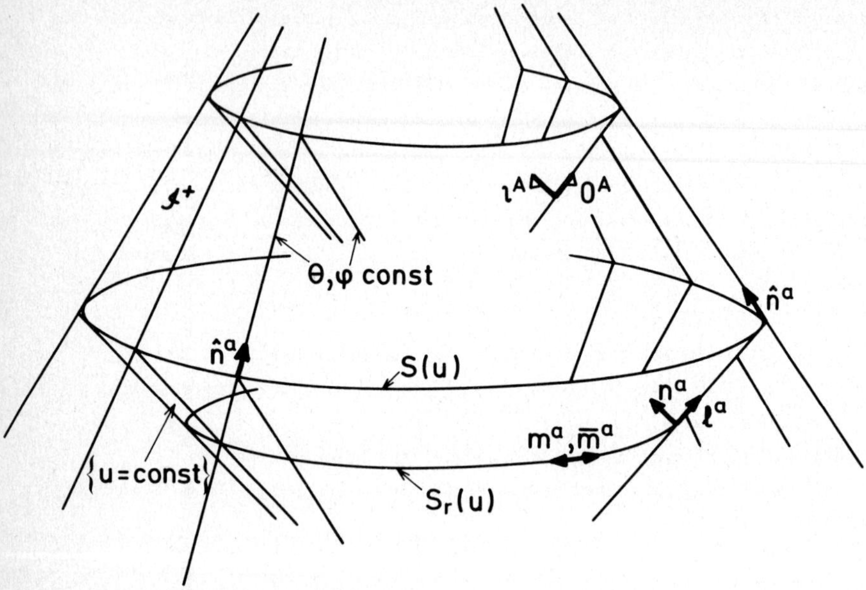

Figure 1

Outgoing null hypersurfaces {u = const} are foliated by a family of spheres $S_r(u)$. They intersect future null infinity $\mathscr{I}^+$ in the spheres S(u). Coordinates, vector- and spin-frames are introduced as described in the text.

Remark:

Bondi et al, and Sachs used a luminosity distance rather than an affine parameter as a radial coordinate.

Given a Bondi chart, a null (NP; Newman and Penrose 1962) frame can be introduced. Define $\ell_a = \nabla_a u$. The null vector field ℓ^a is orthogonal to the spherical surfaces $S_r(u) = \{u = \text{const}, r = \text{const}\}$. Denote by n^a the other (future-directed) null normal to the surfaces $S_r(u)$, normalized against ℓ^a by $\ell^a n_a = 1$. Finally, denote by m^a and $\bar{m}^a$ a pair of conjugate complex null vectors, normalized by $m^a \bar{m}_a = -1$, whose real and imaginary parts are spacelike vectors tangent to the surfaces $S_r(u)$. It follows that

$$g_{ab} = 2\ell_{(a}n_{b)} - 2m_{(a}\bar{m}_{b)} \; . \qquad (1)$$

Finally, denote by o^A and ι^A one of the two pairs of spinors related to the NP frame $\ell, m, \bar{m}, n$ by $\ell^a = o^A\bar{o}^{A'}$, $m^a = o^A\bar{\iota}^{A'}$, $\bar{m}^a = \bar{o}^{A'}\iota^A$, $n^a = \iota^A\bar{\iota}^A$. From (1) follows $o_A\iota^A = 1$, or $\varepsilon_{AB} = 2o_{[A}\iota_{B]}$, where $g_{ab} = \varepsilon_{AB}\varepsilon_{A'B'}$.

Remark:
ℓ^a is geodesic, $\ell^c\nabla_c\ell^a = 0$, by virtue of ℓ_a being a gradient. m^a and $\bar{m}^a$ can be rotated, if necessary, to achieve $\ell^c\nabla_c o^A = 0$ also. The vectors m^c, $\bar{m}^c$ and n^c, and the spinor ι^A are not parallel along the generators of $\{u = \text{const}\}$ in general. Therefore this frame is not that of Exton et al (1969). In order to get from theirs to this one, a null rotation about their o^A is required, its parameter being their function $-\bar{\omega}$. The reason for choosing the frame so that the real and imaginary parts of m^a are tangent to the spheres $S_r(u)$ is that the surface element of these spheres is then proportional to the antisymmetric product of m^a with its complex conjugate. This will be convenient later on, when integrals over these spheres will play an important role.

Acting on scalars, the differential operators associated with the NP frame just defined can be written

$$\ell^c\nabla_c = D = \partial/\partial r ,$$

$$m^c\nabla_c = \delta = \xi^{\underline{i}}\,\partial/\partial x^{\underline{i}} , \qquad (2)$$

$$\bar{m}^c\nabla_c = \bar{\delta} = \bar{\xi}^{\underline{i}}\,\partial/\partial x^{\underline{i}} ,$$

$$n^c\nabla_c = \Delta = \partial/\partial u + (U + \omega\bar{\omega})\partial/\partial r + (X^{\underline{i}} - \bar{\omega}\,\xi^{\underline{i}} - \omega\bar{\xi}^{\underline{i}})\partial/\partial x^{\underline{i}} .$$

Here $x^1 = \theta$, $x^2 = \phi$, so $\underline{i} = 1,2$. The real functions $U, X^{\underline{i}}$ and the real and imaginary parts of the complex functions $\xi^{\underline{i}}$ and ω define the components, with respect to the Bondi chart, of the metric via the component version of (1).

Remark:
If the vector m^a were propagated parallely along ℓ^a, it would have a component in the $\partial/\partial r$ direction in a Bondi chart, this component being the function ω.

The asymptotic behaviour of the affine connection and the curvature components required later can be described by giving the behaviour of these components with respect to the NP or spin-frame constructed above. Recall that the Weyl tensor is related to the Weyl spinor ψ_{ABCD} by

$$C_{abcd} = \psi_{ABCD}\,\varepsilon_{A'B'}\,\varepsilon_{C'D'} + \varepsilon_{AB}\,\varepsilon_{CD}\,\bar{\psi}_{A'B'C'D'} . \qquad (3)$$

The components of the affine connection and Weyl tensor are defined by NP according to the following scheme:

∇	$o^A\nabla o_A = m^c\nabla\ell_c$	$o^A\nabla\iota_A = \frac{1}{2}(n^c\nabla\ell_c - \bar{m}^c\nabla m_c)$	$\iota^A\nabla\iota_A = -\bar{m}^c\nabla n_c$
$\bar{\delta}$	ρ	α	λ
δ	σ	β	μ
Δ	τ	γ	ν
D	κ	ε	π

(4)

$$\psi_0 = \psi_{ABCD}o^A o^B o^C o^D = -C_{abcd}\,\ell^a m^b \ell^c m^d$$

$$\psi_1 = \psi_{ABCD}o^A o^B o^C \iota^D = -C_{abcd}\,\ell^a n^b \ell^c m^d$$

$$\psi_2 = \psi_{ABCD}o^A o^B \iota^C \iota^D = -C_{abcd}\,\ell^a m^b \bar{m}^c n^d \qquad (5)$$

$$\psi_3 = \psi_{ABCD}o^A \iota^B \iota^C \iota^D = -C_{abcd}\,\ell^a n^b \bar{m}^c n^d$$

$$\psi_4 = \psi_{ABCD}\iota^A \iota^B \iota^C \iota^D = -C_{abcd}\,n^a \bar{m}^b n^c \bar{m}^d$$

Also useful is the following table:

∇	$m^c\nabla\bar{m}_c$	$n^c\nabla\ell_c$
$\bar{\delta}$	$\alpha - \bar{\beta}$	$\alpha + \bar{\beta}$
δ	$\beta - \bar{\alpha}$	$\beta + \bar{\alpha}$
Δ	$\gamma - \bar{\gamma}$	$\gamma + \bar{\gamma}$
D	$\varepsilon - \bar{\varepsilon}$	$\varepsilon + \bar{\varepsilon}$

(6)

A convenient technical tool for describing the asymptotic behaviour of spacetimes is a certain covariant derivative operator on the sphere, introduced by Newman and Penrose (1965). The spheres involved arise as the intersection of outgoing null hypersurfaces with $\mathscr{I}^+$. This operator, called "edth" and written $\eth$, is most conveniently introduced as follows (cf. Geroch et al, 1973). Consider a metric two-sphere of radius $\sqrt{2}$ (the square root of two is due to Penrose, 1965). Take vectors m^a and $\bar{m}^a$ tangent to it, with $m^a m_a = 0$, $m^a \bar{m}_a = -1$, as above, except that these vectors are two dimensional. Define $\delta^o = m^c\nabla_c$, where ∇_c now denotes the covariant derivative on the two-sphere. The corresponding connection components can be written

$$\delta^o m^a = -(\bar{\alpha}^o - \beta^o)m^a ,$$
$$\delta^o \bar{m}^a = (\bar{\alpha}^o - \beta^o)\bar{m}^a . \qquad (7)$$

The combination $\bar{\alpha}^o - \beta^o$ is for later convenience.

Consider a scalar on the sphere of the form

$$\eta = m^{a_1} \ldots m^{a_{p+s}} \bar{m}^{b_1} \ldots \bar{m}^{b_p} \eta_{a_1 \ldots a_{p+s} b_1 \ldots b_p} .$$

Then η has the property that

$$m^a \rightarrow e^{i\psi} m^a \quad \Rightarrow \quad \eta \rightarrow e^{is\psi} ,$$

and is said to have spin weight s. Define the action of $\eth$ on η by

$$\eth\eta = -m^{a_1} \ldots m^{a_{p+s}} \bar{m}^{b_1} \ldots \bar{m}^{b_p} m^c \nabla_c \eta_{a_1 \ldots b_p} .$$

It is obvious that $\eth\eta$ has spin weight s+1, and that $\bar{\eth}\eta$ has spin weight s-1. One readily shows that

$$-\eth\eta = \delta^o\eta + s(\bar{\alpha}^o - \beta^o)\eta . \qquad (8)$$

Observe that $\eth$ can be defined, via (8), for half integral values of s, which arise as components of spinors.

The operators $\eth$ and $\bar{\eth}$ do not commute; if η has spin weight s,

$$(\bar{\eth}\eth - \eth\bar{\eth})\eta = 2s\eta . \qquad (9)$$

The eigenfunctions of $\bar{\eth}\eth$ are called spin-weighted spherical harmonics: for s = 0, $\pm 1, \ldots, \pm \ell$,

$$\bar{\eth}\eth\, {}_sY_{\ell m} = -(\ell-s)(\ell+s+1)\, {}_sY_{\ell m},$$
$${}_oY_{\ell m} = Y_{\ell m} . \qquad (10)$$

These functions form complete sets for each spin weight, and have the following properties:

$$\overline{{}_sY_{\ell m}} = (-1)^{m+s}\ {}_{-s}Y_{\ell -m}\ ,$$

$$\eth\ {}_sY_{sm} = 0\ , \qquad (11)$$

$$\bar{\eth}\ {}_{-s}Y_{sm} = 0\ ,$$

and, if the spin weight of A plus the spin weight of B is minus one,

$$\int_S (\eth A)B\,dS = -\int_S A\bar{\eth}B\,dS\ . \qquad (12)$$

With these preliminaries, the asymptotic behaviour of those components of the metric, affine connection, and curvature tensor along generators of {u = const}, which will be required in the following can be given. The asymptotic behaviour of the metric is contained in that of the directional derivatives corresponding to the NP frame introduced above:

$$D = \partial/\partial r$$

$$\Delta = \partial/\partial u - \partial/\partial r - r^{-2}[(\bar{\eth}\sigma^o)\delta^o + (\bar{\eth}\sigma^o)\bar{\delta}^o] + O(r^{-3}) \qquad (13)$$

$$\delta + s(\bar{\alpha}-\beta) = -r^{-1}\eth + \sigma^o r^{-2}\,\bar{\eth} - \sigma^o\,\bar{\sigma}^o r^{-3}\eth + O(r^{-4})\ .$$

The connection coefficients behave as

$$\rho = -r^{-1} + O(r^{-3}) \qquad \left.\begin{matrix}\alpha\\ \\ \beta\end{matrix}\right\}\ \text{incorporated in } \delta + s(\bar{\alpha} - \beta)$$

$$\sigma = r^{-2}\sigma^o + O(r^{-4})$$

$$\tau = r^{-2}(\sigma^o\eth\bar{\sigma}^o - \bar{\eth}\,\sigma^o) + O(r^{-3}) \qquad \gamma = r^{-2}(\alpha^o\bar{\eth}\sigma^o - \bar{\alpha}^o\eth\bar{\sigma}^o - \tfrac{1}{2}\psi^o{}_2) + O(r^{-3})$$

$$\kappa = 0 \qquad \varepsilon = 0$$

$$\lambda \quad \text{not required} \qquad (14)$$

$$\mu = -r^{-1} - (\psi_2^o + \sigma^o\dot{\bar{\sigma}}^o + \eth^2\bar{\sigma}^o) + O(r^{-3})$$

$$\nu \quad \text{not required}$$

$$\pi = -D\bar{\omega} = -\,r^{-2}\,\eth\bar{\sigma}^o + O(r^{-3})$$

The sole curvature component required has the behaviour

$$\psi_2 = r^{-3}\,\psi_2^o + O(r^{-4}). \tag{15}$$

Remarks:

The functions with a superscript ^{o} are functions of u, θ, φ only; a dot denotes $\partial/\partial u$. With the spherical coordinates chosen here, $\alpha^o = -\frac{1}{2}\cot\theta$. The only remaining unknown functions are σ^o and ψ_2^o. Geometrically, σ^o measures the shear of the hypersurfaces {u = const}. $\dot{\bar{\sigma}}^o$ corresponds to the news function of Bondi et al and Sachs. ψ_2^o is the amplitude of the r^{-3} part of the curvature tensor; it is -m for the Schwarzschild solution if $\ell_a = \frac{1}{\sqrt{2}}\nabla_a(t-r-2m\ell n(r/2m))$, $n_a = \frac{1}{\sqrt{2}}\nabla_a(t+r+2m\ell n(r/2m))$ in the usual coordinates. The coefficient of r^{-2} in μ will play an important role later; it is real (Exton et al 1969). This coefficient arises from the asymptotic integration of one of the vacuum field equations, $D\mu = \mu\rho + \lambda\sigma + \psi_2$, along null geodesics in {u = const}; see Newman and Unti (1962), Eqs. (9f), (24f), (40e), recalling that the present frame is null-rotated with respect to theirs. The asymptotic behaviour of the frame components U, $X^{\underline{i}}$ will not be required.

III The asymptotic symmetry group for gravitation

Symmetry groups are usually defined by specifying some geometrical object on a manifold and then asking for diffeomorphisms of the manifold leaving the geometrical object invariant. For a physical theory, the manifold and geometrical object should be universal. They should not depend on any particular solutions of the theory. Thus for electrodynamics, the manifold is Minkowski space and the geometrical object is the Minkowski metric. The corresponding symmetry group is the Poincaré group. For gravitation, both the spacetime manifold and its geometrical structure are determined by the field equations, and vary from solution to solution. These solutions have no symmetries in general. But if asymptotically flat spacetimes are considered, a universal manifold offers itself, namely the hypersurface $\mathscr{I}^+$ at future null infinity itself. What universal structure do all asymptotically flat spacetimes have on $\mathscr{I}^+$? They have a degenerate metric, $d\hat{s}^2|_{\Omega=0}$, but this depends on the choice of conformal factor used to define $\hat{g}_{ab}$ (and $\mathscr{I}^+$). A geometrical object which is invariant under conformal rescalings can be constructed as follows (Penrose 1974). Define a tangent vector to the null geodesic generators of $\mathscr{I}^+$ by

$$\hat{n}^a = -\hat{g}^{ab}\hat{\nabla}_b\,\Omega|_{\Omega=0}\,. \tag{16}$$

The - sign is so that $\hat{n}^a$ is future directed. Then the tensor $\hat{g}_{ab}\hat{n}^c\hat{n}^d$ is invariant under $\Omega \to \Theta\Omega$, where the function Θ is strictly positive on $\mathscr{I}^+$ in order that $\Theta\Omega$ be a permissible conformal factor.

The universal structure on the manifold $\mathscr{I}^+ = \mathbb{R} \times S^2$ is therefore: (i) a conformal class of degenerate metrics of signature (0 - -), (ii) the tensor, $\hat{g}_{ab}\hat{n}^a\hat{n}^b$, invariant under conformal rescalings (Schmidt et al 1975). The BMS group is the group of automorphisms of this structure. They can be exhibited explicitly as follows. Choose Ω so that $-\hat{g}_{ab}$ on $\mathscr{I}^+$ is the unit sphere metric. This choice fixes the parametrization of $\hat{n}^a$; let u be a function on $\mathscr{I}^+$ so that $\hat{n}^a\hat{\nabla}_a = \partial/\partial u$ when applied to functions. Let ζ and $\bar{\zeta}$ be complex stereographic coordinates on the unit sphere which is the space of null geodesic generators of $\mathscr{I}^+$. $\zeta = e^{i\phi}\cot\theta/2$ in terms of the coordinates for which the unit sphere metric is $d\theta^2+\sin^2\theta d\phi^2$. $\{u,\zeta,\bar{\zeta}\}$ is a chart on $\mathscr{I}^+$. Now the collection of transformations preserving (i) is the conformal group of the two-sphere. Introducing an orientation on the space of generators of $\mathscr{I}^+$ and requiring that this orientation be preserved, this group is the proper, orthochronous Lorentz group $L_+^\uparrow$. The universal cover of $L_+^\uparrow$ is SL(2,C), whose action is given in terms of ζ, $\bar{\zeta}$ by the fractional linear transformations

$$\zeta \to A(\zeta) = \frac{z_o\zeta + z_1}{z_2\zeta + z_3} \; ; \; z_o, z_1, z_2, z_3 \in \mathbb{C}, \; z_oz_3 - z_1z_2 = 1. \qquad (17)$$

It remains to see how u transforms so that $\hat{g}_{ab}\hat{n}^c\hat{n}^d$ is left invariant. A transformation (17) induces a conformal rescaling of the unit sphere metric by

$$K_A(\zeta) = (1 + \zeta\bar{\zeta})/\{|z_o\zeta + z_1|^2 + |z_2\zeta + z_3|^2\} \; . \qquad (18)$$

Therefore $\hat{n}^a \to K_A(\zeta)^{-1}\hat{n}^a$ to preserve $\hat{g}_{ab}\hat{n}^c\hat{n}^d$, whence $\partial/\partial u \to K_A(\zeta)^{-1}\,\partial/\partial u$. Since $K_A(\zeta)$ is independent of u, this can be integrated to give

$$u \to K_A(\zeta)(u + f(\zeta,\bar{\zeta})) \; , \qquad (19)$$

f a smooth real function on the sphere. In a Bondi chart, therefore, the BMS group acts on $\mathscr{I}^+$ by

$$(u,\zeta) \to (A,f)(u,\zeta) = (K_A(u + f), A(\zeta)) \; , \qquad (20)$$

where f is an arbitrary function on the sphere, and $A(\zeta)$ and $K_A(\zeta)$ are defined by (17) and (18).

The transformations with $A(\zeta) = \zeta$ leave each generator of $\mathscr{I}^+$ as a whole invariant, and are called supertranslations. In order to get an intuitive picture of these transformations, consider for a moment Minkowski space in retarded null coordinates $\{u,r,\zeta,\bar{\zeta}\}$. The metric is

$$ds^2 = du^2 + 2\, dudr - 4r^2(1+\zeta\bar{\zeta})^{-2}d\zeta d\bar{\zeta} \ . \tag{21}$$

The conformal factor $\Omega = r^{-1}$ satisfies the conditions of the definition of asymptotic flatness, and the coordinates $(u, \zeta, \bar{\zeta})$ and metric induced on $\mathscr{I}^+$ are of the type introduced above. With pseudo-cartesian coordinates

$$t = u+r,\ x = r(\zeta+\bar{\zeta})/(1+\zeta\bar{\zeta}),\ y = ir(\bar{\zeta}-\zeta)/(1+\zeta\bar{\zeta}),\ z = r(\zeta\bar{\zeta}-1)/(1+\zeta\bar{\zeta}), \tag{22}$$

in flat space, consider a translation given by

$$t \to t+a,\ x \to x+b,\ y \to y+c,\ z \to z+d;\ a,b,c,d \in R.$$

One finds $\zeta \to \zeta + O(r^{-1})$ and

$$u \to u+(1+\zeta\bar{\zeta})^{-1}\,[a(1+\zeta\bar{\zeta}) + b(\zeta+\bar{\zeta}) + ic(\bar{\zeta}-\zeta) + d(\zeta\bar{\zeta}-1)] + O(r^{-1}) \ ,$$

along u = const, $r \uparrow \infty$. The action on $\mathscr{I}^+$ is therefore

$$\zeta \to \zeta\ ,\ u \to u + a + b\sin\theta\,\cos\phi + c\sin\theta\,\sin\phi + d\cos\theta\ , \tag{23}$$

where the usual spherical coordinates have been reintroduced.

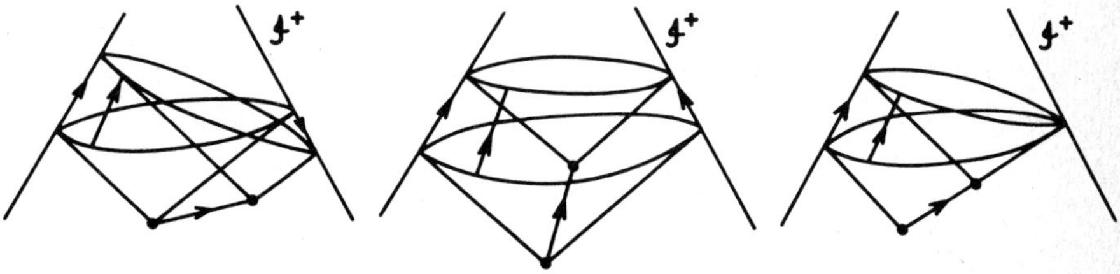

Space translation Time translation Null translation

Figure 2
The effect of translations in flat spacetime on $\mathscr{I}^+$.

Returning now to the general case (20), expanding f in spherical harmonics,

$$f = f^{oo}Y_{oo} + f^{1-1}Y_{1-1} + f^{10}Y_{10} + f^{11}Y_{11} + \sum_{\ell=2}^{\infty}\ \sum_{m=-\ell}^{\ell} f^{\ell m}Y_{\ell m}, \tag{24}$$

and comparing (20) with (23), it is apparent that the first four spherical harmonics correspond to translations. In fact Sachs (1962b) has shown that the translation subgroup is characterized uniquely by group theoretical considerations alone: it is the only four-parameter normal subgroup of the BMS group. He proves this by showing that any normal subgroup with a generator having $\ell \geq 2$ in (24) has dimension greater than four, using the commutation relations for the Lie algebra of the group.

The vectorfields on $\mathcal{I}^+$ generating supertranslations are of the form $Y_{\ell m}\,\partial/\partial u$, or $Y_{\ell m}\hat{n}^a$, in a Bondi chart. Those generating translations are of the form $f\hat{n}^a$ with f a constant linear combination of the spherical harmonics having $\ell = 0$ and 1. The difficulties and ambiguities associated with identifying generators of rotations have been hinted at in the Introduction. They will not be discussed here; see, eg., Walker (1979), or Geroch and Winicour (1981) for clear formulations of the problem.

Of particular interest later will be future directed null translations. These are translations $u \to u + f$, where f is a constant linear combination of the first four spherical harmonics which is greater than or equal to zero on the sphere, and vanishes at exactly one point. This point corresponds to the null direction which is left invariant by a null translation. A basis for the 4-dimensional space of translations can be constructed from generators of future directed null translations, for example $\{K^a_{\underline{a}} \mid \underline{a} = 1,2,3,4\}$ defined by

$$K^a_1 = (1 + \cos\theta)\hat{n}^a , \qquad K^a_2 = (1 - \cos\theta)\hat{n}^a,$$

$$K^a_3 = (1 + \sin\theta\cos\phi)\hat{n}^a, \quad K^a_3 = (1 + \sin\theta\sin\phi)\hat{n}^a . \tag{25}$$

Introduce the other future directed null vector in $\hat{M}$ orthogonal to the spheres S(u) on $\mathcal{I}^+$, $\hat{\ell}^a$, normalized against $\hat{n}^a$ by $\hat{\ell}_c\hat{n}^c = 1$ ($\hat{\ell}^a$ can be obtained from the vector ℓ^a in M by $\hat{\ell}^a = \Omega^{-2}\ell^a$). The basis $\{K^a_{\underline{a}}\}$ then defines four functions

$$K_{\underline{a}} = \hat{\ell}_c K^c_{\underline{a}} \tag{26}$$

on $\mathcal{I}^+$. From the complex-conjugation properties of the spin weighted spherical harmonics, and the fact that the $K_{\underline{a}}$ have spin weight zero (by definition), there exist complex numbers a and b (one pair for each value of $\underline{a}$) such that $K_{\underline{a}} = Y^o\bar{Y}^o$, where

$$Y_o = a_{\frac{1}{2}}\, Y_{\frac{1}{2}\frac{1}{2}} + b_{\frac{1}{2}}\, Y_{\frac{1}{2}-\frac{1}{2}} . \tag{27}$$

Thus the spinors $Y^o\hat{\iota}^A$ on $\mathcal{I}^+$, with Y^o as in (27), generate future directed null translations on $\mathscr{I}^+$. Such spinors will be of great interest in section V.

Remark:

Vectors in the four dimensional space of translations at null infinity correspond to vector <u>fields</u> on $\mathscr{I}^+$. They are labelled by the functions K_a, and are elements of the Lie algebra of the BMS group. The vectorfields on $\mathscr{I}^+$ are linearly dependent at each point, being multiples of $\hat{n}^a$. Therefore the four dimensional space of translations is distinct from the tangent space in $\hat{M}$ to points of $\mathscr{I}^+$.

IV The energy-momentum of isolated gravitational systems

In flat space-time, the local energy-momentum p_a of a system assigns to the timelike unit vector t^a tangent to the world-line of an observer the energy $p_a t^a$ of the system measured by that observer, and to a spacelike vector η^a in his rest frame, the corresponding component $p_a\eta^a$ of momentum. This is true at any event. For the determination of a total energy-momentum there are preferred timelike and spacelike vectors, those which generate translations in Minkowski space. These preferred vectors are related by Lorentz transformations, and the total energy-momentum transforms as a covector under such transformations. The energy-momentum of a system is a real-valued, linear function of the constant vectorfields generating translations in flat space-time.

In gravitation, in curved spacetimes, there is no local energy-momentum of the gravitational field. Nor are there constant vectorfields, or generators of symmetries, in general, with respect to which to define global energy-momentum. For isolated gravitational systems, however, there are asymptotic symmetries. As was shown in section III, there is a preferred four-dimensional space of vectorfields on future null infinity which generate translations in the BMS group. The problem of defining the total energy-momentum of an isolated gravitational system, asymptotically flat at future null infinity, therefore becomes that of defining in a physically convincing manner a real-valued, linear functional on generators of BMS translations on $\mathscr{I}^+$, a covector on the Lie algebra of BMS translations.

There have been essentially two different attempts to achieve this goal. One, mainly associated with Winicour (Winicour and Tamburino 1965, Tamburino and Winicour 1966, Winicour 1967, Geroch and Winicour 1981) starts from structures in the physical spacetime and then takes a limit to $\mathscr{I}^+$. The other, proposed by Ashtekar and carried through by Ashtekar and Streubel (1981), works entirely with structures on $\mathscr{I}^+$ from the start.

Winicour's approach, as described by Geroch and Winicour (GW) will be adopted below to define energy-momentum. GW define generators of BMS translations to be vectorfields on spacetime having smooth extensions to $\mathscr{I}^+$, and generating translations there in the sense of section III. This terminology is misleading, however, since the BMS group does not act on spacetime, and such vectorfields will be called here asymptotically constant. Two asymptotically constant vectorfields generating the same translation on $\mathscr{I}^+$ are called equivalent.

Each cross section of $\mathscr{I}^+$ defines a "retarded time" corresponding to the outgoing null hypersurface in M which meets that section orthogonally in $\hat{M}$. The idea is to associate with each such section and with each generator of translations the corresponding component of energy-momentum at the retarded time defined by the section. If a spacetime admits a Killing field ξ^a, then the Komar (1959) integral $\int_S \varepsilon_{abcd} \nabla^c \xi^d \, dS^{ab}$ is independent of the topological sphere S surrounding the sources. Moreover, in spacetimes with symmetries there are good physical arguments as to what these integrals represent, and they are the corresponding components of energy-momentum. GW show that the corresponding integrals in the spacetime with conformally rescaled metric are always finite on sections of $\mathscr{I}^+$ for asymptotically constant vectorfields, and are invariant under conformal rescalings. They are, however, not equal for equivalent asymptotically constant vectorfields. GW therefore impose a gauge condition on asymptotically constant vectorfields, and modify the Komar integral, so that the new asymptotic integrals are equal for equivalent asymptotically constant vectorfields satisfying the gauge condition.

These new asymptotic integrals are called linkages, and are shown by GW to enjoy the following properties: (i) they are defined for any asymptotically constant vectorfield and any section of $\mathscr{I}^+$, and are linear in the former; (ii) they are invariant under conformal rescalings and passage to an equivalent asymptotically constant vectorfield; (iii) they depend only on the vectorfield and geometry in a neighbourhood of the section; (iv) they reduce to the Komar values for Killing fields; (v) they possess a flux, so that the difference in a linkage between any two cross sections is the integral of the flux over the region of $\mathscr{I}^+$ between the sections; (vi) they also apply in the presence of radiating matter. GW conjecture that these properties characterize the linkages uniquely.

Ashtekar and Streubel, on the other hand, do not need to impose any gauge condition, but they do need global restrictions (in the infinite past and future) to ensure that certain integrals converge. They define a phase space of radiative modes of the gravitational field on $\mathscr{I}^+$, and show that this space admits a (weakly non-degenerate, conformally invariant) symplectic structure. BMS transformations leave this symplectic structure invariant. The generating functions of these canonical transformations represent the flux through all of $\mathscr{I}^+$ of the corresponding quantity associated with the BMS transformation (energy for time-translations, etc.). For translations, the global flux formula leads to a local expression, the energy-momentum at a retarded time corresponding to a section of $\mathscr{I}^+$, which is unique up to a constant independent of section. This constant can be fixed by a further global restriction.

There are therefore two quite different approaches to the energy-momentum of isolated systems. One uses local arguments, but requires a gauge condition; the other is free of gauge conditions, but requires global (in time) restrictions on the gravitational field. Both lead to the same expressions. Taken together, therefore, they provide a convincing relation between the translation subgroup of the asymptotic symmetry group and the energy-momentum of isolated systems.

It is remarkable that Komar (1959) credits Sachs with having arrived independently at what are now called the Komar integrals, since Ashtekar's symplectic approach is a classical version of Sachs' (1962b) "quantum commutation relations at infinity". Ideas of Sachs therefore lie at the roots of both approaches to a total energy momentum of isolated gravitating systems.

Since asymptotically constant spinor fields will play an important role in section V, they will be considered before a gauge choice is made and the GW linkages for translations used to obtain an expression for energy-momentum in terms of the asymptotic field given in section II. A spinor field λ^A on M will be called asymptotically constant if the null vector $K^a = \lambda^A \bar{\lambda}^{A'}$ is asymptotically constant and generates null translations on $\mathscr{I}^+$.

Choose a spin frame o^A, ι^A in M as in section II, and define a spin frame $\hat{o}^A$, $\hat{\iota}^A$ in $\hat{M}$ by $\hat{o}^A = \Omega^{-1} o^A$, $\hat{\iota}^A = \iota^A$. Write $\lambda^A = Xo^A + Y\iota^A$. Then λ^A is asymptotically constant if X is bounded on $\mathscr{I}^+$ and Y is smooth with $Y = Y^o$ on $\mathscr{I}^+$ satisfying (27). This follows from $\hat{\lambda}^A = \lambda^A = \Omega X\hat{o}^A + Y\hat{\iota}^A$. From (27) and (11), $\eth Y^o = 0$. Since $Y = \hat{o}_A \hat{\lambda}^A$, Y has spin weight $\frac{1}{2}$, and (27) is in fact the general time-independent solution to $\eth Y^o = 0$.

Asymptotic constancy alone, however, is too weak a condition. Several arguments to follow require a condition that Bramson (1975) calls "alinement of frames on $\mathscr{I}^+$", and which will be called here strong asymptotic constancy.

Definition:

$\lambda^A = \hat{\lambda}^A$ will be called strongly asymptotically constant if it is asymptotically constant, $\hat{\lambda}^A$ is smooth on $\hat{M}$, and $\hat{\nabla}_{(A}{}^{A'}\hat{\lambda}_{B)} = 0$ on $\mathscr{I}^+$.

Lemma 1 (Bramson 1975):

Expand $\lambda^A = Xo^A + Y\iota^A$. Further, expand X and Y along outgoing null geodesics in a Bondi chart as

$$X = X^o(u,\theta,\phi) + r^{-1}X^1(u,\theta,\phi) + O(r^{-2}),$$
$$Y = Y^o(u,\theta,\phi) + r^{-1}Y^1(u,\theta,\phi) + O(r^{-2}) \; . \qquad (29)$$

Assume that (29) can be formally differentiated once. Then λ^A is strongly asymptotically constant if

$$\dot{Y}^o = 0, \quad ðY^o = 0, \quad \bar{ð}Y^o = X^o, \quad Y^1 = 0 \ . \tag{30}$$

Proof:

The proof consists of taking the spin-frame components of $\nabla_{(A}{}^{A'}\lambda_{B)} = 0$, and using the asymptotic forms of the derivative operators in (2), (13), and the connection coefficients in (14), and (29). Then $\hat{\nabla}_{(A}{}^{A'}\hat{\lambda}_{B)} = 0$ is imposed. Since similar arguments will occur below, this one will not be given.

Let ξ^a be an asymptotically constant vectorfield in M. Expand $\xi^a = A\ell^a+Bn^a+C\bar{m}^a+$ $+\bar{C}m^a$.

Definition:

ξ^a will be called strongly asymptotically constant if the following conditions hold

$$\begin{aligned} A &= A^o(u,\theta,\phi) + r^{-1}A^1(u,\theta,\phi) + O(r^{-2}) \\ B &= B^o(u,\theta,\phi) + O(r^{-2}) \\ C &= C^o(u,\theta,\phi) + O(r^{-2}) \ , \end{aligned} \tag{31}$$

$$\dot{B}^o = 0, \quad ðC^o = 0, \quad ð\bar{C}^o = A^o - B^o, \quad B^o > 0. \tag{32}$$

Remark:

If $\xi^a = \lambda^A\bar{\lambda}^{A'}$ for a strongly asymptotically constant spinor λ^A, then $A^o = X^o\bar{X}^o$, $B^o = Y^o\bar{Y}^o$, and $C^o = \bar{X}^oY^o$. (31) and (32) then follow from (29) and (30).

The following lemma is needed in order to be able to employ strongly asymptotically constant vectorfields to evaluate GW's linkages.

Lemma 2.

Any strongly asymptotically constant vectorfield is equivalent to one that is divergence-free. An asymptotically constant divergence-free vectorfield is strongly asymptotically constant.

Proof:

Write $\nabla_c\xi^c = g^{ab}\nabla_a\xi_b$

$$= [2\,\ell^{(a}n^{b)} - 2m^{(a}\bar{m}^{b)}]\,\nabla_a\xi_b$$

$$= n^cD\xi_c + \ell^c\Delta\,\xi_c - \bar{m}^c\delta\xi_c - m^c\bar{\delta}\xi_c\ ,$$

and use $\xi^a = A\ell^a + Bn^a + C\bar{m}^a + \bar{C}m^a$, and $Do^A = 0$ to obtain

$$\nabla_c\xi^c = DA - 2\rho A + (\Delta-\gamma-\bar{\gamma}+2\mu)B + (\bar{\delta}+\alpha-\bar{\beta}+\pi-\bar{\tau})C + (\delta+\bar{\alpha}-\beta+\bar{\pi}-\tau)\bar{C}.$$

Inserting (13), (14), and (31) gives

$$\begin{aligned}\nabla_c \xi^c &= \dot{B}^o + r^{-1}(2A^o - 2B^o - \bar{\eth}C^o - \eth\bar{C}^o) \\ &+ r^{-2}\,[A^1 - (\eth\bar{\sigma}^o)\eth B^o - (\bar{\eth}\sigma^o)\bar{\eth}B^o - \tfrac{1}{2}(\psi_2{}^o + \bar{\psi}_2{}^o)B^o \\ &- 2(\psi_2{}^o + \sigma^o\dot{\bar{\sigma}}^o + \eth^2\bar{\sigma}^o)B^o + \sigma^o\bar{\eth}\bar{C}^o + \bar{\sigma}^o\,\eth C^o \\ &+ (\sigma^o\,\eth\bar{\sigma}^o)C^o + (\bar{\sigma}^o\bar{\eth}\sigma^o)\bar{C}^o] + O(r^{-3}).\end{aligned}$$

Strong asymptotic constancy implies that the first two terms vanish. A^1 is unrestricted and can be chosen to make the third term vanish. The remaining coefficients are unrestricted by strong asymptotic constancy, so $\nabla_c\xi^c = 0$ can always be achieved, leaving A^o, B^o, C^o and (32) unaltered.

If ξ^a is asymptotically constant and divergence-free, on the other hand, the expression for $\nabla_c\xi^c$ given above implies that ξ^a is strongly asymptotically constant. Strong asymptotic constancy is therefore a weaker condition than divergence-freeness. That the divergence of an asymptotically constant vectorfield should vanish is GW's gauge condition. The linkage integral for ξ^a, which equals the the Komar integral for ξ^a in this gauge, can be written

$$\lim_{\substack{r\uparrow\infty \\ u\ \mathrm{const}}} \frac{1}{4\pi}\int_{S_r(u)} \ell^{[a}n^{b]}\nabla_a\xi_b\, dS_r\,, \tag{33}$$

the vectors ℓ^a, n^a and the surfaces $S_r(u)$ being as defined in section II: $\ell_a = \nabla_a u$, $\ell^a\nabla_a = \partial/\partial r$ applied to functions, n^a is null, orthogonal to the surfaces $S_r(u) = \{u = \mathrm{const}\} \cap \{r = \mathrm{const}\}$, and normalized against ℓ^a by $\ell_c n^c = 1$. Since the surface element dS^{ab} of S_r is $2im^{[a}\bar{m}^{b]}dS_r$, the GW integral becomes (33).

Definition:

Let K^a be an asymptotically constant divergence-free vectorfield on M. Let $S(u) = \lim_{r\uparrow\infty} S_r(u)$ be a unit sphere where $\{u = \mathrm{const}\}$ intersects $\mathscr{I}^+$. Then the component of the total energy-momentum $P^B(u)$ of the isolated system described by (M, g_{ab}), in the direction given by K^a on $\mathscr{I}^+$, at the retarded time u is

$$< P^B(u), K > = \lim_{r\uparrow\infty} \frac{1}{4\pi}\int_{S_r(u)} \ell^{[a}n^{b]}\,\nabla_a K_b\, dS_r \tag{34}$$

Here $< P^B(u), K >$ denotes the action of the Bondi-Sachs energy-momentum covector P^B on the element K of the translation sub-Lie-algebra of the BMS group.

Lemma 3.

Let K^a be an asymptotically constant divergence-free vectorfield. Then

$$< P^B(u), K > = -\frac{1}{4\pi}\int_S B^o(\psi_2{}^o + \sigma^o\dot{\bar{\sigma}}^o + \eth^2\bar{\sigma}^o)\, dS. \qquad (35)$$

Remark:

(35) is, with the present choice of frame field in which m^a and n^a are not parallel in the direction of ℓ^a, precisely the expression obtained by Penrose (1964) from the results of Bondi et al and Sachs.

Note that the expression on the right hand side of (35) depends only on the value of K^a on $\mathscr{I}^+$, and not on its behaviour in spacetime. Thus the total engergy-momentum could have been defined by (35) as that linear functional on the Lie algebra of the translation subgroup of the BMS group. The GW approach was taken to bring out the physical idea behind (35).

Proof:

Expand $K^a = A\ell^a + Bn^a + C\bar{m}^a + \bar{C}m^a$ as usual and insert this into $2\ell^{[a}n^{b]}\nabla_a K_b$ to obtain

$$2\ell^{[a}n^{b]}\nabla_a K_b = n^a DK_a - \ell^a \Delta K_a$$

$$= DA + (\pi+\bar{\tau})C + (\bar{\pi}+\tau)\bar{C} - (\Delta-\gamma-\bar{\gamma})B.$$

Use the expansion of $\nabla_c\xi^c = 0$ from the proof of Lemma 2 (with $\xi^c = K^c$) to rewrite this as

$$2\ell^{[a}n^{b]}\nabla_a K_b = 2DA - 2\rho A + 2\mu B + (\bar{\delta}+\alpha-\bar{\beta}+2\pi)C + (\delta+\bar{\alpha}-\beta+2\bar{\pi})\bar{C}.$$

Using (13), (14) and (31) give

$$2\,DA = -2A^1 r^{-2} + O(r^{-3})$$

$$-2\rho A = 2A^o r^{-1} + 2A^1 r^{-2} + O(r^{-3})$$

$$(\delta+\bar{\alpha}-\beta)C = -r^{-1}\,\eth\bar{C}^o + r^{-2}\sigma^o\bar{\eth}\bar{C}^o + O(r^{-3})$$

$$2\pi C = -2r^{-2}C^o\,\eth\bar{\sigma}^o + O(r^{-3})$$

$$2\mu B = -2r^{-1}B^o - 2r^{-2}B^o\,[\psi_2{}^o + \sigma^o\bar{\sigma}^o + \eth^2\bar{\sigma}^o] + O(r^{-3}).$$

Putting these into $2\ell^{[a}n^{b]}\nabla_a K_b$ gives

$$-r^{-1}(\eth\bar{C}^o + \bar{\eth}C^o - 2A^o + 2B^o) + r^{-2}[-2B^o(\psi_2{}^o + \sigma^o\dot{\bar{\sigma}}^o + \eth^2\bar{\sigma}^o)] + O(r^{-3}).$$

The first term vanishes by (32). From (13), $dS_r = r^2 dS + O(r)$, and (35) follows immediately from (34).

Remark:
From the proof just given, and the expression for $\nabla_c\xi^c$ in the proof of lemma 2, it follows that the divergence of ξ^a only need vanish up to order r^{-2} in order to obtain eq. (35) from eq. (34).

V. Positivity of total gravitational energy at retarded times

A vector in spacetime is future directed and timelike or null if its inner products with four linearly independent future directed timelike or null vectors are all non-negative. It is future directed and strictly timelike if its inner product with all future directed null vectors is strictly positive.

Before stating the theorem asserting positivity of total gravitational energy, a certain spinor expression due to Nester (1981) will be introduced, and a lemma relating it to P^B will be proved.
For any spinor field λ^A on M, define a symmetric spinor ϕ_{AB} by

$$\phi_{AB} = \frac{1}{2}\,[\lambda_{(A}\nabla_{B)}{}^{C'}\bar{\lambda}_{C'} - \bar{\lambda}_{C'}\nabla^{C'}{}_{(A}\lambda_{B)}]\ . \qquad (36)$$

ϕ_{AB} in turn defines a bivector F_{ab} by

$$F_{ab} = \phi_{AB}\,\varepsilon_{A'B'} + \varepsilon_{AB}\;\bar{\phi}_{A'B'}. \qquad (37)$$

Remark:
F_{ab} is not the antisymmetrized covariant derivative of the vector $\lambda^A\bar{\lambda}^{A'} = K^a$, due to the minus sign in (36). ϕ_{AB} and F_{ab} here are the negatives of the corresponding quantities in Ludvigsen and Vickers (1981, 1982) and Horowitz and Tod (1981). This eliminates minus signs later on.

Lemma 4 (Nester, 1981):
Taking NP and spin frames, and the family of spheres $S_r(u)$ going out to $\mathscr{I}^+$ along {u = const } as before, let λ^A in (36) be a strongly asymptotically constant spinor. Then

$$\lim_{r\uparrow\infty} \frac{1}{4\pi} \int_{S_r(u)} F_{ab}\ell^a n^b dS_r = \langle P^B(u), K \rangle\ .$$

Remark:

In section IV, the GW linkage approach was used to define total energy-momentum in terms of the limit on $\mathscr{I}^+$ of a certain surface integral. In lemma 3, this limit was evaluated and shown to depend only on quantities defined on $\mathscr{I}^+$ itself. Unlike lemmas 2 and 3, in lemma 4 the vector K^a need not be divergence-free. The weaker condition of strong asymptotic constancy is sufficient to establish the limit claimed. Indeed, total energy-momentum could have been defined in this way from the beginning, but perhaps with some loss of intuitive content.

Proof:

This sort of proof is routine by now. Write $\lambda^A = Xo^A + Y\iota^A$. Then

$$F_{ab}\ell^a n^b = X\bar{X} + Y\bar{Y} + \mathrm{Re}\,[\bar{Y}(\delta+\beta)X - \bar{X}(\bar{\delta}-\alpha)Y] .$$

With $X = X^o(u,\theta,\phi) + r^{-1}X^1(u,\theta,\phi) + O(r^{-2})$ and $Y = Y^o(u,\theta,\phi) + O(r^{-2})$, and the asymptotic behaviour of the connection coefficients and operators from section II,

$$(\delta+\beta)X = -r^{-1}\,X^o - r^{-2}\eth X^1 + r^{-2}\sigma^o\bar{\eth}X^o + O(r^{-3}),$$

$$(\bar{\delta}-\alpha)Y = -r^{-1}\bar{\eth}Y^o + r^{-2}\sigma^o\eth Y^o + O(r^{-3}).$$

One uses (30) and its consequences, $\eth X^o = -Y^o$ and $\bar{\eth}X^o = 0$, which follow from properties (8) and (11) of the operator $\eth$. One applies eq. (12) to the term $\bar{Y}^o\eth X^1$ in the integral, and finds that strong asymptotic constancy of λ^A makes the coefficient of r^{-1} in $F_{ab}\ell^a n^b$ vanish identically and the r^{-2} coefficient reduce to $-Y_o\bar{Y}_o(\psi_2{}^o + \sigma^o\dot{\bar{\sigma}}^o + \eth^2\bar{\sigma}^o)$, which proves the lemma.

Theorem (Ludvigsen and Vickers 1982):

Let (M,g_{ab}) be a spacetime satisfying the following: (i) It is asymptotically flat at future null infinity. (ii) The material sources satisfy the dominant energy condition: $T^a{}_b t^b$ is future directed and timelike for all future directed and timelike t^a. (iii) A section S of $\mathscr{I}^+$ can be connected to a compact spacelike hypersurface with boundary Σ , in M by a null hypersurface N orthogonal both to S and to the boundary $\partial\Sigma$ of Σ. Then $P^B(S)$ is future-directed and timelike or null.

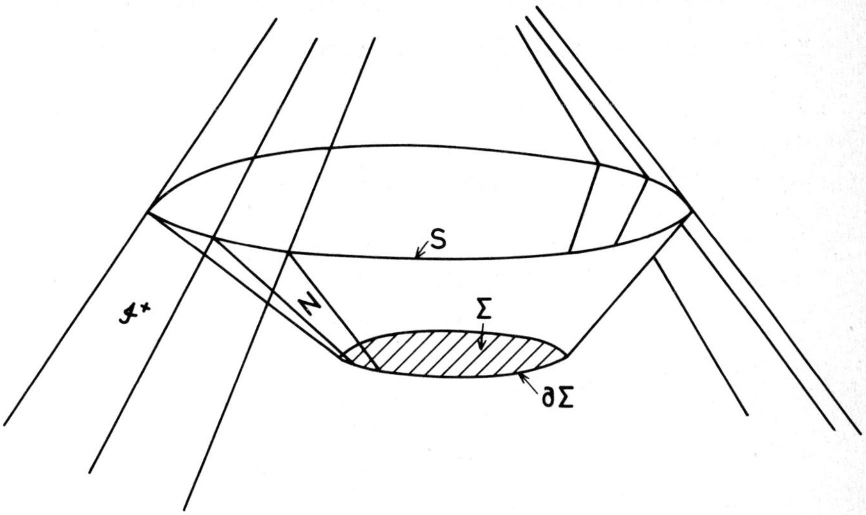

Figure 3

A compact spacelike hypersurface Σ with boundary $\partial\Sigma$ is connected to $\mathscr{I}^+$ by a null hypersurface N meeting $\mathscr{I}^+$ in a sphere S.

Proof:

The idea is to integrate the divergence of the F_{ab} of Lemma 4 (or the exterior derivative of the dual of F, for purists) over the hypersurfaces Σ and N. Gauss' theorem applied to $\Sigma \cup N$ then gives

$$\int_\Sigma \nabla^b F_{ab} d\Sigma^a + \int_N \nabla^b F_{ab} dN^a = \lim_{r\uparrow\infty} \int_{S_r} \ell^a n^b F_{ab} dS_r = 4\pi \langle P^B, K^a \rangle ,$$

by Lemma 4. If every strongly asymptotically constant spinor λ^A can be chosen to make the integrals over Σ and over N nonnegative, then $\eta(P^B, K^a)$ is nonnegative for a basis of generators of future directed null translations on $\mathscr{I}^+$. It follows that $P^B(S)$ is future directed and timelike or null.

From (36) and (37),

$$2\nabla^b F_{ab} = (\nabla_{A'}{}^B \bar\lambda_{C'}) \nabla^{C'}{}_{(A}\lambda_{B)} - (\nabla_{A'}{}^B \lambda_{(A}) \nabla_{B)}{}^{C'} \bar\lambda_{C'}$$

$$+ \bar\lambda_{C'} \nabla_{A'}{}^B \nabla_{(A}{}^{C'} \lambda_{B)} - \lambda_{(A} \nabla_{|A'|}{}^B \nabla_{B)}^{C'} \bar\lambda_{C'} + \quad \text{complex conjugate} \qquad (38)$$

where $|A'|$ indicates that A' is excluded from the symmetrization. The third term on the right of (38) is

$$\frac{1}{2}\bar{\lambda}^{C'}\nabla_{A'B}\nabla_{C'A}\lambda^{B} + \frac{1}{2}\bar{\lambda}^{C'}\nabla_{A'B}\nabla^{B}{}_{C'}\lambda_{A}$$

$$= \frac{1}{2}\bar{\lambda}^{C'}\nabla_{A'B}\nabla_{C'A}\lambda^{B} + \frac{1}{4}\bar{\lambda}^{C'}\varepsilon_{A'C'}\Box\lambda_{A} + \frac{1}{2}\bar{\lambda}^{C'}\nabla_{B(A'}\nabla_{C')}{}^{B}\lambda_{A}$$

$$= \frac{1}{2}\bar{\lambda}^{C'}\nabla_{A'B}\nabla_{C'A}\lambda^{B} - \frac{1}{4}\bar{\lambda}_{A'}\Box\lambda_{A} + \frac{1}{2}\Phi_{ABA'B'}\lambda^{B}\bar{\lambda}^{B'} ,$$

on using the spinor Ricci identity in the last term. The last term in (38) is

$$-\frac{1}{2}\lambda_{A}\nabla^{B}{}_{A'}\nabla_{B}{}^{C'}\bar{\lambda}_{C'} - \frac{1}{2}\lambda_{B}\nabla_{A'}{}^{B}\nabla_{A}{}^{C'}\bar{\lambda}_{C'}$$

$$= -\frac{1}{2}\lambda_{A}\nabla_{BA'}\nabla^{B}{}_{C'}\bar{\lambda}^{C'} - \frac{1}{2}\lambda^{B}\nabla_{BA'}\nabla_{AC'}\bar{\lambda}^{C'}$$

$$= -\frac{1}{2}\lambda_{A}\nabla_{B(A'}\nabla_{C')}{}^{B}\bar{\lambda}^{C'} - \frac{1}{4}\varepsilon_{A'C'}\lambda_{A}\Box\bar{\lambda}^{C'} - \frac{1}{2}\lambda^{B}\nabla_{AC'}\nabla_{BA'}\bar{\lambda}^{C'}$$

$$-\frac{1}{2}\lambda^{B}\varepsilon_{BA}\nabla_{E(A'}\nabla^{E}{}_{C')}\bar{\lambda}^{C'} - \frac{1}{2}\lambda^{B}\varepsilon_{A'C'}\nabla_{E'(A}\nabla^{E'}_{C)}\bar{\lambda}^{C'}$$

$$= \frac{3}{2}\Lambda\lambda_{A}\bar{\lambda}_{A'} - \frac{1}{4}\varepsilon_{A'C'}\lambda_{A}\Box\bar{\lambda}^{C'} - \frac{1}{2}\lambda^{B}\nabla_{A'C}\nabla_{BA'}\bar{\lambda}^{C'}$$

$$+\frac{3}{2}\Lambda\lambda_{A}\bar{\lambda}_{A'} + \frac{1}{2}\Phi_{ABA'B'}\lambda^{B}\bar{\lambda}^{B'}$$

$$= \frac{1}{4}\lambda_{A}\Box\bar{\lambda}_{A'} - \frac{1}{2}\lambda^{B}\nabla_{AC'}\nabla_{BA'}\bar{\lambda}^{C'} + 3\Lambda K_{a} + \frac{1}{2}\Phi_{ab}K^{b} ,$$

where Ricci identities have been used again. Here, $\Phi_{ab} = -\frac{1}{2}(R_{ab} - \frac{1}{4}Rg_{ab})$ and $\Lambda = \frac{1}{24}R$.

Substituting back into (38) gives for the second derivative terms,

$$\bar{\lambda}_{C'}\nabla_{A'}{}^{B}\nabla^{C'}_{(A}\lambda_{B)} - \lambda_{(A}\nabla_{|A'|}{}^{B}\nabla_{B)}{}^{C'}\bar{\lambda}_{C'} + \begin{matrix}\text{complex}\\ \text{conjugate}\end{matrix}$$

$$= 2(\Phi_{ab} + 3\Lambda g_{ab})K^{b} .$$

But by Einstein's equation, $\Phi_{ab} + 3\Lambda g_{ab} = 4\pi T_{ab}$, so finally,

$$\nabla^{b}F_{ab} = 4\pi T_{ab}K^{b} + \frac{1}{2}[(\nabla_{A'}{}^{B}\bar{\lambda}_{C'})\nabla^{C'}_{(A}\lambda_{B)} - (\nabla_{A'}{}^{B}\lambda_{(A})\nabla_{B)}{}^{C'}\bar{\lambda}_{C'} + \text{c.c.}] . \quad (39)$$

The integral over N is

$$\int_N \ell^a \nabla^b F_{ab}\, dN$$

$$= \int 4\pi T_{ab} \ell^a K^b dN + \frac{1}{2} \int o^A \bar{o}^{A'} [(\nabla_{A'}{}^{B} \bar{\lambda}_{C'}) \nabla^{C'}_{(A} \lambda_{B)} - (\nabla_{A'}{}^{B} \lambda_{(A}) \nabla_{B)}{}^{C'} \bar{\lambda}_{C'} + \text{c.c.}] dN. \quad (40)$$

The first term on the right hand side of (40) is nonnegative by condition (ii) of the theorem. For the second term, expand $\lambda^A = X o^A + Y \iota^A$ as usual, and define

$$P = o^A \delta\lambda_A,\ Q = o^A \bar{\delta}\lambda_A,\ R = o^A D\lambda_A,\ S = \iota^A D\lambda_A,\ T = \iota^A \delta\lambda_A.$$

The integrand of the second term on the right hand side of (40) then becomes

$$P\bar{P} - Q\bar{Q} - (\bar{T}R + T\bar{R}) + \bar{S}Q + S\bar{Q}\ . \quad (41)$$

Ludvigsen and Vickers (1982) choose a propagation equation for λ^A along N which 1) is compatible with strong asymptotic constancy of λ^A, and 2) makes (41) nonnegative. Setting $D\lambda^A = S o^A$, so that the propagation is in N, puts R = 0. Since $D\iota^A = \bar{\pi} o^A$ from (4), this propagation gives DY = 0, $DX = S - \bar{\pi}Y$. With S = nQ, (41) becomes $P\bar{P} + (2n-1)Q\bar{Q}$, which is nonnegative for $n \geq \frac{1}{2}$. Putting the usual asymptotics into this propagation equation gives

$$Y = Y^o(u, \theta, \phi)$$

from DY = 0, and successive powers of r^{-1} in $DX = nQ - \pi Y$ give

$$r^{-1}:\ \bar{\eth} Y^o = X^o$$

$$r^{-2}:\ (n-1)X^1 = (1-n)Y^o\, \eth\bar{\sigma}^o - n\bar{\sigma}^o\, \eth Y^o$$

$$r^{-3}:\ (n-2)X^2 + n\sigma^o\bar{\sigma}^o X^o = n\sigma^o\bar{\sigma}^o\bar{\eth}Y^o + (n-2)(\bar{\sigma}^o\bar{\eth}\sigma^o - \frac{1}{2}\psi_1{}^o),$$

etc.

The expansion here has been taken one step further than is given in (13), (14) and (15) to illustrate the structure. Solutions are possible for any n, with $\eth Y^o = 0$, and $n \geq \frac{1}{2}$ gives positivity. The propagation equation is therefore compatible with strong asymptotic constancy for any n. n = 1 is perhaps most natural since it requires $\eth Y^o = 0$ without restricting X^1. Ludvigsen and Vickers (1982) take n = 2 , which is also possible. It follows that λ^A can always be taken on N so that $\int_N \ell^a \nabla^b F_{ab} dN \geq 0$.

The remaining integral is that over the compact spacelike 3-ball Σ. Denoting the unit timelike future directed normal to Σ by t^a , this integral is

$$\int_\Sigma t^a{}^bF_{ab}d\,\Sigma$$

$$= 4\pi\int_\Sigma t^aK^bT_{ab}d\Sigma + \frac{1}{2}\int_\Sigma t^{AA'}[(\nabla_{A'}{}^{B}\bar{\lambda}_{C'})\nabla^{C'}{}_{(A\ B)} - (\nabla_{A'}{}^{B}\lambda_{(A})\nabla_{B)}{}^{C'}\bar{\lambda}_{C'} + \text{c.c.}]d\Sigma\,. \quad (42)$$

Again the first integral is nonnegative by the dominant energy condition. Ludvigsen and Vickers (1982) make the second intergral positive by imposing Witten's (1981) equation on Σ. Letting $h^{ab} = g^{ab} - t^at^b$ denote the projection operator onto Σ, and $D_a = h_a{}^b\nabla_b$, Witten's equation is

$$D_{AA'}\lambda^A = 0\ , \quad (43)$$

or

$$\nabla_{AA'}\lambda^A = t_{AA'}t^c\nabla_c\lambda^A\ . \quad (44)$$

With (43) satisfied, (42) becomes

$$\int_\Sigma t^a\nabla^bF_{ab}\,d\Sigma = 4\pi\int_\Sigma t^aK^bT_{ab}d\Sigma - \int_\Sigma h^{mn}t^{AA'}(D_m\lambda_A)(D_n\bar{\lambda}_{A'})d\Sigma\ . \quad (45)$$

Introducing an orthonormal frame $\xi_{\underline{\alpha}}^a$, $\underline{\alpha} = 1,2,3$, on Σ, and defining $\phi_{\underline{\alpha}}{}^A = \xi_{\underline{\alpha}}^c D_c\lambda^A$, the integrand in the second term on the right hand side of (45) is seen to be minus the inner product of t^a with the sum of three future directed null vectors $\phi_{\underline{\alpha}}^A\bar{\phi}_{\underline{\alpha}}^{A'}$. The minus sign comes because h^{ab} is negative definite. The two minus signs give a plus, so the second term is nonnegative also.

As Ludvigsen and Vickers point out, it is important that the propagation equation along N guarantees that $\bar{\eth}Y^o = X^o$ for any X on the boundary $\partial\Sigma$ of Σ. The reason is that Y^o must take on four independent values on $\partial\Sigma$ (hence on S), and positivity must hold for each of them. For this of course, it is also essential that the Witten equation has a solution on Σ for any value of Y^o on $\partial\Sigma$. Existence, but not uniqueness, of solutions to the Dirichlet problem for the Witten operator follows from the generalization on p. 273 of Theorem 10.6.1 of Hörmander (1976). From the remark above concerning X^o, uniqueness is not necessary, so the theorem is proved.

Corollary 1 (Horowitz and Perry 1982):
If P^B vanishes on S, then spacetime is flat to the future of the maximal extension in M of N.

Proof:
If P^B vanishes, then from the negative definiteness of h^{ab}, $\xi_{\underline{\alpha}}^m D_m\lambda^A$ vanishes on Σ for the basis $\xi_{\underline{\alpha}}^m$, whence $D_m\lambda^A$ vanishes on Σ. This implies from the spinor Bianchi identities that certain components of the curvature tensor vanish on Σ.

But the integral over Σ in (45) is independent of Σ if $\partial\Sigma$ is fixed, because $\nabla^a\nabla^b F_{ab} = 0$. Σ can therefore be varied in its domain of dependence, $\mathcal{D}[\Sigma]$, so that all components of the curvature vanish at all points of $\mathcal{D}[\Sigma]$. Sliding $\partial\Sigma$ out along N towards $\mathscr{I}^+$ and repeating the argument shows that spacetime is flat everywhere to the future of N.

Corollary 2 (Ashtekar and Horowitz 1982):
If P^B is null, then it vanishes.
The proof is given by Ashtekar and Horowitz and will not be repeated here. They also establish the analogous result for the energy-momentum at spacelike infinity.

Corollary 3 (Gibbons, Hawking, Horowitz and Perry, 1982):
If the hypersurface Σ of the theorem contains an apparent horizon, the conclusion of the theorem still holds. In addition, if the black hole is charged, then the mass is greater than the absolute value of the change.

The proof of Gibbons et al will not be repeated here.

Concluding remarks:
It was remarked above that the double divergence of F_{ab} vanishes identically. This means that the covector $P_a = \frac{1}{4\pi}\nabla^b F_{ab}$ is conserved, so that the integral of F_{ab} over the boundary of compact spacelike hypersurfaces Σ is independent of Σ. If $\partial\Sigma$ can be joined to $\mathscr{I}^+$ by a null hypersurface N, then the requirement that λ^A be strongly asymptotically constant at $S = N \cap \mathscr{I}^+$ implies that there are exactly four independent values of Y^o on $\partial\Sigma$, corresponding to a null basis of the BMS translation Lie algebra. If solutions of Witten's equation on Σ were unique, there would then be exactly four independent values of $\frac{1}{4\pi}\int_{\partial\Sigma} F_{ab}\, dS^{ab}$. These can be interpreted as the energy-momentum content within the surface $\partial\Sigma$. The formulation of Ludvigsen and Vickers (1982) therefore provides, in the above sense, a quasi-local definition of energy-momentum for gravitation. It seems likely that methods similar to those of section 4 of the paper of Parker and Taubes (1982) can be used to establish uniqueness for the Dirichlet problem with the Witten operator. Compare also Reula (1982).

Acknowledgements:

The author is grateful to his colleagues at the MPI for Astrophysics in Garching and to the participants at the Les Houches school for discussions and clarifying remarks, especially to Michael Streubel, Abhay Ashtekar and Gary Horowitz. Thanks also to James Vickers for explaining some points in his letters with Ludvigsen. The hospitality of the Physics Department of the Middle East Technical University in Ankara, where part of these notes were prepared, is gratefully acknowledged.

References

Ashtekar A. and Dray T. (1981) Commun. math. Phys. 79 581 - 599

Ashtekar A. and Horowitz G.T. (1982) Phys. Lett. 89A 181 - 184

Ashtekar A. and Streubel M. (1981) Proc.Roy.Soc. A 376 585 - 607

Bičák J. (1968) Proc. Roy. Soc. A 302 201 - 224

Bondi H., van der Burg M.G.J. and Metzner A.W.K. (1962) Proc. Roy. Soc. A 269 21 - 52

Bramson B.D. (1975) Proc.Roy.Soc. A 341 451 - 461

Exton A.R., Newman E.T., Penrose R. (1969) J.Math.Phys. 10 1566 - 1570

Friedrich H. (1981) "On the existence of analytic null asymptotically flat solutions of Einstein's vacuum field equations", preprint. See also H. Friedrich Proc.Roy.Soc A 375 (1981) 169 - 184 and A 378 (1981) 401 - 421.

Geroch R. (1971) in Proceedings of the International Summer School of Physics "Enrico Fermi" Course XLVII, ed. R. Sachs (Academic Press)

Geroch R., Held A. and Penrose R. (1973) J. Math. Phys. 14 874 - 881

Geroch R. (1976) in Asymptotic Structure of Space-Time, ed. F.P. Esposito and L. Witten (Plenum Press)

Geroch R. and Horowitz G. (1978) Phys. Rev. Lett. 40 203 - 206

Geroch R. and Winicour J. (1981) J.Math.Phys 22 803 - 812

Gibbons G., Hawking S., Horowitz G., and Perry M. (1982) "Positive mass theorems for black holes", preprint

Hawking S.W. and Ellis G.F.R. (1973) The Large Scale Structure of Space-Time (Cambridge University Press)

Hörmander L. (1976) Linear Partial Differential Operators (Springer Verlag)

Horowitz G.T. and Tod P. (1981) "A relation between local and total energy in General Relativity", Oxford University preprint

Horowitz G.T. and Perry M.J. (1982) Phys.Rev.Lett 48 371 - 374

Komar A. (1959) Phys. Rev. 113 934 - 936

Ludvigsen M. and Vickers J.A.G. (1981) J.Phys. A 14 L389 - L391

Ludvigsen M. and Vickers J.A.G. (1982) J.Phys. A 15 L67 - L70

Ludwig G. (1976) Gen. Rel. Grav. 7 293 - 311

Misner C.W., Thorne K.S. and Wheeler J.A. (1973) Gravitation (W.H. Freeman and Company)

Newman E. and Penrose R. (1962) J.Math.Phys. 3 566 - 578, errata 4 (1963) 998

Newman E.T. and Penrose R. (1965) J.Math.Phys 7 863 - 870

Newman E.T. and Unti T.W.J. (1962) J. Math. Phys. 3 891 - 901

Nester J.M. (1981) Phys. Lett. 83A 241 - 242

Parker T. and Taubes C.H. (1982) Commun.math.Phys. 84 223 - 238

Penrose R. (1963) Phys.Rev.Lett 10 66 - 68

Penrose R. (1964) in Relativity Groups and Topology, ed. C. De Witt and B. De Witt (Gordon and Breach)

Penrose R. (1965) Proc.Roy.Soc. A 284 159 - 203

Penrose R. (1967) in Relativity Theory and Astrophysics 1. Relativity and Cosmology ed. J. Ehlers (American Mathematical Society)

Penrose R. (1968) in Battelle Rencontres ed. C.M. De Witt and J.A. Wheeler (W.A. Benjamin Inc.)

Penrose R. (1974) in Group Theory in Non Linear Problems ed. A.O. Barut (D. Reidel Publishing Company)

Pirani F.A.E. (1965) in Lectures on General Relativity , ed. S. Deser and K.W. Ford (Prentice-Hall Inc.)

Reula O. (1982) J. Math. Phys. 23 810 - 814

Sachs R. (1962a) Proc.Roy.Soc A270 103 - 126

Sachs R. (1962b) Phys.Rev. 128 2851 - 2864

Sachs R. (1964) in Relativity Groups and Topology, ed. C. De Witt and B. De Witt (Gordon and Breach)

Schoen R. and Yau S.T. (1979a) Commun.math.Phys. 65 45 - 76

Schoen R. and Yau S.T. (1979b) Phys.Rev.Lett. 43 1457 - 1460

Schoen R. and Yau S.T. (1982) Phys.Rev.Lett. 48 371 - 374

Schmidt B. (1981) Commun. math. Phys. 78 447 - 454

Schmidt B., Walker M. and Sommers P. (1975) Gen.Rel.Grav. 6 489 - 497

Tamburino L.A. and Winicour J.H. (1966) Phys.Rev. 150 1039 - 1053

Walker M. (1979) in Isolated Gravitating Systems in General Relativity, Proceedings of the International School of Physics "Enrico Fermi", Course LXVII , ed. J. Ehlers (North Holland Publishing Company)

Winicour J. and Tamburino L. (1965) Phys.Rev.Lett. 15 601 - 604

Winicour J. (1968) J.Math.Phys. 9 861 - 867

Witten E. (1981) Commun.math.Phys. 80 381 - 401

THE INITIAL VALUE PROBLEM AND DYNAMICS

James W. York, Jr.
Department of Physics and Astronomy
University of North Carolina
Chapel Hill, North Carolina 27514
U.S.A.

INTRODUCTION

The physical predictions of general relativity are often hard to obtain even in fairly simple situations because of the complexity of the partial differential equations of the theory and the non-uniqueness of the solutions for the spacetime metric $g_{\mu\nu}$. The former property has to do with the non-linearity and coupling of the equations for the ten $g_{\mu\nu}$ while the latter is a result of the freedom of choosing the spacetime coordinate system. One approach to managing these problems, the subject of these lectures, is to view general relativity as a dynamical theory of gravity in which one has an initial data surface, constraint equations on the data that result from the coordinate freedom, and evolution equations. When the initial data surface and subsequent surfaces are three-dimensional spacelike slices that form a "foliation" of spacetime of codimension unity, then one is dealing with a Cauchy problem and one has dynamics in the ordinary sense, say, of Lagrangian or Hamiltonian mechanics.

In these lectures the dynamical or "three-plus-one" approach to Einstein's theory is reviewed. This of course is in some ways a rather old story. However, it is only in the past decade that the initial-value problem, which is the foundation of this approach, has been understood in the necessary detail and generality. Similarly, the theoretically "incidental" question of the choice of slicings and propagation of coordinates has seen great progress recently. This crucially practical problem has come into its own because nowadays people actually construct spacetime, rather than just talk about it, by numerical methods and computers.

A few words about the organization of these lectures: In order not to interrupt the discussion of essential ideas, notes have been relegated to the next-to-last section. The notes in turn point to the references, which are last.

METRIC, CONNECTION, AND CURVATURE

The object of the game is to construct the spacetime metric $g_{\mu\nu}$. The metric signature is (- + + +) with the minus sign for time. Thus, constant time surfaces--spacelike surfaces--are distinguished and we write the metric in a form adapted to this view:

$$ds^2 = -(\alpha^2 - \beta_i \beta^i)dt^2 + 2\beta_i dx^i dt + \gamma_{ij} dx^i dx^j \ . \qquad (1)$$

Here $ds^2 = g_{\mu\nu}dx^\mu dx^\nu$ has been given in an "adapted" coordinate basis. Spatial (Latin) indices run from one through three. The spatial metric of a slice t = constant is γ_{ij} with inverse defined by $(\gamma^{ij}\gamma_{jk} = \delta^i{}_k)$. The shift vector is $\beta^i = \gamma^{ij}\beta_j$, $\beta_j = g_{tj}$ and the lapse function is $\alpha = (-g^{tt})^{-1/2}$.

The geometry associated with the metric splitting is easy to see. If $\partial/\partial n$ is the timelike future-oriented unit normal vector of the slice, then we have

$$\frac{\partial}{\partial t} = \alpha \frac{\partial}{\partial n} + \beta^i \partial_i \quad (2)$$

where $\alpha\delta t$ is the orthogonal proper time separation of slices $t = t_o$ and $t = t_o + \delta t$. The signature of $g_{\mu\nu}$ is correctly (- + + +) when $\alpha > 0$ and γ is a positive metric. Since $\partial/\partial n$ is the four-velocity of an observer at rest in the slice, $\alpha^{-1}\beta^i$ measures the velocity of the spatial coordinate basis with respect to his origin in his local proper time. The acceleration vector of this observer is tangent to the slice and is given by $a^i = \gamma^{ij}\partial_j \ell n\alpha$.

As far as local observers at rest in the slices are concerned, the metric $g_{\mu\nu}$ is divided into the intrinsic metric γ_{ij} of a slice t = constant and the lapse α and the shift vector β^i. The latter two quantities depend on his subsequent motion (α; choice of next slice) and on the motion of the spatial coordinates (β^i). The natural rate-of-change of the metric concerns only the instantaneous state and hence deals only with the velocity of γ_{ij} with respect to local orthogonal proper time. By convention, one describes this with the second fundamental tensor, or extrinsic curvature tensor,

$$K_{ij} = -(1/2)\partial_n \gamma_{ij} = -\alpha\Gamma^t_{ij} \quad (3)$$

where Γ^t_{ij} are particular connection coefficients determined by $g_{\mu\nu}$. These are also singled out by the fact that (γ_{ij}, K_{ij}) determine the embedding of the slice in the ambient spacetime through the Gauss-Codazzi equation (below). The metric velocity determined by $\partial/\partial t$ is

$$\partial_t \gamma_{ij} = -2\alpha K_{ij} + D_i\beta_j + D_j\beta_i \quad (4)$$

where D_i is the spatial covariant derivative determined by γ_{ij}.

Visualization of K_{ij} is aided by noting that its trace ($\mathrm{tr}K = \gamma^{ij}K_{ij}$) is minus the expansion $\nabla_\mu n^\mu$ of the unit normal field n^μ and its trace-free part is minus the shear of n. The twist of n vanishes because it is hypersurface-orthogonal.

The curvature tensors ${}^{(4)}R^\mu{}_{\nu\alpha\beta}$ of $g_{\mu\nu}$ and $R^i{}_{jkl}$ of γ_{ij} are related by the Gauss-Codazzi equations,

$$ {}^{(4)}R_{ijk\ell} = R_{ijk\ell} + K_{ik}K_{j\ell} - K_{i\ell}K_{jk} \quad (5)$$

$$ {}^{(4)}R_{ijk\mu}n^\mu = D_jK_{ik} - D_iK_{jk} \; . \quad (6)$$

These formulas constitute the integrability conditions for the embedding of a slice characterized by the pair $(\gamma_{ij}, K_{k\ell})$ into the ambient spacetime. They give 14 of the 20 components of ${}^{(4)}R_{\mu\nu\alpha\beta}$.

The remaining six components of the spacetime curvature tensor involve second time derivatives of the metric. They can be written conveniently in the form

$$ {}^{(4)}R_{i\mu j\nu}n^\mu n^\nu = \alpha^{-1}(\partial_t - \pounds_\beta)K_{ij} + K_{i\ell}K^\ell{}_j + \alpha^{-1}D_iD_j\alpha \quad (7)$$

where $\pounds_\beta$ denotes the Lie derivative along the shift,

$$\pounds_\beta K_{ij} = \beta^k D_k K_{ij} + K_{ik}D_j\beta^k + K_{kj}D_i\beta^k \; . \quad (8)$$

EINSTEIN EQUATIONS AND CONSERVATION LAWS

From the above curvature equations one can write the Einstein equations $G_{\mu\nu} = 8\pi T_{\mu\nu}$ ($G = c = 1$). One has

$$G_{\mu\nu}n^\mu n^\nu = \tfrac{1}{2}(R + (\mathrm{tr}K)^2 - K_{ij}K^{ij}) = 8\pi\rho \tag{9}$$

where ρ is the proper energy density determined on a slice by the stress-energy tensor. This initial-value equation is called the scalar or Hamiltonian constraint. The three vector or momentum constraints are given by

$$-(\delta^i_\mu + n^i n_\mu)G^\mu_\nu n^\nu = D_j(K^{ij} - \gamma^{ij}\mathrm{tr}K) = 8\pi j^i \tag{10}$$

where j^i is the momentum density determined by $T_{\mu\nu}$ on the slice. If $\omega^{\hat{a}}{}_i$ denotes an orthonormal basis of one-forms on the slice, then $\omega^{\hat{a}}{}_i\, j^i$ is the proper momentum density of sources determined on the slice by the local ("rest") observer whose four-velocity is n^μ.

There are six remaining "dynamical" Einstein equation. To express these we need to project the Einstein equations in the form ${}^{(4)}R_{\mu\nu} = 8\pi(T_{\mu\nu} - \tfrac{1}{2}g_{\mu\nu}g^{\sigma\rho}T_{\sigma\rho})$. The projection $(\delta^\mu_i + n^\mu n_i)(\delta^\nu_j + n^\nu n_j)T_{\mu\nu} = S_{ij}$, the spatial stress tensor. The same projection on ${}^{(4)}R_{\mu\nu}$ then yields

$$(\partial_t - \pounds_\beta)K_{ij} = -D_iD_j\alpha + \alpha(R_{ij} - 2K_{i\ell}K^\ell{}_j + K_{ij}\mathrm{tr}K)$$
$$-8\pi\alpha(S_{ij} - \tfrac{1}{2}\gamma_{ij}\mathrm{tr}S + \tfrac{1}{2}\rho\gamma_{ij}) \,. \tag{11}$$

We have also

$$(\partial_t - \pounds_\beta)\gamma_{ij} = -2\alpha K_{ij} \,, \tag{12}$$

which amounts to the definition of K_{ij}. These last two equations are essentially the Hamilton equations for Einstein's theory, as we shall see below.

The contracted Bianchi identity $\nabla_\mu G^{\mu\nu} \equiv 0$ becomes the "conservation law" $\nabla_\mu T^{\mu\nu} = 0$. By projection, the latter can be conveniently written as a "continuity equation"

$$\partial_t\rho + \alpha D_i j^i = \alpha(S^{ij}K_{ij} + \rho\,\mathrm{tr}K) - 2j^iD_i\alpha + \beta^iD_i\rho \tag{13}$$

and an "Euler equation"

$$\partial_t j^i + \alpha D_j S^{ij} = \alpha(2K^{ij}j_j + j^i\mathrm{tr}K) - S^{ij}D_j\alpha - \rho D^i\alpha + \pounds_\beta j^i \,, \tag{14}$$

where $\pounds_\beta j^i = [\beta, j]^i = \beta^j D_j j^i - j^j D_j \beta^i$. This completes the formal re-writing of the Einstein equations in a form adapted to analysis of initial-value and evolution problems.

CANONICAL VARIABLES

The geometrically defined gravitational initial data $(\gamma_{ij}, K_{k\ell})$ are closely related to the canonical variables appropriate for writing Einstein's theory with $T_{\mu\nu} = 0$ as a constrained Hamiltonian system. The canonical formalism has proven to be useful in studying problems such as the positivity of energy, invariant decomposition of gravitational perturbations, and canonical quantization. The position or "q" variable is the spatial metric γ_{ij} and the momentum "p" variable is related to the extrinsic curvature by

$$\pi^{ij} = \sqrt{\gamma}\,(\gamma^{ij}\,\mathrm{tr}K - K^{ij}) \tag{15}$$

where $\gamma \equiv \det(\gamma_{ij})$. Notice that π^{ij} is a spatial tensor density of weight one. (In this section only, units are such that ($16\pi G = c = 1$ instead of $G = c = 1$). The Poisson bracket relations are

$$[\gamma_{ij}(x),\ \gamma_{k\ell}(x')] = [\pi^{ij}(x),\ \pi^{k\ell}(x')] = 0\ , \tag{16}$$

$$[\gamma_{ij}(x),\ \pi^{k\ell}(x')] = \tfrac{1}{2}(\delta^k_i\delta^\ell_j + \delta^k_j\delta^\ell_i)\delta(x,x')\ . \tag{17}$$

The vacuum constraints are written as

$$\mathcal{H}(\gamma,\pi) \equiv \frac{1}{2\sqrt{\gamma}}\,(\gamma_{im}\gamma_{jn} + \gamma_{jm}\gamma_{in} - \gamma_{ij}\gamma_{mn})\pi^{ij}\pi^{mn} - \sqrt{\gamma}\,R = 0 \tag{18}$$

$$\mathcal{H}_i(\gamma,\pi) \equiv -2\gamma_{im}D_j\pi^{jm} = 0\ . \tag{19}$$

The total Hamiltonian depends on the boundary conditions as well as a choice of lapse α and shift β^i, which are not determined by the theory. In general, one has

$$H = \int(\alpha\,\mathcal{H} + \beta^i\,\mathcal{H}_i)d^3x + [\text{surface terms}]\ . \tag{20}$$

Here α and β^i are "c-number" functions of the coordinates, not of the canonical variables. For compact slices, the surface terms are absent. The value of H is zero, but of course the constraints $\mathcal{H} = 0$, $\mathcal{H}_i = 0$ are only imposed after the equations of motion

$$\partial_t\gamma_{ij} = \frac{\delta H}{\delta\pi^{ij}}\ ;\ \partial_t\pi^{ij} = -\frac{\delta H}{\delta\gamma_{ij}} \tag{21}$$

have been calculated.

For asymptotically flat slices, the surface term is necessary both physically, because it defines among other things the total energy, and mathematically, to render the functional derivatives in (21) well defined. Appropriate conditions for asymptotic flatness "at spatial infinity" will be described in detail later. In the most important case, where $\partial/\partial t$ goes to a time translation at large distances ($\alpha \to 1 + \mathcal{O}(r^{-1})$, $\beta^i \to 0 + \mathcal{O}(r^{-1})$), the surface term is the total energy E(ADM energy)

$$E = \oint_\infty (h^i_j - \delta^i_j h^k_k)_{|j}\, d^2S_i\ . \tag{22}$$

Here the metric has been written as $\gamma_{ij} = f_{ik}(\delta^k{}_j + h^k{}_j)$, where f_{ik} is flat, $h^i{}_{j,k} = \mathcal{O}(r^{-1})$, and $h^i{}_{j,k} = \mathcal{O}(r^{-2})$. (If $G = c = 1$, the integral is multiplied by $(16\pi)^{-1}$). If $\alpha \to 0$ and $\beta^i \to \phi^i$ = a translational Killing vector of f_{ik}, there is a surface term defining the linear momentum:

$$P_i\phi^i = -2\oint_\infty \pi^i_j\phi^j d^2S_i = \frac{1}{8\pi}\oint_\infty (K^i_j - \delta^i_j\,\mathrm{tr}K)\phi^j d^2S_i\ . \tag{23}$$

It has been known for a long time that $P^{\mu} = (E,P^i)$ forms a conserved Lorentz four-vector of energy-momentum at large distances. A long series of investigations has recently culminated in proofs that P^{μ} is a non-zero timelike future-oriented four-vector except in the case of flat spacetime, when $P^{\mu} = (0,0)$. Thus one has a positive energy theorem for non-flat spacetime geometries whenever the energy can be defined. The total energy is defined neither for closed slices (compact without boundary), unless it is taken there to be zero, which is reasonable, nor for open slices that are not asymptotically flat and empty, such as occur in some cosmological models.

The mass (rest mass) of an asymptotically flat field is defined by $M = (E^2 - P_i P^i)^{1/2}$ and is non-negative. The quantities $E, P_i \phi^i$, and M are constants of the motion.

The angular momentum is also an important concept for asymptotically flat systems. The natural definition in the canonical framework defines this by replacing the asymptotic translational symmetry vector ϕ^i of γ_{ij} by an "asymptotic rotational symmetry vector" $\phi^i{}_{rot}$ in (23). However, there is some ambiguity in the resulting expression.

INITIAL VALUE EQUATIONS

The dynamical approach to general relativity leads us to solve the equations as a Cauchy problem. This means we must first satisfy the constraints (initial value problem) and then propagate the data with some judicious choice of the lapse and shift (evolution problem = kinematics (α and β^i) + dynamics ($\partial_t \gamma_{ij}$ and $\partial_t K_{ij}$)). The heart of this method is to understand the constraints, which we write as

$$\nabla_j (K^{ij} - \gamma^{ij} \mathrm{tr}K) = 8\pi j^i \qquad (24)$$

$$K_{ij} K^{ij} - (\mathrm{tr}K)^2 - R = -16\pi\rho \qquad (25)$$

where we have written ∇_j instead of D_j for the spatial covariant derivative and $G = c = 1$. These equations are best thought of as dealing with the embedding of one surface in spacetime. Thus a good analogy is to think of the structure of a "thin shell" or "elastic membrane" as in continuum mechanics. A "gauge" transformation in general relativity is then analogous to deforming the shell with its boundary held fixed ($\alpha \to 0$, $\beta^i \to 0$), while "evolution" has the boundary displaced orthogonally by a fixed positive amount ($\alpha \to 1, \beta^i \to 0$).

The key point about the initial value problem is to decide which parts of γ_{ij} and K_{ij} to specify freely and which then to determine to force the equation to hold. The free data can then be thought of as corresponding to the "true degrees of freedom" of the gravitational field from the viewpoint of the Cauchy problem. A successful approach is described subsequently. First, consider an unsuccessful one.

I shall mention briefly the "two surfaces" interpretation of the initial value equations ("thin sandwich" problem), as this view is of at least historical interest. It is assumed that the free data are two infinitesimally different metrics γ_{ij} and $\gamma_{ij}' = \gamma_{ij} + \delta\gamma_{ij}$ on two nearby slices that bound the thin sandwich. One interprets $\delta\gamma_{ij}$ as $\dot{\gamma}_{ij}\delta t$ and attempts to solve (24) and (25) for α and β^i. The resulting equations are quite unwieldy and impractical to solve. Unless one requires that α has no zeros (keeps the same sign, say positive) then one has great difficulties in building K_{ij} (which is what one needs) and, moreover, the surfaces either touch or intersect. Excluding these cases, I have found a large class of simple but important counterexamples to the conjecture. (The literature I have seen, all of it, I believe, contains no correct counterexamples to the thin sandwich conjecture with $\alpha > 0$, or even $\alpha \geq 0$). Thus, consider a slice with the topology of a three-sphere and $R < 0$ everywhere--there are many such metrics. Take the normal physical case $\rho \geq 0$. From $R < 0$ and (25) it follows that (trK) is non-vanishing and cannot change signs on the slice. Suppose γ_{ij} is unrestricted except for the global condition that the volume it determines on the nearby slice is the same as that on the first one. Then

$$\begin{aligned} \frac{d}{dt}\int\sqrt{\gamma}\, d^3x = 0 &= -\int(\alpha \mathrm{tr}K - \nabla_i\beta^i)\sqrt{\gamma}\, d^3x \\ &= -\int\alpha \mathrm{tr}K\sqrt{\gamma}\, d^3x \quad . \end{aligned} \tag{26}$$

Equation (26) is impossible from the fact that (trK) cannot change signs and that α is not allowed to do so by hypothesis. The thin sandwich approach will not be considered further here. It possesses many other difficulties that the reader can readily determine.

DECOMPOSITIONS OF SYMMETRIC TENSORS

Solution of the momentum constraint will involve decomposing the symmetric tensor K_{ij} in a certain way. There is more than one way to perform splittings of symmetric tensors. Hence I shall first give a discussion that I hope is of some general interest.

It is convenient to think of any symmetric tensor h_{ij} as a perturbation of a (positive) Riemannian metric g_{ij} in n dimensions (here $n \geq 3$). I shall consider four forms of the metric that have proven to be of interest in geometry and in relativity: g_{ij} = (ordinary) Riemannian metric; $\tilde{g}_{ij} = g^{-1/n}g_{ij}$ = conformal metric (unimodular); $g^{1/2}g^{ij}$ = harmonic metric; and gg^{ij} = "energy" metric. If we consider the action of an infinitesimal diffeomorphism generated by a vector field X^i, we act on the metric with the Lie derivative along X^i. This gives a special vector-generated perturbation (gauge transformation). For the four metrics we have

Metric	Metric Perturbation	Gauge Transformation
1. g_{ij}	h_{ij}	$\nabla_iX_j + \nabla_jX_i$
2. $\tilde{g}_{ij}$	$h_{ij} - \frac{1}{n}g_{ij}\mathrm{tr}h$	$\nabla_iX_j + \nabla_jX_i - \frac{2}{n}g_{ij}\nabla_kX^k$
3. $g^{1/2}g^{ij}$	$h_{ij} - \frac{1}{2}g_{ij}\mathrm{tr}h$	$\nabla_iX_j + \nabla_jX_i - g_{ij}\nabla_kX^k$
4. gg^{ij}	$h_{ij} - g_{ij}\mathrm{tr}h$	$\nabla_iX_j + \nabla_jX_i - 2g_{ij}\nabla_kX^k$

Here the perturbations are represented by the corresponding covariant symmetric tensors (no tensor denisities are used here).

Tensors are split by separating them into parts with zero covariant divergence ("transverse") plus parts of the vector type. The vector is determined by equating the covariant divergence of the "gauge" pieces to the divergence of the original tensor and solving (if possible) for X^i. Here the resulting second order operators are all formally self-adjoint. We want, however, to know if the operators are elliptic, which mainly determines the solvability. For this we construct the "symbol" of the operator, a matrix obtained by replacing derivatives in the second order part by non-zero vectors ξ^i. This yields

	Operator	Symbol Matrix
1.	$\Delta X_i + \nabla_i(\nabla_j X^j) + R_{ij}X^j$	$g_{ij}(\xi_k\xi^k) + \xi_i\xi_j$
2.	$\Delta X_i + (\frac{n-2}{n})\nabla_i(\nabla_j X^j) + R_{ij}X^i$	$g_{ij}(\xi_k\xi^k) + (\frac{n-2}{n})\xi_i\xi_j$
3.	$\Delta X_i + R_{ij}X^i$	$g_{ij}(\xi_k\xi^k)$
4.	$\Delta X_i - \nabla_i(\nabla_j X^i) + R_{ij}X^j$	$g_{ij}(\xi_k\xi^k) - \xi_i\xi_j$

Here $\Delta = g^{ij}\nabla_i\nabla_j$. It is easily seen that all the symbol matrices have non-zero determinants (non-singular) and positive eigenvalues (elliptic) except the last one. In general, this operator cannot be inverted. This is related to the gauge invariance of the ADM energy (for n = 3) and to a difficulty of the thin-sandwich problem, namely, that the linear part of the shift operator there is equivalent to operator 4. The symbol of this operator is the same that occurs in some gauge theories, e.g., for "curl curl" in Maxwell's theory. In those theories however it can be rendered non-singular by imposing a gauge condition like $\nabla_i X^i = 0$. This is allowed because of a conserved current. In general this trick fails in relativity and geometry owing to the non-existence of an appropriate locally conserved current!

Geometrically, the "canonical" splitting 1 is equivalent to 3. However, 1 and 2 are fundamentally different because of the conformal invariance of $\tilde{g}_{ij}$ (when $g_{ij} \to \bar{g}_{ij} = \psi^p g_{ij}$; $\psi > 0$; p = 4 for n = 3, p = 2 for n = 4, etc.). Equivalently, one sees that a perturbation of g_{ij} is tracefree, while the others are not. Method 2 corresponds to the TT (transverse-tracefree) decomposition that is useful in solving the constraints (n = 3):

$$h_{ij} = \overset{*}{h}_{ij} + (\nabla_i X_j + \nabla_j X_i - \frac{2}{3} g_{ij}\nabla_k X^k) + \frac{1}{3} g_{ij} \mathrm{tr} h \qquad (27)$$

where * denotes the TT part. The geometry of the relation of the canonical (C) and TT splittings is illustrated by a "commuting diagram"

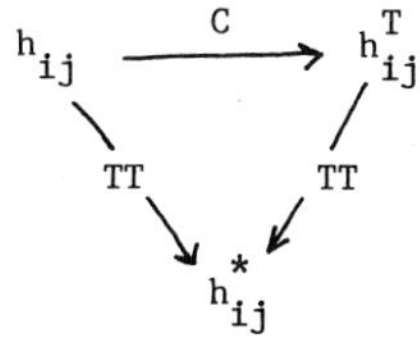

Here T = transverse. In others words, acting on symmetric tensors, TT ∘ C = C ∘ TT = TT.

CONFORMAL TRANSFORMATIONS

I have hinted that conformal transformations of the three-metric (referred to as either γ_{ij} or g_{ij} hereafter) will be used in solving the constraints. Let us recall the movitation for this by writing the standard Schwarzschild metric in "isotropic" coordinates

$$ds^2 = -(1 - \frac{M}{2r})^2(1 + \frac{M}{2r})^{-2}dt^2 + (1 + \frac{M}{2r})^4(f_{ij}dx^i dx^i) \tag{28}$$

where f_{ij} is flat and r is the radial distance determined by f_{ij} (the horizon is at $r = M/2$ here). Thus $\psi = (1 + M/2r)$ acts like a scalar potential.

Important general formulas for conformal transformations ($\psi > 0$) in n dimensions ($n \geq 3$) are

$$g_{ab} = \psi^{4(n-2)^{-1}} \hat{g}_{ab}$$

$$R = \hat{R} \ \psi^{-4(n-2)^{-1}} - 4(\frac{n-1}{n-2}) \hat{\Delta} \psi$$

$$C^a{}_{bcd} = \hat{C}^a{}_{bcd}$$

where the latter is the Weyl tensor. It vanishes identically for n = 3, where the corresponding role is played by the "Bach" tensor

$$B_{ijk} = \nabla_j(R_{ik} - \frac{1}{4} g_{ik}R) - \nabla_k(R_{ij} - \frac{1}{4} g_{ij}R) .$$

For the subsequent work, it is useful to know that for n=3, the connection transforms as

$$\Gamma^i_{jk} = \hat{\Gamma}^i_{jk} + 2\psi^{-1}(\delta^i_j\hat{\nabla}_k\psi + \delta^i_k\hat{\nabla}_j\psi - \hat{g}_{jk}\hat{g}^{im}\hat{\nabla}_m\psi) .$$

From these simple formulas one can show that every completely trace-free tensor, symmetric or skew, has a useful scaling property for its covariant divergence. Take from here on the case n = 3. Consider a vector E^i and when there is a conformal transformation $g_{ij} = \psi^4\hat{g}_{ij}$, let $E^i = \psi^{-6}\hat{E}^i$. Then one finds

$$\nabla_i E^i = \psi^{-6}\hat{\nabla}_i\hat{E}^i .$$

This can be understood by considering Gauss's theorem. Because $g^{1/2} = \psi^6\hat{g}^{1/2}$ we have

$$\int\nabla_i E^i g^{1/2} d^3x = \int\hat{\nabla}_i\hat{E}^i\hat{g}^{1/2} d^3x = \int_S E^i d^2S_i = \text{number of flux lines piercing S.}$$

Clearly this number is independent of the conformal scaling. For more complicated objects there are similar interpretations.

The case of most interest is a tracefree symmetric tensor T^{ij}. When the metric is transformed conformally, we define $T^{ij} = \psi^{-10}\hat{T}^{ij}$. The zero trace is preserved and also

$$\nabla_j T^{ij} = \psi^{-10}\hat{\nabla}_j\hat{T}^{ij}$$

SOLVING THE MOMENTUM CONSTRAINTS

The machinery is in place for writing the momentum constraints (24) as an elliptic system for a vector potential. First write K^{ij} in terms of its tracefree part (A^{ij}) and its trace part. We assume that the scalar trK is given once and for all as part of the free data.

We do not give g_{ij} as free data but rather $\hat{g}_{ij}$ where they are in conformal relation. The conformal factor ψ is regarded as unknown--the scalar potential to be found later--but we do have to assume $\psi > 0$. Likewise define $\hat{A}^{ij}$ by $A^{ij} = \psi^{-10}\hat{A}^{ij}$. $\hat{A}^{ij}$ can be split by the TT method (27) with the given metric $\hat{g}_{ij}$ as free data. Its vector part is denoted by

$$(\hat{L}W)^{ij} = \hat{\nabla}^i W^j + \hat{\nabla}^j W^i - \frac{2}{3}\hat{g}^{ij}\hat{\nabla}_k W^k . \tag{29}$$

Recall that

$$\hat{\nabla}_j(\hat{L}W)^{ij} \equiv (\hat{\Delta}_L W)^i = \hat{\Delta}W^i + \frac{1}{3}\hat{\nabla}^i(\hat{\nabla}_j W^j) + \hat{R}^i_j W^j \tag{30}$$

is formally self-adjoint and elliptic. Moreover it is positive and the only non-trivial vectors it can annihilate are conformal Killing vectors. As none of these, if present, can vanish at spatial infinity (with asymptotically flat boundary conditions), the kernel of Δ_L is empty and it can always be inverted for a unique solution. This is very helpful, for the momentum constraint now has the form

$$(\hat{\Delta}_L W)^i = \frac{2}{3}\psi^6\hat{\nabla}^i(\mathrm{tr}K) + 8\pi\psi^{10}j^i .$$

We shall see shortly that the matter current j^i can be scaled by $j^i = \psi^{-10}\hat{j}^i$ for natural reasons. So we find

$$(\hat{\Delta}_L W)^i = \frac{2}{3}\psi^6\hat{\nabla}^i(\mathrm{tr}K) + 8\pi\hat{j}^i . \tag{31}$$

Hence one can find W^i independently of ψ and of the other constraint except for the term involving the gradient of trK. We have the happy circumstance that on a maximal slice (trK = 0) or a constant mean curvature slice (trK = constant ≠ 0), (31) is completely independent of ψ. Since we are in these lectures interested only in asymptotically flat spacetimes, we usually employ only trK = 0. These slices go to spatial infinity (i^o on a Penrose diagram). On the other hand, trK = constant ≠ 0 are analogous to the mass hyperboloids of flat spacetime. They are spacelike but become null asymptotically. They hit null infinity ("scri" plus or minus). They deserve careful study in the present context but I shall not consider them further here. I shall assume that spacelike slices go to spatial infinity (trK goes to zero as r^{-2} or faster).

Now the momentum constraint is under control and in fact the same ideas give a unique formulation for compact slices as well. However, there is a word of warning. If the slice is open but not asymptotically flat, the splitting used here may not produce unique results; such things always require decent boundary conditions. Clearly, this can also happen on asymptotically flat spaces with inner boundaries (cut-out places) or on incomplete spaces. These last two cases do not raise serious problems, however.

We have a momentum constraint theorem for the cases of interest. For any $\psi > 0$, every K^{ij} such that (24) holds has the form

$$K^{ij} = \psi^{-10}[\hat{A}_*^{ij} + (\hat{L}W)^{ij}] + \frac{1}{3}\psi^{-4}\hat{g}^{ij}\mathrm{tr}K \tag{32}$$

where W^i is given by (31). The problem now is to find a suitable ψ. First, I consider a few simple examples of $\hat{K}^{ij}$.

SOME EXTRINSIC CURVATURE TENSORS

Assume $\hat{g}_{ij} = f_{ij}$ (flat) and solve

$$(\hat{\Delta}_L W)^i = \nabla^2 W^i + \frac{1}{3}\nabla^i(\nabla_j W^j) = 0 \tag{33}$$

for W^i's that vanish as r^{-1} at large distances. There are three such solutions which, combined, yield

$$(\hat{L}W)^{ij} = \frac{3}{2r^2}[P^i n^j + P^j n^i - (P_k n^k)(f^{ij} - n^i n^j)] \tag{34}$$

where P^i is a constant vector and $n^i = r^{-1}(x,y,z)$ is the unit normal of a sphere. Note that because of the r^{-2} factor, we have in effect a point-like source at the origin and $(\hat{L}W)^{ij}$ holds outside the source. Suppose further that $\mathrm{tr}K = 0$ and that $\hat{A}_*^{ij}$ is zero or at least vanishes faster than r^{-2}. Then (34) is our $\hat{K}^{ij}$ while the physical $K^{ij} = \psi^{-10}\hat{K}^{ij}$ for some $\psi > 0$. Since $\psi \to 1 + \mathcal{O}(r^{-1})$, the dominant asymptotic behavior of the physical K^{ij} is fixed. The physical meaning of P^i is that it is the total linear momentum, as we see by calculating in Cartesian coordinates the linear momentum surface integral

$$P_i = \frac{1}{8\pi} \oint_\infty (K_i^j - \delta_i^j \mathrm{tr}K) d^2S_j .$$

The corresponding angular momentum surface integral and other moments of (34) are zero.

As another simple but significant example, take $\hat{g}_{ij} = f_{ij}$, $\mathrm{tr}K = 0$, $\hat{A}_*^{ij} = \mathcal{O}(r^{-p})$, $p > 3$, and solve (33) for W^i's with asymptotic behavior r^{-2}. Among these are three characterized by a constant skew tensor J_{ij} or a three-vector J_i that is its dual. One finds

$$(\hat{L}W)^{ij} = \frac{3}{r^3}(n^k J_{ki} n_j + n^k J_{kj} n_i) . \tag{35}$$

Contracting this with a translational Killing vector of f_{ij} and integrating over a large sphere, we see that the corresponding physical K^{ij} possesses zero linear momentum. Taking a rotational Killing vector ϕ^i of f_{ij} and performing the surface integration yields a component of angular momentum

$$J_i \phi^i = \frac{1}{8\pi} \oint_\infty \frac{3}{r^3}(n^k J_{ki} n_j + n^k J_{kj} n_i) \phi^i d^2S^j . \tag{36}$$

There are three W^i's $\sim \mathcal{O}(r^{-3})$ obtained from (33) that yield an interesting extrinsic curvature tensor which can be written as

$$\hat{B}^{ij} = \frac{3a^2}{2r^4}[P^i n^j + P^j n^i + (P_k n^k)(f^{ij} - 5n^i n^j)] \tag{37}$$

where $a > 0$ is a constant and P^i is a constant vector. The r^{-4} decay shows immediately that (37) generates no linear or angular momentum as $r \to \infty$. What is its meaning? This can be answered by considering the action of a transformation of inversion through a sphere of radius a centered at the origin. This transformation is defined on $R^3 - \{0\}$. In Cartesian coordinates we have

$$\bar{x}^i = \frac{a^2}{r^2} x^i \quad ; \quad \frac{\partial \bar{x}^i}{\partial x^j} \equiv \mathcal{J}^i_j = \frac{a^2}{r^2}(\delta^i_j - 2n^i n_j) . \tag{38}$$

It is not difficult to verify that, if we denote our first example above as $K^{ij}(P)$, that

$$\hat{K}_{ij}(P;x) = -\left(\frac{a}{r}\right)^2 \mathcal{J}^m_i \mathcal{J}^n_j \hat{B}_{mn}(\bar{x}) \tag{39}$$

where $\bar{x}$ denotes the inverted point. Since (38) sends the origin to infinity, (39) suggests that $\hat{B}_{ij}$ may have to do with linear momentum at "another infinity" if we can give $R^3-\{0\}$ a two-sheeted topology with two asymptotically flat "ends." The completion of this interpretation awaits the construction of an appropriate conformal factor ψ, which I postpone until after a treatment of the Hamiltonian constraint. What we are aiming for here is a two-sheeted vacuum model, the sheets connected by a "throat", of initial data for a moving black hole.

We can now see from the linearity of (33) that $\hat{K}_{ij}(P)$ and $\hat{B}_{ij}$ can be combined to yield a solution

$$\hat{K}_{ij}(P,a) = \hat{K}_{ij}(P) + \hat{B}_{ij} \tag{40}$$

with the elegant inversion property

$$\hat{K}_{ij}(P,a;x) = -(\frac{a}{r})^2 \mathcal{J}^m_i \mathcal{J}^n_j \hat{K}_{mn}(P,a;\bar{x}) \ . \tag{41}$$

Property (41) turns out to be essential for the eventual construction of ψ to yield a moving black hole.

In the same spirit of examinining the effect of inversions on $\hat{K}_{ij}$'s that satisfy the constraints, in order to construct black hole data, let us recall our second example, which we denote by $\hat{K}_{ij}(J)$. A simple calculation shows that it already has the inversion property (41):

$$\hat{K}_{ij}(J;x) = -(\frac{a}{r})^2 \mathcal{J}^m_i \mathcal{J}^m_j \hat{K}_{mn}(J;\bar{x}) \ . \tag{42}$$

Note that this example is independent of the inversion radius a.

ENERGY CONDITIONS

We have already given all the formulas needed to write the Hamiltonian constraint (25) as a scalar potential equation for ψ. Before displaying the result, let us turn our attention briefly to the scaling of ρ and j_i.

If ρ and j_i arise from some other fundamental field, then their behavior under our conformal transformations--which we should note in general are not identical to the conformal changes that would be induced by a conformal transformation of the full spacetime metric--is dictated by their physical character and by the possible need to solve, simultaneously with the gravity constraints, any constraints inherent in the field equations of the sources. Examples are abundant: consider that ρ and j^i correspond to some gauge field. Here, however, we shall treat them as essentially phenomenological sources whose scalings are determined by considerations of physical causality. This turns out to give the same formulas as for massless gauge field sources like Maxwell fields. The present approach has the advantage not only of simplicity but also of being independent of the equation of state of the matter sources.

Recall that $j^i = \psi^{-10}\hat{j}^i$ was introduced to decouple the current from the Hamiltonian constraint. In fact, taking $j^i = (\vec{E} \times \vec{B})^i$ and remembering that E^i and B^i have zero divergence gives our formula. What about ρ? We could take a hint from $(E^2 + B^2)$ or, more to the point, we can inforce the idea that, at least classically, the sources cannot have a spacelike energy-momentum four-vector. This is the "dominant energy" condition $\rho^2 \geqslant g_{ij}j^i j^j$. We can add further the "weak" energy condition that $\rho \geqslant 0$ and unite the two by the requirement

$$\rho \geqslant +(g_{ij}j^i j^j)^{1/2} . \tag{43}$$

From the previous transformations, then, it follows that $\rho = \psi^{-8}\hat{\rho}$ will guarantee that

$$\hat{\rho} \geqslant +(\hat{g}_{ij}\hat{j}^i\hat{j}^j)^{1/2} . \tag{44}$$

implies (43) for all $\psi > 0$. Thus, we can build (43) into the initial data from the beginning. Hence, although these scalings of ρ and j^i are not unique, and in fact permit useful changes without doing violence to the general scheme, we shall adopt them in what follows.

Because the initial value equations do not depend on the pressures or spatial stresses of the sources, the material equation of state is left arbitrary. For the same reason, the "strong" energy condition $(\rho + \text{tr}S) \geq 0$ is not involved. However, the latter can be important in the evolution problem in constructing a lapse function.

HAMILTONIAN CONSTRAINT

Collecting our previous formulas enables us to write the Hamiltonian constraint (24) as a semi-linear elliptic potential-type equation for the conformal factor:

$$-8\hat{\Delta}\psi = -\hat{R}\psi + M\psi^{-7} + 16\pi\hat{\rho}\psi^{-3} - N\psi^{5} \tag{45}$$

where

$$M = \hat{g}_{ij}\hat{g}_{k\ell}\hat{A}^{ik}\hat{A}^{j\ell} = \hat{A}^{2} \tag{46}$$

$$N = \frac{2}{3}(\text{tr}K)^{2} . \tag{47}$$

Note that all ψ-dependence in (45) is shown explicitly. Only the terms with $\hat{R}$ and N have proven to cause any real difficulties in analyzing this equation in the case of asymptotically flat data. The scalar curvature is the real "black beast" of the problem. The presence of a non-constant N also raises interesting problems, to which I shall return, even apart from the fact that $\hat{\nabla}_i \text{tr}K \neq 0$ causes the momentum and Hamiltonian constraints not to be uncoupled.

The physical meaning of (45) is partly revealed by the observation, which goes back to Brill's pioneering analysis of time-symmetric, axisymmetric gravitational waves, that the difference between the energies (ADM energies) of two metrics $\hat{g}_{ij}$ and $g_{ij} = \psi^4\hat{g}_{ij}$ that form parts of asymptotically flat data can always be expressed as

$$E(g) - E(\hat{g}) = -\frac{1}{2\pi}\int(\hat{\nabla}^{i}\psi)d^{2}S_{i} . \tag{48}$$

This follows from (22) and $\psi \to 1 + \mathcal{O}(r^{-1})$. Therefore, for example, if $\hat{g}_{ij}$ is chosen to fall off faster than r^{-1}, or more generally if its ADM integral is zero (how to arrange this is discussed later), then the $\mathcal{O}(r^{-1})$ part of the solution of (45) is the energy. We now know that $E > 0$ except in the flat case, so we see that the solution of (45) is always decreasing at large r: $\psi = 1 + E(2r)^{-1} + \mathcal{O}(r^{-(1+\varepsilon)})$, $\varepsilon > 0$.

Quite generally, consider the case where $\hat{R} \geq 0$ and look for a ψ that maps $\hat{g}_{ij}$ conformally to a metric of zero scalar curvature. We have to solve the linear equation

$$8\hat{\Delta}\psi - \hat{R}\psi = 0 . \tag{49}$$

The maximum principle applies here and one can establish that there is one and only one ψ satisfying (49) with $\psi \to 1$ at infinity. Moreover $0 < \psi \leq 1$. Therefore, we conclude that every metric with non-negative scalar curvature is conformally related to one with zero scalar curvature and the former has the greater energy. This lemma ($\bar{\text{O}}$ Murchadha and York) was used by Schoen and Yau in the final version of their proof of the positive energy theorem.

Zero scalar curvature metrics are significant because they are solutions of the time-symmetric $(K_{ij} = 0)$ vacuum $(\rho = 0)$ initial value problem. From the above lemma it follows that every initial data set on a maximal slice $(\text{tr}K = 0)$ has greater energy than that of some time-symmetric data set whose metric is in the same conformal class. This means that the addition of matter $(\rho \geq 0)$ and "kinetic energy" $(M \geq 0)$ always increases the energy. This result is intuitively expected but shows that the build-up of "negative gravitational potential energy" in the non-linear interaction cannot overwhelm the positive matter and kinetic energy.

If $\hat{R} \leqslant 0$ it is not always possible to solve (49) for $\psi > 0$ and even if it is, the maximum principle does not apply. Suppose, however, that $\hat{R}$ is not "too negative" and we get a positive ψ that goes to one at infinity. Then the energy of the zero scalar curvature metric is greater than that of the negative scalar curvature metric. If, moreover, the latter were zero, we would have positive energy for R = 0 metrics, if they could all be obtained from $\hat{R} \leqslant 0$ metrics. Unfortunately one does not know this. Of course, we do know the $E \geqslant 0$ result independently.

We see that the scalar curvature is the hard part. We need to know when $\hat{R}$ is "too negative" and also to understand the cases where $\hat{R}$ has a variable sign. To get a handle on this question, I generalized slightly some early ideas of Brill and Wheeler. Consider (49) when the Laplacian is flat and $\hat{R}$ is a negative constant for $0 \leqslant r \leqslant a$ and is zero outside. (Now $\hat{R}$ is not really scalar curvature, but never mind.) Then we can get $\psi > 0$, $\psi \to 1$ if and only if $|\hat{R}|^{1/2}a < \sqrt{2}\pi$. As one approaches the critical value from below, the energy increases. At the critical value one drops $\psi \to 1$ and interprets the data as a closed slice with zero energy. Beyond the critical value one may again have $\psi \to 1$ but ψ has a node (a zero) and the slice contains a "bag of gold" singularity with negative-energy that is "visible", that is, is not enclosed by a minimal two-surface (which in this case would be an apparent horizon). This shows why the positive energy theorems necessarily require the restriction that any singularities must be "hidden" behind apparent horizons! (It is interesting that some of the early papers on positive energy did not contain this obviously necessary caveat.) As we push still further beyond the critical value, E becomes positive again but the singularity is still naked. Finally a minimal surface forms, the energy is positive, and the bag of gold is hidden. Then one reaches another critical value and the sequence repeats. Cantor and Piran have made all this more general and precise and have offered a possible physical interpretation.

The best results on this general question of the sign of the scalar curvature have been given by Cantor and Brill. They show that (49) can be solved with $\psi > 0$, $\psi \to 1$, whenever

$$\left(\int_{V^-} |\hat{R}|^{3/2}\, \hat{g}^{1/2}\, d^3x\right)^{2/3} \leqslant C \tag{50}$$

where C is a positive constant that can be estimated. V^- denotes the support of the negative part of $\hat{R}$ only. The spherical model suggests $|\hat{R}|a^2 \lesssim \pi^2 \cong 10$. (The value of C in this case turns out to be 8.) Moreover, these authors have shown explicitly the existence of regular asymptotically flat metrics for which (49) has no acceptable solution. We shall see that this means that no acceptable initial data of any kind, with trK = 0, can be built up from such metrics on R^3.

Combining the previous results with the positive energy theorem, one sees the important geometrical result (well known for n = 2) that one cannot have a lump of scalar curvature $R \geqslant 0$, $R \neq 0$ with compact support on an asymptotically Euclidean three-geometry, "Euclidean" meaning here that the metric becomes flat and spheres have areas $4\pi r^2$ in the usual way (no "conical" embedding of the three space in a flat enveloping space could be allowed--by analogy to the two-dimensional problem).

The question of embedding at large distances brings up an important point about the physical problem. Eardley has shown that there are positive-energy asymptotically flat spacetimes, with $g_{ij} \to f_{ij}$ and $K_{ij} \to 0$, such that the ADM energy integral is zero. What is going on is that in these cases $K_{ij} \sim \mathcal{O}(r^{-3/2})$ and this is too slow. In fact, 3/2 is the critical value. One needs the exponent of r to be $-(3/2 + \varepsilon)$, $\varepsilon > 0$. One usually takes $\mathcal{O}(r^{-2})$ so that the linear momentum integral is guaranteed to converge as $r \to \infty$. Then the ADM integral gives the true energy.

ASYMPTOTIC FLATNESS

In the present setting, "asymptotically flat" refers to initial data on a spacelike slice and includes both conditions on the fall-off of the metric on the slice and on the embedding, that is, on the extrinsic curvature (and therefore on the sources).

The conditions on the metric are that (here we work on R^3) for large r we can write

$$g_{ij} = f_{ik}(\delta^k_j + h^k_j)\ ,\ h^k_j = \mathcal{O}(r^{-1})\ ,$$
$$\pounds_X h^k_j = \mathcal{O}(r^{-2})\ ;\ \pounds_X \pounds_X h^k_j = \mathcal{O}(r^{-3})\ , \qquad (51)$$

where X^i is a translational Killing vector of the flat metric f_{ij}. It is assumed that the formulas hold for all three of the linearly independent X^i's. The faster fall-off of derivatives is in keeping with the idea that there are no gravitational waves at spatial infinity (spatial infinity is beyond any wave fronts).

For the embedding to be acceptable in this framework, one has

$$K^i_j = \mathcal{O}(r^{-2})\ ,\ \pounds_X K^i_j = \mathcal{O}(r^{-3})\ . \qquad (52)$$

To preserve this asymptotic flatness with respect to temporal evolution, we require

$$(\alpha - 1) = \mathcal{O}(r^{-1})\ ,\ \beta_i X^i = \mathcal{O}(r^{-1})\ , \qquad (53)$$

plus successively faster fall-off for the derivatives. In a similar vein, we take for the sources

$$\rho = \mathcal{O}(r^{-4})\ ,\ j_i X^i = \mathcal{O}(r^{-4}) \qquad (54)$$

which guarantee finite energy, momentum, and angular momentum for the sources just as in Newtonian gravity.

The above conventional description of asymptotic flatness is not adequate for the proving of rigorous theorems about the constraints. One uses instead "weighted Sobolev spaces" that capture our differentiability and fall-off conditions. These are like the usual Sobolev spaces $W_{s,p}$ but have an extra index attached--the weight--to force the fall-off we require. The new spaces are denoted $M^p_{s,\delta}$ where p is a power (as in Hilbert spaces where p = 2), s is some number of derivatives (not a point to be dwelled upon here) and δ is the weight. The type of most interest are $M^2_{s,\delta} \equiv H_{s,\delta}$ and we define them over R^3. The functions in $H_{s,\delta}$ are the C^∞ functions of compact support completed by those functions with a finite norm defined by

$$\|f\| = \int |\sigma^\delta f|^2 dv + \int |\sigma^{\delta+1} \partial f|^2 dv + \int |\sigma^{\delta+2} \partial\partial f|^2 dv + \ldots \ . \qquad (55)$$

One goes through all s derivatives and $\sigma = (1 + r^2)^{1/2}$. The appropriate weight in three dimensions turns out to be $-3/2 < \delta < -1/2$. Then functions $f = \mathcal{O}(r^{-1})$ are in $H_{s,\delta}$, as is appropriate for potentials in three-space. For functions that fall off like r^{-3}, one uses $\delta+2$, etc. It is interesting that apparently "bad" potentials like, for example, $f \sim (\ell n r) r^{-1}$ are also in $H_{s,\delta}$. This causes no troubles in the initial value problem as we shall see.

The reason for using these spaces is that in them the initial value equations involve second order elliptic operators that define "isomorphisms" between such spaces. This means essentially that the equations can be solved uniquely. For example, consider the Laplacian on an asymptotically flat slice. Assume that the metric has components such that the h_{ij}'s live in $H_{s,\delta}$, $s \geqslant 4$. Then Δ: $H_{s,\delta} \to H_{s-2,\delta+2}$ is an isomorphism, meaning that $\Delta f = \rho$ has a unique solution for $\rho \in H_{s-2,\delta+2}$ and $f \in H_{s,\delta}$.

CONSTRAINT THEOREMS ON MAXIMAL SLICES

First consider the constraints (31) and (45) with trK = 0 (a maximal initial data surface). The constraints have the form

$$(\hat{\Delta}_L W)^i = 8\pi\hat{j}^i , \tag{56}$$

$$-8\hat{\Delta}\psi = -\hat{R}\psi + M\psi^{-7} + 16\pi\hat{\rho}\psi^{-3} . \tag{57}$$

We have used, as before, $j^i = \psi^{-10}\hat{j}^i$ and $\rho = \hat{\rho}\psi^{-8}$. In fact the results which follow are true also for $\rho = \hat{\rho}\psi^{-\lambda}$, $\lambda > 5$. For example, if $\lambda = 6$ we have the sometimes useful condition that the total matter energy can be pre-specified:

$$\int \rho g^{1/2} d^3x = \int \hat{\rho}\hat{g}^{1/2} d^3x \quad \text{if} \quad \rho = \hat{\rho}\psi^{-6} . \tag{58}$$

In any event, suppose that the data are asymptotically flat in the sense that, in Cartesian components, we have $\hat{g}_{ij} - \delta_{ij} \in H_{s,\delta}$, $\hat{K}_{ij} \in H_{s-1,\delta+1}$, $(\hat{\rho},\hat{j}^i) \in H_{s-2,\delta+2}$ and $\hat{\rho} \geqslant 0$. Take a large enough s, say $s \geqslant 4$, and $-3/2 < \delta < -1/2$. Taking a large s is physically not restrictive because spacelike infinity is always beyond any wave fronts by assumption. Then (56) has a unique solution $W^i \in H_{s,\delta}$, which is to say that the "vector Laplacian" Δ_L is an isomorphism. This result is also true for (31) (dropping trK = 0) for any ψ such that $\psi - 1 \in H_{s,\delta}$. However, in this case (31) and (45) are coupled. In other words the momentum constraints <u>per se</u> are completely under control.

The constraint (57) is more subtle. However, we have the following powerful theorem due to Cantor and others: There is a unique positive solution ψ of (57) such that $\psi - 1 \in H_{s,\delta}$ if and only if in the conformal equivalence class of $\hat{g}_{ij}$ there is a zero scalar curvature metric. In other words the solvability of (57) is equivalent to the solvability of the vacuum time-symmetric initial value problem for $\hat{g}_{ij}$. The latter has been discussed above in terms of the Cantor-Brill scalar curvature theorem. Thus, the procedure I have outlined completely removes any difficulties associated with K_{ij}, ρ, and j^i provided trK = 0.

There would appear superficially to be a small difficulty with the fact that $\psi - 1 \in H_{s,\delta}$ in that this appears to allow solutions such that the surface integral of $\nabla_i\psi$ may not converge and thus that the energy might be logarithmically divergent. However, there is really no problem as I now show.

In the first place, within the present framework of asymptotic flatness, one can always combine a diffeomorphism and a conformal change on the initial slice (before solving for ψ) such that the ADM energy integral associated with $\hat{g}_{ij}$ is zero. This means all of the energy resides in the solution ψ of (57):

$$E = -\frac{1}{2\pi}\oint_\infty (\hat{\nabla}^i\psi) d^2S_i . \tag{59}$$

Now consider condition (54), $\hat{\rho} = \mathcal{O}(r^{-4})$, which is slightly stronger than the fall-off implied by the condition $\rho \in H_{s-2,\delta+2}$. Then by integrating both sides of (57) and using Gauss's theorem, one sees that E must in fact be finite and therefore that $\psi - 1$ is strictly $\mathcal{O}(r^{-1})$. The condition $\hat{\rho} = \mathcal{O}(r^{-4})$, more precisely

$$\int \hat{\rho} \hat{g}^{1/2} d^3x < \infty \, , \tag{60}$$

would also be necessary in obtaining finite energy even in Newtonian theory. The condition that we need on $\hat{\rho}$ arises automatically if $\hat{\rho}$ is quadratic in some external field strength f such that $f \in H_{s-1,\delta+1}$.

A similar argument shows that W^i is strictly $\mathcal{O}(r^{-1})$. For this, analogously to the above, one uses $\hat{j}^i = \mathcal{O}(r^{-4})$, more precisely

$$\int \hat{j}_i X^i \hat{g}^{1/2} d^3x < \infty$$

for the translation symmetries X^i of f_{ij}.

NON-MAXIMAL SLICES

If trK is not zero but vanishes at infinity, its gradient is non-zero and this introduces the extra current-like term $\psi^6 \hat{\nabla}^i \mathrm{trK}$ in (31). As I have remarked, for any given ψ, this causes no problem in solving for W^i.

The real difficulties with trK ≠ 0 are (1) the coupling between the constraints makes the analysis more difficult, and (2) the right hand side of the Hamiltonian constraint now has the term $-N\psi^5$, $N = (2/3)(\mathrm{trK})^2$, as in (45). No complete analysis of the coupled problem has been given; this is an outstanding problem for someone to solve.

There are, however, some important conclusions that we can draw. Let us consider (45) and assume that we have zero scalar curvature in the conformal class of $\hat{g}_{ij}$. This was necessary and sufficient for a solution with N = 0. It will not play such a dominant role with N ≠ 0, but we assume it as a basis for discussion. Then we can write (45) in the form

$$8\hat{\Delta}\psi + M\psi^{-7} + 16\pi\hat{\rho}\psi^{-3} - N\psi^5 = 0 \, . \tag{61}$$

Suppose there is a solution of (61) such that $(\psi - 1) \in H_{s,\delta}$ for $s \geq 4$ and $-3/2 < \delta < -1/2$. Then we can show such a solution must be unique. If it were not, there would be a point x_o where $h = \psi_1 - \psi_2$ (two solutions) would have a positive maximum, since $h \to 0$ at infinity. However, using (61) we see that $\Delta h(x_o) > 0$, which is a contradiction. Hence a solution of (61) must be unique.

Moreover, note that because $\hat{\nabla}\mathrm{trK} \neq 0$ in the momentum constraint, we cannot have M = 0 in (61) in the physical problem of interest. Hence we can always assume in (61) that $M \geq 0$, $M \neq 0$, and of course $N \neq 0$. Because $\psi - 1 \in H_{s,\delta}$, ψ must be C^2 (an embedding theorem for Sobolev spaces) and therefore $\Delta\psi$ is continuous. Since $M \neq 0$ we see that if $\psi = 1$ at infinity, it must be positive because otherwise $M\psi^{-7}$ would blow up somewhere. Hence, any solution of (61) will be necessarily both unique and positive, if it exists. This is gratifying and does not follow unless the coupling of the constraints is taken into account.

I shall now state briefly another new result about the coupled problem, assuming again that we can take the scalar curvature of $\hat{g}_{ij}$ equal to zero: If $\mathrm{trK} \in H_{s-1,\delta+1}$ and is sufficiently small everywhere on R^3, there exists a unique solution (ψ, W^i) of the coupled problem, and of course $\psi > 0$. This result is not surprising, of course, but it does rely on a nice "order-by-order" uncoupling property of the constraints in a neighborhood of <u>any</u> solution (ψ_o, W^i_o) of the problem at trK = 0.

ROBIN BOUNDARY CONDITIONS

If the constraints are solved numerically, it must be done on a finite grid with a largest radius $R < \infty$. Therefore we consider a compact slice with a boundary being the two-sphere $r = R$.

The analog of $\psi \to 1$ as $r \to \infty$ would be a Dirichlet condition $\psi(R) = 1$. Clearly, this will force ψ to be too steep at $r = R$ and the total energy E will be over-estimated. We can avoid this problem by using a procedure devised by Piran and York, involving so-called Robin boundary conditions, which involve a mix of Dirichlet and Neumann conditions.

Let f be a scalar function operated on by an elliptic operator that obeys a maximum/minimum principle. Work on a domain Ω of R^3 with boundary B, whose outward unit normal is $\partial/\partial n$. Then the following Robin condition will produce a unique solution:

$$\frac{\partial f}{\partial n} + gf = h \quad \text{on} \quad B \tag{62}$$

where $g \geq 0$.

Recall that we expect $\psi = 1 + E(2r)^{-1} + \mathcal{O}(r^{-2})$ and $\partial\psi/\partial r = -E(2r^2)^{-1} + \mathcal{O}(r^{-3})$. Eliminating E between these two equations gives, with $u = \psi - 1$,

$$\frac{\partial u}{\partial r} + \frac{1}{R}\, u = \mathcal{O}(R^{-3}) \tag{63}$$

at $r = R$, which has the form of (62). For a reasonably large grid we can usually estimate $h = \mathcal{O}(R^{-3})$ by zero. Numerical work involving the $\hat{K}_{ij}$'s discussed previously (using inversion symmetry, etc.) has demonstrated the feasibility and accuracy of this procedure.

A similar problem would arise in putting $W^i(R) = 0$ in the momentum equation. This would yield an unacceptable estimate of the total linear momentum P^i (usually we want this to be zero--we work in a rest frame). A procedure similar to that employed above for E, using (34) to characterize W^i and $(LW)^{ij}$, results in a new kind of Robin condition applicable to vectors:

$$(\hat{L}W)^{kj} n_j (\delta^i_k - \tfrac{1}{2} n^i n_k) + \frac{6}{7R} W^k (\delta^i_k - \frac{1}{8} n^i n_k) = \mathcal{O}(R^{-3}) , \tag{64}$$

where n^i is the unit outward normal of the large sphere. It can be shown that (64) used in conjunction with vector elliptic operators like $\hat{\nabla}_j(\hat{L}W)^{ij}$ that define isomorphisms with Dirichlet conditions also yields unique solutions. I understand that Nakamura (this volume) has successfully used (64) in computing initial data for rotating collapse. There one expects a W^i such that $P^i = 0$ but the angular momentum $J^i \neq 0$. One cannot in general construct directly a Robin condition to sharpen the value of J^i because such W^i's $= \mathcal{O}(r^{-2})$ but the fundamental solutions in three dimensions of Laplace-type operators are $\mathcal{O}(r^{-1})$.

NON-STANDARD BLACK HOLE DATA

We return to the example $\hat{K}_{ij}$'s discussed in equations (33)-(42). The objective is to solve the Hamiltonian constraint, which has the form

$$\nabla^2\psi + \frac{1}{8} M\psi^{-7} = 0 , \tag{65}$$

where ∇^2 is the flat-space Laplacian. Recall that we are working on $R^3 - \{0\}$. We want the physical solution, however, to have two isometric sheets joined by a throat, that is, we want the origin to become "another" normal spatial infinity. The result is supposed to represent a topologically non-trivial model of a black hole. The top sheet, say, represents the observable exterior geometry.

To enforce the idea that the data represent a black hole, we will make the inversion sphere r = a into a minimal two-surface of the three-geometry. The reason we do this can be seen by recalling the equation of an apparent horizon, written in terms of the Cauchy data:

$$\nabla_i s^i - \mathrm{tr}K + K_{ij} s^i s^j = 0 \,. \qquad (66)$$

Here trK = 0. The trace of the extrinsic curvature of a two surface with outward unit normal s^i embedded in a three space is $\mathrm{tr}X = -\nabla_i s^i$. The formula trX = 0 defines a minimal two-surface. (Actually this gives an extremal surface. In our examples it is easy to prove it is in fact minimal.)

In terms of the conformal data (66) becomes

$$\hat{\nabla}_i \hat{s}^i + 4\hat{s}^i \hat{\nabla}_i \ell n\psi + \psi^{-4} \hat{K}_{ij} \hat{s}^i \hat{s}^j = 0 \,. \qquad (67)$$

where $s^i = \psi^{-2}\hat{s}^i$.

In general, even with trK = 0, the apparent horizon is not a minimal surface. However, I conjecture that if there is a minimal surface, there will always be an apparent horizon "nearby." This conjecture is true in the examples I discuss here. Once we have an apparent horizon, we assume cosmic censorship and infer that the evolved data will possess an event horizon also, coinciding with or outside of the apparent horizon. Therefore, the data represent a black hole.

We demand that the inversion $\mathcal{J}$: $\bar{r} = a^2 r^{-1}$ on $R^3 - \{0\}$ be an isometry of the physical metric $g_{ij} = \psi^4 f_{ij}$. This means

$$g_{ij}(x) = \mathcal{J}^m_{\ i} \mathcal{J}^m_{\ j} (g_{mn} \circ \mathcal{J}(x)) \qquad (68)$$

which implies

$$\psi(x) = \frac{a}{r} \psi \circ \mathcal{J}(x) \qquad (69)$$

or $\psi(r,\theta,\phi) = (ar^{-1})\psi(a^2 r^{-1},\theta,\phi)$. It can then be seen that if $\psi \to 1 + E(2r)^{-1}$ on one "end" ($r \to \infty$), then also $\psi \to 1 + E(2\bar{r})^{-1}$ on the other end ($\bar{r} \to \infty, r \to 0$) as well.

Differentiating (69) gives (not a Robin condition because $\partial_r = -\partial_n$)

$$\frac{\partial \psi}{\partial r}(a) + \frac{1}{2a}\psi(a) = 0 \qquad (70)$$

which implies r = a is a minimal surface in the physical geometry. (In fact, being a submanifold that is the fixed point set of an isometry, r = a is a totally geodesic subspace, that is, not only trX = 0 but $X_{ij} = 0$.)

We can now use (70) as an inner boundary condition on the top sheet and one has only to solve (65) for $r \geq a$ such that (70) holds and $\psi > 0$, $\psi \to 1$ as $r \to \infty$. If there is a solution to this problem it can be shown to be unique. Moreover, the solution on the top sheet can always be extended smoothly and uniquely to a ψ on all of $R^3 - \{0\}$ such that the top and bottom sheets are isometric and the throat has a metrically non-spherical minimal surace at r = a. A proof of this assertion has been presented in detail in the literature. This depends crucially on using either Kij (P-type) of (41) or the K_{ij} (J-type) of (42) to form M in (65). The result is either a boosted or a spinning black hole. It has been proven theoretically that the resulting holes are neither, respectively, standard boosted Schwarzschild holes or Kerr holes (There will be no timelike Killing vector.) Ours are accompanied by, in effect, some gravitational waves whose behavior cannot be known quantitatively until our data have been evolved. However, Piran has solved (65) numerically for the ψ's and (67) for the apparent horizons in both cases. Details are presented elsewhere.

It is worth noting that the above procedure goes through if we add the $\hat{K}_{ij}$'s of (41) and (42). This produces a translating spinning hole. Furthermore, similar techniques enable us also to give the hole an electric charge. None of this, however, has been worked through in detail nor solved numerically. I think the results would be very interesting.

Of greater importance in extending this program, and in fact its goal, is to contruct initial data for two holes that have orbital angular momentum and therefore will undergo a spiraling encounter, and, presumably, produce gravitational radiation efficiently. This problem has been solved by simply adding two of the $\hat{K}_{ij}$'s as in (41), with different inversion centers. The impact parameter and initial separation are adjustable parameters, along with the two P^i's and the two a's. If they are initially far apart, one can even give ψ to very good accuracy. However, the result is a three-sheeted manifold: the top ("physical") sheet has both holes, but the throats connect to inequivalent bottom sheets. This picture results because the sum of the two $\hat{K}^{ij}$'s does not invert in the proper way through either center of inversion. Presumably, to achieve this one needs an infinite series of "image" $\hat{K}_{ij}$'s. If this could be done, and it has not been, then the resulting ψ would have the correct inversion properties to allow two isometric sheets only. The advantage of such generalized "Misner-matched" data would be that each throat would have a minimal surface and we would know precisely, rather than approximately, what boundary conditions analogous to (70) to employ in a numerical solution. I think the resolution of this would be an outstanding result, even though our present data should give good results ultimately (when the data--non-axisymmetric!) are evolved.

ENERGY FLUX

I will not say much on this subject as I cannot improve much the analysis given by Smarr in 1979. He lists eight energy flux formulas that are classified by whether they are based on the connection ($\Gamma \sim \partial g$) or on the curvature. The first type is more physical but has attendant "gauge" sensitivity. (Example: modernized ADM "Poynting" vector.) The curvature formulas are nice but do not have the physical dimensions of energy flux unless some appropriate Fourier analysis is performed, which is not easy in curved space. However, often one can read off the dominant wave length from graphs of the metric behavior at moderate values of r. (Example: Bel-Robinson flux vector.) Smarr also distinguishes formulas based on Cauchy data and those based on characteristic data. (The latter can readily be written in terms of the Cauchy data used in 3+1 evolution.)

Bardeen and Piran (see Bardeen, this volume) have refined the treatment of energy flux calculations in the 3+1 format. Another very promising approach uses the characteristic initial value and evolution equations directly. There are several articles on this subject in this volume. Ultimately one wants to be able to solve the equations and compute fluxes by both methods. An advantage of the 3+1 method is that it has been developed and tested more extensively at this time (1982). Moreover, one knows from the work of many people, most recently Christodoulou and Ō Murchadha and Ashtekar, a precise description of spatial infinity as a mathematical construct and, most importantly, one knows that it correctly characterizes the asymptotic behavior of solutions of Einstein's equations. One has achieved this nice situation from analysis of the initial value problem and from the "boost" theorem (below).

I will add one suggestion about finding the total energy radiated away in computations on a finite spatial grid. One knows the initial total energy at the initial time by using the Robin condition to fix E. On a subsequent slice, then one may extract from the 3-metric g_{ij} a conformal metric $\tilde{g}_{ij}$ that satisfies

$$\tilde{g}_{ij} = f_{ik}(\delta^k_j + \tilde{h}^k_j) \tag{71}$$

where

$$\mathrm{grad}_f \mathrm{tr}_f \tilde{h}^k_j = \mathcal{O}(r^{-3}) \quad , \tag{72}$$

$$\mathrm{div}_f \tilde{h}^k_j = \mathcal{O}(r^{-3}) \ . \tag{73}$$

Then $E_{ADM}(\tilde{g}) = 0$. From $g_{ij} = \psi^4 \tilde{g}_{ij}$ in this gauge, one uses ψ to compute $E_{ADM}(g)$ at the edge of the grid. It would be interesting to check the resulting value of "ΔE_{ADM}" at finite r and compare it to results obtained by other methods. It should be accurate provided one does not have much wave energy reflecting back from r = R (impedance mismatch). The reliability of any method is of course dependent on understanding the latter problem in a numerical context.

EVOLUTION

We can think of the 3+1 evolution problem as first order equations (for $\partial_t g_{ij}$ and $\partial_t K_{ij}$) or second order equation (for $\partial_t \partial_t {}^{(4)}g_{\mu\nu}$). The first method is geometrically clearer as it uses the variables natural to the initial value problem. The second is easier to handle in the sense of proving mathematical theorems. In both cases one has to employ "gauge" conditions to control α and β^i.

The gauge conditions people have used can be divided into elliptic type, hyperbolic type (e.g., "harmonic" conditions), and either of these two mixed with algebraic conditions. I cannot add much to extensive discussions given in previous works, but I will make a few remarks.

I think the best choice is to use elliptic type gauges that control the velocities of the two primary variables $\tilde{g}_{ij}$ and trK that determine the initial "state" as described in the preceding sections. The most pressing problem is to obtain a good foliation of spacetime by spacelike slices. One can do this by fixing the velocity of trK

$$\partial_t \mathrm{tr}K = -\Delta\alpha + \alpha\left[K_{ij}K^{ij} + 4\pi(\rho + \mathrm{tr}S)\right] + \beta^i \nabla_i \mathrm{tr}K \ . \tag{74}$$

The operator for α is linear, elliptic, and obeys a maximum/minimum principle if the "strong" energy condition $(\rho + \mathrm{tr}S) \geqslant 0$ holds.

The choice of β^i is less important and is often dictated by convenience, such as preserving a manifest symmetry in the data or by simply setting $\beta^i = 0$ ("Pythagorean gauge"). A more elegant choice is the "minimal distortion" condition, which, given a slicing, filters the action of spatial diffeomorphisms out of $\tilde{g}_{ij}$ by the demand $\nabla^j(\partial_t \tilde{g}_{ij}) = 0$ or

$$\nabla_j (L\beta)^{ij} = 2\nabla_j\left[\alpha(K^{ij} - \tfrac{1}{3} g^{ij}\mathrm{tr}K)\right] \ . \tag{75}$$

Note that the vector Laplacian acting on β^i is the same one that gives us W^i in the momentum constraints (except here one uses g_{ij} instead of $\hat{g}_{ij}$). It follows that β^i and W^i are closely related in their asymptotic behavior.

If the constraints hold, then the system of equations for $\partial_t g_{ij}$, $\partial_t K_{ij}$, $\partial_t \mathrm{tr}K$ (fixed), and (75) should give a unique development for the spacetime metric $g_{\mu\nu}$ in vacuum. However, there is no theorem for this mixed evolution system. The idea of uniqueness here is a conjecture that I would like to see sharpened, proved, or disproved.

Apart from recent work of Friedrich (this volume) and Choquet-Bruhat (this volume) the strong theorems on evolution in either first or second order form employ the "harmonic gauge." I give here four equivalent forms of the harmonic gauge

$$(\sqrt{-g}\, g^{\mu\nu})_{,\nu} = 0 \tag{76}$$

$$\Gamma^{\mu} = g^{\alpha\beta}\Gamma^{\mu}_{\alpha\beta} = 0 \tag{77}$$

$$\partial_t \alpha = \beta^j \partial_j \alpha - \alpha^2 \mathrm{tr}K \tag{78a}$$

$$\partial_t \beta^i = \beta^j \partial_j \beta^i - \alpha^2 [\gamma^{ij}\partial_j(\ln\alpha) + \Gamma^i] \tag{78b}$$

where γ_{ij} and $\Gamma^i = \gamma^{jk}\Gamma^i_{jk}$ in (78b) refer to the spatial metric. The fourth form employs a background metric formalism with $g_{\mu\nu}$ as a background spacetime metric. The harmonic condition is then

$$\hat{\nabla}_{\nu}[\sqrt{-g}\, g^{\mu\nu}] = 0 \ . \tag{79}$$

The latter shows its natural relation to gauge conditions in other field theories. However, I do not understand the geometrical content of the harmonic conditions in terms of foliations of slices threaded by curve congruences in the way that is clear if one uses (74) and (75).

Mme. Choquet (this volume) has introduced a gauge that suffices for obtaining the Einstein equations in a new hyperbolic form. The equations have third order form, i.e., they look like

$$g^{\mu\nu}\nabla_{\mu}\nabla_{\nu}(K^{ij} - \gamma^{ij}\mathrm{tr}K) = \ldots \tag{80}$$

with the gauge

$$\beta^i = 0 \ ; \quad \alpha = (\sqrt{\gamma})(\sqrt{f})^{-1} \tag{81}$$

where $\sqrt{f}$ denotes an arbitrarily chosen fixed scalar density of weight one. The relation of (81) to the harmonic gauge can be seen by dropping (78b) and putting $\beta^i = 0$ in (78a). Then one has

$$\partial_t \alpha = -\alpha^2 \mathrm{tr}K \tag{82}$$

which is satisfied by (81).

BOOST THEOREM

The mathematical soundness of the 3+1 approach to Einstein's theory was advanced by the "boost theorem" of Christodoulou and Ō Murchadha. This result also shows rigorously the existence of "spatial infinity." The result is worth going through in detail. Fortunately, the paper by these authors gives a clear exposition, so I shall limit myself to a few remarks. This theorem was made possible by the fact that results on both the initial-value and evolution problems can be established in the $H_{s,\delta}$ spaces. Harmonic gauge was employed so that the evolution problem is strictly hyperbolic in the usual technical sense.

One's intuitive idea is that you have an asymptotically flat spacelike slice with a strong field region "in the middle" and a weak field far away. One should therefore be able to push (evolve) the slice far into the future, asymptotically, while perhaps not so far in the strong field region. The boost theorem shows you can do this, with the proper timelike "distance" between the initial data surface and the future (or past) surface growing linearly with spatial distance from the strong field region. The notion of distances used here can be made precise and one finds that the effective "boost" being made asymptotically corresponds to a physical velocity (or "slope") $v < c$.

It is interesting that the theorem was proved using a very weak notion of asymptotic flatness, namely

$$g_{ij} \to f_{ij} + \mathcal{O}(r^{-\varepsilon}) \tag{83}$$

$$K_{ij} \to \mathcal{O}(r^{-(1+\varepsilon)}) \tag{84}$$

where $\varepsilon > 0$. The usual way of thinking has $\varepsilon = 1$. This might give rise to a speculation that one could extend the theorem such that $v = c$ and the spacelike slices are asymptotically null, i.e., that the slices hit null infinity. However, it seems that one would need $\mathrm{tr}K = \mathcal{O}(r^{-1})$, that is, $\varepsilon = 0$, to do this. I believe that the slow fall-offs in (83) and (84) can be gauged away and do not assert anything of physical importance. This should be investigated.

ACKNOWLEDGMENTS

Over the past ten years I have benefitted from discussions with many colleagues. I would especially like to thank Murray Cantor, Yvonne Choquet-Bruhat, Niall Ō Murchadha, Tsvi Piran, and Larry Smarr. I also acknowledge continued support from the National Science Foundation of the U.S.A.

NOTES

These notes follow the text in order by sections. They are intended to give only references that are recommended for easy access to the problems. As such, they reflect strongly my personal biases and are not complete nor do they attempt to establish priority. More extensive bibliographies are found in Choquet-Bruhat and York (1980) and York (1979).

Introduction

The 3+1 approach to Einstein's theory is found in Arnowitt, Deser, and Misner (hereinafter referred to as ADM) (1962), Misner, Thorne, and Wheeler (MTW) (1973), and Wheeler (1963). I use MTW conventions throughout. For numerical relativity, see Smarr (1979).

Metric, Connection, and Curvature

The role of metric, extrinsic curvature, lapse, and shift is seen in Lichnerowicz (1944), Choquet-Bruhat (1962), and ADM (1962). The material is worked out in detail in general form, including non-coordinate bases in York (1979).

Einstein equations and Conservation Laws

This is a continued elaboration of the previous section. It follows York (1979).

Canonical Variables

See ADM (1962). A recent review is Isenberg and Nestor (1980). Discussions of energy and momentum surface integrals are found in Regge and Teitelboim (1974) and York (1980). The positive (ADM) energy theorem is reviewed by York (1980). The result is in Schoen and Yau (1981) and Witten (1981).

Initial Value Equations

The one-surface approach is due to Lichnerowicz (1944) and Choquet-Bruhat (1962). The thin-sandwich approach is discussed by Wheeler (1963) and in MTW (1973). The counter-examples (when $\alpha \geqslant 0$) were found by the author.

Decompositions of Symmetric Tensors

This is a new presentation of the material. See York (1973) and (1974). I was strongly influenced by Deser (1967) and Berger and Ebin (1967). The singular splitting is especially interesting because it arises in so many problems. Another example is in "Euclidean" (++++) general relativity where the "special" gauge that explicitly eliminates in perturbation theory the problem of "negative-action conformal modes" (in path integration) does not exist in general. For this "special" gauge see Gross, Perry, and Yaffe (1982). Problems of the singular type were recognized in the thin sandwich problem by Pereira (1981).

Conformal Transformations

Conformal transformations were introduced in the constraint problem by Lichnerowicz (1944) and Choquet-Bruhat (1962). For the "rules" on trK, ρ, j^i, etc. see Ō Murchadha and York (1973;1974a), Isenberg, Ō Murchadha, and York (1976), and Isenberg and Nestor (1977).

Solving the Momentum Constraints

This is the simpler of two possible applications of the TT splitting to the momentum constraints. See York (1979) for discussion. On compact manifolds, the kernel of Δ_L consists of conformal Killing vectors. See Cantor (1979a) and (1979b) for the asymptotically flat case.

Some Extrinsic Curvature Tensors

This work is based on Bowen (1979), Bowen and York (1980), and York and Piran (1982).

Energy Conditions

Energy conditions on $T_{\mu\nu}$ in the context of the singularity theorems are discussed by Hawking and Ellis (1973).

Hamiltonian Constraint

For the physical interpretation of ψ, see Brill (1959) and Ō Murchadha and York (1974b). Specification of scalar curvature is in Cantor and Brill (1981). The model for negative scalar curvature is based on Wheeler (1963). For flat slices when $E_{ADM} \neq 0$, see Eardley (1975).

Asymptotic Flatness

The weighted Sobolev spaces were introduced by Cantor (1974; 1979). Generalizations to p=2 are given in McOwen (1979), Choquet-Bruhat and Christodoulou (1981) and Cantor and Brill (1981). For a detailed exposition, see Cantor (1981).

Constraint Theorems on Maximal Slices

The principal results are found in Cantor (1977; 1979), Chaljub-Simon and Choquet-Bruhat (1980), and Christodoulou and Ō Murchadha (1981).

Non-Maximal Slices

The results stated in this section are due to the author (1982).

Robin Boundary Conditions

An elementary treatment for the scalar Laplacian is found in Duff (1959). The application to ψ in this problem is in York and Piran (1982). Cantor (private communication) showed that the ψ-equation on R^3 with Robin conditions has a unique solution. The vector Robin condition was apparently new when introduced in York and Piran (1982).

Non-Standard Black Hole Data

Details are given in Bowen and York (1980) and York and Piran (1982).

Energy Flux

Smarr (1979) has given a detailed treatment. A forthcoming article by Bardeen and Piran has new results. Spatial infinity has been established clearly thanks to Ashtekar and Hansen (1978) and Christodoulou and Ō Murchadha (1981). For the asymptotic gauges (71), (72), (73), see York (1980).

Evolution

Comprehensive reviews are found in Fischer and Marsden (1979) and Choquet-Bruhat and York (1980). Discussion of gauges is given in some detail in York (1979). Note that the form of the harmonic gauge condition analogous to (79) is given incorrectly in Hawking and Ellis (1973), who used $(-g)$ instead of $\sqrt{-g}$. However, no error resulted from this in their later analysis.

Boost Theorem

This nice result is due to Christodoulou and Ō Murchadha (1981) and is based in part on Christodoulou (1981). Ō Murchadha and the author did extensive work on this problem in the middle 1970's before the advent of the $H_{s,\delta}$ spaces made rigorous proofs possible.

REFERENCES

Ashtekar, A. and Hansen, R. (1978). A unified treatment of null and spatial infinity in general relativity. J. Math. Phys. 19, pp. 1542-1566.

Arnowitt, R., Deser, S. and Misner, C. W. (1962). The dynamics of general relativity. In Gravitation, ed. L. Witten, pp. 227-265. Wiley, New York.

Berger, M. and Ebin, D. (1969). Some decompositions of the space of symmetric tensors. J. Diff. Geom. 3, pp. 379-392.

Bowen, J. (1979). Initial-value problems on non-Euclidean topologies. Ph.D. thesis, University of North Carolina, Chapel Hill.

Bowen, J. and York, J. W. (1980). Time asymmetric initial data for black holes and black hole collisions. Phys. Rev. D21, pp. 2047-2056.

Brill, D. (1959). On the positive-definite mass of the Bondi-Weber-Wheeler time-symmetric gravitational waves. Ann. of Phys. 7, pp. 466-483.

Cantor, M. (1974). Spaces of functions with asymptotic conditions. Indiana Univ. Math. J. 24, pp. 897-902.

Cantor, M. (1977). The existence of non-trivial asymptotically flat initial data for vacuum spacetimes. Commun. Math. Phys. 57, pp. 83-96.

Cantor, M. (1979a). A necessary and sufficient condition for York data to specify an asymptotically flat spacetime. J. Math. Phys. 20, pp. 1741-1744.

Cantor, M. (1979b). Some problems of global analysis on asymptotically simple manifolds. Compositio Math. 38, pp. 3-35.

Cantor, M. (1981). Elliptic operators and the decomposition of tensor fields. Bull. Amer. Math. Soc. 5, pp. 235-262.

Cantor, M. and Brill, D. (1981). The Laplacian in asymptotically flat manifolds and the specification of scalar curvature. Compositio Math. 43, pp. 317-330.

Cantor, M. and Piran, T. (1982). Conformally connected universes. (preprint).

Chaljub-Simon, A. and Choquet-Bruhat, Y. (1980). Global solutions of the Lichnerowicz equation in general relativity on an asymptotically Euclidean complete manifold. Gen. Rel. and Grav. 12, pp. 175-185.

Choquet-Bruhat, Y. (1962). The Cauchy problem. In Gravitation, ed. L. Witten, pp. 130-168. Wiley, New York.

Choquet-Bruhat, Y. and Christodoulou, D. (1981). Elliptic systems in Hilbert spaces on manifolds which are eculidean at infinity. Acta. Math. 146, pp. 129-150.

Choquet-Bruhat, Y. and York, J. W. (1980). The Cauchy problem. In General Relativity and Gravitation, ed. A. Held, pp. 99-172. Plenum, New York.

Christodoulou, D. (1981). The boost problem for weakly coupled quasilinear hyperbolic systems of the second order. J. Math. pures et appliquees 60, pp. 99-130.

Christodoulou, D. and Ō Murchadha, N. (1981). The boost problem in general relativity. Commun. Math. Phys. 80, pp. 271-300.

Deser, S. (1967). Covariant decompositions of symmetric tensors and the gravitational Cauchy problem. Ann. Inst. Henri Poincare 7, pp. 149-188.

Duff, G. F. D. (1959). Partial Differential Equations. Univ. of Toronto Press, Toronto.

Eardley, D. (1975). Gravitational collapse of marginally bound spheroids: Initial conditions. Phys. Rev. D 12, pp. 3072-3076.

Fischer, A. and Marsden, J. (1979). The initial value problem and the dynamical formulation of general relativity. In General Relativity, eds. S. W. Hawking and W. Israel, pp. 138-211. Cambridge University Press, Cambridge.

Gross, D., Perry, M., and Yaffe, L. (1982). Instability of flat space at finite temperature. Phys. Rev. D25, pp. 330-355.

Hawking, S. and Ellis, G. (1973). The Large Scale Structure of Space-time. Cambridge University Press, Cambridge.

Isenberg, J. and Nestor, J. (1977). Extension of the York field decomposition to general gravitationally coupled fields. Ann. of Phys. 108, pp. 368-386.

Isenberg, J. and Nestor, J. (1980). Canonical gravity. In General Relativity and Gravitation, ed. A Held, pp. 23-98. Plenum, New York.

Isenberg, J., Ó Murchadha, N., and York, J. W. (1976). Initial value problem of general relativity III. Phys. Rev. D13, pp. 1532-1537.

Lichnerowicz, A. (1944). L'integration des equations de la gravitation relativiste et le probleme des n corps. J. Math. Pures et Appl. 23, pp. 37-63.

McOwen, R. (1979). Behavior of the Laplacian on weighted Sobolev spaces. Commun. Pure Appl. Math. 32, pp. 783-795.

Ō Murchadha, N. and York, J. W. (1973). Existence and uniqueness of solutions of the Hamiltonian constraint of general relativity on compact manifolds. J. Math. Phys. 14, pp. 1551-1557.

Ō Murchadha, N. and York, J. W. (1974a). Initial-value problem of general relativity I. Phys. Rev. D10, pp. 428-436.

Ō Murchadha, N. and York, J. W. (1974b). Gravitational energy. Phys. Rev. D10, pp. 2345-2357.

Pereira, C. M. (1981). Nonglobal proof of the thin sandwich conjecture. J. Math. Phys. 22, pp. 1064-1074.

Regge, T. and Teitelboim, C. (1974). Role of surface integrals in the Hamiltonian formulation of general relativity. Ann. of Phys. 88, pp. 286-318.

Smarr, L. (1979). Gauge conditions, radiation formulae and the two black hole collision. In Sources of Gravitational Radiation, ed. L. Smarr, pp. 245-274. Cambridge University Press, Cambridge.

Schoen, R. and Yau, S.-T. (1981). Proof of the positive mass theorem II. Commun. Math. Phys. 79, pp. 231-260.

Wheeler, J. A. (1963). Geometrodynamics and the issue of the final state. In Relativity, Groups, and Topology, eds. C. DeWitt and B. DeWitt, pp. 316-520. Gordon and Breach, New York.

Witten, E. (1981). A new proof of the positive energy theorem. Commun. Math. Phys. 80, pp. 381-402.

York, J. W. (1973). Conformally invariant orthogonal decomposition of symmetric tensors on Riemannian manifolds and the initial-value problem of general relativity. J. Math. Phys. 14, pp. 456-464.

York, J. W. (1974). Covariant decompositions of symmetric tensors in the theory of gravitation. Ann. Inst. Henri Poincare 21, pp. 319-332.

York, J. W. (1979). Kinematics and dynamics of general relativity. In Sources of Gravitational Radiation, ed. L. Smarr, pp. 83-126. Cambridge University Press, Cambridge.

York, J. W. (1980). Energy and momentum of the gravitational field. In Essays in General Relativity, ed. F. Tipler, pp. 39-58. Academic Press, New York.

York, J. W. (1982). Initial value problems and coupled constraints (to appear).

York, J. W. and Piran, T. (1982). The initial value problem and beyond. In Spacetime and Geometry, eds. R. Matzner and L. Shepley, pp. 145-176. University of Texas Press, Austin.

METHODS OF NUMERICAL RELATIVITY

Tsvi Piran

Racah Institute for Physics
Hebrew University
Jeruselem 91904
ISRAEL

and

Institute for Advanced Study
Princeton, New Jersey 08540
U.S.A.

Numerical Relativity is an alternative to analytic methods for obtaining solutions for Einstein equations. Numerical methods are particularily useful for studying generation of gravitational radiation by potential strong sources. We review the analytical background, the numerical analysis aspects and techniques and some of the difficulties involved in numerical relativity.

INTRODUCTION

After a decade of theoretical work on sources of gravitational radiation it is clear that the most interesting and promising sources cannot be studied using analytic methods [1,2]. Dimensional analysis, and order of magnitude estimates, suggest that gravitational radiation is produced efficiently only in a strong field, dynamical configuration. Moreover, the quadrupole nature of gravitational radiation demands that the sources will be aspherical, the larger the deviation from spherical symmetry, the better. Current analytic methods cannot yield an exact solution under these conditions. Perturbation methods depend on an expansion parameter (typical parameters are ratios of masses involved, or specific angular momentum). This expansion parameter is often too large, for the expansion to be valid, whenever a significant amount of gravitational radiation is produced. (see Eardley's lecture in this volume, [3]). We turn therefore, to numerical relativity to study these sources.

May and White [4] and Hahn and Lindquist [5] performed in the mid-sixties the first general relativistic numerical calculations. May and White [4] calculated successfully spherical collapse of matter and formation of neutron stars. They were able to calculate the initial stages of a black hole formation, but their coordinate system became singular before its completion. Hahn and Lindquist [5] tried to calculate a two black hole collision. They calculated the initial infall phase but they were not able to evolve the initial data all the way to the merge of the two black holes. In many senses these pioneering attempts were somewhat premature. Theoretical techniques were not developed well enough and computational power was not large enough to achieve these goals.

A second wave of activity in numerical relativity began in the early seventies. This was partly motivated by the growing interest in gravitational radiation and in physics of collapsed objects. Theoretical developments, led by York and his collaborators [6,7,8] and larger computational power enabled Smarr and Eppley [9,10,11,12] to finish the project that was begun by Hahn and Lindquist and followed by Cadez and DeWitt [12] and to solve numerically the axisymmetric, non rotating two black-hole collision problem. The results of these calculations are well known and their physical implication on sources of gravitational radiation are summarized in Eardley's lectures [3]. The most important impact of these calculations was the demonstration of the ability to solve major relativistic problems numerically. This work, together with Wilson's work [13,14] on numerical relativistic hydrodynamics and with his introduction of advanced numerical techniques to numerical relativity [14] led to the current realization of the power of numerical relativity. By now more than a dozen solutions to Einstein equations have been calculated using numerical methods, and a few review articles [15,16,17,18,19] summarize different aspects of this field.

In these lectures we present a review, not of the numerical solutions, but of the basic ideas and techniques involved in numerical relativity. We discuss questions concerning the formulation of Einstein equations in a form suitable for numerical solution (York's lectures in this volume provide an extensive source of additional information on this matter). We examine the numerical analysis aspects and introduce a few numerical considerations. We attempt to explore the prospects and limitations of numerical relativity and to examine the features and approximations involved in a numerical solution. The discussion is general but the main problem that we have in mind is the numerical evaluation of the amount and signature of gravitational radiation emitted by a strong source in an asymptotically flat space time. The related astrophysical problems are gravitational collapse, collision of two black holes or merge of a neutron star binary.

NUMERICAL METHODS - ADVANTAGES AND LIMITATIONS

Numerical relativity yields an approximate solution to Einstein equations. Like in standard perturbation calculation the approximation depends on an expansion parameter. The crucial difference between numerical calculation and other approximation methods is the nature of the expansion parameter. The numerical expansion parameter is not a physical parameter of the problem. Therefore, numerical methods are suitable for solution of strong field, non-linear problems when all natural expansion parameters are large. To examine the nature of the numerical expansion parameter we turn to a brief discussion of numerical analysis.

The central idea in a numerical solution of a differential equation is conversion of the equation to a set of algebraic equations. One way to do so is finite differencing. A continuous function $f(x)$ is defined on a discrete grid x_I with $f_I = f(x_I)$. Capital roman subscript, I, J, K... denotes the integer numerical grid index. We write $x_I = X_o + Idx$, but the grid spacing may be variable in general. We approximate the continuous derivative as :

$$\left.\frac{\partial f}{\partial x}\right|_{x_I} = \frac{f_{I+1} - f_{I-1}}{2dx} + o(dx) \qquad (1)$$

The second term on the l.h.s. is the truncation error, which is proportional to $f'''dx^2$. This form is second order accurate since the truncation error is quadratic in dx. Higher order approximations can be written, but these generally involve more complicated expressions which include f_{I+2}, f_{I-2} etc.. The ratio between the truncation error and the other terms in the equation is the numerical expansion parameter.

In an n'th order scheme this ratio is of order $\left(\frac{dx}{\ell}\right)^n$ where ℓ is a typical length scale over which the function f varies. If there is only one such length scale in the problem then L, the numerical grid size is of order (a few)ℓ and

$$\left(\frac{dx}{\ell}\right)^n \simeq \left(\frac{dx}{L}\right)^n \simeq N^{-n} \quad , \tag{2}$$

where N is the number of grid points in the x direction (the more complicated situation in which there are two very different length scales is discussed later).

Unlike standard perturbation expansion parameters N is not related directly to any physical parameter of the problem. Rather it is limited by technical considerations - computer memory size, speed etc...

In principle we can imagine letting $N \to \infty$. The scheme is consistent if the approximate (finite difference, or other) numerical equations converge to the differential equations in this limit. Numerical convergence is if $f^N \xrightarrow[N \to \infty]{} f$ (where f is the solution of the differential equation). Consistency of the approximate equation is necessary, but not sufficient for convergence of the solution. An additional factor that determines the convergence is stability. Roughly speaking, a scheme is stable if small errors which are introduced into the numerical solution (for example, round off errors) remain bounded throughout the solution. An unstable scheme involves divergence of the numerical solution, divergence which does not exist in the analytic solution (for more precise definitions see [20,21]). Clearly an unstable scheme cannot yield a reasonable solution. A priori it is difficult to guess whether a given finite differencing approximation will be stable or not. In particular, very often, there is an interplay between accuracy and stability and the more accurate (higher order) approximation turn to be unstable. A typical example is the simple equation:

$$\frac{\partial f}{\partial t} = u \frac{\partial f}{\partial x} \tag{3}$$

The second order (in space) and first order (in time) form:

$$\frac{f_{I,j+1} - f_{I,J}}{dt} = u \frac{f_{I+1,J} - f_{I-1,J}}{2dx} \quad , \tag{4}$$

is unconditionally (for every dt, dx) unstable. While the first order form:

$$\frac{f_{I,J+1} - f_{I,J}}{dt} = u \frac{f_{I+1,J} - f_{I,J}}{dx} \quad , \tag{5}$$

which is only first order accurate (in space) is stable for $0 < u \frac{dt}{dx} < 1$ Lax theorem states that for a linear initial value problem consistency and stability are sufficient for convergence. This theorem is very powerful since for linear problems both consistency and stability can be examined analytically before performing any numerical calculations. Unfortunately there is no analog theorem for non-linear systems. Even the questions of stability of a non-linear system can be generally studied only after linearization.

A practical test of stability of a finite difference form of a non-linear set of equations is usually done by trial and error. Numerical instability is manifested by divergence of the solution. The fact that numerical instabilities exist is the basic reason why an appearance of a singularity in a numerical solution does not necessarily mean that the actual physical solution diverges as well!

Convergence is tested by construction of a series of numerical solutions with increasing grid size f^N, f^{2N}, f^{4N} etc... A study of such series can give estimates of both the error:

$$(f^{2N} - f^N)/f^{2N} \quad , \tag{6}$$

and of the rate of convergence:

$$(f^{4N} - f^{2N})/(f^{2N} - f^N) \quad . \tag{7}$$

Additional convergence problems appear when solving problems defined on an open manifold, such as in the asymptotically flat case. The manifold extends in such cases to infinity and the physical boundary conditions are defined there, while the numerical grid is finite. We adopt, therefore, a numerical (artificial) boundary[2] of finite size L. The boundary conditions on L have to reproduce those at spatial infinity. Convergence means also that $f^{N,L} \underset{N\to\infty;\, L\to\infty}{\longrightarrow} f$. Recently, Cantor [23] has shown that with proper boundary conditions one can proof convergence in this sense. Again in practice, a series of solutions f^L, f^{2L}, f^{4L} yields estimates for both errors and convergence rate of the numerical solution.

Physical considerations appear in the determination of L and dx. L should be such that "nothing interesting" happens at $x > L$. Similarily "nothing important" should be taking place on length scales $\ell <$ dx. These considerations determine the necessary grid size N. Technical difficulties appear if N is too large. If there is only one length scale in the problem and if $L \sim$ (a few) x ℓ the problem is simple. Technical difficulties appear when there are two or more different length (or temporal) scales. In such cases L is determined by the largest scale, ℓ_2 while dx by the smallest scale, ℓ_1 $(dx \ll \ell_1 \ll \ell_2 < L)$ Practical limitations limit our ability to solve problems with very large ℓ_2/ℓ_1

$$N = \frac{L}{dx} = \frac{L}{\ell_2}\ \frac{\ell_2}{\ell_1}\ \frac{\ell_1}{dx} \ , \tag{8}$$

is simply too large in such cases. (Sometimes but not always this problem can be solved by a variable grid spacing, or by an appropriate coordinate transformation, see for example Adler and Piran [24]).

For example, (see Figure 1) in calculations of a source of gravitational radiation the numerical grid should extend into the local wave zone (see Thorne's lecture in this volume). A typical length of variation in this outer region is λ, the wavelength of the resulting radiation. With at least four grid points per wave length and $L \simeq (20 \div 40)\ \lambda$ we obtain $N \geq 80$! With $\lambda \sim M$ we expect variation on a scale $\ell < \lambda$ inside the source. This problem can be solved by a variable grid size. On the other hand, an attempt to follow the radiation, numerically, all the way from the source to a variable cosmological background will fail due to the enormous difference in scale length ($L \sim$ typical cosmological radius of curvature).

The numerical expansion parameter N^{-n} governs the accuracy of the numerical approximation. Technical considerations (computer memory and speed) limit N. These limitations determine, to a large extent what can be practically computed. We denote by m the total number of equations. The actual m value (for general relativistic calculations) is a function of d - the number of spatial dimensions of the problem (Note that by one dimensional problem we mean one space + one time dimension, etc.) and g - the number of gravitational degrees of freedom $g = 0,1,2$ depending on the symmetry of the configuration ($g = 0$ for spherical symmetry).

In general, a general relativistic calculation involves evolution (integration in tim) of six second order equations, (these correspond to twelve first order equations) and four coordinate conditions which are usually elliptic (or parabolic) equations. Hydrodynamics (with perfect fluid) adds five first order equations and an equation of state. Thus, $m \lesssim 21$.

These equations involve $m\ p$ algebraic operation (addition, subtraction, multiplication and division) per time step per grid point. Where we estimate $p \simeq 50$ (evaluation of a Rieman tensor component may involve up to a thousand algebraic operations in the general case). With $r N^d$ grid points the total number of operations per time step is $r N^d m\ p$. ($r \leq 1$, $r < 1$ if the grid is not rectangular).

The number of time steps needed is $q N = T/dt$ with T the total integration time which is of order of (a few) x (L/c_s) or larger (c_s is a typical velocity

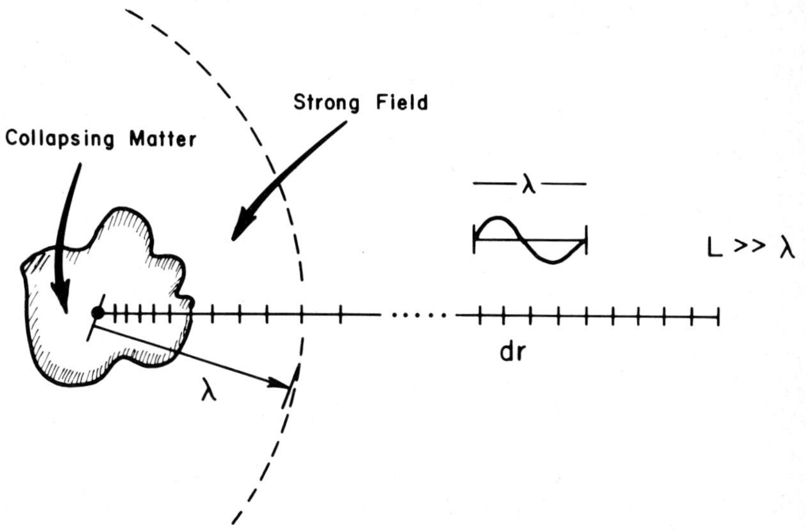

Figure 1: Numerical grid in a typical collapse problem. Note that the grid is varying.

in the source, and dt determined by the Courant condition $dt < \frac{dx}{c}$). Thus, q is of order 10 or more.

The total number of algebraic operations in a calculation is of order:

$$q N^{d+1} r m p = 10^{6+2d} r\left(\frac{N}{100}\right)^{d+1} \left(\frac{m}{20}\right) \left(\frac{p}{50}\right) \left(\frac{q}{10}\right) . \qquad (8)$$

With R_c the rate of operation of the computer ($R_c \simeq 10^7$ algebraic operations/CPU sec for the currently best available computer). We estimate the CPU time needed for a calculation as:

$$\text{CPU Time} = 10^{2d-1} r\left(\frac{N}{100}\right)^{d+1} \left(\frac{p}{50}\right) \left(\frac{m}{20}\right) \left(\frac{q}{10}\right) \left(\frac{R_c}{10^7}\right)^{-1} . \qquad (9)$$

For three dimensional calculations this amounts to about 30 hours on a proper computer! Additional limit is memory size. It is essential to store

$$2\ 10^{2d+1} r\left(\frac{N}{100}\right)^{d} \left(\frac{m}{20}\right) \quad \text{numbers,} \qquad (10)$$

which is about 20 10^6 numbers for a three dimensional calculation!

These limitations determine the physical problems that can be approached numerically in the near future. (The situation may change with a futuristic introduction of a hypercomputer, designed specifically for solution of partial differential equations [25]). Typical problems that can be solved currently are:

1) The issue of the final state, i.e. final fate of a collapsing configuration. This classical question that was addressed by Wheeler [26] in the early sixties was solved recently for axisymmetric configurations by Nakamura and his co-workers (see lecture in this volume and ref. [27,28]). If we are interested only in the resulting compact object (black hole etc...) we can ignore the production, and generation of gravitational radiation. One may use $L \simeq 15M$ (where M is the mass of the collapsing object and L is expressed in gravitational units, $c = G = 1$) and $N \simeq 30$ may be sufficient. This problem may even be considered for three dimensional configurations.

2) Amount and nature (frequency, pulse characteristic, etc...) of graviational radiation produced in various potential astrophysical scenarios: rotating collapse, collision of two black holes, decay and merge of a binary system of two neutron stars. This problem needs a relatively large L, say about $L \simeq 50M$, and small dx, $dx \lesssim \frac{M}{4}$. With $N \simeq 200$, this problem could be barely solved for two dimensional (i.e. exisymmetric) configurations.

3) For initial value calculations, there is no time dependence. There is therefore a gain of factor of qN in the CPU time, also m is fairly small, about 4. Apart from some mathematical difficulty, which is discussed in a later section, this problem can be solved for the general, three dimensional case.

4) It should be stressed again that problems that involved appearance of a singularity can usually be handled only when combined with an analytical procedure that eliminates the singularity from the numerical solution. This can usually be done only if some information is known in advance on the nature of the expected singularity. Otherwise, it might be extremely difficult to distinguish between a real singularity which develops in the solution and a singularity due to a numerical instability.

NUMERICAL RELATIVITY AND THE STRUCTURE OF EINSTEIN EQUATIONS

Einstein equations in their abstract form

$$G_{\mu\nu} = 8\pi\, T_{\mu\nu} \quad , \tag{11}$$

are not suitable for numerical integration. These equations have to be written first explicitly as a set of first order quasi-linear partial differential equations:

$$\frac{\partial t}{\partial t} = L(f,x) \quad . \tag{12}$$

Only then a finite differencing approximation can be worked out. The immediate question arising is what are the best variables and what is the best quasi-linear first order system of equations?

Intuitively one may wish to use ${}^{(4)}g_{\mu\nu}$, the four dimensional metric, and its time derivative ${}^{(4)}g_{\mu\nu}/\partial t$ as variables. This approach was very effective in a few simple special cases. Misner and Sharp [29] for example wrote Einstein equations in an especially simple form for the shperically symmetric case. This form was used by May and White [4] in their pioneering work on spherical collapse. Hahn and Lindquist [5] used ${}^{(4)}g_{\mu\nu}$, and ${}^{(4)}\Gamma^{\sigma}_{\mu\nu}$ as variables in the first calculations of the two black holes collision problem. The Jordan-Ehlers-Kompaneetz metric for cylindrical geometry yields a very simple form for Einstein equations [30,31]. This form was used by Piran and Stark [32] for a numerical study of the interaction of gravitational radiation. However, this approach cannot be generalized.

Before examining this, consider once more, the nature of numerical relativity. The problem addressed by numerical relativity is the general relativistic Cauchy problems. Initial data is defined on an initial hypersurface and is evolved into the future. It is evident that in such a problem space-time must be foliated into the initial hypersurfaces on which data is defined and to subsequent hypersurfaces onto which the data is evolved. The choice of variables should reflect this structure, and this depends on the type of foliation. Two different types of foliations are used: folization to spacelike hypersurfaces, and foliation to null hypersurfaces. In the former case we obtain the "3+1" formalism [33,34,6] while in the later case we obtain a characteristic "2+2" Cauchy problem [35,36, 37]. It is also possible to obtain a mixed foliation, in which the initial data is specified partly on spacelike and partly on null hypersurfaces [35] (see Fig. 2). Almost all numerical work up to now employed the "3+1" formalism, and the following discussion focuses on this approach.

Turning now to the question of equations and variables we notice that four of the Einstein equations:

$$G_{o\mu} = 8\pi T_{o\mu} \tag{13}$$

do not contain second time derivative of the metric. These are four constraint equations that constrain the initial data, or data on any spacelike hypersurface. The solution of these equations is the general relativistic initial value problem.

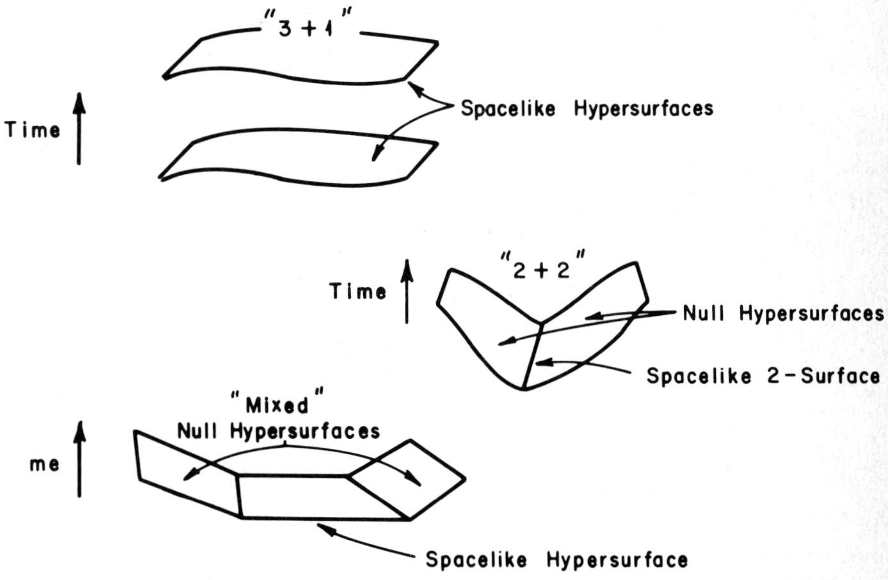

Figure 2: Different slicing of space-time, schematic.

A detailed discussion of the initial value problem is given in York's lecture in this volume, (see also [38,39]). For numerical relativity, the most important conclusion of this work, which was originated by Lichnerowicz [40] and Choquet-Bruhat [41] is that generally the metric of the three-dimensional spacelike hypersurfaces, ${}^{(3)}g_{ij}$ (we omit later the superscript (3), but keep the superscript (4) to denote the four dimensional metric) and K_{ij} the extrinsic curvature tensor of these hypersurfaces are the natural geometrical variables. This conclusion is supported by work on Hamiltonian formulation of general relativity [33,42,43] which reaches the same conclusion.

We employ therefore, the "3+1" equations of general relativity, using as variables g_{ij} and K_{ij}. In some works [9,44] ${}^{(3)}\Gamma^i_{jk}$ were added to g_{ij} and K_{ij} as additional variables. These are only auxiliary variables without a direct physical or geometrical interpretation. Their addition simplifies the calculation of R_{ij} (reduce p) but there is a heavy penalty in the increase of m, the number of variables. In particular, this may turn to be too heavy a burden on the computer's memory capacity.

In general it is very difficult to solve the relativistic Cauchy problem using the components of ${}^{(4)}g_{ij}$ as variable. However, in special cases [4,5,32], use of ${}^{(4)}g_{ij}$ can be very effective. These problems have a few common features. First there is quite high symmetry in these problems. Partially because of symmetry it was possible to obtain analytic solutions for the initial value problem in those cases (by reducing the problem to quadrature in the spherical and cylindrical cases and by an ingenious ansatz of Misner [45] for the two black hole collision). A second feature is the use of the normal coordinate condition:

$$ {}^{(4)}g_{oj} = 0 \quad . \tag{14} $$

This condition leads to:

$$ {}^{(4)}g^{ij} = g^{ij} \quad (i,j = 1,3) \quad , \tag{15} $$

(${}^{(4)}g_{ij} = g_{ij}$ always holds) which makes these schemes very close to a "3+1" scheme. However, in general the condition ${}^{(4)}g_{oj} = 0$ is not convenient. It does not cause difficulties in the cylindrical waves and the special collapse calculations because of the high symmetry, even though we see later that the spherical collapse problem can be improved greatly by relaxing this condition. This condition, however, caused some difficulties in the two black-hole collision problem.

For completeness we review the essential equations of the "3+1" approach to general relativistic dynamics further details are given in [6]. The four-dimensional line element is written in the form

$$ ds^2 = -(N^2 - N^i N_i)dt^2 - 2N_i\, dx^i\, dt + g_{ij}\, dx^i\, dx^j \tag{16} $$

The time coordinate $x^o = t$ labels spacelike hypersurfaces with intrinsic geometry specified by the spatial metric tensor g_{ij}. The unit timelike four-vector normal to the hypersurface at each point is n^a, with

$$ n^o = N^{-1} \quad ; \quad n^i = N^{-1} N^i \quad . \tag{17} $$

Folliwng Bardeen and Piran [46] the shift vector N^i is the coordinate 3-velocity of the normal and has the opposite sign from what is commonly called the shift vector [6] (see Fig. 3). The proper time interval along the normal between two neighboring hypersurfaces is the lapse function N times the coordinate time interval Δt. Three-vectors like N^i, have indices raised and lowered by the spatial metric g_{ij} and its inverse, i.e. $N_i \equiv g_{ij} N^j$. Clearly four vectors raised and lowered by the full metric tensor ${}^{(4)}g_{\mu\nu}$ and its inverse.

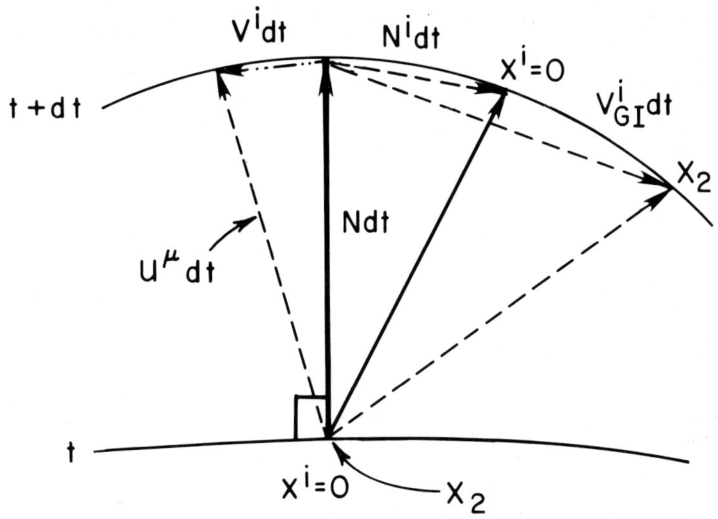

Figure 3: Varying vectors in the "3+1" formalism. The thick line is the orthogonal, a coordinate point moves along the narrow solid line, a grid point moves along the dashed line while a matter elements moves along u^μ.

The extrinsic curvature tensor K_{ij} is the three-tensor in the t = constant hypersurface which describes how the hypersurface is locally embedded in the four-dimensional spacetime. An explicit formula is

$$K_{ij} = -n_{i;j} = -\frac{1}{2N}[g_{ij,o} + N_{i|j} + N_{j|i}]. \tag{18}$$

Here ";" denotes a four-dimensional covariant derivative, "|" a three-dimensional covariant derivative with respect to g_{ij}, and "," an ordinary partial derivative. In fact, $N_{i|j} + N_{j|i}$ is the Lie derivative of g_{ij} along N^i, and Eq. 18 can be written as:

$$dg_{ij}/dt + N^k{}_{,i} g_{kj} + N^k{}_{,j}\, g_{ki} = -2NK_{ij} \quad , \tag{19}$$

where $d/dt \equiv \partial/dt + N^i\, \partial/\partial x^i$ is the convective time derivative along the normal.

In the "3+1" formalism, the identity (19) evolves the metric, while the extrinsic curvature evolves according to the six dynamic Einstein equations in the form, say,

$$K_{j,o}^{\ i} + (L_{N^k}K)_j^{\ i} \equiv \frac{d}{dt}K_j^{\ i} - N^i{}_{,k}\, K_j^{\ k} + N^k{}_{,j}\, K_k^{\ i} =$$

$$- N^{|i}{}_{|j} + N[R_j^{\ i} + KK_j^{\ i} + 4\pi(S-E)\,\delta_j^{\ i} - 8\pi S_j^{\ i}] \quad . \tag{20}$$

where $R_j^{\ i}$ is the intrinsic Ricci curvature tensor of the constant - t hypersurface, $K \equiv K_i^{\ i}$, E is the matter energy density in the hypersurface, and S_{ij}, with $S \equiv S_i^{\ i}$, is the matter stress tensor in the hypersurface. Specifically, if $T_\mu^{\ \nu}$ is the energy-momentum tensor,

$$E \equiv T^{\mu\nu} n_\mu n_\nu = N^2 T^{oo} \tag{21}$$

$$S_{ij} \equiv T_{ij} \ , \tag{22}$$

and one can also define a momentum density three-vector J_i by

$$J_i \equiv -n_\mu T_i^{\ \mu} \tag{23}$$

The four initial value equations are the energy or Hamiltonian constraint equation

$$\frac{1}{2}\left[R - K_j^{\ i} K_i^{\ j} + K^2\right] = 8\pi E \ , \tag{24}$$

and the three momemtum constraint equations are

$$K_i^{\ j}{}_{|j} - K_{|i} = 8\pi J_i \tag{25}$$

THE NUMERICAL INITIAL VALUE PROBLEM

g_{ij} and K_{ij} satisfy the initial value equations, Eqs. 24,25 on any spacelike hypersurface. This holds, in particular, on the initial hypersurface and the solution of this equation on this hypersurface is the general relativistic initial value problem. York [6,7,8,38,39] stresses that the freely specified data on the initial hypersurface is γ_{ij} the conformed metric and E_{ij} the transverse-traceless part of the extrinsic curvature tensor. In principle it is possible to specify other parts of the initial data, however, York's procedure is the only one that we know that leads to an elliptic set of equations for which proofs of existence of a unique solution exist [47,48]. γ_{ij} and E_{ij} are related to g_{ij} and K_{ij} as:

$$g_{ij} = \psi^4 \gamma_{ij} \tag{26}$$

and

$$K^{ij} = \psi^{-10} \hat{K}^{ij} = \psi^{-10}\left[E^{ij} + (\hat{\ell}W)^{ij}\right] + \frac{1}{3}\psi^{-4} \, \mathrm{tr}K \, g^{ij} \tag{27}$$

where "^" means that the quantity is calculated relative to γ_{ij}.

ψ, the conformal factor, and W^i satisfies the transformed constraint equations [6]:

$$8\hat{\Delta}\psi = \hat{R}\psi + \frac{2}{3}\psi^5 (\mathrm{tr}K)^2 - \psi^{-7}\hat{K}_{ij}\hat{K}^{ij} + 16\pi\hat{E}\psi^{-3} \tag{28}$$

and

$$(\hat{\Delta}_\ell W)^i = \frac{2}{3}\psi^6 \hat{\nabla}^i \, \mathrm{tr}K + 8\pi\hat{J}^i \ . \tag{29}$$

The operators $\hat{\Delta}$, $\hat{\Delta}_\ell$ and $\hat{\ell}$ are:

$\hat{\Delta} \equiv \Delta(\gamma_{ij})$ (the Laplacian of the conformal metric γ_{ij})

$$(\hat{\Delta}_\ell W)^i \equiv \hat{\nabla}_j (\ell W)^{ij} = (\hat{\Delta}W)^i + \frac{1}{3}\hat{\nabla}^i(\hat{\nabla}_j W^j) + R_j^{\ i} W^j \tag{30}$$

and

$$(\hat{\ell}W)^{ij} \equiv \hat{\nabla}^i W^j + \hat{\nabla}^j W^i - \frac{2}{3}\hat{\gamma}^{ij}\hat{\nabla}_k W^k \tag{31}$$

$\hat{E}$ and $\hat{J}^i$ relate to physical E and J^i like:

$$E = \psi^{-8}\hat{E} \tag{32}$$

$$J^i = \psi^{-10}\hat{J}^i \tag{33}$$

These initial value equations constitute a coupled set of four elliptic equations. To complete the mathematical formulation of this problem we add boundary conditions. For asymptotically flat spaces these are [7]:

$$\psi \underset{r \to \infty}{\to} 1 + \frac{E_\infty}{2r} \text{ (with } \gamma_{ij} \simeq f_{ij} \text{ asymptotically)} , \tag{34}$$

and

$$K_j^{\ i} \underset{r \to \infty}{\to} \frac{3}{2r^2} [P_j \nu^i + P^i \nu_j - (\nu \cdot P)(\delta_j^{\ i} - \nu_i \nu^j)] \tag{35}$$

f_{ij} is a flat space metric, E_∞ and $\vec{P}$ are the total mass and linear momentum and ν^i is the unit vector normal to a two sphere. These boundary conditions are stronger than what is usually given in an elliptic Dirichlet problem, in which the value of the function is specified on a boundary. This is very useful. The actual boundary is at infinity, however, the numerical grid usually extends only to a finite distance L. Specifying, for example, $\psi = 1$ is only $0(r^{-1})$. A better boundary condition for ψ at a finite boundary [38] is:

$$\frac{\partial \psi}{\partial r} + \frac{1}{r}(\psi - 1) = 0(r^{-3}) \tag{36}$$

The analog boundary condition for $K_i^{\ j}$ is given in terms of the vector W^i:

$$(\hat{\ell} W)^{kj} \nu_j [\delta_k^{\ i} - \frac{1}{2}\nu^i \nu_k] + \frac{6}{7r} W^k [\delta_k^{\ i} - \frac{1}{8}\nu^i \nu_k] \doteq 0(r^{-3}) \tag{37}$$

Both boundary conditions are accurate to order $0(r^{-3})$.

An alternative method is to use a coordinate transformation that brings spacelike infinity to a finite point, or sphere, in this case the boundary conditions $\psi = 1$ and $K_i^{\ j} = 0$ are used. The transformation is essentially singular, but the problem associated with such singularity can be handled (see for example [22]).

Numerical solutions of the Hamiltonian constraint were obtained a few special cases. (see Fig. 4) [38,49,50,51]. In these cases the corresponding momentum constraints were satisfied either trivially ($K_i^{\ j} \equiv 0$; $J^i \equiv 0$) or solved analytically [52].

The elliptic Hamiltonian constraint is a quasi-linear elliptic equation. It is usually solved numerically using a SOR (Successive over relaxation) method [21], or by a more sophisticated improvement of SOR [e.g. 22].

$$L_{fd}(\psi_{IJ}) = 0 \tag{38}$$

is the finite differencing approximation for an elliptic equation (IJ stands for the grid indices). In a relaxation method we derive the (n+1) approximation for the solution from the n'th approximation:

$$\psi_{IJ}^{(n+1)} = \psi_{IJ}^{(n)} + \omega \left[- \frac{L_{fd}(\psi^{(n)}, \psi^{(n+1)})}{\partial L_{fd}/\partial \psi_{IJ} (\psi^{(n)}, \psi^{(n+1)})} \right] \tag{39}$$

ω is the over-relaxation parameter (usually $1 \leq \omega \leq 2$) and $L_{fd}(\psi^{(n)}, \psi^{(n+1)})$

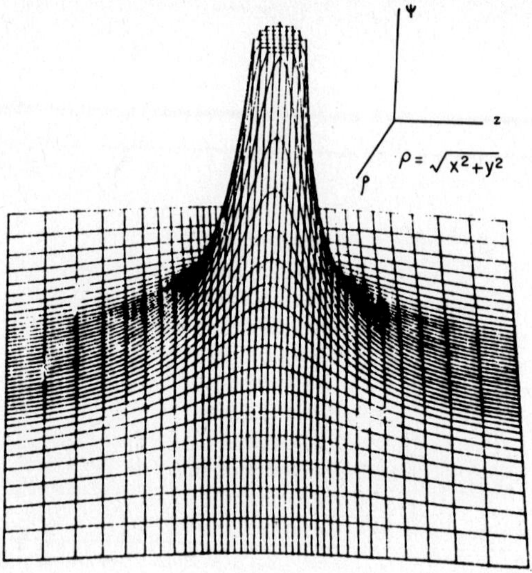

Figure 4: The conformal factor ψ for a rotating black hole initial data, from [38].

$\frac{\partial Lfd}{\partial \psi_{IJ}} (\psi^{(n)}, \psi^{(n+1)})$, denotes that these quantities are evaluated using values of $\psi^{(n+1)}$ for grid points where these values are already available (this depends on the way the grid is swept). For a linear problem Eq. 39 reduced to the standard SOR relaxation cycle. Additional terms appear in the non-linear case. These may be omitted, but their inclusion which reflect better the non-linearity, accelerate usually the convergence.

A good initial guess for $\psi_{IJ}^{(o)}$ can reduce significantly the number of itterations needed. A way to obtain an approximate guess is to solve the problem first on a small grid and to interplate the solution to obtain a initial guess on a grid which is twice as large. By a few doubling of the grid size one can obtain, in this way, a good approximate solution, for a very large grid. When using this method comparison of ψ(N grid points) with ψ(2N grid points) yields an immediate important estimate on the accuracy of the numerical solution.

Back and forth interpolation between grids of different sizes (i.e. from small size coarse grid to large size fine grid and back from large to small) is an important improvement of this idea. This method was used recently successfully by Choptuik [22].

Wheeler [26] pointed out that when solving the Hamiltonian constraint, ψ, the conformed factor may vanish on a topologically spherical surface. This leads to a singular geometry which Wheeler calls a "bag of gold" singularity. Cantor and Piran [53] refined recently Wheeler's suggestion to rule out spaces in which ψ vanishes as aphysical. They show that in some cases a minimal surface, and hence an apparent horizon engulfs the "bag of gold" singularity. Thus, this singularity is hidden from an observer at infinity, and the solution is physical. A schematic embedding diagram of these solutions is shown in Fig. 5.

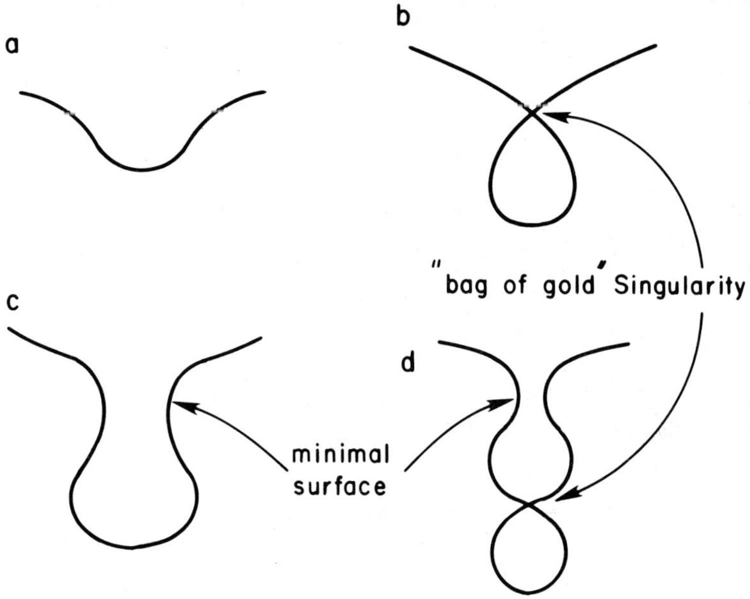

Figure 5: Embedding diagram of a three-dimensional hypersurface R^n after a conformal transformation a) $\psi>0$; b) $\psi=0$ at the "bag of gold" singularity; c) Appearance of a minimal surface; d) A minimal surface hides the singularity. From reference [53].

The general (general relativistic) initial value problem involves a solution of four coupled elliptic equations. On a constant mean curvature hypersurfaces (trK = const), and in particular, on a maximal slice ($trK = 0$) the Hamiltonian constraint decouples from the momentum constraints. In this case application of the SOR method is straightforward. The linearity (in W^i) of the momentum constraints guarantees that a numerical SOR algorithm for the three coupled equations will converge. The convergence may be slow, though, since we solve a coupled set of equations. So far there was no attempt to solve these equations numerically.

For $\nabla^i trK \neq 0$ all four equations are coupled, and in fact it is not proved yet that these equations have a solution (see York's lecture in this volume). One can still construct a numerical SOR algorithm for these equations. If there is no solution it is very unlikely that the numerical solution will converge. A good general numerical solution may demonstrate, therefore, existence of solutions for these equations. Failure to obtain such a solution (lack of convergence of the SOR scheme, for example) will not indicate the opposite since analytic inconsistency is almost certain to induce numerical instability, there are many numerical instabilities that have nothing to do with analytic features of the system of equations that are being solved.

Open Problem: Construct a full general initial value numerical code, for all four constraint equations, using the York procedure.

So far we have discussed the initial value problem - or the solution of the constraint equations in terms of the York procedure. Although this is the only method for which general (global in space) proofs of existence of unique solution exist [47,48] other ad hoc approaches can be adopted for specific problems. Once a proper initial data is obtained, it is not important how it was obtained. A typical adhoc approach is to solve one of the constraint equations for a specific component of g_{ij} or $K_i^{\,j}$. This method was suggested by Wilson [14] as a way to evaluate specific components during the evolution procedure. However, it has been used successfully at the initial value stage as well. An example of this method is discussed later.

EVOLUTION AND CONSTRAINT EQUATIONS - THE MAIN OPEN QUESTION

The evolution equations (Eqs 19,20) evolve constraint initial data (satisfying the constraint equations, Eqs 24,25) to constraint initial data on future spacelike hypersurfaces. This is essential for the consistency of the theory [43,38]. Similar constraints and consistency features appear in electromagnetism and other gauge theories.

We cannot, in general, satisfy the consistency condition in a finite differencing approximation. This is related to the well-known difficulty in writing general relativity on a lattice. To see the difficulty assume that the initial value equations are satisfied and that the evolution equations are second order accurate (in both space and time). A typical equation is:

$$\frac{\overset{N+1}{g}_{mk} - \overset{N}{g}_{mk}}{\Delta t} = L_{fd}(g_{ij},K_{ij}) + O(\Delta x^2, \Delta t^2) \quad , \tag{40}$$

where $\overset{N}{g}_{mk}$, $\overset{N+1}{g}_{mk}$ are the metric functions on N and N+1 time steps, L_{fd} is the appropriate finite differencing operator, and Δt, Δx are the temporal time step and grid spacing. With $\Delta t = O(\Delta x)$

$$\overset{N+1}{g}_{mk} = g_{mk}(t^{N+1}) + O(\Delta x^3) \quad , \tag{41}$$

where $g_{mk}(t^{N+1})$ is the exact solution. Accumulation of error after many successive steps leads to:

$$\overset{N+M}{g}_{mk} = g_{mk}(t^{N+M}) + O(\Delta x^{2+\varepsilon}), \qquad 0<\varepsilon<1 \tag{42}$$

The solution is second order accurate, (or slightly better).

Numerical derivatives will be of lower accuracy:

$$\frac{\partial \overset{N+1}{g}_{mk}}{\partial x} \simeq \frac{\overset{N+1}{g}_{mk,I+1} - \overset{N+1}{g}_{mk,I-1}}{2\Delta x} = \frac{\partial g_{mk}(t^{N+1})}{\partial x} + O(\Delta x) \tag{43}$$

and

$$\frac{\partial^2 \overset{N+1}{g}_{mk}}{\partial x} \quad \frac{\overset{N+1}{g}_{mk,I+1} - 2\overset{N+1}{g}_{mkI} + \overset{N+1}{g}_{mk,I-1}}{(\Delta x)^2} = \frac{\partial^2 g_{mk}(t^{N+1})}{\partial x^2} + O(1) \quad , \tag{44}$$

The constraint equations include first and second derivatives of the metric and the extrinsic curvature. Therefore, while the deviations from the evolution equation are of order $O(dx^2)$, the deviations from the constraint are of order $O(dx)$ or worse! Consistency is lost in the numerical approximation. By inconsistency we mean here, that the constraint equations are satisfied to a lower order of accuracy than the evolution equations or vise versa.

Open Question (basic): Write a consistent lattice, and in particular finite differencing, approximation for Einstein equation. Regge calculus [54] is in a way an answer to the lattice but not to the finite differencing problems.

One approach to the consistency problem is to ignor it and to use only the evolution equations. We call such a scheme a free evolution scheme. It was suggested that the deviations from the constraints:

$$H = \sqrt{g}(K_{ij}K^{ij} - (\mathrm{tr}K)^2 - R - 8\pi E) \tag{45}$$

and

$$H^i = -2\sqrt{g}\,[(K^{ij} - g^{ij}\mathrm{tr}K)_{,j} - 8\pi J^i] \tag{46}$$

can be used to check the accuracy (and validity) of the numerical solution. To see this we examine the evolution of H and H^i. Once H and H^i do not vanish they may generate further diviations, even if we use the exact Einstein equations. If N and N^i are not functionals of g_{ij} and K_{ij} a straight forward calculation, [16,55] using the commutation relations between H and H_i [56], yields:

$$\frac{\partial H}{\partial t} = 2H^i N_{,i} + NH^i{}_{,i} + (HN^j)_{,j} = 2H^i N_{,i} + NH^i{}_{,i} + L_{N^j} H \tag{47}$$

and

$$\frac{\partial H_i}{\partial t} = HN_{,i} + (N^j H_i)_{,j} + H_j N^j{}_{,i} = HN_{,i} + L_{N^j} H_i \quad . \tag{48}$$

L_{N^j} here is the Lie derivative along N^j.

Perturbations of a general relativistic solution can be devided under the Moncreif decomposition [57] to real, gauge and constraint perturbations. In a special case of linearized perturbation from Minkowski space-time one can easily show [55] that the constraint perturbation generates further gauge and constraint perturbation, but they do not generate real perturbations.

Open Questions: a) Do the constraint perturbation (according to the Moncreif decomposition) generate real perturbation? b) Is there a covariant unique way to factor out the constraint perturbations when g_{ij} and K_{ij} are not far from an unknown background g°_{ij}, K°_{ij} satisfying the constraints?

A partial solution for this problem is suggested in the text, following York's procedure. However, it is unlikely that this procedure agrees with the Moncreif decomposition.

γ_{ij}, the conformal metric ($\det \gamma_{ij} \equiv 1$) and E_{ij}, the transverse-traceless part of the extrinsic curvature tensor, are the natural "free" part of the gravitational field. From the discussion of the initial value problem [6] we saw that they come nearest to describing the degrees of freedom of gravity. A potential solution for the consistency problem would be to evolve γ_{ij} and E_{ij} and to impose the constraint, via York's procedure, we substract the evolution of $g \equiv \det g_{ij}$:

$$\frac{dg}{dt} = -2\alpha g\,\mathrm{tr}K - 2gN^i{}_{,i} \tag{49}$$

from Eq. 19 to obtain

$$\frac{d\gamma_{ij}}{dt} = -2N\left(\gamma_{i\ell}K^{\ell}_{\ j} - \frac{1}{3}\gamma_{ij}\,\mathrm{tr}K\right) - N^{k}_{\ ,j}\gamma_{ik} + N^{k}_{\ ,i}\gamma_{jk} - \frac{2}{3}\gamma_{ij}N^{k}_{\ ,k}) \qquad (50)$$

After evolution of γ_{ij} using Eq. 50 we solve the conformal factor version of the Hamiltonian constraint (Eq. 28) for $\psi = g^{1/12}$ to obtain the full metric. This procedure is possible since Eq. 28 is insensitive to errors in the solution of Eq. 50 that will cause det $\gamma \neq 1$.

For the extrinsic curvature tensor we would like to evolve the transverse-traceless part, $\hat{E}^{ij}$:

$$\frac{d\hat{E}^{ij}}{dt} = \frac{d}{dt}(\psi^{10}K^{ij}) - \frac{1}{3}\frac{d}{dt}(\psi^{6}\,\mathrm{tr}K\,g^{ij}) - \frac{d}{dt}(\hat{\ell}W)^{ij} \qquad (51)$$

where "^" means that the quantity is calculated relative to the conformal metric γ_{ij}, ($\hat{E}^{ij} = \psi^{10}E^{ij}$). The evolution of K_{ij}, ψ, g_{ij} and trK can be substituted using Eqs. 20, 49, 19 and:

$$\frac{d\,\mathrm{tr}K}{dt} = -N^{|i}_{\ \ |i} + N[R + K^{2} - 4\pi(3E-S)] \qquad (52)$$

However,

$$\frac{d(\hat{\ell}W)^{ij}}{dt} = \frac{d}{dt}\,(\hat{\nabla}_{j})^{-1}\,[\tfrac{2}{3}\psi^{6}\hat{\nabla}^{i}\,\mathrm{tr}K + 8\pi\hat{J}^{i}] \qquad (53)$$

and we cannot write an explicit evolution equation for E^{ij}, or $\hat{E}^{ij}$ without inverting the operator $\hat{\nabla}_{j}$ analytically.

Still we can evolve K_{ij} using Eq. 19. Deviation from the constraint will appear in the numerical evolution. We constrain the evolved $\tilde{K}_{ij}$ by adding to it $(\ell W)_{ij}$:

$$K_{ij} = \tilde{K}_{ij} + (\ell W)_{ij} \qquad (54)$$

with

$$\Delta_{\ell}W^{i} = \nabla_{j}(\tilde{K}^{ij} - g^{ij}\,\mathrm{tr}\tilde{K} - 8\pi J^{i}) \quad . \qquad (55)$$

trK does not change in this procedure. There are two difficulties with this proposed scheme: First the conformal Hamiltonian constraint (Eq. 28) and Eq. 55 are coupled. Second, numerical derivatives which are taken in the procedure (both in $\nabla_{j}\tilde{K}^{ij}$ and in $R(\gamma_{ij})$) may spoil the accuracy of the sources for ψ and W^{i} and may make the whole scheme useless.

The consistency problem stems from the apparent over-determination problem; there are sixteen Einstein equations and twelve variables. Of course, there is no over-determination, there are four identities, the four Bianchi identities. We are free to substitute combinations of the constraint equations into the evolution equations (Eqs. 19,20). Such substitutions could either simplify the equations or yield equations that can be solved more accurately. We achieve the latter task by elimination of divergent or potential singular terms.

The Hamiltonian constraint, for example, can be substituted into the evolution equations for trK (Eq. 52) to eliminate the Ricci scalar R. With this we replace the long (and numerically less accurate) evaluation of R by the relatively simpler evaluation of $K_{ij}K^{ij}$. One can also try to improve the consistency of the finite differencing approximation by varying the equations in this manner. One set of equations may produce smaller deviations than another. It is not known how to do so systematically, but of course one can always use trial and error.

Wilson [14] suggests to consider the constraint as (elliptic) equations for specific components of the metric or the extrinsic curvature tensor. We solve the Hamiltonian constraint (Eq. 24) for the variable g_{ab} (a,b, fixed) with g_{ij}, (ij $\neq$ ab), and K_{ij} serving as sources and coefficients. Similarily we solve the momentum constraints (Eq. 25) for three specific components, say K_{cd}, K_{ef} and K_{gh} of K_{ij}. This procedure has a few drawbacks. Clearly it is not covariant and it is difficult to generalize from one case to another. The coordinate choice determines to a large extent which component can be evaluated in this way; sometimes there is no clear choice. Furthermore, when considered as an equation for specific components of g_{ij} and K_{ij} the constraints might not be proper elliptic equations. This may lead to difficulties (a solution may not exist, or worse may not be unique). The resulting equations are usually coupled. Rigorously we have to solve all of them simultaneously. This is usually a technically impossible task and we have to be satisfied with the approximation that the constraint equations are decoupled.

In spite of all these drawbacks, this method was very successful when applied in a few recent calculations [14,58,71,77]. It seems that it leads to stable finite differencing schemes [58].

Overall, there are twelve evolution equations and four constraint equations. The different schemes can be classified according to the equations used [17]. Let N_{coor} be the number of specific components of g_{ij} and K_{ij} that are eliminated by coordinate conditions (this includes components that are eliminated trivially, due to asymmetry). We denote by N_{evol}, (N_{aux}) and N_{cons} the number of evolution equations for g_{ij} or K_{ij} (and for auxiliary quantities, like Γ^i_{jk}) and the number of constraint equations solved. The following inequality holds:

$$N_{evol} \geq 8 + 2g - N_{coor} - N_{cons} + N_{aux} \tag{56}$$

This inequality allows us to classify the different schemes.

TABLE I: CLASSIFICATION OF NUMERICAL SCHEMES

SCHEME			REMARKS
Free Evolution	$N_{cons} = 0$	1	Constraints are not imposed
Partially Constrained Evolution	$1 \leq N_{cons} \leq 3$	1	Some constraints are imposed
Constrained Evolution	$N_{cons} = 4$	1,2	All constraints are imposed
Fully Constrained Evolution	$N_{evol} = 2g$	1,2	$N_{coor} = 4$ is necessary
Chopped Evolution	Usually $0 \leq N_{cons} \leq 3$ Sometimes $1 \leq N_{cons\,2} \leq 4$ $N_{cons} < N_{cons2}$		Free (or partially constrained) evolution on which additional constraints are imposed every fixed time interval.
Covariantly Constrained Evolution	Eq. 56 becomes an inequality		Constraints are imposed continuously but not by evaluation of specific g_{ij} or K_{ij} components.
Auxiliary (constrained) Evolution	$N_{aux} \neq 0$ $(\bar{N}_{cons} > 0)$	1	Auxiliary quantities are evolved (together with imposing some or all of constraints)

1. Eq. 56 satisfied as an equality
2. Constraint equations that are satisfied trivially are counted in N_{cons}, in these cases only.

So far, free, partially constrained and fully constrained schemes, as well as auxiliary free evolution schemes have been tried. There have been no attempts to construct a covariantly constrained scheme, or even a partially covariantly constrained one (with only the Hamiltonian constraint imposed). This is partially due to the theoretical difficulties involved, and partially due to the numerical complexity of such a procedure.

From a numerical point of view, a solution of a constraint equation which is generally elliptic, (even though the constraints can become parabolic in special cases [46]) is more (CPU) time consuming than the solution of an evolution equation. An elliptic equation is solved by a relaxation method and the grid have to be swept several times in order to obtain a convergent solution. The effective p (number of floating point operations per grid point per time step) increases. This difficulty disappears for a parabolic constraint in which the numerical grid is swept only once.

Empirical tests [58] seem to indicate that fully constraint schemes are less prone to numerical instabilities than free evolution ones. The final choice depends strongly on the coordinate conditions and on the exact form of the resulting constraint equations.

To conclude this section we make some practical remarks. The consistency problems seem very worrisome. It may be impossible to solve analytically all the questions related to this problem. Similar questions are still open in numerical analysis of simpler systems of equations. However, we have to remember that simple practical tests, like comparison of the results calculated with a different grid size are always available. In addition, we can compare results of free, chopped and constrained evolution [58]. Reasonable agreement between these suggests that in spite of all the doubts the numerical solution is probably correct!

COORDINATE CONDITIONS

The coordinate conditions have a crucial role in the success of a numerical solution. We have seen that it is currently impossible to write a general code, which could handle various coordinate conditions. By a general code we mean a code using, for example, Cartezian coordinate x,y,z, with general metric functions $g_{ij}(x,y,z)$. The huge numbers of algebraic operations needed to evaluate R_{ij} for such general metric makes such a code impractical. To simplify the calculation one has to make a special coordinate choice.

Bardeen (lecture in this volume) [59] (see also [7,9]) review various features of different coordinate systems. We discuss here the numerical aspects of gauge conditions. We have the following demands from a good coordinate system:

a) Singularity avoidance: The coordinates must not develop coordinate singularities, apart from simple singularities which can be factored out, like the singularity at the origin of polar coordinates. Moreover, the coordinates must avoid physical singularities that are developing in the solution.

Avoidance of physical singularity is achieved by slowing down the evolution in the spatial region near the singularity when such a singularity is approached. This is controlled by the temporal gauge condition, i.e. by the lapse function. If the spacelike hypersurfaces are regular, normal coordinates will always yield a regular metric. An additional condition on any other spatial gauge condition is that it does not generate additional coordinate singularities.

b) Simplification: The coordinate must simplify the metric and Einstein equations in a way that will make the numerical calculations feasible.

c) Asymptotic Propagation of Radiation: Asymptotically the coordinates should turn to a natural radiation gauge in which gravitational radiation has a wavelike propagation nature [59,60]. This suggests that the coordinates should be asymptotically polar - to correspond to the radial propagation of gravitational radiation away from a central source.

d) Gravitational Degrees of Freedom: The gravitational degrees of freedom should be isolated as much as possible. The scheme evolves variables corresponding to these degrees of freedom; other variables are evaluated preferably using the constraint equations. This helps to obtain accurate propagation of gravitational rediation.

e) Unique Form of Known Exact Solution: It is advantageous when known exact solutions (in particular the Kerr solution) have a unique form in the chosen coordinate system. In such cases development towards a known exact solution can be easily identified.

Coordinate conditions are imposed in the "3+1" formalism via choice of the lapse function and the shift vector [see for example 6]. Both N and N^i can be freely specified as they are not determined by Einstein equations. In the following sections we divide the discussion to lapse function and hypersurface conditions and to the shift vector and spatial gauge.

LAPSE FUNCTION AND HYPERSURFACE CONDITIONS:

The lapse function, N, (see Fig. 2) determines the temporal coordinate by fixing the distance between two neighboring spacelike hypersurfaces. The choice of N is usually, but not necessarily, related to a condition on the extrinsic curvature.

a) Gaussian Coordinates: The choice $N = 1$ (which is usually associated with $N^i = 0$) leads to Gaussian normal coordinates. This coordinate condition is simple and it has been used in some works [5,32,44]. However, apart from elimination of N from the scheme it does not lead to any simplification of Einstein equations. A serious problem is the tendency of this coordinate to converge and to form caustics and singularities which are pure coordinate singularities. Thus, these coordinates are "singularity seeking" rather than "singularity avoiding" and should not be used.

b) Lagrangian Slicing: For spherical flow Misner and Sharp [29] use Lagrangian slicing:

$$(Nu^t) = 1 \tag{57}$$

where u^t is the t component of the matter four velocity. Clearly $u^i \equiv 0$, and the spacelike hypersurfaces are orthogonal to the flow lines (this is always possible in a one dimensional flow). With $N^i = 0$ the spacelike coordinates follow the matter flow lines. The Lagrangian condition simplifies the hydrodynamic equations, however, the penalty is very severe. The matter flow lines converge towards a singularity when it forms. This is the reason that the May and White [4] could not follow a black hole formation - the Lagrangian hypersurfaces touch the black hole's central singularity as soon as it forms and the calculation cannot continue. This happens long before all the matter falls into the black hole.

c) Maximal Slicing:

In a given space-time the maximal slicing condition [40,7,61,62] maximizes the three volume of each of the spacelike hypersurfaces:

$$V = \int_{\text{hypersurface}} \sqrt{{}^{(3)}g}\; d^3x \; . \tag{58}$$

The variation

$$\delta V = 0 \quad , \tag{59}$$

leads to

$$trK = 0 \quad . \tag{60}$$

On a given maximal slice the evolution equation for trK, Eq. 52, yields a linear elliptic equation for the lapse that keeps the future hypersurfaces maximal:

$$\frac{dtrK}{dt} = -N^{|i}{}_{|i} + N[K_{ij}K^{ij} + 4\pi(E + trS)] = 0 \quad . \tag{61}$$

This equation has been modified by substitution of R from the Hamiltonian constraint, Eq. 24.

Asymptotic flatness demand that $N \underset{r \to \infty}{\to} 1$. If there is an inner boundary surface like on the throat in Schwartzschold solution another boundary condition is needed which can be either $N = 1$ or $\partial N/\partial r = 0$ [61].

Maximal slicing has excellent singularity avoidance features. In particular, maximal hypersurfaces avoid a large class of singularities, called by Eardley and Smarr [63] crushing singularities. For Schwartzschild black hole, for example, maximal slices (with $\partial N/\partial r = 0$ boundary condition) freeze the evolution at $r = 1.5M$ and do not touch the singularity at $r = 0$! Similar features appear in maximal slicing of Kerr metric. The lapse function "collapses" near the singularity, [62], i.e. N vanishes exponentially near the singularity, allowing the maximal slices to span the rest of the future development of the initial data.

Maximal slicing simplifies the numerical scheme eliminating terms from the momentum constraint (Eqs. 25 or 29) and the $K_j^{\ i}$ evolution (Eq. 20) equations. $TrK = 0$ leads to a separation of York's equations for the initial value problem. Finally, the algebraic equation $trK = 0$ can be used to eliminate a chosen component of $K_i^{\ j}$ from the scheme. Gravitational radiation can propagate micely on maximal slices [59,61].

With all these features it is clear why maximal slices were so popular in recent numerical works [14,58,64,65]. A basic drawback of these slices is lack of uniqueness. The necessity of two boundary conditions outer (at infinity) and inner (on the throat) for black hole solutions means that maximal slices are not unique. This might lead to difficulties in identifying a given metric on these slices. Another drawback is the need to solve an elliptic equation at each time step. Furthermore, in spite of recent progress [66,67] it is still not clear whether under which condition a general space-time admits such hypersurfaces.

d) Constant Mean Curvature Hypersurfaces:

The slicing condition:

$$trK = k \quad , \tag{62}$$

includes maximal slices as a special case. Like maximal hypersurfaces, these hypersurfaces have crushing singularity avoidance feature [63,68]. For asymptotically flat space times the basic difference between these and maximal hypersurfaces is that while the later reach I^{o}, constant mean curvature hypersurfaces become asymptotically null and reach null infinity (either $\mathscr{I}^+$ or $\mathscr{I}^-$ depending on the sign of k). This might be advantageous for studying propagation of gravitational radiation. If we begin with a hypersurface with $trK = k$ and if $k \neq k(t)$, the condition $\partial trK/\partial t = 0$ (Eq. 61) yields the slicing condition for the lapse function. For cosmological problems $k = k(t)$ leads to York's slicing [69]. In a closed Universe these slices are the natural generalization of the constant time slices the Robertson-Walker metric. Their use is almost essential when studying cosmological problems, since it guarantees that we can distinguish real deviation from Robertson-Walker metric from gauge ones [69,70,58].

Only a slight modification of Eq. 63 is needed to allow $k = k(t)$:

$$N^{|i}{}_{|i} - N[K_{ij}K^{ij} + 4\pi(E + trS)] = - \frac{\partial k}{\partial t} \tag{63}$$

So far constant mean curvature slices have been used only in cosmological work [19,58,71], and their interesting asymptotic null features [69] have not been exploited numerically.

e) Algebraic and Hypergeometric Slicing:

Nakamura [28] suggests to use the equation:

$$\frac{1}{r^2} \frac{d}{dr} (r^2 \frac{dN}{dr}) = V_o \ \text{sech}^2(dr)N \tag{64}$$

with V_o and d, free parameters, for the lapse function. With boundary conditions $N \underset{r\to\infty}{\to} 1$ and $dN/dr\,|_{r=0} = 0$ the solution can be expressed in terms of hypergeometric functions. This condition imitates with a proper choice of V_o and d the singularity avoidance feature of maximal slicing. In Nakamura's calculations [28] it slowed down the evolution successfully near the central singularity when black holes were formed. The basic advantage of this hypergeometric slicing over maximal slicing is the simplicity of Eq. 64 which yields an immediate solution (in terms of hypergeometric functions [28]) while the maximal slicing equations (Eq. 61) is an elliptic equation whose SOR solution is time consuming. This condition does not have further simplifying features or a direct useful geometrical meaning.

Choquet-Bruhat [72] suggested recently a different algebraic slicing condition:

$$N = \sqrt{g} \tag{65}$$

With this condition, (and with the normal coordinate condition) she was able to write Einstein equations as a set of third order partial differential equations, and to prove that this set is hyperbolic [72]. It is not clear what are the singularity avoidance features of this slicing condition. Clearly this condition accelerates the evolution whenever g becomes large, and slows it down for $g \to 0$. We suspect, therefore, that these hypersurfaces will be attracted to singularities on which $g \to \infty$. So far this condition was not tested in any numerical scheme.

f) Polar Hypersurfaces

Polar hypersurfaces [46] are compatible with spherical polar coordinates (r,θ,ϕ). The coordinate condition is:

$$trK = K_r{}^r \tag{66}$$

with r the radial coordinate. This slicing condition leads to a parabolic equation for N:

$$\frac{dtrK}{dt} - \frac{dKr^r}{dt} = -(N^{|i}{}_{|i} - N^{|r}{}_{|r}) + N[R-R_r{}^r) + K(K-K_r{}^r) - 8\pi(E-S_r{}^r)] +$$

$$+ N^r{}_{|\theta}K_r{}^\theta + N^r{}_{|\phi}K_r{}^\phi - N^\theta{}_{|r}K_\theta{}^r - N^\phi{}_{|r}K_\phi{}^r = 0 \ . \tag{67}$$

Only the first derivative $N_{|r}$ appears in this equation. The equation is integrated inwards. The boundary condition: $N = 1$, is specified at spatial infinity. Parabolic equations have a few advantages over elliptic equations. First, the numerical solution is obtained after a single sweep of the numerical grid, versus the necessity of a few (or more) iterations for convergence of an elliptic solution. Second, with a simple boundary condition (even when there is an inner throat) the polar hypersurfaces are unique. In fact, for Schwartzschild and Kerr metrics these are common constant time hypersurfaces.

The polar slicing appears very natural when combined with the radial gauge [46], which we discuss later. In this combination it seems to have singularity avoidance feature that is even stronger than the singularity avoidance of maximal slices. At least in spherical collapse examples the polar hypersurfaces slow the evolution so that even an apparent horizon does not form.

When the hypersurface condition is related to the extrinsic curvature it is not surprising that it determines the nature of the momentum constraint equations. With polar hypersurfaces it is easy to see that $K_r{}^r{}_{,r}$ does not appear in any of the momentum constraint equations. This enables us to combine the momentum constraint equations (Eq. 25) to a parabolic equation when considered as an equation for $K_r{}^r$. Unfortunately, this form is not very useful as it has a singular homogeneous solution.

The polar slicing condition has two disadvantages. Unlike in prior slicing conditions, the shift vector, N^i, appears in the polar slicing lapse function equation. The lapse function equation is coupled to the spatial gauge condition equations for the shift vector. The combination may lead us back to an elliptic system if both conditions are solved simultaneously.

Additional dificulties lead to irregular behavior of polar hypersurfaces at the origin. To avoid this irregularity, an inner portion of the polar hypersurface must be replaced by another, say maximal, hypersurface. Smooth fit between the two hypersurfaces is obtained by the mixed condition:

$$\mathrm{tr}K = C\left(\frac{r}{r_c}\right) K_r{}^r \tag{68}$$

with $C(0) = 0$ and $C(x) = 1$ for $x \geq 1$ and a smooth transition between. The lapse function equation is:

$$(N^{|i}{}_{|i} - CN^{|r}{}_{|r}) - N[(R-CR_r{}^r) - 4\pi(3-C)E + 4\pi(1-C)S + 8\pi CS_r{}^r]$$
$$+ C[N^r{}_{,\theta}K_r{}^\theta + N^r{}_{,\phi}K_r{}^\phi - N^\theta{}_{,r}K_\theta{}^r - N^\phi{}_{,r}K_\phi{}^r] - K_r{}^r C'\left[\left(\frac{r}{r_c^2}\right)\dot{r} - \frac{N^r}{r_c}\right] \quad . \tag{69}$$

SHIFT VECTOR AND SPATIAL COORDINATES

The spatial coordinates are determined by the shift vector N^i. The shift vector generates a continuous coordinates transformation during the time evolution. This can be seen from the contribution of N^i to the evolution equations of $g_{ij}:L_{N^k}g_{ij}$ which is equivalent to a coordinate transformation generated along a vector field N^i with a parameter t. The choice of N^i is naturally, but again not necessarily, related to the metric functions. We discuss a few coordinate conditions:

a) <u>Normal Coordinates</u>:

The normal coordinate condition:

$$N^i = 0 \quad , \tag{70}$$

is the simplest condition possible. This coordinate condition was used frequently in the early works in numerical relativity [4,5,10,11,15,44], it is also called sometimes the Eulerian gauge [9,59,62].[3]

The trajectories of these coordinates are orthgonal to the spacelike hypersurfaces. The great advantage of the normal gauge is that is never leads to a coordinate singularity. The normal coordinates do not become singular unless the hypersurfaces themselves develop a singularity. Clearly this condition leads to the disappearance of N^i from the convective derivative, $d/dt = \partial/\partial t$ and from the rest of the evolution equations. This simplification of Einstein equations is very minor. The major drawback of these coordinates is that they do not simplify g_{ij} and R_{ij}. Moreover, at a given time the form of the metric depends on the past history of g_{ij} - and it might be very difficult to identify the formation of a specific geometry in this case.

b) Lagrangian Coordinates:

Lagrangian coordinates follow the matter. The coordinate condition:

$$N_i = u_i/u_t \quad . \tag{71}$$

leads to $u^i = 0$. These coordinates will not develop coordinate singularity unless a physical hydrodynamic singularity appears. Some difficulties may appear, though, if a shock wave is encountered. The Lagrangian coordinates simplify the hydrodynamics, but complicate the geometry [72,74]. It may be very difficult to propagate the gravitational radiation through the coordinate shear produced by the matter motion. Apart from the problem of spherical collapse this seems a very bad coordinate choice.

c) Minimal Shear:

Minimal shear coordinates were proposed as a natural radiation gauge by Smarr and York [60,7]. The minimal shear condition:

$$\nabla^j (g^{1/3} \, \partial\gamma_{ij}/\partial t) = 0 \tag{72}$$

leads to a vector elliptic equation for N^i. This condition has many virtues and it seems to be an excellent radiation gauge [59]. In spite of the nice analytic properties of the minimal shear gauge it was not shown that this condition will not develop coordinate singularities. Furthermore, for practical applications the minimal shear conditions have a few major drawbacks. The minimal shear vector elliptic equations are very complex (These are more or less equivalent to Eq. 30 for W^i). Furthermore, the minimal shear condition does not lead to any simplification of Einstein equations (which remain as cumbersome as in the general case). Finally, like in the normal coordinate case, the metric g_{ij} in this gauge depends on the past history of g_{ij}. These drawbacks limit the use of the minimal shear condition. So far it was used only in the (trivial) spherical case and for (one dimensional) cylindrical problems [58].

d) Simplifying Gauge:

Simplifying gauge conditions compose a large group of conditions that are constructed to simplify the metric and subsequently Einstein's equations [14,9,16,17]. Assume that the metric g_{ij} satisfies a general algebraic relation on the initial hypersurface:

$$F(g_{ij}, x^i) = Q(x^i) \quad . \tag{73}$$

An important special case of Eq. 73 is vanishing of a particular component of the metric:

$$g_{ab} = 0 \quad . \tag{74}$$

The condition:

$$\frac{\partial F}{\partial t} = \frac{\partial F}{\partial g_{ij}} \frac{\partial g_{ij}}{\partial t} = \frac{\partial F}{\partial g_{ij}} \left[2NK_{ij} + \mathcal{L}_{N^k} g_{ij}\right] = 0 \quad , \tag{75}$$

guarantees that Eq. 73 holds on all future surfaces and enables us to use Eq. 73 to eliminate variables and to simplify Einstein equations. The existence of a fixed form (Eq. 73) of g_{ij} makes it easier to identify a known solution once it appears.

With three components of N^i we can impose up to three coordinate conditions of the form of Eq. 73. After substitution of Eq. 19, Eq. 74 becomes a first order equation for N^i. Let $A(A = 1,2,3)$ label the conditions, we combine the three equations as:

$$\frac{\partial F_A}{\partial g_{ij}} \circ \mathcal{L}_{N^k} g_{ij} = \frac{\partial F_A}{\partial g_{ij}} \circ (2NK_{ij}) \tag{76}$$

$\frac{\partial F_A}{\partial g_{ij}}$ should be viewed, after rearranging ij as a six vector, as a three by six projection operator, whose coefficient can be functions of x^i and g_{ij}.

Open Question: What are the conditions on $\frac{\partial F_A}{\partial g_{ij}}$ *so that Eq. 76 has a solution?*

It is known that with some projection operators, Eq. 76 does not have a solution. A second question is the long-time existence of the solution.

Open Question: When do simplifying conditions, (of the form of Eq. 73) lead to coordinate singularity?

In view of this great simplifying power, such conditions have been widely used in recent numerical work [14,16,58,71]. We review now a few examples.

e) Diagonal Gauge:

In this gauge:

$$ds^2 = g_{xx}dx^2 + g_{yy}dy^2 + g_{zz}dz^2 \tag{77}$$

The three metric is the simplest possible. The shift vector equations are:

$$g_{xx}N^x{}_{,y} + g_{yy}N^y{}_{,x} = 2NK_{xy} \tag{78a}$$

$$g_{yy}N^y{}_{,z} + g_{zz}N^z{}_{,y} = 2NK_{yz} \tag{78b}$$

$$g_{zz}N^z{}_{,x} + g_{xx}N^x{}_{,z} = 2NK_{zx} \tag{78c}$$

It seems, even though not rigorously proven, that in general, (with two modes of degrees of freedom of the gravitational field, i.e. $g = 2$) Eq. 78 does not have a solution. With $g = 1$, a solution may exist, if one of Eq. 78 is satisfied trivially. Such a solution is not unique and an additional condition has to be added (see [58] for example of application of this gauge to axisymmetric non-rotating collapse).

f) Radial Gauge:

The radial gauge is particularly useful as a simplifying gauge for asymptotically flat configurations in which gravitational radiation is propagating away from a central source and which do not include initially a black hole. These coordinates were suggested recently by Bardeen and Piran [46]. They are a special case of coordinates suggested by Geroch [75]. Analog conditions were used by Piran and Rotenberry [76] for cylindrical configurations.

The radial gauge employs polar coordinates (r,θ,ϕ). The three dimensional line element has the form:

$$d\ell^2 = A^2 dr^2 + r^2 B^{-2} d\theta^2 + r^2 B^2 (\sin\theta\, d\phi + \xi\, d\theta)^2 . \qquad (79)$$

The simplifying conditions are:

$$g_{r\theta} = g_{r\phi} = 0 \quad , \qquad (80ab)$$

and

$$g_{\theta\theta} g_{\phi\phi} - g_{\theta\phi}{}^2 = r^4 \sin^2\theta \quad . \qquad (80c)$$

From Eq. 80c we notice that the coordinate r obtains a direct geometrical meaning. The area of a constant - r sphere is $4\pi r^2$. The radial gauge is, therefore, a natural generalization of Schwartzschild coordinates.

The shift vector equations become parabolic:

$$\left(\frac{2N^r}{r}\right)_{,r} - \frac{1}{\sin\theta} (\sin\theta A^2 N^{r,\theta})_{,\theta} - (A^2 N^{r,\phi})_{,\phi} = -[2N(K_\theta{}^\theta + K_\phi{}^\phi)]_{,r} +$$

$$+ \frac{1}{\sin\theta} (2N\sin^2\theta K_r{}^\theta)_{,\theta} + (2NK_r{}^\phi)_{,\phi} \quad . \qquad (82)$$

Eq. 82 is integrated outwards with a boundary condition $N^r = 0$ at the origin. The other shift vector components are obtained from N^r by a simple integration:

$$N^{\theta,r} = -2NK^{r\theta} - N^{r,\theta} \quad , \qquad (83a)$$

$$N^{\phi,r} = -2NK^{r\phi} - N^{r,\phi} \quad . \qquad (83b)$$

The boundary condition $N^\theta = N^\phi = 0$ fixes the integration constant. Eqs. 83a,b have a unique regular solution as long as the sources are regular. The exponential decay of a homogeneous solution of linear parabolic equations leads to $N^r \underset{N \to \infty}{\to} 0$, and therefore also to $N^\theta \underset{r \to \infty}{\to} 0$ $N^\phi \underset{r \to \infty}{\to} 0$.

The radial gauge becomes asymptotically a natural transverse-traceless radiation gauge [59] with the dynamical variables (η, K_+) and (ξ, K_-) displaying simple radial wavelike propagation, where:

$$\eta \equiv B^2 - 1, \qquad (84)$$

$$K_+ \equiv \frac{1}{2}(K_\phi{}^\phi + 2(\xi/\sin\theta)K_\phi{}^\theta - K_\theta{}^\theta), \qquad (85)$$

and

$$K_- \equiv (\sin\theta)^{-1} B^{-2} K_\phi{}^\phi \quad . \qquad (86)$$

Other equations also simplify greatly, in particular, the Hamiltonian constraint becomes an outward integrated parabolic equation for A. When $g = 1$, ξ and K_- vanish and the radial gauge becomes automatically a diagonal gauge.

The basic advantages of the radial gauge are its simple form, the resulting simplicity of Einstein equations which is combined with natural propagation of radially outgoing gravitational radiation and the fact that known solutions like

Schwartzschild and Kerr are easily expressed in these coordiantes. The radial gauge will develop a singularity when a minimal two surface surrounding the origin, which usually corresponds to an apparent horizon, appears. This is just the well-known coordinate singularity of Schwartzschild coordinates at $r = 2M$. r, that measures the area of two sphere, cannot grow monotonically from the origin to infinity. This is manifested by divergence of A. To solve this problem we propose to use the radial gauge in conjunction with polar hypersurfaces. Polar hypersurfaces slow down the evolution sufficiently, so that an event horizon does not form on them. We conjecture that other coordinate singularities will not develop, using this gauge.

g) Isothermal Gauge:

The isothermal gauge is another simplifying condition. This version [46] is a generalization of the isothermal gauge used by Dykema and Wilson [77] which in turn is a generalization of the spherical isotropic coordinates. Unlike Smarr and Wilson [9,14], this isothermal gauge employs polar coordinates, (r,θ,ϕ). This makes it more convenient for studying propagation of radiation from an isolated system. The main advantage of this gauge over the radial gauge is the disappearance of the singularity on minimal surfaces. Thus, the isothermal gauge can be used for configuration that includes initially a black hole.

The three dimensional line element is:

$$d\ell^2 = \psi^4[B^{-2}(dr^2 + r^2 d\theta^2) + B^2 r^2 (\sin\theta\, d\phi + \xi\, d\theta)^2] \quad . \tag{87}$$

The gauge conditions are:

$$g_{r\theta} = g_{r\phi} = 0 \quad , \tag{88a,b}$$

and

$$g^{rr} = g^{\theta\theta} \quad . \tag{88c}$$

The shift vector equations are:

$$N(K^{\theta\theta} - \frac{1}{r^2} K^{rr}) = \frac{1}{r} (\frac{N^r}{r})^{,r} - N^{\theta,\theta} \quad ,$$

together with Eqs. 83a,b.

The isothermal gauge leads to considerable simplification of Einstein equations. However, the simplification is not as impressive as in the radial gauge case. General equations for the isothermal gauge for axisymmetric configurations are given in Appendix B of [46].

AXISYMMETRIC ROTATING COLLAPSE WITH RADIAL GAUGE AND POLAR (MIXED) SLICING - AN EXAMPLE

A numerical scheme for axisymmetric rotating collapse calculations have been recently worked out in details by Bardeen and Piran [46]. We review in this section some of the basic ideas and results of this scheme, as an example for a numerical approach to a relativistic calculation. The general radial gauge and polar (or mixed) gauge conditions have been summarized earlier. In this section we specialize to the axisymmetric case. The physical problem that we have in mind when constructing this example is collapse of a rotating star in an asymptotically flat background. The basic physical question that we are interested in is how much gravitational radiation does the collapsing star emit? In the discussion we examine specific questions that are important for the construction of a numerical scheme: Use of triad components, combinations of the original "3+1" equations and normalized variables, all in order to isolate the "true degrees of freedom" and to minimize the errors in the propagation of gravitational radiation.

Examination of the consistency of the scheme and its potential singular behavior near the origin. Treatment of the degeneracy of the equations on inner boundaries, like the origin or the axis and a staggered grid structure that is compatible with these features.

Triad Components

To obtain "physical" components, we project tensors on an orthonormal triad of basis vectors $\vec{e}_{(i)}$: $\vec{e}_{(1)}$ is along the radial direction, $\vec{e}_{(3)}$ is along the ϕ direction and $\vec{e}_{(2)}$ is then fixed by orthonormality and the right-hand rule:

$$e_{(1)}{}^{i} = \psi^{-2}[A^{-1},0,0] \quad , \tag{90a}$$

$$e_{(2)}{}^{i} = \psi^{-2}[0,r^{-1}B, -(r\sin\theta)^{-1}\xi B] \quad , \tag{90b}$$

$$e_{(3)}{}^{i} = \psi^{-2}[0,0(r\sin\theta)^{-1}B^{-1}] \quad . \tag{90c}$$

The projection of the extrinsic curvature tensor, for example, is related to coordinate components by

$$K_{(1)(1)} = K_r{}^r \quad , \tag{91a}$$

$$K_{(1)(2)} = (r/AB)K_r{}^\theta \tag{91b}$$

$$K_{(1)(3)} = (r\sin\theta)^{-1}(A/B)K_\phi{}^r \quad , \tag{91c}$$

$$K_{(2)(2)} = K_\theta{}^\theta - (\xi/\sin\theta)K_\phi{}^\theta \quad , \tag{91d}$$

$$K_{(3)(3)} = K_\phi{}^\phi + (\xi/\sin\theta)K_\phi{}^\theta \quad , \tag{91e}$$

$$K_{(2)(3)} = (\sin\theta)^{-1}B^{-2}K_\phi{}^\theta \quad . \tag{91f}$$

We label specially some linear combinations of these triad components:

$$K_T \equiv K_{(2)(2)} + K_{(3)(3)} \tag{92a}$$

and

$$K_+ \equiv \frac{1}{2}(K_{(3)(3)} - K_{(2)(2)}) \quad , \tag{92b}$$

and

$$K_- \equiv K_{(2)(3)} \quad , \tag{92c}$$

K_+ and K_- are the even and odd parity transverse-traceless parts of the extrinsic curvature at large r and are conjugate to the "dynamical" metric functions η and ξ, respectively. As we see later, the evolution equations for η, ξ, K_+ and K_- constitute wave equations for the "dynamical" variables η and ξ. The waves apparently propagate only in the radial direction, since there are no angular derivatives of η or ξ in these equations. Propagation in angular directions is expressed through the angular derivatives of A and through the shift vector terms. The usage of K_+ and K_T rather than $K_{(3)(3)}$ and $K_{(2)(2)}$ is crucial for minimizing the errors in propagation of gravitational radiation.

Behavior Near the Origin

Local flatness and reflection symmetry about the equatorial plane require that the metric function η satisfies:

$$\eta \sim e\, r^2(1-x^2) \quad . \tag{93}$$

Pure local flatness considerations might seem to allow ξ to vanish like $\xi \sim r^2(1-x^2)x$ near the origin. However, one cannot satisfy the gauge condition $g_{r\phi} = 0$ with this behavior. The leading behavior compatible with the radial gauge condition is:

$$\xi \approx q r^4(1-x^2)x \tag{94}$$

for some coefficient $q(t)$.

In locally Cartesian coordinates at $r = 0$ the general axisymmetric form for the extrinsic curvature tensor is:

$$K_x{}^x = \tfrac{1}{3}K+K_+, \qquad K_y{}^y = \tfrac{1}{3}K+k_+, \qquad K_z{}^z = \tfrac{1}{3}K-2k_+, \tag{95}$$

all other components vanish. The coefficient k_+ is the amplitude of the shear in the extrinsic curvature at $r = 0$. When the basis vectors are rotated by the appropriate angles to correspond to the triad (Eq. 90), the result is

$$K_{(1)(1)} = \tfrac{1}{3}K-2k_+P_2(x) \quad , \tag{96a}$$

$$K_{(1)(2)}/\sin\phi = 3k_+x \tag{96b}$$

$$K_T = \tfrac{2}{3}K+2k_+P_2(x) \tag{96c}$$

$$K_+ = \tfrac{3}{2}k_+(1-x^2) \quad , \tag{96d}$$

where $P_2(x)$ is the Legendre polynomial. The other two components, $K_{(1)(3)}$ and $K_{(2)(3)} = K_-$ are necessarily zero and must vanish as r^2 at $r = 0$.

Note that in spherical coordinates individual components of $K_{(i)(j)}$ may be a *function of angle* at $r = 0$, because the orientation of the triad $\vec{e}_{(i)}$ relative to fixed directions in space is a function of angle at $r = 0$.

At $r = 0$ we take regularity to mean that the changes in *locally Cartesian* coordinates $x \equiv r\sin\theta\cos\phi$, $y \equiv r\sin\theta\sin\phi$, $z \equiv r\cos\phi$, have expansions in non-negative integer powers of x,y, and z. Axisymmetry then requires N^x, N^y, and N^z to have the form

$$N^x = f_1(z,\tilde\rho^2)x-f_2(z,\tilde\rho^2)y \quad , \tag{97a}$$

$$N^y = f_1(z,\tilde\rho^2)y+f_2(z,\tilde\rho^2)x \quad , \tag{97b}$$

$$N^z = f_3(z,\tilde\rho^2) \quad , \tag{97c}$$

where $\tilde\rho^2 \equiv x^2 + y^2 = r^2\sin^2\theta$. The f_n are regular functions of their arguments in the above sense. Transform back to the spherical coordinates to find

$$N^r/r = \sin^2\phi f_1 + r^{-1}\cos\phi f_3 \quad , \tag{98a}$$

$$N^\phi/\sin\phi = \cos\phi f_1 - r^{-1}f_3 \quad , \tag{98b}$$

$$N^\theta = f_2 \quad . \tag{98c}$$

With symmetry about the equatorial plane f_1 and f_2 must be even functions of z and f_3 must be an odd function of z.

Shift Vector Equations

The basic axisymmetric shift vector equation, with $G \equiv N^{\theta}/\sin\theta$ and x $\cos\theta$ is:

$$[(1-x^2)G]_{,xx} - 2r(AB)^{-2}G_{,r} = [NK_T]_{,x} + 4(AB)^{-1}NK_{(1)(2)}/\sin\theta \quad . \tag{99}$$

This is an outward-parabolic equation. The appearance of parabolic instead of elliptic equation in the radial gauge is the essential feature which we believe makes the radial gauge the preferred gauge for numerical calculations of stellar collapse. Once G is found, N^r is given by:

$$N^r/r = \frac{1}{2}[(1-x^2)G]_{,x} - \frac{1}{2}NK_T \quad , \tag{100}$$

and N^{ϕ} is calculated by integrating

$$N^{\phi,r} = -\left(\frac{2AN}{rB}\right)\frac{K_{(1)(3)}}{\sin(\theta)} - \xi G_{,r} \quad , \tag{101}$$

radially inward from infinity. Substituting Eq. 98 in Eqs. 100a,b we find that the boundary condition for the shift vector are:

$$G(0) = -3k_+N_o x \tag{102a}$$

where $N_o = N(r=0)$ and $k^+ = K_+(0)$, and

$$N^r/r = 2k_+N_oP_2(x) - N_oK_o/3 \quad . \tag{102b}$$

Hamiltonian Constraint

The Hamiltonia constraint equation, Eq. 24 takes the form:

$$[r(1-A^{-2})]_{,r} - A^{-1}[(1-x^2)B^2A_{,x}]_{,x} = r^2[8\pi E + K_+^2 + K_-^2 + K^2_{(1)(2)} +$$

$$K^2_{(1)(3)} + \frac{3}{4}K_T^2 - KK_T + \frac{1}{4}A^{-2}(B^{-4}(\eta_{,r})^2 + B^4(\xi_{,r})^2)] + \frac{1}{2}[(1-x^2)\eta]_{,xx} \tag{103}$$

Equation 103, in contrast to the Hamiltonian constraint elliptic equation for the conformal factor ψ Eq. 28, is a *parabolic* equation for A. The stable direction of integration is *outward*, with local flatness requiring the initial condition $A = 1$ at $r = 0$.

If E. the $K_{(i)(j)}$, η, and ξ fall off sufficiently rapidly as $r \to \infty$, the solution for A automatically satisfies asymptotic flatness, $A \to 1 + O(r^{-1})$. When linearized in (A-1) the homogeneous solutions of Eq. 103 go as $A-1 \approx r^{-[1+\frac{1}{2}\ell(\ell+1)]}P_\ell(x)$. The linear contribution to A from an oscillatory gravitational wave in η, $\eta \approx \frac{e^{ikr}}{r}$, falls off as r^{-2} once $kr \gg 1$.

By analogy to the Schwartzschild metric one can define a *mass aspect* function

$$m(r,\theta) \equiv \frac{1}{2}\, r(1-A^{-2}) \tag{104}$$

The angular average of $m(r,\theta)$ over an r = constant two-surface,

$$M(r) \equiv \frac{1}{4}\iint m \sin\theta d\theta d\phi = \frac{1}{2}\int_{-1}^{1} m dx \tag{105}$$

can be interpreted as the total energy inside the two-surface. In the limit $r \to \infty$, M is the gauge-invariant ADM mass on the hypersurface, and as first noted by Geroch [75] M(r) increases monotonically outward on a maximal hypersurface (K = 0).

The most likely difficulty in stellar collapse calculations is that during the evolution the energy density, say, will become large enough over a large enough region that $2m/r \to 1$ at some finite radius, i.e., that $A \to \infty$. This heralds the development of a minimal two-surface. It seems likely that minimal two-surfaces only occur inside apparent event horizons and therefore, modulo cosmic censorship, only inside the true event horizon. If so, it may be possible to make the minimal two-surface or apparent event horizon the inner boundary of the grid, instead of $r = 0$, all without compromising the calculation in the astrophysically relevant part of the spacetime. Note that the singular part of A, provided that η, ξ, E, and the $K_{(i)(j)}$ are regular functions of r and x, is, thanks to the parabolic character of Eq. 103, a factor depending only on the radius r. Whether minimal two-surfaces actually develop in a stellar collapse calculation will depend on the choice of hypersurface condition.

Evolution equations

The convective time derivatives of the three metric functions in the radial gauge along the hypersurface normal are:

$$A^{-1}dA/dt = -N^r{}_{,r} - NK_{(1)(1)} \tag{106a}$$

$$B^{-2}dB^2/dt = -(1-x^2)G_{,x} - 2NK_+ \tag{106b}$$

$$B^2 d\xi/dt = (1-x^2)B^2[N^\theta{}_{,x} + \xi G_{,x}] - 2NK_- \quad . \tag{106c}$$

The metric function, A, may be altimately determined from the Hamiltonian con- constraint (Eq. 103) at every time step in a numerical calculation. However, Eq. 103 is a non-linear parabolic equations, and Eq. 106a is likely to be useful in order to produce trial values for the non-linear part of Eq. 103.

The simplest form of the evolution equations is obtained by projecting Eq. 20 onto the orthonormal triad Eq. 90. The time derivatives of the metric functions generated when the triad vectors are brought inside the time derivative of K^i_j are evaluated from Eqs. 106. Some further simplification is obtained by using the shift vector equations to express derivatives of the shift vector in terms of $K_{(i)(j)}$.

The evolution of the two "dynamical" components of $K_{(i)(j)}$, K_+ and K_-, is given by

$$\begin{aligned} & dK_+/dt + N[2K_-^2 + K^2_{(1)(3)} + K^2_{(1)(2)}] + (AB)^{-1} r\sin\theta\, G_{,r} K_{(1)(2)} = \\ & -\frac{1}{2}\frac{1}{AB^2r^2}[r^2NA^{-1}\eta_{,r}]_{,r} + \frac{1}{2}\frac{B^2}{r^2}(1-x^2)[N_{,xx} + \frac{N}{A}A_{,xx}] \\ & + \frac{1}{2}NA^{-2}[B^{-4}(\eta_{,r})^2 + B^4(\xi_{,r})^2] + NKK_+ - 4\pi N(S_{(3)(3)} - S_{(2)(2)}) \end{aligned} \tag{107}$$

and

$$\begin{aligned} & dK_-/dt - 2NK_+K_- - (AB)^{-1} r\sin\theta G_{,r} K_{(1)(3)} = \\ & -\frac{1}{2}\frac{1}{B^2AR^2}[r^2NB^4A^{-1}\xi_{,r}]_{,r} + N[KK_- - 8\pi S_{(2)(3)}] \quad . \end{aligned} \tag{108}$$

From the remaining four components one degree of freedom is taken up by the hypersurface condition, for instance, the maximal hypersurface condition, for which $K = 0$. The remaining three independent components of $K_{(i)(j)}$ could in principle be determined from the three momentum constraint equations, but in practice, it may be not feasible to solve all of the momentum constraint equations during the evolution. The evolution equations for these components are:

$$dK_{(1)(1)}/dt - 2N[K^2_{(1)(2)} + K^2_{(1)(3)}] + 2AB\sin\theta N^r{}_{,x}K_{(1)(2)}/r = \tag{109a}$$

$$-A^{-1}[A^{-1}N_{,r}]_{,r} - \frac{1}{Ar^2}[(1-x^2)NB^2A_{,x}]_{,x}$$

$$+N\{\frac{2}{r}A^{-3}A_{,r} - \frac{1}{2}A^{-2}[B^{-4}(\eta_{,r})^2 + B^4(\xi_{,r})^2] + KK_{(1)(1)} + 4\pi(S_{(2)(2)}$$

$$+ S_{(3)(3)} - S_{(1)(1)} - E)\} \quad .$$

$$dK_{(1)(2)}/dt - 2NK_{(1)(3)}K_- + (K_{(2)(2)} - K_{(1)(1)})[NK_{(1)(2)} \tag{109b}$$

$$+ (AB)^{-1}r\sin\theta G_{,r}] = \frac{B\sin\theta}{r}(A^{-1}N_{,r})_{,x} - \frac{B\sin\theta}{A^2r^2}(NA)_{,x}$$

$$+\frac{1}{2}\frac{1}{Br\sin\theta}[(1-x^2)NA^{-1}\eta_{,r}]_{,x} + N[KK_{(1)(2)} - 8\pi S_{(1)(2)}] \quad ,$$

$$dK_{(1)(3)}/dt + 2NK_{(1)(2)}K_- + N(K_{(1)(1)} - K_{(3)(3)})K_{(1)(3)} \tag{109c}$$

$$+ (AB)^{-1}r\sin\theta G_{,r}K_- = -\frac{1}{2}\frac{1}{Br\sin\theta}[(1-x^2)NB^4A^{-1}\xi_{,r}]_{,x}$$

$$+ N[KK_{(1)(3)} - 8\pi S_{(1)(3)}] \quad ,$$

and

$$dK_T/dt + 2N[K^2_{(1)(2)} + K^2_{(1)(3)}] - 2AB\sin\theta N^r{}_{,x}K_{(1)(2)}/r = \tag{109d}$$

$$-\frac{2}{A^2r}N_{,r} - \frac{1}{r^2}[(1-x^2)B^2N_{,x}]_{,x}$$

$$+ N\{\frac{4m}{r^3} + \frac{2}{rA^3}A_{,r} - \frac{1}{Ar^2}[(1-x^2)B^2A_{,x}]_{,x} - r^{-2}[(1-x^2)\eta]_{,xx}$$

$$+ KK_T + 8\pi(S_{(1)(1)} - E)\} \quad .$$

where $m_{(i)}$ is the mass aspect defined by Eq. 104. The evolution equation for $K \equiv K_{(i)}{}^{(i)}$, (simplified by substituting the Hamiltonian constraint), is

$$dK/dt = -A^{-1}r^{-2}[(r^2A^{-1}N_{,r})_{,r} + [(1-x^2)B^2AN_{,x}]_{,x}] \tag{110}$$

$$+ N[4\pi(E+S) + 2K_+^2 + 2K_-^2 + 2K^2_{(1)(2)} + 2K^2_{(1)(3)} + K^2_{(1)(1)} + \tfrac{1}{2}K_T^2] \quad .$$

These last two equations are used to determine the lapse function.

Momentum constraint equations

The three components of Eq. 25 are projected onto the orthonormal triad of Eq. 90, with the result

$$-[rK_T]_{,r} + 2K_{(1)(1)} - A^{-1}[(1-x^2)(AB)^2(\frac{K_{(1)(2)}}{B\sin\theta})]_{,x} \tag{111a}$$

$$+ B^{-2}r\eta_{,r}K_+ + B^2r\xi_{,r}K_- = rAJ_{(1)} \quad ,$$

$$r^{-2}[r^3(\frac{K_{(1)(2)}}{B\sin\theta})]_{,r} + [AK_{(1)(1)}]_{,x} + \frac{1}{2}A^2[A^{-1}K_T]_{,x} \tag{111b}$$

$$+ \frac{B^{-2}}{(1-x^2)}[(1-x^2)^2B^2AK_+]_{,x} + r\xi_{,r}\frac{BK_{(1)(3)}}{\sin\theta} = \frac{rA}{B\sin\theta}J_{(2)},$$

$$r^{-2}[r^3(\frac{BK_{(1)(3)}}{\sin\theta})]_{,r} - \frac{1}{(1-x^2)}[(1-x^2)^2B^2AK_-]_{,x} = \frac{rAB}{\sin\theta}J_{(3)} \quad . \tag{111c}$$

The solution of these equations depends on the slicing condition and is discussed later.

Consistency at the origin

An important check on any gauge choice is that the time evolution preserves *automatically* the limiting behavior of the metric functions and extrinsic curvature near $r = 0$ necessary for physical regularity at the origin. Starting the radial integration is straightforward given Eq. 93 and Eq. 96 for the extrinsic curvature tensor:

$$A \sim 1+r^2[\frac{4\pi}{3}E_o + \frac{1}{2}k_+^2 - \frac{1}{18}K_o^2 + \frac{1}{3}eP_2(x)] + \ldots \tag{112}$$

Note that the gravitational shear term appears here like an energy density: $(\frac{3}{8\pi})k_+^2$, of the gravitational field.

The condition $\xi \approx O(r^4)$ is consistent with the evolution equations, even though the individual terms on the r.h.s. of Eq. 105c are of order r^2. Such automatic cancellations near $r = 0$ do not appear in the evolution equations for the extrinsic curvature, and we are able to derive straight forward equations for dk_+/dt, dk_-/dt, and dK_o/dt. To do so represent the general leading behavior of the lapse function N near $r = 0$ (assuming axisymmetry and equatorial plane symmetry) by

$$N \approx N_o[1+r^2(n_o+n_2P_2(x)) + O(r^4)] \quad , \tag{113}$$

where n_o and n_2 are found either locally or non-locally from the hypersurface conditions on each constant-t slice.

Using Eqs. 107, 112, 113, 96 and 102a we obtain:

$$\frac{dk_+}{dt} = N_o[n_2 - \frac{5}{3}e + K_ok_+ - \frac{8\pi}{3}(S_{(3)(3)} - S_{(2)(2)})_o] \quad . \tag{114}$$

The corresponding result for k_- from Eqs. 108 and 94 is:

$$\frac{dk_-}{dt} - 2N_ok_+k_- - \frac{2}{3}N_oK_ok_- = N_o[K_ok_- - \frac{2}{3}q - \frac{8}{15}(\frac{S_{(2)(3)}}{r^2x(1-x^2)})_o] \quad . \tag{115}$$

The stress tensor driving term in Eq. 115 is regular at $r = 0$ by the general regularity conditions for symmetric second-rank tensors. Finally, from Eq. 110

$$\frac{dK_o}{dt} = N_o[4\pi(E_o + S_o) - 6n_o + 6k_+^2 + \frac{1}{3}K_o^2] \quad . \tag{116}$$

Comparison of Eqs. 116 and 112 shows that the effective pressure associated with the shear in the normal worldlines at $r = 0$ is equal to the corresponding energy density, as expected.

The evolution equations for K_T, $K_{(1)(2)}$, and $K_{(1)(3)}$ at $r = 0$ are consistent with Eqs. 114-116. Of course, this must be true given that the leading behavior of $K_{(i)(j)}$ is compatible with the momentum constraint equations.

Given proper starting values at $r = 0$ the solution for G from Eq. 99 automatically satisfies the regularity conditions of Eq. 98. However, if $k_+ \neq 0$, the radial integration of G away from $r = 0$ using Eq. 99 requires some care, since unles the cancellation between $K_{(1)(2)}$ and the angular derivatives of G is enforced exactly, the radial derivative will be singular at $r = 0$.

Polar Hypersurfaces

With the polar hypersurface condition $K_T = 0$ the evolution equations for K_T becomes the equation for the lapse function N. It seems worthwhile to suggest for this purpose, a lapse equation in which the Hamiltonian constraint is used to eliminate the $2mr^{-3}$ term (rather than use Eq. 109d). This leads to an equation for the product (NA), which has the form:

$$2A^{-2}r^{-1}(NA)_{,r} + A^2r^{-2}[(1-x^2)(B/A)^2(NA)_{,x}]_{,x} = \tag{117}$$

$$2B^{-1}r\sin\theta K_{(1)(2)}G_{,r} + (NA)\{\,2r^{-2}[(1-x^2)B^2A^{-1}A_{,x}]_{,x}$$

$$+ \frac{1}{2}A^{-2}[B^{-4}(\eta_{,r})^2 + B^4(\xi_{,r})^2] + 4K^2_{(1)(2)} + 2K_-^2$$

$$+ 8\pi(E+S_{(1)(1)})\,\} \quad .$$

After A is found by integrating the Hamiltonian constraint outward in radius, the solution of Eq. 117 as a parabolic equation for (NA) requires integration *inward*.

The advantage of Eq. 117 is that while $N = 1 + 0\,(r^{-1})$ as $r \to \infty$, $(NA) = 1+0(r^{-2})$. Furthermore, $(NA) = 1$ is exact everywhere outside a spherically symmetric star. As an approximate boundary condition imposed at the outer edge of the grid in a numerical calculation, $NA = 1$ is the analogue of the Robin boundary condition suggested earlier. The slow variation of (NA) compared with N in the exterior region means that using Eq. 117 instead of Eq. 107d should help the numerical accuracy, particularly at late times in a black hole formation problem when the hypersurfaces are getting close to the event horizon and N and A are each varying rapidly with radius.

A very important property of polar hypersurfaces, particularly for use with the radial gauge condition, is the way they seem to automatically avoid a region of spacetime with minimal two-surfaces surrounding the origin. Integrate equation 117 over x. The result is, after integration by parts,

$$\frac{2}{r}\int_{-1}^{1} dx\,[A^{-2}(NA)_{,r}] = 2\int_{-1}^{1} dx[B^{-1}r\,\sin\theta K_{(1)(2)}G_{,r}] \tag{118}$$

$$+ \frac{1}{2}\int_{-1}^{1} dx\,\frac{N}{A}\,[B^{-4}(\eta_{,r})^2 + B^4(\xi_{,r})^2]$$

$$+ 2\int_{-1}^{1} dx\,(NA)[K_+^2 + K_-^2 + 2K^2_{(1)(2)} + 4\pi(E+S_{(1)(1)})] \quad .$$

Only the first term on the r.h.s. is not positive definite, which suggests very strongly that on polar hypersurfaces any tendency for A to get very large will result in N becoming so small in that region that the evolution will never reach the point that A is actually singular.

The freezing of evolution in regions of strong gravitational fields is stronger with polar hypersurfaces than with maximal hypersurfaces, which is desirable for astrophysical purposes. Minimal effort is wasted on calculating dynamics in regions of spacetime which have no causal influence on the outside universe. The only potential problem in this regard is that the hypersurfaces will become null somewhere, i.e., $N = 0$ at some finite time, but this seems unlikely.

Another advantage of the polar hypersurface is the simple form of the momentum constraint equations. With $K_T = 0$, Eq. 111a determines $K_{(1)(1)} = K$ directly from $K_{(1)(2)}$ without any radial integration as required on maximal hypersurfaces. Furthermore, the equation for $K_{(1)(2)}$, given K_+, now becomes a parabolic equation. Eliminate $K_{(1)(1)}$ from Eq. 111b to get

$$r^{-2}\left(r^3 \frac{K_{(1)(2)}}{B\sin\theta}\right)_{,r} + \frac{1}{2}\left[(1-x^2)(AB)^2 \frac{K_{(1)(2)}}{B\sin\theta}\right]_{,xx} =$$

$$\frac{rA}{B\sin\theta} J_{(2)} - \frac{1}{2}\left[rA^2 J_{(1)}\right]_{,x} + \frac{1}{2}\left[A(B^{-2} r\eta_{,r} K_+ + B^2 r\xi_{,r} K_-)\right]_{,x} - \tag{119}$$

$$\frac{B^{-2}}{(1-x^2)}\left[(1-x^2)B^2 AK_+\right]_{,x} - r\xi_{,r}\frac{BK_{(1)(3)}}{\sin\theta} .$$

The stable direction of integration is *inward*, with an outer boundary condition that $K_{(1)(2)} = 0$ at $r = \infty$.

Appearance of Singularities

The inward integration of the parabolic equation (Eq. 117) on polar hypersurfaces does not allow any freedom to enforce regularity of N at $r = 0$. Near $r = 0$, since $A, B \to 1$ and $\xi \to 0$, the homogeneous solutions of Eq. 117 are approximately the solutions in a flat background. These are

$$N \sim r^{\frac{\ell(\ell+1)}{2}} P_\ell(x) . \tag{120}$$

The coefficients of these terms near $r = 0$ are determined uniquely by the global integration from $r \sim \infty$. The $t = 0$ homogeneous solution is just the central value of N, N_o. The $\ell = 2$ solution gives a contribution to N.

$$N_3 \approx N_o n_3 r^3 P_2(x) . \tag{121}$$

This term is present as long as there are any departures from spherical symmetry. It is not regular at $r = 0$, since it cannot be represented by integer powers of Cartesian coordinates.

Irregularity at $r = 0$ is also generically present in the extrinsic curvature tensor. Since the hypersurface condition enforces $K_T = 0$, regularity requires, by Eq. 98, that $k_+ = K = 0$, so $K, K_{(1)(2)}$, $K_+ = 0(r^2)$ at $r = 0$. We evolve $K_{(i)(j)}$ with this as an initial condition. Eqs. 109, 109b, and 110 give, after cancellations of terms which are non-zero at $r = 0$.

$$\frac{dK_+}{dt} = \frac{3}{2} N_o n_3 (1-x^2) r + 0(r^2) , \tag{122a}$$

$$\frac{d}{dt}\left[\frac{K_{(1)(2)}}{\sin\theta}\right] = 2N_o n_3 \frac{dP_2}{dx} r + 0(r^2) , \tag{122b}$$

$$\frac{dK}{dt} = -6N_o n_3 P_2(x)r+0(r^2) \quad . \tag{122c}$$

This irregular behavior induced in $K_{(i)(j)}$ produces, through the matter evolution equations, irregular behavior in E and $J_{(i)}$, e.g., a term in E proportional to $rP_2(x)$ with a coefficient which depends in detail on the properties of the matter. This in tern contributes to a term in A proportional to $r^3P_2(x)$.

Irregular behavior, while unpleasant, can perhaps be managed in a numerical calculation if its form is known in advance. Unfortunately, the irregular behavior $\sim r^3P_2(x)$ induced in A acts back through Eq. 117 to give a term $\sim r^3(\ln r)P_2(x)$ in N, which when recycled repeatedly through the evolution equations as described above gives a whole infinite power series in (lnr). This sums to modify the *power* of r governing the irregular behavior in an uncontrolled way. We conclude that the polar hypersurface condition should not be applied near $r = 0$ in a numerical calculation involving deviations from spherical symmetry.

The homogeneous solutions to Eq. 119 as an equation for $\frac{K_{(1)(2)}}{\sin\theta}$ in a flat background, valid asymptotically as $r\to\infty$ and $r\to 0$, are

$$\frac{K_{(1)(2)}}{\sin\theta} \sim r^{\frac{1}{2}\ell(\ell+1)-3} \frac{dP_\ell(x)}{dx} \tag{123}$$

For all $\ell \geq 2$ the boundary conditions as $r\to\infty$ is incompatible with the homogeneous solutions, and therefore the solution of Eq. 119 should be unique. At $r = 0$, given numerical errors and a not perfectly good choice for $K_+(r,x)$, one can expect a non-zero contribution from the $\ell = 2$ homogeneous solution. This is more seriously irregular than the irregularities discussed above, in view of $K_T = 0$, and seems definitely unacceptable, but is not problem if the solution of Eq. 119 is only used well away from $r = 0$.

Mixed Hypersurfaces

To solve the regularity problem we consider a hypersurface condition which is polar, $K_T = 0$, outside some radius $r_c(t)$. Inside this radius we modify the hyperface condition in such a way that it is maximal near $r = 0$ and that the lapse function is at least C^2 at $r = r_c$. Such a hypersurface condition was already given in Eq. 68: $K_T = -C(r/r_c)K_{(1)(1)}$, with $C = 1$ at $r = 0$ and $C = 0$ at $r = r_e$.

For $\frac{r}{r_c} < 1$ the lapse function equation is

$$0 = \frac{d}{dt}\left[K_T = C\left(\frac{r}{r_c}\right)K_{(1)(1)}\right] = \frac{dK_T}{dt} = C\frac{dK_{(1)(1)}}{dt} = \frac{dC}{dt}K_{(1)(1)} \tag{124}$$

Eq. 69 becomes, after elimination of the radial derivative of A with the Hamiltonian constraint:

$$\begin{aligned} &C[A^{-1}(A^{-1}N,_r),_r + A^{-1}r^{-2}(1-x^2)B^2N,_xA,_x] + 2A^{-2}r^{-1}N,_r \\ &+ r^{-2}[(1-x^2)B^2N,_x],_x = \left(\frac{r}{r_c}\right)C\left(\frac{N^r}{r} - \frac{r_c}{r_c}\right)K_{(1)(1)} \\ &+ 2(1-C)AB\sin\theta(N^r/r),_xK_{(1)(2)} + N\{(1-C)[2mr^{-3} - \tfrac{1}{2}r^{-2}((1-x^2)\eta),_{xx} \\ &+ \tfrac{1}{4}A^{-2}(B^{-4})\eta,r)^2 + B^4(\xi,r)^2)] + (1+C)[K_+^2 + K_-^2] \end{aligned} \tag{125}$$

$$+ (3C-1)[K^2_{(1)(2)} + K^2_{(1)(3)}] + C(1 - \frac{1}{4}C)(1+C)K^2_{(1)(1)}$$

$$+ 4\,C[E + S_{(2)(2)} + S_{(3)(3)}] + 4\,(2-C)S_{(1)(1)}\} \quad .$$

If $C \equiv 1$, Eq. 125 reduces to maximal slicing, while if $C \equiv 0$, Eq. 125 reduced to polar slicing.

The equation for N in the polar region, $r > r_c$, should be the same equation as the limit $C \to 0$ of Eq. 125. Otherwise, numerical errors will introduce discontinuities in the derivatives of N at $r = r_c$. Making Eq. 125 an equation for (NA), so the polar limit is Eq. 117, is *not* desirable because the second order radial derivative of N, converted into a second order radial derivative of (NA), would leave a second order radial derivative of A. The Hamiltonian constraint can only eliminate a first order radial derivative of A without introducing a lot of other radial derivatives.

A simple form for $C(r/r_c)$ in Eq. 125 which should, then, give smooth solutions across $r = r_c$ is

$$C(r/r_c) = [(1-(r/r_c)^2]^n \quad , \tag{126}$$

with $n > 1$. In practive, with N represented on a grid, the solution will be smooth across $r = r_c$ only if there are at least a few radial grid points in the region just inside $r = r_c$ where $0 < C << 1$. In order that C increase slowly away from $r = r_c$, it seems best to take n fairly large, say $n = 3$ or $n = 4$. The transition radius r_c should be near or a bit inside the point where A reaches its maximum value. The main concern is to take full advantage of the singularity-avoidance property of polar hypersurfaces, without introducing any abrupt distortions in the hypersurface near $r = 0$.

The momentum constraint equations must also be handled with care in order that the $K_{(i)(j)}$ all vary smoothly across $r = r_c$. For example, one cannot take advantage of Eq. 119 for $K_{(1)(2)}$, given K_+, in the region $r > r_c$, because there is no corresponding equation in the region $r < r_c$. However, Eq. 111a, with K_T eliminated using the hypersurface condition Eq. 68 becomes

$$[rCK_{(1)(1)}]_{,r} + 2K_{(1)(1)} - A^{-1}[(1-x^2)(AB)^2 \frac{K_{(1)(2)}}{B\sin\theta}]_{,x} \tag{127}$$

$$+B^{-2}r\eta_{,r}K_+ + B^2 r\xi_{,r}K_- = rAJ_{(1)} \quad .$$

Suppose that $K_{(1)(2)}$, K_+, and K_- are known from the evolution equations. At each value of $x = \cos\theta$, treat this as an ordinary differential equation for $K_{(1)(1)}$, with boundary condition

$$K_{(1)(1)} = \frac{1}{3}[(1-x^2)\frac{K_{(1)(2)}}{\sin\theta}]_{,x} = -2k_+ P_2(x) \tag{128}$$

at $r = 0$. It is easy to see that $K_{(1)(1)}$ and all its derivatives are continuous across $r = r_c$ if $n > 1$.

Once $K_{(1)(1)}$ and therefore K_T are known, one might integrate Eq. 111b in angle (i.e. x) to find corrected values of K_+. If $K_{(1)(1)}$ and $K_{(1)(2)}$ are smooth across $r = r_c$, the new values of K_+ will be C^{n-1} at $r = r_c$, where n is the exponent in Eq. 126. It would seem best not to correct K_+, and just evolve both K_+ and $K_{(1)(2)}$, unless n is rather large.

The mixed hypersurface condition has the advantage over the maximal hypersurface condition that the elliptic region of the equation for N need occupy only a fraction of the grid, which should substantially reduce the number of operations required in this portion of a computer calculation.

Normalized Variables

Proper choice of variables can greatly reduce the amount of numerical errors introduced into the calculations [14]. The variables that are best suitable for the numerical calculations are not always those that appear immediately in the analytic formulation of the problem, and special care should be taken to use proper variables. Consider, for example, a situation when a physical quantity is the difference (or sum) of two other quantitites β, and γ. If $\beta >> \alpha$ and $\gamma >> \alpha$, $\alpha = \beta - \gamma$ is much less accurate than β and γ, i.e. $|\Delta\alpha|/\alpha >> |\Delta\beta|/\beta$. In this case, it is advantageous to use α as a variable. Use of the triad components, and in particular, the combinations K_T, K_+ and η is partially motivated by these considerations.

Similarily, accuracy is lost when exact concellations appear at a special point (say near the origin or near the axis) in some of the equations. Typical cancellations are $(\alpha - \beta)/\sin(\theta)$ with $\alpha(\theta = 0) - \beta(\theta = 0) = 0$. Most of these problems were eliminated, again, by use of the combinations of the triad components.

Finally, a third kind of terms, that should be avoided are $\alpha/\sin(\theta)$ with $\alpha(\theta = 0) = 0$. Such a term has a finite limit but it is almost always impossible to obtain this limit accurately numerically. We can eliminate such terms by using proper combinations of either the evolution or the evolution and the constraint equations. When this method is not useful we can avoid the singular behavior by transforming to normalized variables: $\tilde{\eta}$, $\tilde{K}_+$, $\tilde{\xi}$ and $\tilde{K}_-$ where:

$$\tilde{\eta} = \sin^2(\theta)\ ,\eta \text{ etc...} \tag{129}$$

and to $\overline{K}_{(1)(2)}$ and $\overline{K}_{(1)(3)}$ where,

$$\overline{K}_{(1)(2)} = \sin(\theta)K_{(1)(2)}\ . \tag{130}$$

The chain of arguments leading to this normalization is as follows: first we normalize $K_{(1)(2)}$ and $K_{(1)(3)}$ so that the source terms in Eqs. 99 and 103 are regular. Evolution of $\overline{K}_{(1)(2)}$ and $\overline{K}_{(1)(3)}$ using Eqs. 109b,c suggest that η and ξ should be replaced by $\tilde{\eta}$ and $\tilde{\xi}$. Further substitution of $\tilde{\eta}$ and $\tilde{\xi}$ either in Eqs. 106b,c or in Eqs. 107 and 107 leads to normalization of K_+ and K_- as $\tilde{K}_+$ and $\tilde{K}_-$. The later normalization agrees with the structure of the momentum constraints, Eqs. 111b,c which is an essential consistency check. The power of $\sin(\theta)$ in this normalization agrees with the powers of $\sin(\theta)$ that appear at the behavior near the origin. However, the total angular behavior of the normalized variables is not the same as the total angular behavior near the origin, since it was not necessary to factor out the powers of $\cos(\theta)$.

Structure of Numerical Scheme

We propose a partially constrained scheme. The equations and the inner and outer (radial) boundary conditions are described in Table II. The hydrodynamic variables are discussed later.

The boundary conditions in the x (i.e. θ) direction are reflection symmetry on the equatorial plane ($x = 0$) and regularity on the axis ($x = 1$). The first condition is simply: $\left.\frac{\partial f}{\partial x}\right|_{x=0} = 0$. The latter regularity condition i.e $\partial G/\partial\theta = 0$,

TABLE II. STRUCTURE OF NUMERICAL SCHEME

VARIABLE	EQUATION	BOUNDARY CONDITION Inner, Origin	Outer, r = L
A	Hamiltonian Eq. 103 †	A = 1	free
η or B	Evolution Eq. 106b	Eq. 93	outgoing waves see [59]
ξ	Evolution Eq. 106c	Eq. 94	- " -
K_+	Evolution Eq. 107	Eq. 96d	- " -
K_-	Evolution Eq. 108	$\sim O(r^2)$	- " -
$K_{(1)(1)}$	Evolution Eq. 109a	Eq. 96a	- " -
$K_{(1)(2)}$	Evolution Eq. 109b	Eq. 96b	- " -
$K_{(1)(3)}$	Evolution Eq. 109c	$\sim O(r^2)$	- " -
K_T	Coordinate Condition Eq. 68	Eq. 96c	- " -
N	Mixed Slicing Eq. 125		NA = 1
N^θ	Radial Gauge Eq. 99	Eq. 98b	free
N^r	Eq. 100	Eq. 98a	free
N^ϕ	Eq. 101	free	$N^\theta = 0$

† We include a solution of the A evolution equation, Eq. 106a. The results of this evolution are used as first approximation for the non-linear parabolic equation Eq. 103 and for comparison.

is satisfied automatically when we write $G = G(x) = G(\cos(\theta))$ rather than writing G as $G(\theta)$.

The lapse function equation (Eq. 125) has an additional boundary; this is the internal boundary at r_c where the equation turns from a parabolic into a elliptic one. Ellipticity is lost as r approaches r_c from below, and r_c becomes another inner boundary. The nature of such boundary depends on the sign of the first derivatives [78]. Roughly speaking, if the first derivative, normal to the boundary has the same sign as the second derivative (whose coefficient vanishes) then boundary values have to be specified otherwise this is a free boundary on which the value of the function is determined from the inner data by the equation. In Eq. 125 ellipticity is lost in a way that we have to specify the boundary values for N on r_c. These values are obtained, however, naturally from the inwards integration of the parabolic part of the equation at $r > r_c$.

A related feature is the vanishing of the second derivative of the parabolic equations for N, A, and G on the axis. Even though, these are parabolic equations the same rule holds. Since, the sign of the first derivative is opposite to the sign of the second derivatives, these boundary values should not be specified, rather they are evaluated by integrating the equations towards the axis.

The staggered grid structure, which we discuss later, should comply with the structure of the x derivatives of these equations. Consider, for example, the following finite differencing approximation of the angular part of Eq. 99:

$$[(1-x^2)G],_{xx} \approx [(1-x^2_{J+1})G_{J+1} - 2(1-x^2_J)G_J + (1-x^2_{J-1})G_{J-1}]/dx^2 \quad , \tag{131}$$

We choose to locate G_J so that the last point G_{Jmax} is on the axis (x = 1). With this choice $G_{Jmax} = G(1)$ disappears from the equation for $G_{Jmax-1} = G(1-dx)$. The value on the boundary is not necessary for the evaluation of the inner points. In fact, G(1) is not needed anywhere in the scheme. Was it needed it would have been evaluated using a limiting procedure. The finite differencing approximation for the angular part of Eq. 125 is:

$$[(1-x^2)B^2N,_x],_x \approx \tag{132}$$

$$[(1-x^2_{J+1/2})B^2_{J+1/2}(N_{J+1}-N_J) - (1-x^2_{J-1/2})B^2_{J-1/2}(N_J-N_{J-1})]/dx^2 \quad .$$

Here we define N_{Jmax} on a grid point located half a grid spacing away from the axis (x = 1) i.e. N_J is defined on (.5dx, 1.5dx, ...etc... (1-.5dx)). From Eq. 130 we see that the equation for $N_{Jmax} = N(1-.5dx)$ contains only $N_{Jmax-1} = N(1-1.5dx)$. Similar features appear in the angular part of the Eq. 103 for A, and similar locations are chosen for A_J.

CYLINDRICAL GRAVITATIONAL RADIATION - AN EXAMPLE

This example is very different from the previous one and from the rest of the text - it does not employ the "3+1" formalism, rather it is based on an ad hoc procedure that is adequate for the cylindrical geometry. In this example we consider the propagation of cylindrical gravitational waves and, we evolve the initial data along null rays. Unfortunately the methods used here cannot be easily generalized to other configurations. The aim of this example is to demonstrate the potential power of analytic considerations and of the characteristic method, and to show that in spite of the "praise" of the "3+1" formalism, described so far, ad hoc methods should not be disregarded all together.

We are interested in the evolution of vacuum cylindrical systems. We use cylindrical coordinates i.e. $[t,r,z,\theta]$. In this section, r is the cylindrical radial coordinate, i.e. $r^2 = x^2 + y^2$. The system has two Killing vectors, one along the θ direction, the other one along the z direction. In general, such configurations can include both modes of gravitational radiation. The numerical evolution of the cylindrical one mode system was considered by Piran [58] using the "3+1" formalism. This approach was generalized to two mode configurations by Rotenberry [79] and Rotenberry and Piran [76]. Here, following Piran and Stark [32] we employ a four dimensional characteristic approach.

The general cylindrical (four dimensional) line element is the Jordan-Ehlers-Komapneetz [30,31] line element:

$$ds^2 = e^{2(\gamma-\psi)}(-dt^2 + dr^2) + e^{2\psi}(dz + \omega d\theta)^2 + r^2e^{-2\psi}d\theta^2 \quad . \tag{133}$$

The Einstein equations obtain the simple form:

$$\psi,_{tt} - \frac{1}{r}(r\psi,_r),_r = \frac{e^{4\psi}}{2r^2}(\omega^2_{,t} - \omega^2_{,r}) \tag{134a}$$

$$\omega,_{tt} = r(\frac{\psi,_r}{r}),_r = 4(\omega,_r\psi,_r - \omega,_t\psi,_t) \tag{134b}$$

$$\gamma,_r = r(\psi_{,t}^2 + \psi_{,r}^2) + \frac{e^{4\psi}}{4r}(\omega_{,t}^2 + \omega_{,r}^2) \tag{134c}$$

$$\gamma,_t = 2r\psi,_t\psi,_r + \frac{e^{4\psi}}{2r}\omega,_t\omega,_r \tag{134d}$$

It is clear, from these equations that ψ and ω correspond to the two dynamical variables (Eqs. 134a,b are second order, and two dynamical variables are sufficient to describe the two gratitational degrees of freedom). ψ corresponds to the + mode while ω corresponds to the x mode. γ corresponds to the gravitational total energy, and it is equal to 1/4 of the C energy in the system [80] (slightly different definition is used in [81,82]).

The Jordan-Ehlers-Kompaneetz coordinates are the cylindrical analog of the Bondi coordinates. The ingoing and outgoing radial null rays are just $t \pm r$. To take advantage of this simple null structure we define the ingoing quantities:

$$\alpha = 2(\psi,_t + \psi,_r) \quad , \tag{135a}$$

and

$$\xi = \frac{e^{2\psi}}{r}(\omega,_t + \omega,_r) \quad . \tag{135b}$$

α and β are defined along the ingoing null coordinates (τ, r_o),i.e.

$$\alpha(\tau, r_o) = \alpha(\tau, r_o + \tau) \tag{136}$$

The outgoing quantities:

$$\beta = 2(\psi,_t - \psi,_r) \quad , \tag{137a}$$

and

$$\delta = \frac{e^{2\psi}}{r}(\omega,_t - \omega,_r) \quad . \tag{137b}$$

are defined along the outgoing null coordinates (τ, r_o), i.e.

$$\beta(\tau, r_o) = \beta(\tau, r_o - \tau) \tag{138}$$

Clear, α and β correspond to the ψ, +, mode, while ξ and δ correspond to the ω, x, mode. The energy density in the radiation becomes:

$$\gamma,_r = \frac{r}{8}(\alpha^2 + \beta^2 + \xi^2 + \delta^2) \quad , \tag{139}$$

which is, of course, just Eq. 134c rewritten using the new variables. We rewrite now the rest of Einstein equations as a set of four couples *ordinary* differential equations:

$$\frac{d\alpha(\tau, r_o)}{d\tau} = \frac{(\alpha(\tau, r_o) - \beta(\tau, r_o - 2\tau))}{2(r_o - \tau)} + \xi(\tau, r_o)\,\delta(\tau, r_o - 2\tau) \quad , \tag{140a}$$

$$\frac{d\beta(\tau, r_o)}{d\tau} = \frac{(\alpha(\tau, r_o + 2\tau) - \beta(\tau, r_o))}{2(r_o + \tau)} + \xi(\tau, r_o + 2\tau)\,\delta(\tau, r_o) \quad . \tag{140b}$$

$$\frac{d\xi(\tau, r_o)}{d\tau} = \frac{(\xi(\tau, r_o) + \delta(\tau, r_o - 2\tau))}{2(r_o - \tau)} - \alpha(\tau, r_o)\,\delta(\tau, r_o - 2\tau) \quad , \tag{140c}$$

$$\frac{d\delta(\tau, r_o)}{d\tau} = \frac{(\xi(\tau, r_o + 2\tau) + \delta(\tau, r_o))}{2(r_o + \tau)} - \beta(\tau, r_o)\,\xi(\tau, r_o + 2\tau) \quad . \tag{140c}$$

Eq. 134d becomes:

$$\gamma_{,t} = \frac{r}{8}(\alpha^2 - \beta^2 + \xi^2 - \delta^2) \tag{141}$$

Eqs. 14a,b,c,d are the evolution equations for the system γ is integrated in r from Eq. 139 and Eq. 141 is satisfied as an identity.

It should be clear in what sense these are ordinary differential equations. The variables α, β, ξ, and δ are still functions of two variables: r_o and τ however, there is no differentiation along r_o in these equations. Furthermore, we were able to write the equations as ordinary differential equations only by using *two different coordinate systems* in this set of equations, where τ is a parameter along either outgoing or ingoing null geodesics.

The numerical grid used for the solution of these equations is described in Fig. 6. For simplicity we consider an equally spaced grid. We label the variables according to their initial position i.e.

$$\alpha_I = \alpha(0, Idr) \quad . \tag{142}$$

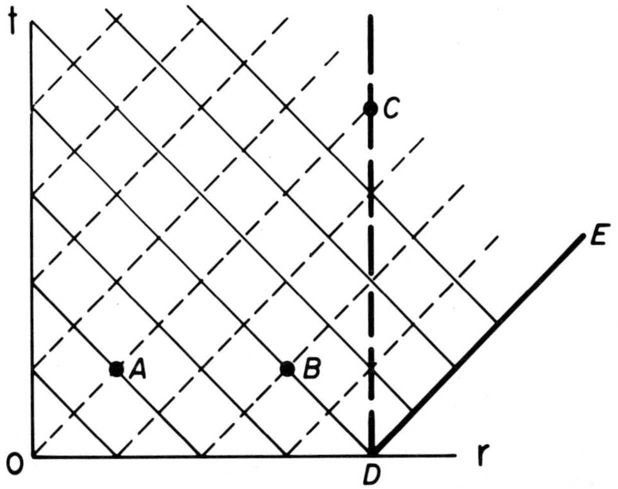

Figure 6: Grid for the cylindrical characteristic problem. Initial data is specified either on OC or on OD. In the latter case boundary values are specified either on DC or on DE. Note that α at A and β at B have the same r_o and τ values.

ξ_I always appears together with α_I in these equations, and similarily β_I appears together with δ_I. To obtain $\beta(\tau, r_o - 2\tau)$ and $\delta(\tau, r_o - 2\tau)$, which are needed for Eq. we interpolate between the appropriate β_I abd δ_I values. For $d\tau = dr$, this interpolation involes, during the N'th time step only β_{I-N} and β_{I-N+1}, and δ_{I-N} and δ_{I-N+1}. We can solve Eqs. 140a,b,c,d as a set of

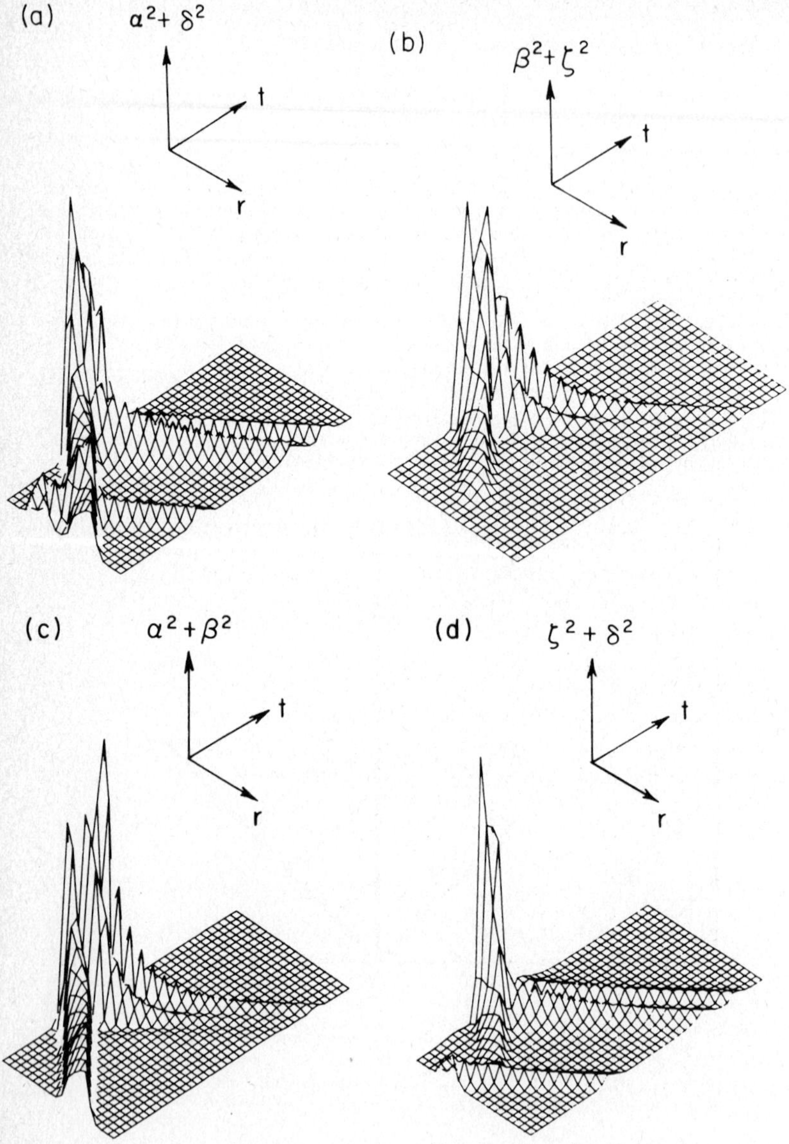

Figure 7: Solution of Cylindrical characteristic problem.
a) Outgoing α and ingoing δ which are at the initial data.
b) α turns to β after reflections at the axis. Note the appearance of ζ at the interaction between α and δ.
c) The t mode α and β.
d) The x mode, ζ and δ. From ref. [32].

4N coupled ordinary differential equations, whose variables are: $\{\alpha_1,,,\alpha_N,\beta_1,,,\beta_N,\beta_1,,,\xi_N,\delta_1,,,\delta_N$. This equations can even be solved using a standard package (like IMSL) integrating subroutines!

Eqs. 139,140 have to be supplemented with boundary conditions. On the axis, $r = 0$ these are:

$$\beta = \alpha \; ; \qquad \delta = -\xi \; ; \qquad \gamma = 0 \tag{143}$$

There are no outer boundary conditions on β or δ, since these are outgoing waves! If we choose to hold the outer grid boundary at a fixed r value R_{max} (see Fig. 6) we need to supply outer boundary conditions for the incoming radaition α and ξ. If R_{max} is large enough we can neglect radiation that will be reflected inwards at $r > R_{max}$, and can approximate an outgoing wave boundary condition simply using:

$$\alpha(R_{max}) = 0 \; ; \qquad \xi(R_{max}) = 0 \tag{144}$$

Alternatively we can consider the problem as a characteristic initial data problem and specify our initial data on a null hypersurface, i.e. on the line: $t - r =$ *constant* (see Fig. 6). In this case, the initial data of α ξ on this line are sufficient to determine the solution and further boundary conditions are not necessary.

In the specific examples of a numerical solution [32] we have chosen to specify the initial data on a spacelike hypersurface ($t = 0$), and to hold the outer boundary fixed at some R_{max}, using Eq. 144 as an outer boundary condition. The influence of this boundary condition on the solution was checked by comparing the solution with R_{max} to a solution with a similar outer boundary condition at $2R_{max}$.

Figure 7 describes the evolution of an initial data that contains two pulses of gravitational radiation, an outgoing x mode polse and an ingoing + mode pulse. The numerical solution was extremely accurate, and in particular, tests like comparison of ψ or γ evaluated from temporal integration versus ψ, or γ evaluated from radial integration were very satisfactory. The main new feature observed in the calculations [32] was generation of an ingoing x mode pulse, due to the interaction of the initial pulses (se Fig. 7).

HYDRODYNAMICS AND MATTER EVOLUTION EQUATIONS

Energy-momentum conservation:

$$T^{\nu}_{\mu\,;\,\nu} = 0 \; . \tag{145}$$

governs the evolution of the sources of the gravitational field. We can solve directly this four dimensional equation. In the spirit of the previous treatment of Einstein equations it is advantegeous, however, to consider projections that lead to simpler three dimensional equations. Using the "3+1" projections (along and orthogonal to n_μ, Eq. 145 becomes:

$$dE/dt = NKE + NK^{ij}S_{ij} + N^{-1}(N^2J^i)_{|i} \tag{146}$$

and

$$dJ_i/dt + N^j{}_{,i}J_j = NKJ_i - (E\,\delta_i{}^j + S_i{}^j)N_{,j} - NS_i{}^j{}_{|j}. \tag{147}$$

We can evolve E and J^i using these equations. The remaining six variables S_{ij} are determined from these four by a local anisotropic equation of state. However, we prefer to use a formulation that will reflect better the nature of the source (matter, EM field, etc.).

In this work we are mainly interested in perfect fluid sources. For a perfect fluid:

$$T_{\mu\nu} = (\rho+p)u_\mu u_\nu + pg_{\mu\nu} \tag{148}$$

where u^μ is the matter four velocity, ρ the total energy density and p, the presure. ρ can be split, further, to nm_b the rest mass density and ε the thermal energy density. ρ, p, n and ε are measured in the matter's comoving frame.

We would prefer to use the hydrodynamic variables, rather than E and J^i in our matter evolution equations. First, we use the conservation of baryon number which (by definition) implies $Nu^\mu_{;\mu} = 0$:

$$\frac{\partial D}{\partial t} + \frac{\partial DV^i}{\partial x^i} = 0 \ . \tag{149}$$

D, is the baryon number density of the hydrodynamic quantities per coordinate volume element:

$$D = (Ng^{1/2}u^o)n \ . \tag{150}$$

and V^i is the matter three veolcity:

$$V^i = \frac{u^i}{u^o} = \frac{g^{ij}S_j}{(\rho+p)u^{o2}} - N^i \tag{151}$$

We define two other densities, H, and S_i which are the thermal energy and momentum densities (per coordiante volume element):

$$H = (N_g{}^{1/2}u^o)\varepsilon \tag{152}$$

and

$$S_i = g^{1/2}J_i = (Ng^{1/2}u^o)(\rho+p)u_i \tag{153}$$

To obtain evolution equations for H, and S_i we project Eq. 146 along the stream lines of the matter field i.e. along u^μ [13,14]

$$\frac{\partial H}{\partial t} + \frac{HV^i}{\partial x^i} = -p \frac{\partial}{\partial t}(Ng^{1/2}u^o) + \frac{\partial}{\partial x^i}(Ng^{1/2}u^o V^i) \tag{154}$$

and

$$\frac{\partial S_j}{\partial t} + \frac{\partial S_j V^i}{\partial x^i} = -g^{1/2} N \frac{\partial p}{\partial x^j} + \frac{1}{2}\frac{S_a S_b}{S^o}\frac{\partial g^{ab}}{\partial x^j} \tag{155}$$

One has to add an equation of state

$$p = p(n,\varepsilon) \ , \tag{156}$$

to get a complete set of equations for the matter variables.

The resemblence of Eqs. 149, 154 and 155 to the Newtonian baryon number conservation, energy conservation and momentum conservation equations is a great advantage. We can apply now numerical techniques, developed for Newtonian hydrodynamics, to these equations.

The comoving quantities ρ, p, n and ε are four-scalars while E and $S = S_i{}^i$ are three-scalars. The "3+1" variables: E, J_i and S_{ij} are related to ρ, p, and u^μ by:

$$E = \rho(Nu^o)^2 + p[(Nu^o)^2-1] \tag{157a}$$

$$J_i = (\rho+p)Nu^o u_i \tag{157b}$$

$$S_{ij} = (\rho+p)u_i u_j + pg_{ij} \tag{157c}$$

After evolving the hydrodynamic equations we use Eqs. 157a-c to obtain the source terms for the extrinsic curvature evolution equations, and for the constraints.

The convective derivatives in the "3+1" equations (Eqs. 19,20,146,147) are along the shift vector. The l.h.s of Eqs. 149,154 and 155 is another convective derivative which is along the matter stream lines. The flux terms in these derivatives, i.e. $\frac{\partial}{\partial x^i}(DV^i)$ describe the matter flow relative to our coordinate system. In some sense these terms are 'artificial' when compared with the 'true' source terms, and in fact, the flux terms disappear when one uses the natural Lagrangian coordinates. One can immediately see the potential danger in Eulerian numerical hydrodynamics (Eulerian coordinates are any coordinate that do not follow the matter flow, i.e. in which u^i does not vanish). The 'artifical' flux term can become very large, when the coordinates are not suitable for the hydrodynamic equations, and numerical errors in these terms can become much larger than the 'real' sources. The disappearance of the flux terms, is a great virtue, which is responsible to a large extent to the success and accuracy of Lagrangian numerical hydrodynamics.

However, as was stressed before, we cannot spare the coordinate freedom to simplify the hydrodynamics. Much more important role is reserved for the coordinates: they have to simplify the geometry! Furthermore, even in Newtonian hydrodynamics, Lagrangian coordinates can become entangled fairly rapidly and this causes problems in all, but one dimensional Lagrangian schemes.

A way out of the problem of large flux terms is to introduce another vector field $V_G{}^i$ (see Fig. 3) which we call the grid velocity [14,73]. We can imagine a set of observers moving along this vector field, but this is not necessary. We choose to calculate the hydrodynamics quantitites along the flow lines of $V_G{}^i$, but not in the frame moving with $V_G{}^i$. This means that we calculate typical quantities, like $D(y^i,t)$ along the curves $y^i(x^i,t)$, where

$$\frac{\partial y^i}{\partial t} = V_G{}^i(y^i,t) \quad . \tag{158}$$

To obtain the time derivative of D we add a convective derivative, along, $V_G{}^i$.

$$\frac{D(y^i,t)}{\partial t} = \frac{\partial D}{\partial t} + V_G{}^i \frac{\partial D}{\partial x^i} \quad . \tag{159}$$

The baryon conservation law, for example, becomes:

$$\frac{\partial D(y^i,t)}{\partial t} + \frac{\partial}{\partial x^i}[(V^i - V_G{}^i)D] + D\frac{\partial V_G{}^i}{\partial x^i} = 0 \quad , \tag{160}$$

along y^i. The other hydrodynamic equations are changed in similar manner.

$V_G{}^i$ is a freely specified fector field. In addition to the freedom to define the coordinates, x^i, we are free to choose the location of the observers, y^i. This allows us, for example, to obtain an *effective Lagrangian scheme* without dispensing with the coordinate freedom. To do so, we chose $V_G{}^i = V^i$. Clearly, the convective term $\frac{\partial}{\partial x^i}[(V^i-V_G{}^i)D]$ disappears with this choice. Notice that we measure all quantities relative to the coordinates x^i and not relative to the, now Lagrangian coordinates y^i. If we transform also to Lagrangian observables, like $\bar{D}$, which are measured relative to the coordinates y^i we obtain, using Eqs. 148-160, the usual Lagrangian form of the hydrodynamic equations, i.e.:

$$\frac{\partial \bar{D}}{\partial t} = \frac{\partial}{\partial t}\left[D\frac{\partial y^i}{\partial x^i}\right] = 0 \quad . \tag{161}$$

In finite differencing schemes our observers $y^i(t)$, are located at the numerical grid points. The grid velocity is a motion of the numerical grid relative to the coordinates x^i. The grid points location vary during the time evolution. Clearly, if the grid points follow the matter we obtain a Lagrangian scheme.

In practive it is not useful to follow the matter in a Lagrangian way. The Lagrangian grid structure could become entangled and too difficult to follow. Moreover, in numerical relativity we would like to keep the numerical mesh spaced more or less evenly to allow for smooth evolution of geometrical structure. Stil, we would like to avoid large convective terms. The practical solution is to introduce an averaging algorithm that allows the global feature of the grid to follow the matter, but keep the local mesh orthogonal and almost evenly spaced. Notice that with non-vanishing grid velocity, the convective term of Eq. 147 has to be added to all evolution equations.

Additional problem in Eulerian collapse type calculations is the accumulation of a large fraction of the matter in the innermost grid zones. Clearly, if the matter is spread over a large fraction of the grid at the beginning of the evolution, such accumulation will happen only when large convective terms appear. These correspond to matter motion between different grid zones. By reducing these flux terms, the grid velocity algorithm eliminates this problem.

NUMERICAL FINE POINTS

There are many fine points that should be considered in the translation of the analytic scheme, such as the one described earlier to a numerical code. In fact, a large fraction of the work involved in constructing a numerical code is devoted to programming considerations of these topics. Still, these questions are very rarely discussed. This is partially because many of these problems depend on the specific configuration that is studied and many of these answers depend on personal preference rather than on clear objective criterions. In this section we consider a few fine points of this type, clearly the selection to topics included is very subjective, but an attempt was made to consider issues that are more important in a general relativistic calculation (see also very useful discussions in [14,20,24]). Most of these considerations were adopted to numerical relativity from other fields of numerical physics, like numerical hydrodynamics, and many of them were introduced to numerical relativity by Wilson [4][14].

Staggered Spatial and Temporal Grids

Consider the simple first order form of the wave equation:

$$\frac{\partial f}{\partial t} = \frac{\partial p}{\partial x} \; ; \; \frac{\partial p}{\partial t} = \frac{\partial f}{\partial x} \tag{162}$$

For a simple second order accurate finite differencing approximation we need to shift the location of p_{NI} by half a grid spacing and by half a time step relative to f_{NI}. Let f_{NI} be $f(Ndt, Idx)$, we define $p_{N+1/2,I+1/2}$ as $p[(N+1/2)dt,(I+1/2)dx]$. The finite differencing approximation to the wave equation becomes:

$$\frac{f_{N+1,I} - f_{NI}}{dt} = \frac{p_{N+1/2,I+1/2} - p_{N+1/2,I-1/2}}{dx} \tag{163a}$$

and

$$\frac{p_{N+1/2,I+1/2} - p_{N-1/2,I+1/2}}{dt} = \frac{f_{N,I+1} - f_{NI}}{dx} \quad . \tag{163b}$$

The grid structure of f and p is staggered both in space and time. Notice that the staggered structure leads to a few advantages over an unstaggered grid. For the latter the equivalent of Eq. 163a is:

$$\frac{f_{N+1,I} - f_{NI}}{dt} = \frac{p_{N,I+1} - p_{N,I-1}}{2dx} \quad . \tag{164}$$

This equation is only first order accurate in time; it leaves the f values on even grid points decoupled from those on the odd grid points, and finally the truncation error in Eq.164 is four times larger than the truncation error in Eq. 163a for the same dx.

An alternative way to write the wave equation is:

$$\frac{\partial g}{\partial t} = k \quad ; \quad \frac{\partial k}{\partial t} = \frac{\partial^2 g}{\partial x^2} \tag{165}$$

With these variables it is simplest to define g and k in the same spatial location, but to keep a staggered temporal structure, i.e. $k_{N+1/2,I}$ is defined at $k[(N+1/2)dt,idx]$. The finite differencing equations are:

$$\frac{g_{N+1,I} - g_{NI}}{dt} = k_{N+1/2,I} \tag{166a}$$

and

$$\frac{k_{N+1/2,I} - k_{N-1/2,I}}{dt} = \frac{g_{N,I+1} - 2g_{NI} + g_{N,I-1}}{dx^2} \quad . \tag{166b}$$

The "3+1" Einstein equations correspond to Eq. 165 and to the set (g,k), while they hydrodynamic equations resemble Eq. 162 and the set (f,p). It is advantageous to employ a staggered grid structure in the numerical relativistic schemes. The particular details of the staggering depend on the exact form of the equations. The basic rules for the staggered are: p is shifted (by half a grid spacing) relative to f if first derivatives of p appear in the equation for f and vice versa, k and g are defined at the same grid point if second derivatives of k, or k itself, appear in the equation for g and vice versa. Usually g_{ij}, N and K_{ij} together with n, ε and p are defined at the same spatial grid point while V^i and N^i are shifted by half a grid spacing. Clearly, N^x and V^x are shifted by half a grid spacing in the x direction but not in the y or z directions. g_{ij}, N, n, ε and p are defined at the same temporal step while K_{ij}, V^i and N^i are shifted by half a time step. Specific components might be staggered differently, depending on the exact nature of the equations.

The grid staggering structure should correspond not only to the relations between different variables, but also to the boundary structure. Some quantities, (like G for the radial gauge example) are defined naturally, on the axis, others (like N and A in that example) are defined naturally half a grid spacing away from it. A proper staggering structure should accommodate all these features.

Variable grid spacing

Any non trivial grid velocity will result in grid points that are separated by unequal intervals between them. Even without a grid velocity variation of the grid spacing can be useful; with a variable grid spacing we can construct a grid structure that includes two length scales, an inner smaller one and an outer longer one (see Fig. 1). With a variable grid spacing, dx, becomes a function of the grid location:

$$x_{I+1} = x_I + dx_I \quad . \tag{166}$$

To see the effects of a variable grid spacing consider the wave equation (Eq. 162). We use a staggered grid, with p defined at the half grid spacing between x_I, i.e.:

$$p_{N+1/2,I+1/2} = p[(N+1/2)dt, x_I + 1/2dx_I] \quad . \tag{167}$$

Eq. 163b is still second order accurate, however, Eq. 163a includes both second and first order truncation errors:

$$\frac{\partial p}{\partial x}\Big|_{x_I} = \frac{p_{N+1/2,I+1/2} - p_{N+1/2,I-1/2}}{1/2(dx_{I-1}+dx_I)} + \frac{1}{4}(dx_I - dx_{I-1})\frac{\partial^2 p}{\partial_x{}^2}\Big|_{x_I} + O(dx^2) \quad . \tag{168}$$

The first order term is in fact second order if:

$$\frac{dx_I - dx_{I-1}}{dx_I} < \frac{dx_I}{\ell} \tag{169}$$

where ℓ is the typical variation length. When this inequality is not satisfied we must replace Eq. 163a by a finite differencing approximation that includes more terms, if we wish to maintain second order accuracy. In practice this is a very cumbersome procedure and inequality 169 is used as a restriction on the variation of dx_I. A grid structure that satisfies this inequality is a 'geometric grid' with:

$$dx_{I+1} = q\, dx_I, \tag{170}$$

with a constant q satisfying:

$$q-1 < \frac{\overline{dx}}{\ell} \tag{171}$$

Inequality 169 turns out to be another argument against application of a Lagrangian grid velocity. It is unlikely that such a grid velocity will result in a grid structure satisfying this inequality. A practical alternative is to choose a constant q such that inequality 169 is satisfied and such that the flux terms are minimized. A new grid structure is calculated, employing this q, and finally the grid velocity is calculated from the variation in the grid structure as:

$$V_{G,I} = \frac{x_I(t+dt) - x_I(t)}{dt} \tag{172}$$

Time step and dragging zone

The time step is determined by the Courant condition which is: $dt < dx/v$. This is necessary since information can propagate only to the nearest neighboring grid points in one time step. In a Newtonian system with a matter velocity, V, and sound speed c_s this corresponds to:

$$\Delta T < \frac{\Delta x}{(V+c_s)} \qquad (173$$

In a general relativistic calculation, gravitational radiation can propagate at the speed of light. The equivalent condition is, therefore, to limit the time step so that the null cone, within ΔT, from a center of a grid element is confined to this grid element (see Fig. 8). This condition corresponds to:

$$-(N\Delta T)^2 + \sum_{\text{noncyclic}\, ij} g_{ij}(\Delta x^i - N^i\Delta T)(\Delta x^j - N^j\Delta T) > 0 \quad , \qquad (174$$

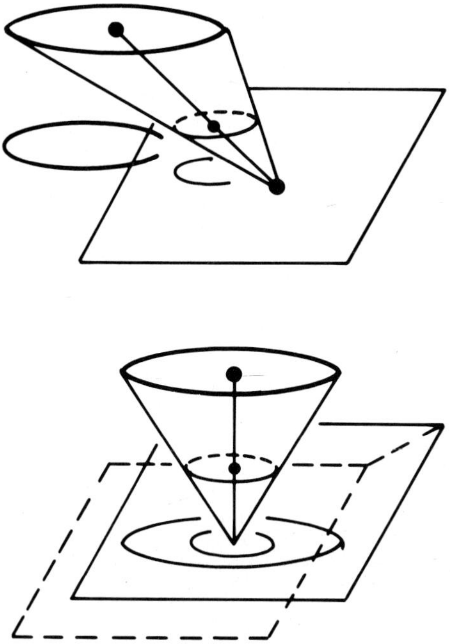

Figure 8: Projection of the null cone and ΔT. Lower Figure: Both projections are within a grid cell and the longer ΔT is allowed. With a grid velocity the grid moves to the dashed grid. The longer ΔT is not allowed. Upper Figure: a dragging zone, the projection of the cone at any $\Delta T \neq 0$ does not include its tip. Still the smaller ΔT is allowed.

which can be rewritten in a form resembling inequality 173. In inequality 174 Δx^i are the grid spacing. There is no grid spacing, Δx^k for a cyclic coordinate, x^k. Therefore, Δx^k should vanish in inequality 174. To emphasize this we denote explicitly that the summation is only over non-cyclic coordinates.

An interesting feature that can appear in a "3+1" formalism is a "dragging zone" [17], (see Fig. 8). In a "dragging zone" the shift vector is relatively large so that ${}^{(4)}g_{tt}$, the four dimensional tt metric component, becomes positive (${}^{(4)}g_{tt} = -N^2 + N_i N^i > 0$). To eliminate a potential source of confusion we stress that a dragging zone region is perfectly regular. The only immediate effect is that just like in a Kerr ergosphere, an observer cannot remain stationary at any coordinate point inside a dragging zone. However, this does not affect the nature of the constant-t hypersurfaces which depend on N^2, and not on ${}^{(4)}g_{tt}$. The constant-t hypersurfaces remain spacelike as long as $N > 0$. Inequality 174 applies for the calculation of ΔT in a dragging zone as well. A grid velocity introduces additional restriction on ΔT. The grid point moves by $V_G{}^i T$ during a time step (see Fig. 8). To take care of this motion we modify inequality 174 by addition of $V_G{}^i$:

$$-(N\Delta T)^2 + \sum_{\text{noncyclic } ij} g_{ij}[\Delta X^i - (N^i + V_G{}^i)\Delta T]\,[\Delta X^j - (N^j + V_G{}^i)\Delta T] > 0 \quad . \tag{175}$$

This inequality guarantees that the light cone remains inside the (moving) numerical grid zone. The matter velocities are smaller than the speed of light. The hydrodynamic inequality 173 is therefore, satisfied whenever inequality 174 is. The minimal ΔT that satisfies inequality 175 for all grid points is used.

CONCLUSIONS AND ACKNOWLEDGEMENTS

In spite of the relative infancy of the field of numerical relativity (it is even younger than experimental gravitational radiation research), its full scope is too wide now to be covered in a single review. Some topics, like the "2+1+1" formalism [28], Characteristic methods [36], outgoing boundary conditions [59] and review of numerical relativistic results had to be left out. Some of these questions are discussed in other contributions to this volume, and the reader is referred to them.

We tried to emphasize the methods, the basic ideas and some of the technical aspects of numerical relativity. We hope that this review will be useful as background material for researchers interested in actual construction of numerical codes and we hope that the open questions and some of the difficulties that were described will not discourage them from doing so.

This research was supported by the USA - Israel Binational Science Foundation, by the Revson Foundation and by an NSF grant PHY79-19884. It is a pleasure to thank B. DeWitt for introducing me to the field of numerical relativity and to express my gratitude to J. Bardeen, J. York and J. Wilson for many discussions on numerical relativity.

---

1. This formula can be derived using Taylor expansion or other more physical methods, see Roache [20].
2. This can be solved by a transformation [22]. However, such a transformation must be singular and hence, introduces other problems.
3. The name Eulerian coordinates is somewhat misleading, since this gauge condition is one of an infinite number of gauge conditions leading to Eulerian hydrodynamics.
4. I thank J. Wilson for many private communications on these subjects.

REFERENCES

[1] Thorne, K.S.,"General Relativistic Astrophysics," in: Leibovitz, N.R., Reid, W. H. and Vandervoort, P.O. (eds.), "Theoretical Principles in Astrophysics and Relativity" University of Chicago Press, Chicago, ILL, 1978.

[2] Thorne, K.S., "The Theory of Gravitational Radiation; An Introductory Review" in this volume.

[3] Eardley, D. M., "Theoretical Models for Sources of Gravitational Waves," in this volume.

[4] May, M.M. and White, R.H., "Hydrodynamic Calculations of General-Relativistic Collapse," Phys. Rev. 141 (1966) 1232-1241.

[5] Hahn, S.G. and Lindquist, R.W., "The Two Body Problem in Geometrodynamics," Ann. Phys. 29 (1964), 304-331.

[6] York, J.W.,Jr., "The Initial Value Problem and Dynamics," in this volume.

[7] York, Jr.W.,Jr., "Kinematics and Dynamics of General Relativity," in: Smarr, L. (ed) "Sources of Gravitational Radiation," Cambridge University Press, Cambridge, England 1979.

[8] $\bar{\text{O}}$Murchadha, N. and York, J.W.,Jr., "Initial Value Problem of General Relativity I," Phys, Rev. D10, 428, 1974.

[9] Smarr, L., "Gauge Conditions, Radiation Formulae and the Two Black Hole Collision," in" Smarr, L. (ed.) Sources of Gravitational Radiation (Cambridge University Press, Cambridge, England, 1979).

[10] Smarr, L., Phd. Thesis, University of Texas, Austin, TX, unpublished, 1975.

[11] Eppley, K.R., Phd. Thesis, Princeton Univeristy, Princeton, NJ, unpublished, 1975.

[12] Smarr, L., Cadez, A, DeWitt, B. and Eppley, K.R., "Collision of two Black Holes, Theoretical Frame Work," Phys, Rev. D14, 2443, 1976.

[13] Wilson, J.R., "Numerical Study of Fluid Flow in a Kerr Space," Ap. J. 173, 431, 1972.

[14] Wilson, J. R., "Relativistic Hydrodynamics," in: Smarr, L. (ed.) Sources of Gravitational Radiation (Cambridge University Press, Cambridge, England, 1979).

[15] Smarr, L., "Space-Time Generated by Computers: Black Holes with Gravitational Radiation," Ann. N.Y. Acad. Sci., 302 (1977), 569-604.

[16] Piran, T., "Problems and Solutions in Numerical Relativity," Ann. NY. Acad. Sci. 375, 1, 1981.

[17] Piran, T. "Numerical Relativity," in: (ed) Ruffini, R. "Proceedings of the second Marcel Grossmann Meeting," North Holland, Amsterdam, 1982.

[18] Nakamura, T. "Numerical Relativity" to appear in "Evolution of the Universe, Stars and the Solar System," Prog. Theor. Phys. Supp., 1982.

[19] Centrella, J., "Numerical Cosmology," to be published in: (eds) Jones B and Jones J. "The Origin and Evolution of Galaxies,", 1982.

[20] Roache, P.J., Computational Fluid Dynamics, (Hermosa Publishers, Albuquerque NM, 1972).

[21] Ames, W.F., Numerical Methods for Partial Differential Equations (Academic Press, New York, 1977).

[22] Choptuik, M., Msc. Thesis, University of British Columbia, unpublished, 1982.

[23] Cantor, M., "Numerical Treatment of Potential Type Equations on R^n: Theoretical Considerations," Preprint, 1981.

[24] Adler, S. and Piran, T., to appear in Rev. Mod. Phys., 1983.

[25] Despain, A., Lecture given at Santa-Barbara Workshop on Computers in Physics, Santa-Barbara, CA, Aug. 1982.

[26] Wheeler, J.A., "Geometrodynamics and the Issue of the Final State," in DeWitt, B. and DeWitt, C. (eds) "Relativity Groups and Topology," Gordon and Breach, New York, NY, 1963.

[27] Nakmura, T.K.,"General Relativistic Collapse of Axially Symmetric Stars Leading to the Formation of Black Holes,"Prog. Theo. Phys., 65, 1876, 1981.

[28] Madea, K., Sasaki, M., Nakamura, T. and Miyama, S., "A New Formation of the Einstein Equations for Relativistic Rotating Systems," Prog. Theo. Phys., 63, 919, 1980.

[29] Misner, C.W. and Sharp, D.H., "Relativistic Equations for Adiabatic Spherically Symmetric Gravitational Collapse," Phys. Rev. 136B, 571, 1964.

[30] Jordan, P., Ehler, J. and Kundt, W., "Strenge Losungen der Feldgleichugen der Algemeinen Relativitatztheorie," Acad. Wiss. Mainz. Abh. Math.-Nat. Kl. Jahrg. No. 2., 1960.

[31] Kompaneets, A.S. "Strong Gravitational Fields in Free Space," Zh. Eksp. Theort. Fiz. 34, 953, Soviet Phys.J.E.T.P., 7, 659, 1958.

[32] Piran, T. and Stark, R. F., unpublished work, 1982.

[33] Arnowitt, R., Deser, S. and Misner, C.W., "The Dynamics of General Relativity," in: Witten, L. (ed.) Gravitation: Introduction to Current Research (Wiley New York, 1962).

[34] Misner, C.W., Thorne, K.S. and Wheeler, J.A. "Gravitation," Freeman, San-Fransico, 1973.

[35] d'Iverno, R.A. and Smallwod, J., "Covariant 2+2 Formulation of the Initial Value Problem in General Relativity," Phys. Rev. D22, 1233, 1980.

[36] Isaacson, R.A., Welling, J.S., and Winicour, Jr., "Null Cone Computation of Gravitational Radiation," preprint, 1982.

[37] Stewart, J.M. and Friedrich, H., "Numerical Relativity I The Characteristic Initial Value Problem," preprint, 1982.

[38] York, J.W.,Jr. and Piran, T., "The Initial Value Problem and Beyond," in Matzner, R. and Shepley, L. (eds) "Spactime and Geometry," Texas University Press, Austin, Tx, 1982.

[39] Choquet-Bruhat, Y. and York, J.W.,Jr., "The Chancy Problem "in" Held A. (ed) "General Relativity and Gravitation," Plenum, New York, NY, 1980.

[40] Lichnerowicz, A., "L'integration des équations de la gravitation relativiste et le problème des n corps," J. Math. Pures et Appl. 23 (1944) 37-63.

[41] Choquet-Bruhat, Y., "The Cauchy Problem," in Witten, L. (ed) "Gravitation" Wiley, New York, NY, 1962.

[42] Dirac, P.A.M., "Fixation of Coordinates in the Hamiltonian Theory of Gravitation," Phys. Rev., 114, 924, 1959.

[43] Hansen, A., Regge, T. and Tertelboim, C., "Constrained Hamiltonian Systems," Acad. National dei Linceri, Rome, 1976.

[44] Centrella, J. and Matzner, R., "Plane Symmetric Cosmology," Ap. J., 230, 311, 1979.

[45] Misner, C.W., "Wormhole Initial Conditions," Phys. Rev. 118, 1110, 1960.

[46] Bardeen, J.M., and Piran T., "General Relativistic Axisymmetric Rotating Systems: Coordinates and Equations," to be published in Physics Reports, 1982.

[47] Cantor, M., "A Necessary and Sufficient Condition for York Data to Specify an Asymptotically Flat Spacetime," J. Math. Phys. 20, 1741, 1979.

[48] Christondonlon, D. and Ō Murchadha, N., "The Boost Problem in General Relativity," Comm. Math Phys. 80, 271, 1981.

[49] Eppley, K.R., "Pure Gravitational Waves," in: Smarr, L. (ed.) Sources of Gravitational Radiation (Cambridge University Press, Cambridge, England, 1979).

[50] Chrzanowski, P., private communication, 1978.

[51] Cantor, M., unpublished results, 1982.

[52] Bowen, J. and York, J.W., Jr., "Time Asymmetric Initial Data for Black Holes and Black Holes Collisions," Phys. Rev. D21, 2047, 1980.

[53] Cantor, M. and Piran, T., "Conformally Connected Universes," preprint, 1982.

[54] Regge, T., "General Relativity without Coordinates," Nuovo Cimiento, 19 (1961) 558-571.

[55] Moncreif, V. and Piran, T., unpublished results, 1981.

[56] DeWitt, B.S., "Quantum Theory of Gravity, I. The Canonical Formalism," Phys. Rev. 160, 1113, 1967.

[57] Moncreif, V., "Decomposition of Gravitational Perturbations," J. Math. Phys. 16, 493, 1975.

[58] Piran, T., "Numerical Codes for Cylindrical General Relativistic Systems," J. Comp. Phys. 35, 254, 1980.

[59] Bardeen, J., "Gauge and Radiation Conditions in Numerical Relativity," Lecture in this volume.

[60] Smarr, L. and York, J.W.,Jr., "Radiation Gauge in General Relativity," Phys. Rev. D. 17 (1978) 1945-1956.

[61] Eastbrook, F., Wahlquist, H., Christiansen, S., DeWitt, B., Smarr, L. and Tsiang, E., "Maximally Slicing a Black Hole," Phys. Rev. D 7 (1973), 2814-2817.

[62] Smarr, L. and York, J.W.,Jr., "Kinematical Conditions in the Construction of Space-time," Phys. Rev. D 17 (1978) 2529-2551.

[63] Eardley, D.M. and Smarr, L., "Time Functions in Numerical Relativity I, Marginally Bound dust Collapse," Phys. Rev. D., D19, 2239, (1980).

[64] Bardeen, J.M., "Gauge Invariant Cosmological Perturbations," Phys. Rev. D22, 1882, 1980.

[65] Shapiro, S.L., and Teukolsky, S.A., "Gravitational Collapse of Neutron Stars and Black Holes: Computer Generation of Spherical Space-times," Ap. J. 235, 199, 1980.

[66] Chouquet-Bruhat, Y., "Maximal Submanifolds and Manifolds with mean Extrinsic Curvature of a Lorentzian Manifold," C.R. Acad. Sci (Paris) 281, (1975).

[67] Marsden, J. and Tipler, F., "Maximal Hypersurfaces and Foliation of Constant Mean Curvature in General Relativity," preprint (1979).

[68] Eardley , D.M., "Global Problems in Numerical Relativity," in Smarr, L. (ed) "Sources of Gravitational Radiation," Cambridge University Press, Cambridge, England, 1979.

[69] York, J.W., Jr., "Role of Conformal Three Geometry in the Dynamics of Gravitation," Phys. Rev. Lett. 28 [1972], 1082-1085.

[70] Centrella, J. and Wilson, J.R., "Planar Numerical Cosmology," preprint, 1982.

[71] Centrella, J. and Wilson, J.R. "Planar Numerical Cosmology II," preprint, 1982.

[72] Choquet-Bruhat, Y., Lecture in this volume.

[73] Piran, T., "Lagrangian Relativistic Hydrodynamics with Eulerian Coordinates," in Tipler, L. (Ed) "Essays in General Relativity: A Festschriff for A. Taub," 1981.

[74] Wilson, J. Smarr, L. and Taubes, C., in Tipler, L. (Ed) "Essays in General Relativity: A Festschriff for A. Taub," 1981.

[75] Geroch, R., "Energy Extraction," Ann. NY Acad. Sci. 224, 108, 1973.

[76] Piran, T. and Rotenberry, M., unpublished results, 1982.

[77] Dykema, P. and Wilson, Jr., unpublished results, 1980.

[78] Olneimik, O. R. and Radkevic, E. V. "Second Order Equations with Nonnegative Characteristic Form," American Math. Soc., Providence, R.I., 1973.

[79] Rotenberry, M., Msc. Thesis, University of Texas at Austin, 1980.

[80] Thorne, K.S., "Geometrodynamics of Cylindrical Systems, PhD Thesis, Princeton University, Princeton, NJ, unpublished, 1965.

[81] Thorne, K. S., "Energy of Infinity Long Cylindrically Symmetric Systems in General Relativity," Phys. Rev. 138, B251, 1965.

[82] Kuchar, K., "Canonical Quantization of Gravitational Waves," Phys. Rev. D10, 955, 1971.

THEORETICAL MODELS FOR SOURCES OF GRAVITATIONAL WAVES

Douglas M. Eardley

Harvard College Observatory
Harvard-Smithsonian Center for Astrophysics
Cambridge, Massachusetts
U.S.A.

Sources of gravitational radiation are never more than 100% efficient, by the Positive Energy Theorems, and efficiencies in likely astronomical sources are considerably less. Stellar core collapse to a neutron star or black hole is one possible source; for high efficiency the core must be deformed somehow. Accretion of bodies onto neutron stars or black holes provides another source, best when two nearly equally massive bodies collide; much theoretical work remains to be done in this case. Binary systems emit gravitational waves; observations of period change in PSR1913+16 confirm this.

1. INTRODUCTION

Gravitational wave antennas have increased in sensitivity over the last 15 years by five orders of magnitude. Detection of gravitational waves would amount to a fundamentally important confirmation of gravitation theory, and would open a new window on the astronomical world. These facts have motivated theorists to carry out many different calculations and estimates of gravitational wave output for possible sources. These calculations are often very difficult, simply because it is always very difficult to model three dimensional and even two dimensional dynamic phenomena of the real world. The application of this work to the real astronomical world still remains quite uncertain, however, both because of the difficulty of the calculations and our lack of knowledge of the actual boundary conditions and rate of occurrence of various types of sources, such as stellar collapses, close binaries, and formation of or accretion onto massive black holes.

This survey of theoretical models is by no means complete. It will concentrate on kinds of sources that seem most interesting for presently operating or feasible experiments at frequencies above ~0.1 mHz; in particular I will not treat long-wavelength cosmological gravitational waves, which were discussed in the lectures of Rees and Hellings at this Summer School. I will discuss the operating principles of sources, but generally the difficult astronomical problem of the actual occurrence rate of sources and their boundary conditions (e.g. event rate for stellar core collapses) will not be reviewed. Finally, this survey is more topical than exhaustive in that recent results play the biggest role, and the older history of the subject will not be presented. Fortunately there are a number of excellent surveys and reviews of this subject, which I have relied on heavily, to which the reader should turn for more information and references to the older primary literature. These include many articles in the proceedings of the last major summer school on gravitational waves, at the Battelle Seattle Research Center in 1978 (Smarr 1979), several reviews by Kip Thorne (1980, 1977, 1975), and Press and Thorne (1972). Introductions to general relativity theory which cover the basic physics of gravitational radiation include Misner, Thorne, and Wheeler (1973; "MTW"), Weinberg (1972), and Landau and Lifshitz (1975).

There are four major subjects surveyed here. Section 2 reviews briefly the fundamental restrictions on sources of gravitational waves which follow directly from the laws of general relativity, which are comprehensively treated in the lectures for Thorne, York, Damour, and Walker; and this section also mentions why plausible sources usually do not approach closer than about a factor of 10 to the fundamental limits for energy efficiency in gravitational waves. Section 3 discusses the gravitational collapse of stellar cores to neutron stars or black holes, with emphasis on the cores of massive, young stars ("supernovae of type II"). Section 4 reviews gravitational wave emission by already-formed neutron stars and black holes, due to collision with another object, or due, in the case of neutron stars but not black holes, to internal excitation by star-quake or phase change. Section 5 treats binary systems, including the "binary pulsar" PSR 1913+16, for which the observations by Joseph Taylor and his collaborators of apparent orbital decay provide indirect but very impressive evidence for the existence of gravitational radiation with properties in accord with the predictions of general relativity theory.

2. FUNDAMENTAL BACKGROUND

2.1 POSITIVITY OF ENERGY

In his lectures, Walker proves a form of the Positive Energy Theorem in general relativity theory. This celebrated result shows that the total energy of an isolated system can never become negative, even though gravitational binding energy is itself negative. (In the literature, this result is sometimes called the Positive Mass Theorem, but the result concerns the time component of the asymptotic 4-momentum of an isolated system, which is conventionally called energy, not mass.) Let us consider an isolated, quiescent system ("state 0") which undergoes a period of violent activity accompanied by the emission of some gravitational waves and then settles down again into a remnant ("state 1"); see Fig. 1. For example, the initial state might consist of a pre-supernova star, and the remnant could then be a neutron star plus the exploding outer layers of the supernova.

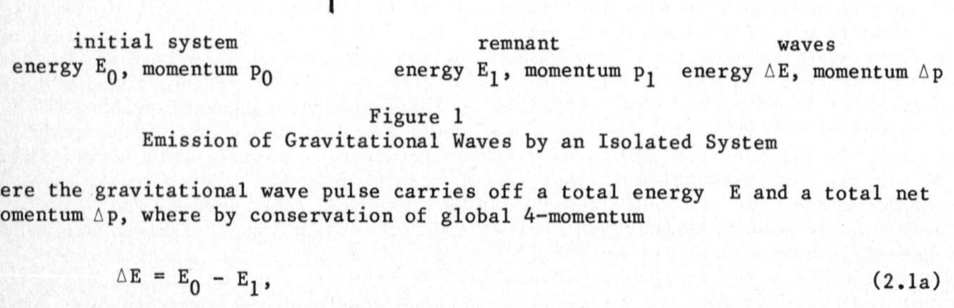

Figure 1
Emission of Gravitational Waves by an Isolated System

Here the gravitational wave pulse carries off a total energy E and a total net momentum Δp, where by conservation of global 4-momentum

$$\Delta E = E_0 - E_1, \tag{2.1a}$$

$$\Delta p = p_0 - p_1. \tag{2.1b}$$

The mass (or rest mass) of the initial system is

$$M_0 = (E_0{}^2 - p_0{}^2)^{1/2} \tag{2.1c}$$

and similarly for the remnant. Positivity of ADM energy gives $E_0 > 0$, $p_0 < E_0$ (unless spacetime is flat and both vanish). Positivity of Bondi energy gives for the remnant $E_1 > 0$, $p_1 < E_1$ (unless the remnant is flat spacetime, i.e. unless the initial system turns entirely into gravitational waves, which is not in principle impossible although it would be extremely difficult to realize.) Finally, positivity of the Bondi-Sachs mass flux at future null infinity states that $\Delta E > 0$, $\Delta p < \Delta E$ (unless the gravitational waves are completely absent; this is the statement that the radiated 4-momentum must be future-pointing and time-like unless it vanishes).

Now one main observable for the event is E, or in dimensionless form the efficiency g for emission of energy as gravitational waves,

$$g = \Delta E/E_0 \tag{2.2}$$

which can be estimated by detecting the gravitational wave pulse, or, in the case of a binary system, can be estimated indirectly by measuring the rate of change of orbital period P, and e.g. using the quadrupole formula for gravitational radiation damping of the orbit. The other main observable is the recoil velocity v, as measured in the frame where the initial system is at rest,

$$v = p_1/E_1 \tag{2.3}$$

which can be obtained by observing or deducing the proper motion of the remnant. The Positive Energy Theorems put these restrictions on the observables:

$$0 < g < 1, \tag{2.4a}$$

$$v < 1. \tag{2.4b}$$

I will generally use units in which $c = 1 = G$, so that $v = 1$ means speed of light. These condition may seem obvious but was a major achievement to prove them rigorously, beginning with the work of Schoen and Yau (1979).

2.2 LAWS OF BLACK HOLE MECHANICS

The Area Theorem or Second Law of Black Hole Mechanics (Hawking 1973; Bardeen, Carter and Hawking 1973) allows us to tighten these limits on g and v if black holes occur in the initial or final state. This theorem implies that

$$A_0 < A_1, \tag{2.5}$$

for the total surface areas A_0 and A_1 of all black holes present in the initial and final states, respectively (unless all black holes present in the system are absolutely stationary in some neighborhood of their horizons, in which case the two areas are equal). We also know by the "No Hair" theorems that each black hole in the initial or final state has a rest mass M in the range

$$A/16\pi \leq M^2 < A/8\pi, \tag{2.6}$$

where A is the surface area of the individual hole; the lower equality is achieved for a nonrotating (Schwarzschild) black hole, while the upper limit is approached for a nearly maximally rotating (Kerr) black hole. For a system of n stationary black holes, far apart from each other, and at rest, it follows that the total rest mass M of all the holes obeys

$$A/16\pi \leq M^2 < nA/8\pi \tag{2.7}$$

where A now denotes the total surface area of all the holes together; the lower limit is achieved for one big nonrotating hole, while the upper limit is approached for n equal, nearly maximally rotating black holes. Finally, for any initial or final configuration of black holes which are far apart and in motion with respect to each other, there is only a lower bound on the total energy,

$$A/16\pi \leq E^2, \tag{2.8a}$$

$$(\text{sum of rest masses of all holes}) \leq E, \tag{2.8b}$$

since we can put as much energy as we please into kinetic energy of holes. It is currently conjectured by experts in positivity of energy that for any configuration of black holes and matter,

$$A/16\pi \leq E^2 - p^2 = M^2. \tag{2.9}$$

Efficiency limits for events involving black holes can now be obtained. Consider the particular initial state consisting of n black holes, far apart from each other, and asymptotically at rest. Here "asymptotically at rest" means approaching each other barely with escape velocity; this does not exclude their having considerable amounts of orbital angular momentum. The initial black holes may be rotating. The black holes collide, or perhaps pass by each other, and the final "remnant" consists of $\leq$n black holes in relative motion, generally in hyperbolic motion. The final energy of the remnant is bounded below by

$$E_1 \geq (A_1/16\pi)^{1/2} > (A_0/16\pi)^{1/2} > M_0/(2n)^{1/2} = E_0/(2n)^{1/2} \tag{2.10}$$

where the successive inequalities follow from Eqs. (2.8a, 2.5, 2.7), and the last equality holds because the initial state is asymptotically at rest. Then the efficiency for n initial black holes at rest is limited by

$$\begin{aligned} g &= \Delta E/E_0 = 1 - E_1/E_0 \\ &< 1 - (2n)^{-1/2}. \end{aligned} \tag{2.11}$$

If we further assume that the initial black holes are all nonrotating black holes, a similar argument gives a tighter limit,

$$g < 1 - n^{-1/2}. \tag{2.12}$$

I must strongly emphasize that these are only theoretical <u>limits</u>; it may be that any practical process, or even realizable process, cannot approach some of these limits. For instance, consider the interesting case of two nonrotating black holes of masses M_{0A} and M_{0B} (with $M_0 = M_{0A}+M_{0B}$), initially far apart and asymptotically at rest. The efficiency limit of Eq. (2.12) gives

$$g < 1 - (M_{0A}{}^2+M_{0B}{}^2)^{1/2}/M_0$$

which has it maximum of g = 29% when $M_{0A} = M_{0B}$, and which vanishes as either mass goes to 0. The <u>actual</u> efficiency for head-on collision of two equally massive nonrotating black holes has been estimated by Eppley and Smarr (Smarr 1979a) from their work in numerical relativity on this problem, and it is about e = 0.07%, a factor of 400 smaller than the limit. The actual efficiency is unknown when the collision is not head-on, but is it undoubtably much greater when the two black holes have enough relative angular momentum to form a distant binary system which then decays by gravitational radiation. Section 4.4 below discusses crude guesses, which suggests $g \sim$ a few %, or a factor of 10 less than the limit.

Similar arguments bound the recoil velocity v. For n initial black holes asymptotically at rest,

$$\Delta p = p_1 = vE_1,$$

$$\Delta p < \Delta E = E_0 - E_1,$$

and elimination of Δp yields

$$E_0 < (1+v)E_1$$

$$< (1+v)(1-v^2)^{-1/2}M_1$$

upon using the special relativistic formula relating E and M. By an argument almost identical to Eq. (2.10), M_1 is in turn bounded in terms of E_0,

$$M_1 > E_0(2n)^{-1/2};$$

eliminating E_0 and solving for v gives the desired limit for n (perhaps rotating) black holes at rest in the initial state,

$$v < (2n-1)/(2n+1). \qquad (2.13)$$

This gives a finite limit $v < 1/3$ even for $n = 1$; this limit can actually be approached by starting with a single, nearly maximally rotating hole, extracting all its energy by the Penrose process, and putting the resulting energy into a graviton rocket to accelerate the black hole. In real life, however, the actual recoil velocities are probably much less than the above limits; see Sects. 3.7, 4.4 below.

A similar argument gives for n nonrotating black holes at rest initially

$$v < (n-1)/(n+1). \qquad (2.14)$$

Another thing to notice is that the limits become greater and greater as n increases, with g and v both approaching 1 as n tends to infinity. In fact, it was pointed out soon after Hawking proved the Area Theorem (attributed by him to Misner and Rees) that one can achieve g very close to 1 by starting with a very large number n of black holes and staging a "tennis tournament". In the first generation one collides all the holes in pairs, yielding n/2 new, larger holes and an efficiency g_1 which may be <<1. One collides the new holes in pairs, in the same way with the same efficiency, ... and so on through $N = \log_2 n$ generations until one final black hole results. The efficiency g_N after N generations is easily seen to be

$$g_N = 1 - (1-g_1)^N \cong 1 - \exp(-Ng_1) \tag{2.15}$$

which becomes very close to 1 for $N >> 1/g_1$. However, $>>2^{(1/g_1)}$ black holes are then needed!

2.3 PRACTICAL LIMITS

There are a number of suggestive (but unpersuasive) arguments that suggest that real efficiencies and recoil velocities will always in the astronomical world be substantially less than the limits discussed above. First, in general relativity theory (unlike most, perhaps all, other relativistic theories of gravity; see Sect. 5.4 below) there are no monopole gravitational waves. Therefore a perfectly spherical star emits no gravitational waves at all, no matter how violently it collapses, and a nearly spherical star is bound to be a poor emitter. Second, plausible astrophysical sources tend to be "poor antennas" [that is, (size of antenna) < (wavelength of wave)], because matter motions (unlike charge motions in a radio antenna) tend to be significantly smaller than c; Thorne in his lecture (see also MTW) gives the estimate for gravitational wave luminosity L_{GW} to total internal luminosity L_{int} as

$$L_{GW} \sim L_{int} \sim (M/r)^{5/2} \sim (v/c)^5$$

$$\sim (\text{number of cycles needed for high } g)^{-1}. \tag{2.16}$$

This estimate suggests that the best sources for high efficiency may be those which exist for many cycles of the wave, e.g. nearly periodic sources such as rapidly rotating stellar cores, rapidly (perhaps nearly extremal) rotating black holes, and extremely close binary systems of compact objects. The best strategy may be to make a poor antenna, then preserve and use it for a long enough time to emit a good deal of energy, rather than try to make an antenna which will have a very high efficiency for a single burst. If so, then observers who wish to detect gravitational waves should search for possible low amplitude but long lived wave trains, probably fairly high Q trains at single frequencies, as well as for single, intense bursts.

Since the efficiency is a single number which is easy to remember, theorists (including me) often emphasize it too much, and tend to ignore other equally important parameters of possible gravitational wave signals that experimentalists would like to know, such as dimensionless amplitude h, frequency, "Q" (reciprocal of number of cycles of roughly constant frequency in waveform), other aspects of waveform, or polarization. The precise value of the efficiency for a given source is less important than how common the source is in the universe. Nevertheless the order of magnitude of the efficiency g is important; observers are unlikely to see sources with $g = 10^{-20}$.

3. GRAVITATIONAL COLLAPSE OF STELLAR CORES

Any star which uses up all its nuclear fuel and finds itself with a mass greater than the Chandrasekhar limit of $\sim 1.4M_\odot$ must undergo gravitational collapse to a neutron star or black hole. Since stars can lose a great deal of mass as a stellar wind (or during mass exchange in a close binary system), not every star with a mass $>1.4M_\odot$ at birth undergoes collapse; there are still substantial uncertainties, but the lower mass limit at birth for single stars which are going to undergo gravitational collapse probably lies in the range of 4 to 8 $M_\odot$. Stars much less massive than this limit will end their lives quietly as white dwarfs, and are poor candidates for sources of bursts of gravitational waves; it is thought possible that some stars too massive to become white dwarfs will explode upon the ignition of carbon and oxygen under degenerate conditions in the core during their evolution, and may disrupt themselves entirely. In any case, above some mass limit in the range just quoted, carbon/oxygen detonation cannot occur because the core is not degenerate at the crucial stage, and gravitational collapse is inevitable after the formation of a core of the ashes of thermonuclear burning, which are iron-group elements.

The collapse of such a massive star is generally thought to give rise to the observed Type II supernovae, which are characterized by rather low explosion velocities and Population I abundances (large content of elements heavier than helium). Theoretically it is the best understood of observed supernovae, although it is by no means completely understood. These are the only kinds of supernova model that I will review here, since the most work has been done on it.

3.1 SPHERICALLY SYMMETRIC COLLAPSE OF STELLAR CORES

There are a number of excellent reviews of this subject available so I will survey only those aspects of the problem which are most relevant to gravitational wave emission; relevant papers are Arnett (1979), Brown, Bethe, and Baym (1982), Wilson (1979), and Hillebrandt and Müller (1981). See footnote 1.

Most of the work done on gravitational collapse of stellar cores assumes that they are spherically symmetric and remain so during collapse. In particular this assumption means that rotation and magnetic fields are not dynamically important, and that no gravitational waves are emitted. This assumption has some indirect observational support, but is not compelled either by astronomical observations or by strong theoretical arguments. It is fair to say that the primary reason that this assumption is made is that the spherically symmetric case is simplest and is by far the easiest to work out, and it is reasonable for the experts to put their effort into solving this case as completely as possible before introducing complications. Some of the experts (the author is not at all an expert in this field), although not all, now believe that a spherically symmetric collapse will in fact lead to the sort of supernova explosion that is observed; however, this consistency with observation does not compel us to believe that all stellar collapses are therefore spherically symmetric; this would require working out the nonspherical case and showing that it does not work.

At endpoint of thermonuclear burning in the stellar core, the core consists of $\sim 1.5M_\odot$ of iron-group elements, with a central density of 3×10^9 g/cm^3 and an adiabatic index γ close to 4/3. By one of the most familiar and important arguments in astrophysics, a star with $\gamma>4/3$ is stable, and one with $\gamma<4/3$ is unstable (see e.g. MTW Chapter 26). [When the effects of general relativity are taken into account, the critical value is $4/3 + O(M/R)$; this relativistic correction is not large for the stellar core, which has a radius of

$>10^3$ km, similar to a white dwarf.] The adiabatic index decreases as electrons become relativistic and also become lost as a source of pressure support as they capture onto nuclei to turn protons into neutrons. The core thus becomes unstable and collapses; it does not stop until the density of nuclear matter, $>10^{14}$ g/cm^3, is reached at the center when the hard-core repulsion of nucleons stiffens the pressure again, and causes the core to "bounce". The total timescale for the collapse is ~1 sec, while the hydrodynamic timescale for the inner part of the core at bounce is ~1 msec.

Great quantities of neutrinos are emitted by the inverse beta reactions that turn electrons and protons into neutrons. A very important effect is trapping of these neutrinos by coherent neutral-current scattering on nuclei, which is one of the predictions of Weinberg-Salam theory. Since neutrinos are trapped, they act as a source of pressure as the collapsing core adiabatically compresses. As a relativistic gas, the neutrinos have $\gamma = 4/3$, which means that instability is only marginal and pressure support never becomes much less than self-gravity of the core. Thus the core is never really in free fall, and collapses a few times more slowly than a freely falling core of the same mass and radius. In particular, less than 10% of the gravitational binding energy released by the collapse goes immediately into bulk kinetic energy, while more than 90% is stored in the stellar material as heat and only slowly diffuses out as neutrinos leave the core, which takes roughly 1 sec. The "inner core" is that part of the star which for which the collapse is always subsonic; its mass is about half that of the core, or $\sim 0.8 M_\odot$. Since the inner core has time to react hydrodynamically to the forces upon it, the collapse of the inner core is nearly "homologous" which means that it keeps the same shape while its overall size changes in a self-similar way:

$$r(y,t) = r(y,0)R(t) \tag{3.1}$$

where y is a Lagrangian or comoving coordinate which labels shells of constant rest mass in the star (or to be precise in general relativity, constant baryon number), and r(y,t) is the radius of shell y at time t; R(t) is the overall scale factor which describes the collapse.

The material outside of the inner core falls supersonically, because the "bottom drops out" as the inner core (which has a greater density and therefore a shorter hydrodynamic timescale) collapses. In this outer region the collapse is strongly nonhomologous. Finally, at roughly the boundary of the original core, the hydrodynamic timescale becomes so slow that the entire core collapse is over with before the material even begins to fall very fast.

When the inner core bounces, it does so smoothly on its timescale but abruptly compared to the slower timescales of the outer core. The bounce is adiabatic, and causes the inner core to bounce outward with nearly its original inward velocity. This motion pushes outward a strong hydrodynamic wave which quickly steepens into a strong shock before it enters the outer core. It is currently hoped that this shock wave will eject all of the star above a certain point, to cause a supernova explosion and leave behind a neutron star with a mass of perhaps $1.4\ M_\odot$. However this point is still uncertain. When born, the shock has enough energy to successfully blow off the rest of the star to infinity, but it is not clear how much energy the shock loses to endothermic nuclear reactions in the material that it passes through, or loses to neutrinos once it breaks through the neutrino photosphere at densities of $\sim 10^{11}$ g/cm$_3$.

The calculations of all these physical processes is, needless to say, quite difficult, and can only be done with the aid of large computers. If the shock fails to blow off the outer layers of the star, they fall back down onto the newborn neutron star; presumably a black hole eventually results in this case, but nobody has followed this evolution through in detail. In any case, it is clear that this model of the supernova explosion is very close to working, and that deciding whether or not it actually works is a delicate question involving competition of nearly equal effects.

The inner core seems to lose most of its kinetic energy in pushing out the wave, though it continues to pulsate radially at rather small amplitude with a period of a few msec according to available detailed calculations, such as that of Wilson (1980). The newborn neutron star is very hot and is supported enough by the pressure of trapped neutrinos that its radius is quite a bit larger than that of a cold neutron star, more nearly 100 km than 10 km.

Goldreich and Weber (1980) have proposed a simple but fairly accurate model of the hydrodynamic collapse of the inner core. They take the equation of state as

$$p = k\rho^{\gamma}, \quad \gamma = 4/3, \quad k = \text{const.} \tag{3.2}$$

and they assume the motion to be homologous, Eq. (3.1). The equations of motion (nonrelativistic Euler equations) then separate to give an equation of motion for the scale factor R(t),

$$\tfrac{1}{2}\dot{R}^2 = (4q/3R)(k^3/\pi G)^{1/2} + E; \quad q, E = \text{const}; \tag{3.3}$$

and a radial equation for a density profile function f(y), where y is Lagrangian radius,

$$y^{-2}(d/dy)(y^2 df/dy) + f^3 = q, \tag{3.4}$$

$$\rho(y) = f^3(y)\rho(0) \quad \text{(definition of density).} \tag{3.5}$$

Equation (3.5) is just the Lane-Emden equation for an N=3 polytrope, except for the nonzero constant q on the right hand side, which arises as a separation constant. The main result for this model is the largest possible mass for a collapsing homologous core,

$$M_c \le 1.045(k_c/k_o)^{3/2} M_o \tag{3.6}$$

where M is mass and k is as in Eq. (3.2); subscript o refers to the precollapse core and subscript c refers to the collapsing core. Since $k_c/k_o \sim 0.7$ from detailed calculations, this model predicts that $M_c \le 0.6\ M_\odot \sim 0.9\ M_\odot$, in good accord with the numerical results.

Goldreich and Weber also analyze the growth of asymmetry in the inner core during collapse, before bounce, by perturbing their model. The homologous core turns out to be stable against growing modes, except for the kinematic effect of adiabatic compression on pre-existing motions. Stability is possible because the motion is subsonic and the core has time to adjust itself if asymmetries appear. All in all, growth in asymmetry during the compression from white dwarf density to neutron star density will not exceed a factor of ~3.

3.2 DEPARTURE FROM SPHERICAL SYMMETRY IN CORE COLLAPSE

Rotation and magnetic fields are the two most important possible causes of departure from spherical symmetry in the precollapse core; see Katz (1980).

If the initial core is rotating, then conservation of angular momentum will increase the centrifugal deformation of the core during collapse. For radius R, mass M, and angular velocity, the eccentricity e of the core is

$$e^2 \sim \text{(rotational energy)}/\text{(total binding energy)}$$

$$\sim MR^2\Omega^2/(GM^2/R) = \Omega^2R^3/GM.$$

Now angular momentum J is conserved during collapse,

$$J \sim MR^2\Omega,$$

so that as a function of R during collapse,

$$e^2 \sim (J^2/GM^3)R^{-1}. \tag{3.7}$$

Since the relative importance of centrifugal forces increase during collapse in the same way as would the pressure forces of an ordinary nonrelativistic free gas ($\gamma = 5/3$) one often says "rotation has an adiabatic index $\gamma = 5/3$." Before collapse, R ~ 1000 km, and after the neutron star settles down, R ~ 10km. Thus e will grow by a factor of ~ 10 during collapse. In fact,

$$e_{\text{initial}} \sim (1 \text{ sec}/P_{\text{initial}}), \tag{3.8a}$$

$$e_{\text{final}} \sim (10 \text{ sec}/P_{\text{initial}}), \tag{3.8b}$$

$$\sim (1 \text{ msec}/P_{\text{final}}). \tag{3.8c}$$

Here P denotes the rotation period of the object. There is no direct knowledge of the period of the core. Massive stars on the main sequence, while they are still burning hydrogen in their cores and before the core has started to contract to high densities, usually have rather short rotation periods on the order of a few days. _If_ angular momentum is conserved during the subsequent evolution, the core will indeed have a period of seconds or shorter when it arrives at white dwarf densities. However there exist possible mechanisms for transferring angular momentum out of the core as it quasi-statically shrinks during stellar evolution; these mechanisms are not understood well enough to support confident theoretical predictions as to the period of the core at collapse. The next point in core history when information exists about period is when they've become neutron stars, which are observable as radio pulsars if they are rotating and magnetized. The fastest pulsar is the one at the center of the Crab Nebula, which has a period of 33 msec, far slower than that required for a large distortion, and there is some reason to believe the period could not have been very much shorter a birth (Ruderman 1972). Although one might like to believe that all pulsars are born with periods near 1 msec, there is no particular reason to believe this, and absolutely no observational evidence for it. Another possible source of information is to look at rotation periods of observed white dwarfs. Since these stars were formed as the cores of less massive stars, they do not bear directly on the problem at hand, but observational evidence is highly desirable, even if indirect. White dwarfs are observed with periods down to 71 sec, much longer than required for great distortion. In fact, white dwarfs with such short periods invariably occur in binary systems, and mass transfer from the companion star has probably spun them up. Single white dwarfs have much longer periods.

The corresponding argument for magnetic deformation invokes the conservation of magnetic flux, or frozen-in magnetic field; since the stellar material is highly conducting, perfect MHD applies. If the field is poloidal (i.e. field lines lie in planes through the symmetry axis, such as for an aligned dipole field) then magnetic flux Φ is conserved during collapse,

$$\Phi \sim BR^2,$$

and

$$e^2 \sim (\text{magnetic energy})/(\text{total binding energy})$$

$$\sim R^3B^2/(GM^2/R) = R^4B^2/GM^2$$

or

$$e^2 \sim \Phi^2/GM^2, \tag{3.9}$$

which is independent of R. In this case the magnetically induced distortion neither increases nor decreases during collapse. "A poloidal magnetic field has $\gamma = 4/3$." In fact, for a poloidal magnetic field,

$$e_{initial} \sim e_{final} \sim B_{initial}/10^{14} \text{ Gauss}$$

$$\sim B_{final}/10^{18} \text{ Gauss}. \tag{3.10}$$

A toroidal magnetic field has the same behavior so long as it is not amplified by differential rotation during collapse. It is possible for such amplification to occur, and if it does the magnetically induced eccentricity can increase.

The fields necessary to cause a large eccentricity are enormously greater than those directly observed on related astronomical objects, which range up to 10^8 Gauss for white dwarfs (corresponding to the initial state), and up to 10^{14} Gauss for neutron stars (corresponding to the final state).

Since there are no direct observations of precollapse cores -- they are hidden inside a large star, probably a red supergiant, and in any case are rare because the timescale for the final stages of thermonuclear burning is days, and such a core collapses in our galaxy only once every 10 - 100 years -- one does not know whether it is possible for cores to support rotation rates or magnetic fields large enough to cause significant eccentricities.

Other causes of distortion are possible. In a carbon detonation supernova, it is possible for the explosion to initiate off-center, causing a geometrical distortion of the core. However such an occurrence is not likely in the "iron" core of the massive stars under discussion, since all thermonuclear burning in the core has ceased. (Burning of silicon-group elements is still going on in a shell which forms the outer boundary of the core, however, and it is conceivable that breaking of spherical symmetry might occur here.)

Therefore no strong conclusion is possible at present on whether core collapse is spherically symmetrical in all, some, or no cases. Thus our attention turns to theoretical models of deformed collapse, even though the theoretical calculations are much more difficult in this case. It now is possible using supercomputers to carry out full hydrodynamical calculations of rotating, collapsing cores in two spatial dimensions (i.e. axial symmetry); see Müller and Hillebrandt (1981). However these calculations are still difficult enough that comprehensive results are not available. In particular, general relativistic calculations of this problem are not yet available (see Piran's lectures in this volume), and estimates of gravitational radiation have not been made. Therefore I will discuss some highly simplified models of nonspherical collapse.

3.3 ELLIPSOIDAL MODELS OF COLLAPSE

Saenz and Shapiro (1978, 1979, 1981), and Saenz (1982), have carried out an interesting program of investigation of nonspherical collapsing cores based on a one-zone ellipsoidal model of the core. The replacement of the very large number of hydrodynamic degrees of freedom of the core by the few degrees of freedom possessed by a homogeneous ellipsoid is a radical approximation, but many interesting results come out. The advantage of the approximation is that the partial differential equations describing the hydrodynamical evolution of the core become a set of a few coupled ordinary differential equations in time, which can readily be solved numerically.

The core is taken as homogeneous with density ρ. The pressure p is fixed at the center of the star by some equation of state, e.g. an adiabatic one such as Eq. (3.2) for some value of γ. The space dependence of p away from the center is then fixed by the requirement that the Euler equations be everywhere satisfied, and that the density remain spatially homogeneous despite changes in its value caused by volume changes. The equations of motion of the three principal axes a,b,c of the core then become

$$\ddot{a} = 2p/\rho a - 2\pi G\rho A_1 + a^2\Omega^2 + \dots \qquad (3.11a)$$

$$\ddot{b} = 2p/\rho b - 2\pi G\rho A_2 + b^2\Omega^2 + \dots \qquad (3.11b)$$

$$\ddot{c} = 2p/\rho c - 2\pi G\rho A_3 + c^2\Omega^2 + \dots \qquad (3.11c)$$

where Ω is the angular velocity of the ellipsoid, which has been assumed axially symmetric for simplicity here, where the A's are gravitational acceleration terms which are known explicitly, and where terms arising from vorticity and gravitational radiation damping have been omitted. Saenz and Shapiro also put in simple one-zone model for neutrino cooling, which in turn affects the equation of state by lowering the adiabat of the matter, and for hydrodynamic dissipation between inner and outer core, which damps inner core bounces.

During the first few bounces (see Saenz and Shapiro 1978, 1979) the amount of gravitational radiation emitted depends strongly on the initial eccentricity of the core, which is assumed due either to rotation or magnetic fields. For instance, as a function of initial rotational period P, the efficiency peaks very strongly at P = 1 sec, with a peak value

$$g \sim 10^{-2} \qquad (3.12)$$

for a "cold" equation of state which is probably not suited for core collapse of a massive star, but which is chosen to maximize compression at bounce, and

$$g \sim 10^{-4} \qquad (3.13)$$

for a "hot" equation of state more reasonable for this particular problem. The efficiency g is proportional to P^{-4} for periods above 1 sec, which is a very steep drop-off. According to these results, a neutron star forming with the presently observed period of the Crab pulsar has $g \sim 10^{-10}$! However, the efficiency can be greatly enhanced if the core keeps bouncing; see below.

The spectrum of gravitational radiation peaks broadly between 100 Hz and 1 kHz for the events of maximal efficiency, while the peak moves to a few kHz for the much less luminous events at low distortion or high P.

Detweiler and Lindblom (1981) have carried out calculations of ellipsoidal models to see what happens at later times, after the core has settled down as a rapidly rotating neutron star and is secularly evolving on a timescale of 1 sec. Efficiencies for gravitational radiation during this late phase are low, but the emission is very narrowly peaked about some frequency f on the order of 1 or 2 kHz,

$$g \sim 10^{-6}, \quad \Delta f/f \sim 10^{-3}. \tag{3.14}$$

Now let us discuss the intriguing results of Saenz and Shapiro (1981) as to what happens if the core keeps bouncing. They find that the eccentricity e always becomes large after enough bounces, even if it starts off small. For instance, a core with an initial eccentricity e = 0.01 at white dwarf density will become strongly deformed after about 10 bounces; at the tenth bounce in this example, the density excursion during each bounce is less than a factor of 2. The consequence is that the efficiency g stays large for any initial period above 1 sec, out at least to several hundred sec. According to this model, the birth of a neutron star with the present spin rate of the Crab pulsar would have $g \sim 10^{-5}$. This growth of asymmetry has potentially quite important implications for gravitational radiation from collapsing stellar cores, because it makes the efficiency almost uniformly high at small initial distortion, and thereby renders estimates of gravitational wave sources less dependent upon unknown initial conditions of the cores, as well as giving optimistic strength estimates.

3.4 PARAMETRIC RESONANCE IN BOUNCING STELLAR CORES

Clark (1979) did some work to try to understand how the growth of asymmetry discovered by Saenz and Shapiro occurred, and what conditions in the core were necessary for the effect to be large. The growth of asymmetry can be viewed as a case of parametric resonance, with the radial pulsation or bouncing of the core acting as the pump oscillator, and with a nonspherical mode of the star acting as the driven oscillator. In the work of Saenz and Shapiro (1981) the nonspherical mode was the quadrupole f-mode, or "Kelvin" mode, of the core. When the core is static, the Kelvin mode is always stable. But when the core is radially pulsating with a great enough amplitude, the Kelvin mode may be driven unstable by parametric resonance with the pulsation.

Parametric resonance is defined as excitation of a mode, not by direct coupling, but by periodic modulation of parameters of the mode such as its frequency. The phenomenon appears in many kinds of systems in physics and engineering; the archtype is a pendulum in which the pivot point is moved up and down periodically by an external force. Discussions may be found in many mechanics and electrical engineering books; see e.g. Landau and Lifshitz (1960). The equation of motion of a mode amplitude x(t) is

$$\ddot{x} + B^2(t)x = 0; \tag{3.15}$$

for instance, for the pendulum, x is angle and

$$B^2(t) = [g + \ddot{h}(t)]/l \tag{3.16}$$

where g = acceleration of gravity, h(t) = height of pivot, a periodic function, and l = length of pendulum.

Let $B(t)$ be periodic at frequency F ("pump frequency"). If B were constant, then $x(t)$ would have a natural frequency

$$f = B/2\pi. \tag{3.17}$$

If B undergoes small-amplitude oscillations about some constant value $2\pi f$, then parametric instability will occur at narrow resonances when the natural frequency f is close to harmonics of F/2,

$$f \approx f_n = nF/2,\ n = 1,2,3,\ldots, \tag{3.18}$$

with the n = 1 resonance being strongest and broadest, with strength and breadth dropping off steeply as n increases. In resonance, the unstable mode is phase-coherent with the pump frequency; in the strongest resonance at n = 1, the unstable mode moves through half a period of its motion during a full pump period.

If the amplitude of change of $B(t)$ becomes large, then the bands of parametric instability also become broad and strong, with again the n = 1 resonance being the most important. If x is taken as a complex mode amplitude, then a suitable measure of growth is the complex factor z that x changes by in one period:

$$x(t+T)=zx(t) \tag{3.18}$$

If $|z| = 1$, then the mode is not unstable (although in this case the phase of z tells how the frequency of the oscillator x is being pulled by the pump). If $|z| > 1$ then the mode is unstable and a convenient measure of growth to quote is $\ln|z|$, the number of e-folds the mode amplitude grows by in one pump period. If the amplitude of change of B is large, parametric resonances are typically very strong at n = 1, with $\ln|z| > 1$. This means that the driven mode x will increase by a factor $> e^2 \sim 8$ during one of its own natural periods 2T.

Clark (1979) studied parametric resonance in homogeneous ellipsoidal core models; some of the microphysics that Saenz and Shapiro kept was ignored, and the core is taken as a perfectly adiabatic spheroid with no vorticity and no gravitational radiation, and no neutrino or hydrodynamic losses. The motion is described by a radial part $R(t)$ and a nonspherical part $x(t)$; x is assumed small and only 0th and 1st order terms in x are kept, while R is not assumed small. The equation of state is

$$p = k\rho^\gamma,\ k = \text{const},\ \gamma = \text{const}, \tag{3.19}$$

and the adiabatic index γ plays an important role because is changes the radial stiffness of the star and hence the pump period; the natural period of the Kelvin mode is exactly independent of γ in these ellipsoids, and depends only weakly on γ in real core models. The three semimajor axes a, b, c, are expressed in terms of R and x,

$$a(t) = b(t) = R(t)[1 + x(t)], \tag{3.20a,b}$$

$$c(t) = R(t)[1 - 2x(t)]. \tag{3.20c}$$

The equations of motion (3.11) become

$$\ddot{R} = - 1/R^2 + 1/R^{(3\gamma-2)}, \tag{3.21}$$

$$\ddot{x} = - (4/5R^2)x, \tag{3.22}$$

where the units have been chosen in such a way that the equilibrium radius of the core is R = 1, and the squared angular frequency of the Kelvin mode is 4/5. Here Eq. (3.21) describes the motion of the radial pump oscillator R; the first term on the right is gravity, and the second is pressure force. Eq. (3.22) describes the motion of the driven nonradial mode x, in the approximation that x is small. The term on the right is gravitational restoring force, and pressure does not enter.

First, the case of small-amplitude radial pulsation can de solved analytically. If

$$R(t) = 1 + s(t), \quad |s| << 1, \tag{3.23}$$

then Eqs. (3.21-22) reduce to

$$\ddot{s} = -(3\gamma - 4)s, \tag{3.24}$$

$$\ddot{x} = -(4/5)(1 - 3s)x \tag{3.25}$$

Equation (3.24) gives the squared angular frequency of radial oscillation as $(3\gamma - 4)$ -- note the famous instability if $\gamma < 4/3$! Equation (3.25) gives the squared angular frequency of the nonradial mode as 4/5 if r = 0. The solution of Eq. (3.24) is a pure sine wave, and Eq. (3.25) can be solved in terms of Mathieu functions (Abramowitz and Stegun 1964, Chap. 20). In accord with the standard results about small-pump-amplitude parametric resonance, there are narrow instabilities at frequencies given by Eq. (3.18),

$$(1/2\ )(4/5)^{1/2} = (n/2)(1/2\ )(3\gamma - 4)^{1/2}, \quad n = 1,2,3,..., \tag{3.26}$$

or

$$\gamma = (4/3)(1 + 4/5n^2), \quad n = 1,2,3,...; \tag{3.27}$$

therefore the following values of adiabatic index will show sharp parametric resonances of the given order n, as listed in Table 1.

Table 1
Parametric Resonances of the Kelvin Mode in Homogeneous Spheroids

n	γ
1	2.40
2	1.60
3	1.45
4	1.40
.	.
.	.
∞	4/3

If the radial pulsation is not small in amplitude, $|s| \sim 1$, then numerical solution is necessary for Eqs. (3.21-22). Clark's method is to integrate Eq. (3.21) for one period (finding the exact period T numerically), and then to determine numerically from Eq. (3.22) the 2x2 matrix Q which takes initial data $\{x, \dot{x}\}$ into itself one period T later. This map Q is called the "Floquet matrix" or "stroboscopic operator" or "Poincaré map". The eigenvalues z of the Floquet matrix Q are then the same as in Eq. (3.18), and $|z| > 1$ signals instability.

Clark's results are that the $n = 1$ parametric resonance is very strong and broad. For instance, when $R(max)/R(min) = 2$, the growth rate at band center ($\gamma = 2.4$) is $|z| \sim 8$, and the instability band extends from $\gamma = 1.8$ nearly to $\gamma = 3$. Since the adiabatic index for nuclear matter is probably above 2 and less than 2.5, a core of cold nuclear matter will undoubtably be trapped in the $n = 1$ parametric resonance for large amplitude pulsation. The results of Saenz and Shapiro (1981) show that their growth of asymmetry is an $n = 1$ parametric resonance, since the period of the nonradial oscillations is half that of the radial pulsation.

The resonances for $n > 1$ are much less strong, in accord with general lore on parametric instability. The $n = 2$ resonance at $\gamma = 1.6$ only has a breadth of $\Delta\gamma = 0.03$ at $R(max)/R(min) = 2$, and the maximum strength is only about 0.3 e-folds per T. Resonances for $n > 2$, while present, are even weaker. Therefore the $n = 1$ resonance is the main one to watch for.

There are two questions about the growth of asymmetry. First, is a homogeneous spheroid a very good model of a real collapsing core, which is more like an $N = 3$ polytrope and is centrally condensed? --I.e. central density greatly exceeds average density. Second, do real cores bounce enough for the growth to be large, even if the tuning is right for a parametric instability? The first question has been addressed by Clark (1980) in some extensive work on more realistic (but still not terribly realistic) models of pulsating cores, the "homologous polytropes". We will describe his model and his results before turning to the second question.

The particular class of stars investigated by Clark (1980), the "homologous polytropes", is set up by making three assumptions. For this class, it is straightforward (involves only numerical solution of ordinary differential equations) to set up solutions of the Euler equations for large-amplitude radial pulsation. These solutions are exact in the sense that no assumption about smallness of pulsation amplitude is made (e.g. no Eq. 3.23). Then it is a sizable but not impossible task to carry out first-order perturbation expansions of the Euler equations for nonradial modes, and to construct numerically and diagonalize the Floquet matrix for the nonradial modes over one period T of the radial pulsation. The assumptions are:

1. The star is able to undergo homologous, spherically symmetric motions,

$$r(y,t) = R(t)y, \tag{3.28}$$

   where y = Lagrangian or comoving radial coordinate, t = time, and r = Eulerian or geometrical radial coordinate.

2. The equation of state for pressure p in terms of density ρ is a sum of two contributions, p_γ for $\gamma > 4/3$ and $p_{4/3}$:

$$p(y,\rho) = k(y)\rho^\gamma + l(y)\rho^{4/3}, \tag{3.29a}$$

$$\equiv \quad p_\gamma + \quad p_{4/3}, \tag{3.29b}$$

   where $k(y)$ and $l(y)$ are functions of Lagrangian radius which specify what adiabat different mass elements are on. These functions are determined when all conditions are imposed. The motion is therefore adiabatic but the material is not isentropic.

3. When the star is static (not pulsating homologously), $p_{4/3}$ is restrict- by a polytropic law

$$p_{4/3} = \text{const}\cdot\rho^{(1+1/N)}, \tag{3.30}$$

where $0 \leq N \leq 5$, just as for the classical polytropes (see, e.g., Chandrasekhar 1939, Zel'dovich and Novikov 1971).

Assumption 1 is made primarily to make the problem tractable; it is a fairly good assumption for the pulsating core itself, but it places the very important restriction that the core cannot interact hydrodynamically with a surrounding envelope, to send out waves or shocks. Therefore this model cannot be used to study damping of core pulsations, only nonradial parametric instability during undamped core motion. One way of lifting this restriction would be to construct solutions of the Euler equations numerically, either periodic solutions or solutions for damped core pulsation following collapse. Assumption 1 was made instead just to avoid this considerable numerical work in making a background model to perturb. Assumption 2 just takes the simplest possible equation of state that leads to interesting models; taking only the first term makes homologous motion impossible, while taking only the second term leads to stars which collapse but do not pulsate, as found by Goldreich and Weber (1980). Similar results could be obtained with other sorts of equations of state, for instance sums or integrals over different γ's. Assumption 3 is likewise inessential and, as for the classical polytropes, is made just to obtain a class of stars with different radial profiles of density.

The resulting model stars and their homologous pulsational motions are then characterized by four essential dimensionless parameters:

N = polytropic index, $0 \leq N \leq 5$,

γ = adiabatic index of p_γ, $\gamma > 4/3$,

q = separation constant = "amount of p_γ compared to $p_{4/3}$, in a rough average sense".

$w = (R_{max} - R_{min})/(R_{max} + R_{min})$ = pulsation amplitude, $0 \leq w < 1$,

The Euler equations for spherically symmetric homologous motion,

$$\partial^2 r(y,t)/\partial t^2 = -Gm(y)/r^2 - (1/\rho)\partial p/\partial r, \tag{3.31}$$

where $m(y)$ is the mass contained within Lagrangian radius y, then separate upon employing Eq. (3.28) into ordinary differential equations in y and t,

$$\ddot{R} = -\text{const}/R^2 + \text{const}'/R^{(3\gamma - 2)}, \tag{3.32a}$$

$$y^{-2}(d/dy)(y^2 df/dy) = q - f^N, \tag{3.32b}$$

where $f(y)$ is a function that determines the density distribution according to

$$\rho \equiv f^N/\text{const } R^3. \tag{3.33}$$

Equation (3.32b) is a generalization of the Lane-Emden equation similar to Eq. (3.4), while Eq. (3.32a) is essentially Eq. (3.19). These models therefore generalize both the spherical motions of the homogeneous ellipsoids, and the collapsing Goldreich-Weber stars. It should be noted that the net adiabatic index γ_{net} of the material is variable; according to Eqs. (3.29),

$$\gamma_{net} \equiv d \log p/d \log \rho \,|_y = [p_\gamma + (4/3)p_{4/3}]/(p_\gamma + p_{4/3}). \qquad (3.34)$$

For any chosen N (independent of γ and w) there is a maximum possible value q_{max} of the constant q, such that $0 \leq q \leq q_{max}$. This turns out to put an upper limit on the contribution of p_γ to p, such that pressure gradients in the star can still support homologous motion. This is so because a star with an adiabatic index of 4/3 can have large homologous motions, since "the adiabatic index of gravity is also 4/3". On the other hand, an adiabatic index much different from 4/3 will preclude homologous motion. At the lower limit, q=0, p_γ vanishes and the equation of state is pure $\gamma = 4/3$.

The Goldreich-Weber models appear as the case N = 3, $\gamma = 4/3$ of the homologous polytropes.

For $N \geq 1$, and for $0 < q < q_{max}(N)$, the density distribution does not differ very much from that of a classical polytrope of index N. The homologous polytropes are generally a little more centrally condensed than the classical ones.

Given these periodically pulsating, spherically symmetric background models, it is straightforward though tedious to carry out first-order perturbation theory for the nonspherical motions of the star. Since the background is spherically symmetric, the perturbations separate in angular variables into spherical harmonics labelled by a total angular momentum l; since it is not stationary the perturbations do not separate in time into Fourier components $\exp(-i\omega t)$, rather it is necessary to integrate the equations of motion of the perturbations as linear partial differential equations in two independent variables (t,y). Because the star is not isentropic, two series of modes appear, the p-modes which are primarily acoustic waves and which are high in frequency; and the g-modes which are primarily gravity waves (not gravitational waves! -- the models are nonrelativistic) and which are generally low in frequency. At the middle of the frequency spectrum the g-modes and p-modes of a given symmetry overlap at the f-mode, which has no radial nodes. There is a third series of modes, the toroidal modes, which are zero frequency, are decoupled from everything else, and play no role. The nature of the modes is very similar to that in perturbations of static stellar models (see Cox 1980), except for the time dependence. The most important mode for gravitational radiation is the quadrupole (l = 2) f-mode, although any low-order quadrupole g- or p- mode may be of interest.

The main numerical task is to construct the Floquet matrix, or time-evolution matrix which maps the space of initial conditions for the perturbation modes into itself one period T later. A discrete zoning of the star is adopted, e.g. into 24 zones. Since the perturbation equations are second order in time, there are two initial conditions per degree of freedom; furthermore, there are two perturbation degrees of freedom per zone, representing p-modes and g-modes, or potential flow and vorticity; therefore the space of initial conditions has 4 dimensions per zone, and is 96-dimensional if the star is carved up into 24 zones, and Q is a square matrix in this dimensionality, e.g. 96x96. The matrix Q is constructed as Q = Q(T) where Q(t) obeys the perturbation equations over a period and has initial condition Q(0) = I = identity. In this case, there is no dissipation, and the star forms a Hamiltonian system. Thereby the matrix Q(t) is symplectic, which is to say it has certain symmetries which can be exploited to reduce the numerical work by about a factor of 8. After Q for a period is constructed, its eigenvalues and eigenvectors are calculated. The eigenvalues z have the same significance as in Eq. (3.18) above, viz. any z with $|z| > 1$ represents an instability, and $\ln|z|$ gives the number of e-folds by which the amplitude of the unstable mode grows over a period T. The shape of the eigenfunctions depends on the amplitude of spherical pulsation w as well as on the parameters (N, γ, q) adopted for the stellar model. The "same" mode at different pulsation amplitudes can be identified only by continuously varying the pulsation amplitude w and following the mode by continuity in w.

This method is related to that of Stellingwerf (1974), who constructed a numercal Floquet matrix as part of a Newton's-method iteration scheme to construct numerical models of large-amplitude radial pulsations of Cepheid variables.

The perturbed nonradial modes of this star represent an example of parametric resonance in a system of many degrees of freedom (e.g. 48 degrees of freedom for a 24-zone star). Parametric resonance in dissipationless systems of many degrees of freedom is discussed in a number of mathematical mechanics books, e.g. Arnol'd (1980), Arnol'd and Avez (1968), Abraham and Marsden (1967). The main results are as follows. If z is an eigenvalue of Q, then so are $1/z$, z^*, and $1/z^*$. If z is on the unit circle, then the four eigenvalues collapse to two, since $1/z = z^*$;

$$|z| = 1 \quad \text{implies a pair } (z, z^*) \text{ of stable eigenvalues.} \tag{3.35}$$

If z is real, and $|z| \neq 1$, then again the quadruple collapses to a pair since $z = z^*$,

$$z \text{ real, } z \neq 1 \text{ implies a pair } (z, 1/z) \text{ of eigenvalues, one stable and one unstable: "principal parametric resonance".} \tag{3.36}$$

Finally, if z is neither real nor on the unit circle, then all four eigenvalues are different,

$$z \text{ not real, } |z| \neq 1 \text{ implies a quadruple of eigenvalues } (z, 1/z, z^*, 1/z^*)\text{, two stable and two unstable: "combination parametric resonance."} \tag{3.37}$$

The onset of instability can occur in two distinct ways. The first way is for a pair of stable eigenvalues (z, z^*) on the unit circle (Eq. 3.35) to collide at the real axis, either at $z = +1$ or $z = -1$, and then move apart again up and down the real axis to form a pair with one unstable mode (Eq. 3.36); this is instability via a principal parametric resonance, and is the only possibility in a system of one degree of freedom, such as the one-zone spheroids discussed above. For a principal parametric resonance, the frequency f of the unstable mode is given by Eq. (3.18),

$$2f = nF, \quad n = 1,2,3,\ldots, \tag{3.38}$$

where $F = 1/T$ is the pump frequency (in our case the frequency of radial pulsation); and where the $n = 1$ resonance is usually strongest, with higher resonances $n = 2,3,4,\ldots$ being successively weaker. A quantum theoretical analogy for Eq. (3.38) is that n quanta of radial pulsation decay into two quanta in some nonradial mode f.

The second way is that two different pairs (z, z*) and (z′, z′*) of stable modes on the unit circle (Eq. 3.35) can collide anywhere on the unit circle, and move off into the complex plane, to create a quadruple of eigenvalues (Eq. 3.37), two of which are unstable; this is instability via a combination parametric resonance. In this case the frequencies f, f′ of the two unstable modes are related to the pump frequency by

$$f + f' = nF, \quad n = 1,2,3,.... \tag{3.39}$$

Again resonance is usually strongest for n = 1, with higher resonances successively weaker. The index n is the order in w at which the instability appears, which makes plausible the strength of the resonance for lowest values of n. The quantum analogy is that n quanta of radial pulsation decay into two quanta, one in some mode f and the other in another mode f′. These two kinds of instability are the only ones that occur to first order in the driven modes; there are no decays into three, four, ... quanta in this order.

The onset of instability in a static, dissipationless star is a familiar topic, the results of which can be phrased in the same language. If a perturbation mode of a static star has complex frequency ω, then a quantity z as above is defined as $z = \exp(i\omega)$. Stable modes have real ω and come in pairs $(\omega, -\omega)$; i.e. $|z| = 1$ and z′s come in pairs (z, z*) as in Eq. (3.35). Unstable modes have pure imaginary ω and come in pairs (ω, ω^*): i.e. z is real and belongs to a pair (z, 1/z), as in Eq. (3.36). There is no analog of Eq. (3.37). Onset of instability in a static star happens when a pair of frequencies ω on the real axis collide at zero, then move up and down the imaginary axis; i.e. a pair of z′s on the unit circle collide at z = 1, then move up and down the real axis, which is analogous to a principal parametric resonance. There is no analog of combination parametric resonance in a static star.

Clark′s numerical results for parametric resonance in radial pulsation of the homologous polytropes are as follows.

First, the mode spectrum is very complicated, and many principal and combination resonances appear and disappear as the pulsation amplitude w is changed. Combination resonances appear only between pairs of modes which obey angular momentum selection rules: most importantly, the total angular momentum l of the two modes must be equal.

Second, the most unstable modes are invariably principal resonances; combination resonances, when they appear, are roughly a factor of ten weaker in $\ln|z|$. This may be a special feature of the homologous polytropes; when q = 0, there is a selection rule which forbids the appearance of any combination resonances at all (this has to do with self-similarity of the background in the case q = 0). For possible models $0 \leq q \leq q_{max}$, there seems to be an approximate selection rule due to the smallness of q.

Tables 2 and 3 give some growth rates for principal parametric resonances in quadrupole modes for a variety of stellar models in fairly vigorous pulsation ($R_{max}/R_{min} = 3$). The value of γ corresponds to the adiabatic index of the component p_γ of the equation of state, Eqs. (3.29); the net adiabatic index of the star is considerably lower, according to Eq. (3.34). An average value of γ_{net} over the whole star is given in the tables; this is the value that should be compared with the adiabatic index of another core model.

Table 2

Growth rates $\ln|z|$ for principal parametric instability of the $l = 2$ f-mode ("Kelvin mode") in homologous polytropes, for $q = 0.8\, q_{max}$, $w = 0.5$, N and γ as shown.

γ	γ_{net}	N = 0.5	N = 0.67	N = 1	N = 1.5	N = 2
3	1.80	0.2	0.3	0.2	0.8	0.0
4	2.06	2.1	1.2	0.4	0.0	0.0
5	2.34	2.1	1.3	0.0	0.8	0.0

Table 3

Growth rates $\ln|z|$ for principal parametric instability of the most unstable mode for $l = 2$, usually the low-order g-modes g_1, g_2, or g_3; in homologous polytropes, for $q = 0.8\, q_{max}$, $w = 0.5$, N and γ as shown.

γ	γ_{net}	N = 0.5	N = 0.67	N = 1	N = 1.5	N = 2
3	1.80	0.2	0.3	0.1	1.1	0.0
4	2.06	2.1	3.1	2.0	1.1	0.1
5	2.34	3.2	3.3	3.2	2.4	0.2

Parametric resonances for $l = 2$ are weak or absent for polytropic index $N \geq 2$, or for adiabatic index $\gamma < 3$, so corresponding growth rates are not given in the tables.

[The homologous polytropes are convectively unstable for $N < 3$, according to the Schwarzschild criterion. Unstable convective modes do indeed show up in the numerical results. However these modes are short in wavelength (are high-order g-modes), have slow growth rates, and are present even in the absence of pulsation ($w = 0$), so that they can easily be distinguished from the global f-modes and low-order g-modes that are driven unstable by parametric resonance.]

The third result is that strong parametric resonance requires values of N and γ (or γ_{net}) to be "tuned" to appropriate ranges so that resonance conditions are satisfied for $n = 1$. In particular, strong resonance requires

$$N < 2, \text{ i.e. core cannot be too centrally condensed,} \tag{3.40}$$

and also

$$\gamma \geq 3 \text{ or } \gamma_{net} \geq 1.8, \text{ i.e. core must be stiff enough.} \tag{3.41}$$

These conditions are not satisfied in current numerical models of collapsing cores; in particular, cores tend to be a bit more centrally condensed. However the conditions are not violated by a great deal and we cannot conclude that actual cores of massive stars will not be tuned correctly for strong parametric resonance into quadrupole modes.

In unpublished work presented by Wilson (1979), Norman and Wilson looked for the existence of growth of asymmetry using a 2-dimensional time-dependent hydrodynamic code. The initial condition was a spherically symmetric, vigorously radially pulsating stellar model. They did find a range of parameters for which growth of quadrupole asphericity occurred, thus confirming the existence of the effect; from the time dependence of the asphericity it can be seen that the quadrupole mode is in n = 1 principal parametric resonance with the pulsation in their model.

Let us now return to the very important question of whether the cores actually bounce enough for large growth of quadrupole asymmetry to occur, even if the modes are in tune. To quantify the amount of bouncing, define the "total excursion" X of the core after the first instant of maximum compression,

$$X = \int |dR/R| = \Sigma |\Delta \ln R|, \text{ added up over all bounces.} \tag{3.42}$$

A simple upper limit to the growth of asymmetry, which is valid for parametric resonance in both homogeneous spheroids and in homologous polytropes, is

$$[\text{total growth of amplitude}] \lesssim \exp(bX) \tag{3.43}$$

where b measures the growth rate per bounce and, as in Eq. (3.42), X measures the total number of bounces. From Clark (1980), maximum values of b are

$$b \sim 1.5, \text{ low-order } l=2 \text{ g-modes in tune,} \tag{3.44a}$$

$$b \sim 1.0, \ l=2 \text{ f-mode (Kelvin mode) in tune.} \tag{3.44b}$$

Currently available hydrodynamic simulations of core collapse generally do show core pulsations going on for several cycles after initial collapse; however the amplitude is small. For instance, Wilson (1980) shows results which correspond to

$$X = 1.4 \tag{3.45}$$

while Van Riper (1979), in a hydrodynamic simulation set up to obtain maximum compression on initial infall, shows bounces which go on for ~10 cycles but amount only to

$$X = 2.0. \tag{3.46}$$

One must ask whether the strong damping observed in these numerical models is a real effect, or whether it is due to numerical viscosity. Wilson (private communication, 1980) feels on the basis of some numerical experiments that the damping seen in his model is probably real.

Brown, Bethe, and Baym (1982) argue by a simple model that core pulsations damp rapidly by emission of outgoing hydrodynamic waves; in the present notation their conclusion can be expressed as

$$X \lesssim 1 \text{ due to wave damping,} \tag{3.47}$$

which is roughly consistent with the numerical evidence.

From Eqs. (3.43-47) it follows that growth of asymmetry is probably not strong in current models of core collapse:

$$[\text{total growth of amplitude}] \lesssim 1.5 \text{ to } 3 \text{ e-folds,} \tag{3.48}$$

simply because the core does not have enough total excursion during its bouncing. <u>However</u>, growth of asymmetry can be very large in models which have only 2 to 3 times the total excursion of current models, because of the exponential in Eq. (3.43). In view of the uncertainties which remain in the models, the growth of asymmetry must certainly be kept in mind as a potentially very significant effect for emission of gravitational waves during core collapse.

3.5 FORMATION OF BLACK HOLES

If the shock is not strong enough to blow off the stellar envelope in the core collapse of a massive star, then a black hole will probably form on a timescale of ~1 sec, which is the timescale for neutrinos to diffuse out of the core, although detailed calculations of this process have not been made. If the distortion of the core away from spherical symmetry is small, then little gravitational radiation will be emitted during formation of the black hole. In the absence of rapid rotation or superstrong magnetic fields, the core will be nearly spherical when it finally collapses to a black hole, because it will have been static for ~1000 hydrodynamic times. A fairly good model of this collapse is the Oppenheimer-Snyder (1939) model of the spherical collapse of pressureless matter to form a nonrotating black hole; see Sect 3.6 below.

Rapidly rotating cores must certainly have a more interesting behavior. For collapse which remains axisymmetric, Nakamura and Sato (1982) have carried out fully general relativistic, 2-dimensional hydrodynamic numerical simulations. They find that for total core angular momentum less than about 95% of the maximum possible value for a rotating (Kerr) black hole,

$$J \lesssim 0.95\, M^2 \text{ (in units } c = 1 = G\text{),} \tag{3.49}$$

a black hole forms promptly; while for greater values of J, the core is able to support itself by centrifugal force and does not collapse immediately. Emission of gravitational radiation by such collapses has not been studied; it is reasonable to conjecture that efficiencies will be rather low (much less than g = 1%) when a black hole forms promptly.

What happens to a centrifugally supported core (high J) is not known. It is an excellent guess that it will eventually get rid of enough J to become a rotating black hole with $J < M^2$, but how and on what timescale is unclear. Such configurations have been studied in protostellar collapse, and it seems that if J is big enough cores will be unstable to non-axisymmetric modes and will evolve into rotating triaxial shapes or even fission into two or more smaller cores ("breakup"). Transient formation of a toroidal configuration is also possible.

Once a stationarily rotating core becomes nonaxisymmetric, it can emit gravitational radiation. One possibility is that gravitational radiation is the main source of angular momentum loss for the system; since a finite amount of angular momentum must be lost, a finite amount of gravitational radiation must be emitted. Another possibility is that angular momentum can be carried away by some matter spun off the system; experience with mass transfer binaries shows that most of the total angular momentum can be lost by ejection of a fairly small proportion of the total matter content. In this case there is no reason for much gravitational radiation to be emitted.

If indeed gravitational radiation is the main means of angular momentum loss, then a core with J substantially exceeding the value for breakup will have an efficiency for gravitational wave emission on the same order as that for final decay of a neutron star/neutron star binary (see Sect. 4.4 below), $g \sim 1\%$. This is the "collapse, pursuit and plunge" scenario of Ruffini and Wheeler (see MTW, Chap. 36), which has not been studied in detail.

3.6 PERTURBATIONS OF PRESSURELESS SPHERICAL COLLAPSE

To study the gravitational radiation given off by a collapsing star which forms a black hole without bouncing, Cunningham, Moncrief, and Price (1978, 1979) looked at perturbations of pressureless spherical collapse. For a summary, see Moncrief, Cunningham, and Price (1980). Strictly speaking, their results apply only to nearly spherical collapse, when the efficiency is very small; however these results are likely to give qualitatively correct information about efficiencies and waveforms even at large distortion, so long as both pressure support and centrifugal support are unimportant outside the event horizon, that is, so long as the matter goes straight down the hole without stopping. This is possible only if the mass of the core is sufficiently great, because degeneracy and nuclear repulsion are always important sources of pressure support for masses near the Chandrasekhar limit. Therefore I will quote their results normalized to a black hole mass M of $10M_\odot$, although they apply also for much larger masses. It is helpful to remember that in everyday units,

$$M_\odot = 0.005 \text{ msec}, \quad M_\odot^{-1} = 200 \text{ kHz} \tag{3.50ab}$$

Cunningham, Moncrief, and Price considered rotational (odd-parity) perturbations of spherical collapse in first order, and also the even-parity perturbations which are induced in second order as centrifugal distortions due to the first-order rotation. The waveform of gravitational waves emitted resembles that from a test particle falling into a black hole (see Sect. 4.2 below), in that it is dominated by ringing in the quasi-normal modes of the black hole, principally in the leading mode. Most of the power appears in a couple of cycles of damped oscillation with a period

$$P \approx 20M \approx 1 \text{ msec } (M/10M_\odot) \tag{3.51}$$

so that the spectral power dE/df is broadly peaked at a frequency f of

$$f \approx 0.05\, M^{-1} \approx 1 \text{ kHz } (M/10M_\odot)^{-1}. \tag{3.52}$$

The efficiency turns out to be, for the second order even parity distortion,

$$g = (1.9\%)(J/M^2)^4; \tag{3.53}$$

strictly speaking these results only apply for $J \ll M^2$. For J/M^2 finite but significantly less than 1, the reasonable conjecture is that the efficiency is about that given in Eq. (3.53), but that the waveform, period and frequency are dominated by the quasi-normal modes of a rotating hole of that J and M.

3.7 RECOIL IN GRAVITATIONAL COLLAPSE

As already mentioned in Section 2, momentum as well as energy is carried off by a gravitational wave. This has potentially significant astrophysical implications. For instance, pulsars have proper motions which imply space velocities of up to about 570 km/sec (Manchester and Taylor 1977). One certain contributor to these velocities is binary breakup due to supernova explosions; but it is interesting to consider other possible causes of these space velocities, among them gravity wave recoil (however in the author's opinion this is unlikely to be an important cause). Begelman, Blandford and Rees (1980) pointed out that supermassive black holes could be kicked out of galactic nuclei by gravity wave recoil during their formation, assuming that they can form there. Bekenstein (1973) suggested that the "runaway OB stars", a certain class of massive young stars with anomalously large proper motions, might have silent black hole binary companions; and that these companions, and hence the binary system, could have received such a kick during the gravitational collapse that created the black hole (there is at present no direct evidence in favor of this idea).

In the slow motion approximation, recoil appears as the result of interference between certain pairs of multipoles; see Thorne, lectures in these proceedings. The dominant contributions, (in powers of 1/c) comes from the (even-parity quadrupole) x (even parity octupole) term and also the (even-parity quadrupole) x (odd parity quadrupole) term; however the latter often vanishes due to symmetry. For the former contribution, the magnitude of the recoil is

$$v = (4/7)^{1/2}\ |\text{overlap integral}|\ (g_2 g_3)^{1/2} \tag{3.54}$$

where g_2 is net energy efficiency in even-parity quadrupole waves, g_3 is ditto in octupole waves, and the overlap integral is between the first time derivatives of the asymptotic (1/r) quadrupole and octopole wave amplitudes, normalized so that the integral is unity of the amplitudes are equal as functions of time.

In exact general relativity, if $dE/d\Omega$ is the energy per steradian emitted to infinity as a function of direction, then the component of momentum along any particular axis that is emitted to infinity is given by the obvious formula

$$p = \quad d\Omega \cos\theta\, dE/d\Omega, \tag{3.55}$$

where θ is angle between the emission direction and the axis in question.

Available calculations on gravitational wave recoil in collapse apply only to the case of collapse to a black hole. On the basis of crude but plausible estimates of the even-parity quadrupole and octupole efficiencies, Bekenstein (1973) finds

$$v \lesssim 300 \text{ km/sec.} \tag{3.56}$$

This is large enough to be very important for a galactic object such as a binary; it is of the same order as escape velocity from a galaxy or galactic nucleus.

Moncrief (1979) calculated, for odd-parity wave emission from the perturbed pressureless collapse results of Cunningham, Moncrief and Price (reviewed above),

$$v \approx (300 \text{ km/sec})(g/1\%) \tag{3.57}$$

where g is the total efficiency, $g = g_2 + g_3$. Since the best efficiency for direct collapse to a black hole may well be on the order of 1% (except perhaps for very rapidly rotating holes), Eqs. (3.56) and (3.57) are, at least roughly, quite consistent with each other.

3.8 SUMMARY OF GRAVITATIONAL WAVES IN CORE COLLAPSE

Spherical collapse in general relativity has zero efficiency g for gravitational radiation. It is possible, but far from clear, that Type II supernovae always involve spherically symmetric cores.

Collapse which is distorted although nonrotating might produce $g \sim 1\%$, if the distortion is big enough to cause a strongly asymmetric bounce at neutron star densities. Wilson (1980) discusses some fully relativistic 2-dimensional hydrodynamic calculations by himself and Smarr of such collapses. In collapse of cores of massive stars, if distorted but nonrotating, the fairly great heat content in the form of trapped neutrinos probably prevents the core from achieving neutron star densities, and the efficiency is conjecturally lower, $g \sim (0.01 - 0.1)\%$?

Rotating cores, for J less than the critical value J_b for breakup, may have efficiencies of $\sim 1\%(J/J_b)^4$ at cold neutron star densities; or, again, for "hot" collapse, the efficiencies are probably a couple of orders of magnitude smaller (as found by Saenz and Shapiro; see Sect. 3.3 above).

The efficiency may not drop off at all with J for $J < J_b$, _if_ the growth of asymmetry found by Saenz and Shapiro in fact occurs. There is reason to doubt that growth of asymmetry occurs in core collapse models of Type II supernovae, as they are presently understood. However, the last word is still not in on these models.

Rapidly rotating cores with $J > J_b$ are not understood in detail theoretically; see Wiita and Press (1976) for discussion of their equilibria and stability. Fission into two or more compact objects may well occur for sufficiently great J, and the efficiency may well be high, $g \gtrsim 1\%$. More work on this case would be most welcome. In particular, Saenz and Shapiro (1981) show the efficiency as dropping off steeply for J increasing above J_b; it may well be that a more complete investigation of the problem, allowing for slow triaxial distortion, fission into a tight binary, and subsequent evolution, would show high efficiency even at large J. It may be that processes which involve a black hole rotating at very close to the maximal rate ($J \approx M^2$) will have the highest efficiencies; see Detweiler (1979).

There is no direct astrophysical evidence that cores have properties which would endow them with high efficiency for gravitational waves at formation; see Katz (1980) for an interesting discussion on this point. But the uncertainties are very great; especially so because there may be several quite different kinds of neutron star or black hole formation events in nature, with some of them emitting virtually no gravitational waves, and others emitting much.

I have been emphasizing the efficiency g in this Section. The relation between g and dimensionless amplitude h for core collapse involving $\sim 1M_\odot$ is

$$h \sim (10^{-21})(g/1\%)^{1/2}(10 \text{ Mpc}/D) \tag{3.58}$$

where D is distance from earth; D ~ 10 Mpc at the Virgo Cluster of galaxies, out to which distance the event rate for stellar collapses ought to be ~ 1/yr. The frequency spectrum of events discussed in this section peaks below 2 kHz in all cases for which it is known. There is a notable tendency (which may partly due to the author's prejudice) for the strongest sources discussed here to have fairly high Q, that is to be quasi-periodic and have strongly peaked frequency spectra, perhaps

$$\Delta f/f \sim 0.1 \text{ ?} \tag{3.59}$$

though the peak frequency may change secularly with time (e.g. as a tight binary decays).

Even if stellar collapse produces gravitational waves with high efficiency only rarely, prospects for detection are not necessarily bad; however it will be necessary to increase sensitivity of detectors in order to detect these rare events at greater range. Since volume of space, and therefore event rate, increases as D^3, it is only necessary to increase sensitivity by the cube root of the proportion of rare events (cf. Eq. 3.58). For instance, if only one out of a thousand stellar collapses produces strong gravity waves, but if these events have g = 1%, then the sensitivity necessary for an event rate of 1 detection/yr is $h = 10^{-22}$, compared to $h = 10^{-21}$ necessary if <u>all</u> stellar collapses have g = 1%. An order of magnitude increase in sensitivity takes great effort to achieve (see the lectures by Blair, Drever, and Michelson in these proceedings), but this is some reason for optimism.

4. EMISSION OF GRAVITATIONAL WAVES BY COMPACT OBJECTS

This Section discusses emission of gravitational waves by already-formed neutron stars and black holes. Most of the available results treat small excitations such as infall of low-mass objects, and are derived from perturbation theory. Perturbation theory fails for the most spectacular events, collisions of nearly equally massive neutron stars or black holes, although extrapolation of the results of perturbation theory provides some idea of what to expect for collisions. Much of this material is already very well reviewed in the literature, so that the treatment will often be brief.

4.1 GRAVITATIONAL WAVES FROM NEUTRON STARS

Oscillations of neutron stars can be treated by standard techniques of stellar perturbation theory, with one essential generalization: Oscillations of the star in general generate gravitational waves which carry energy off to infinity and damp the motion. Fully general relativistic perturbation theory is used to compute normal modes and their damping times (see e.g. Thorne 1975).

If the time dependence of a mode is $\exp(-i\omega t)$, with ω a complex angular frequency, then the real part of ω gives the frequency of oscillation,

$$f = \mathrm{Re}\,\omega/2\pi \sim (G\rho)^{1/2}/2\pi \sim (GM/Rc^2)^{3/2}(c^3/GM) \tag{4.1a}$$

$$\sim 1 \text{ Hz for a white dwarf,} \tag{4.1b}$$

$$\sim 1 \text{ kHz for a neutron star,} \tag{4.1c}$$

$$\sim 10 \text{ kHz } (M_\odot/M) \text{ for a black hole.} \tag{4.1d}$$

Nonradial modes with angular momentum quantum number $l \geq 2$ will couple to gravitational radiation; then the damping of the mode due to gravitational waves, as described by $\mathrm{Im}\,\omega$, is

$$2\,\mathrm{Im}\,\omega/\mathrm{Re}\,\omega \sim L_{GW}/L_{int} \sim (GM/Rc^2)^{5/2} \tag{4.2}$$

and the damping time t_d is then given by

$$t_d = 1/2\pi\,\mathrm{Im}\,\omega \sim (GM/Rc^2)^{-4}(GM/c^3) \tag{4.3a}$$

$$\sim \text{years for a white dwarf (other damping mechanisms will certainly dominate)} \tag{4.3b}$$

$$\sim 0.1 \text{ sec for a neutron star,} \tag{4.3c}$$

$$\gtrsim 0.1 \text{ msec } (M/M_\odot) \text{ for a black hole.} \tag{4.3d}$$

A sample of normal mode frequencies for cold neutron stars as calculated by Detweiler and by Thorne (see Thorne 1975) are displayed in Table 3.

Table 3
Examples of quadrupole ($l = 2$) normal modes of cold neutron stars, as described in text.

M ($M_\odot$)	ω (sec^{-1})	f (Hz)	t_d (sec)
0.37	7930 -0.3i	1260	1.7
0.86	12130 - 3i	1930	0.17
1.63	18070 - 12i	2880	0.04

Excitation of normal modes can happen during formation of the neutron star in nonspherical core collapse. In this case the neutron star will still be hot enough over the first ~ 1 sec, because of trapped neutrinos, that its normal mode frequencies will be significantly lowered. Neutrinos may also damp the oscillations (Kazanas and Schramm 1979).

Normal modes could be excited in a cold neutron star by some internal disturbance such as a crustquake, corequake, or phase change (see Schumaker and Thorne 1982, Ramaty et al. 1980). The amount of energy released will be very small compared to that in a core collapse ($E \sim 10^{-9}$ to 10^{-5} Mc^2 ??) but these events could still be detectable on earth because they may occur at ranges of $D \sim 1$ kpc with significant event rates.

Impact of small bodies such as asteroids or comets on neutron stars is not likely to be an interesting source of normal mode excitation. The collision is almost perfectly inelastic because of the "impedance mismatch" between two bodies of very different masses, $M \sim 1M_\odot$ and $\mu \sim 10^{-15}$ $M_\odot$,

$$E_{total} \sim (GM/Rc^2)\mu c^2 \sim \mu c^2, \tag{4.4a}$$

$$E_{osc} \sim (\mu/M)E_{total} \sim (\mu/M)^2 Mc^2, \tag{4.4b}$$

where E_{osc} is the amount of energy coupled into stellar oscillations and therefore available for gravitational wave emission. See footnote 2.

4.2 GRAVITATIONAL WAVES FROM BLACK HOLES

The review by Detweiler (1979) on black hole perturbation theory is quite recent and complete; see it for further details and discussion of history of the subject.

Black holes also have normal modes, which are strongly damped by gravitational radiation; they are called "quasi-normal modes". They can be thought of as packets of gravitational radiation temporarily caught in the unstable photon orbit around a black hole, and their period is nearly that determined from the the photon orbit,

$$\text{Re}\,\omega/l \simeq 2\pi/(\text{period of photon orbit}) \tag{4.5a}$$

$$\simeq 1/27^{1/2}M \text{ for } J = 0 \tag{4.5b}$$

$$\simeq 1/2M \text{ for } J = M^2. \tag{4.5c}$$

Here ω is again the complex angular frequency of the mode, l is its total angular momentum ($l = 2$ means quadrupole, and so forth); and M is mass of black hole, J is angular momentum of black hole. Table 4 displays some normal modes of black holes; notation is same as for Table 3.

Table 4
Normal mode frequencies of black holes (see Detweiler 1979).
Shown are the frequencies for the $l = m = 2$ corotating quasi-normal mode that is most slowly damped.

J/M^2	ω ($10M_\odot/M$ sec^{-1})	f ($10M_\odot/M$ Hz)	t_d ($M/10M_\odot$ msec)
0.	7500 - 1800i	1200	0.28
0.5	9400 - 1700i	1500	0.29
0.9	14000 - 1300i	2200	0.38
0.99	19000 - 700i	3000	0.71
1.	20000 - 0i	3200	(becomes large)

These numbers are normalized to a black hole mass of $10M_{\odot}$. The most striking point is that the Q becomes very large as the black hole approaches the maximum possible value of angular momentum, $J = M^2$.

There have been many perturbation calculations of the gravitational waves emitted by a small particle of mass μ falling into a black hole of mass M and angular momentum J, $\mu << M$. The energy efficiency for gravitational radiation depends very much on whether the particle goes straight into the hole without orbiting ("plunge orbits") or whether it starts off in a stable orbit around the hole, which then slowly decays ("bound orbit"). By linearity of the perturbation theory, once results are computed for a single particle, waves can be superposed for any distribution of mass falling into the hole, so long as the total mass of the distribution is small enough.

For "plunge" orbits, the total efficiency is of order $(\mu/M)^2$, so that only a fraction (μ/M) of the rest mass energy of the infalling particle is radiated; the remainder is swallowed by the hole as kinetic energy of infall. This small efficiency can be viewed as due to impedance mismatch, just as in the case of a small mass falling onto a neutron star. Here the efficiency is defined with respect to the total mass energy of the system. The efficiency is of the form

$$\begin{aligned} g &= E/(M+\mu) \\ &= (\mu/M)^2 f(J/M^2, \text{orbit}) \end{aligned} \tag{4.6}$$

where f is a dimensionless function of dimensionless variables which may be computed from the perturbation wave equations.

Several recent calculations of gravitational waves from distributions of matter falling into black holes (Nakamura and Sasaki 1981, Haugen, Shapiro and Wasserman 1981, Shapiro and Wasserman 1981) have found a lack of coherence that depresses the efficiency when the matter takes the form of an extended distribution of total mass μ which takes a long time $T >> M$ to fall down. Then the efficiency is of order

$$g \sim (M/T)(\mu/M)^2 \tag{4.7a}$$

$$\sim (T/M)(\mu M/TM)^2 \tag{4.7b}$$

where the form of Eq. (4.7b) indicates that one can think of this process as the separate and incoherent infall of some number $\sim(T/M)$ of separate mass distributions, each of mass $(\mu M/T)$, and each with its own efficiency, Eq. (4.6).

The efficiencies for plunge orbits into nonrotating holes are as follows. For a particle falling straight in with no angular momentum (Davis, Ruffini, Press, and Price 1971),

$$g = 0.01\ (\mu/M)^2; \tag{4.8a}$$

for a particle which has 97.5% of the specific angular momentum that would be necessary to go into stable orbit, so that it spirals through about one complete revolution around the hole before plunging in (Detweiler 1979),

$$g = 0.50\ (\mu/M)^2. \tag{4.8b}$$

The waveforms are generally dominated by the $l = 2$ quasi-normal mode of the black hole (cf. Table 4). It is regrettable that no recoil velocities v have been computed for any of these processes. Recoil velocities are straightforward to calculate from e.g. Eq. (3.54) when multipole waveforms at infinity are available, or from Eq. (3.55) when the gravitational wave energy distribution over the sphere at infinity is known. For instance, Davis, Ruffini and Tiomno (1972) published waveforms and energy distributions for the straight-in plunge orbit into a nonrotating black hole, and from their energy distribution over the sphere at infinity one can roughly estimate the recoil velocity as

$$v \sim 10^{-3} (\mu/M)^2 \tag{4.9}$$

Experts in black-hole perturbation theory are urged to publish recoil velocities as well as energy efficiencies. For further discussion of recoil, see Fitchett (1982) and Sects. 3.7 above, 4.4 below.

Complete results for plunge orbits into rotating holes are not available, although efficiencies may be expected to be higher for prograde orbits.

For bound orbits, in which the particle cannot fall into the black hole until it has lost enough energy to descend to the innermost stable orbit, the efficiency per orbit is still of order $(\mu/M)^2$, but the particle undergoes of order (M/μ) orbits before it falls down the hole, so that the total efficiency is of order (μ/M). In fact, just from the binding energies of the innermost stable particle orbits about black holes, the total efficiency for a particle that starts out in a distant circular orbit and slowly spirals in is

$$g_{total} = 6\% \; (\mu/M) \text{ for } J = 0 \tag{4.10a}$$

$$g_{total} = 42\% \; (\mu/M) \text{ for prograde orbit and } J = M^2. \tag{4.10b}$$

In this case the efficiency per orbit can be computed from the wave equations,

$$g \text{ per orbit} = (\mu/M)^2 f(J/M^2, \text{orbit}) \tag{4.11}$$

parallel to Eq. (4.6). Waveforms for circular bound orbits generally have the periodicity of the orbit; there is a trend toward a waveform consisting of a sharp spike once a period as J approaches M^2.

4.3 COLLISIONS OF NEUTRON STARS WITH EACH OTHER

Neutron stars and black holes might collide with each other at the endpoint of binary decay due to gravitational radiation, in very dense star clusters, or in a transient tight binary formed in the collapse of a rapidly rotating stellar core. Collision events form an interesting class of possible gravitational wave sources because they probably have very high efficiencies, $g \gtrsim 1\%$, since the impedance match is good and the collision is highly nonspherical; but one has only the roughest idea of the event rate for any of the collision processes just mentioned (see Clark 1979).

Perturbation theory cannot be used when two bodies of roughly equal masses collide with each other. Available results on collisions of compact objects with each other come from numerical simulations, extrapolations of perturbation theory (a reckless but tempting course), rough guesswork, and judicious combinations of all of these.

For collisions of neutron stars, Shapiro (1980) estimates g ~ 1%, based on some numerical calculations of a hydrodynamical model in one space and one time dimension. Wilson and Smarr also carried out some unpublished 2+1 dimensional calculations of colliding neutron stars (see Wilson 1979 for the code).

For final decay of the orbit of a neutron star/neutron star binary, Clark and Eardley (1977) carried out some crude estimates. The efficiency for gravitational radiation was about g = 0.5%, while the efficiency for neutrino pair emission was about four times this big. The waveform was periodic with a slowly changing frequency, which might range up to ~ 2 - 3 kHz.

Neutron star collisions might also emit observable x- or γ-rays, or optical radiation. The efficiencies might be very low for these, but instruments are much more sensitive to electromagnetic radiation than gravitational or neutrino radiation. It is an interesting speculation that some Type I supernovas could be decaying neutron star binaries.

For collisions of one neutron star and one black hole, the neutron star will be tidally disrupted if the black hole mass is less than a few $M_\odot$. For greater black hole mass there will be no disruption and the collision will resemble the collision of two black holes with corresponding masses (cf. Lattimer and Schramm 1974).

4.4 COLLISIONS OR BLACK HOLES WITH EACH OTHER

Eppley and Smarr (see Smarr 1979a), in a major project in numerical relativity, calculated what happens when two equally massive, nonrotating black holes collide head on in general relativity. The product is a single larger nonrotating black hole and gravitational radiation amounting to an efficiency of roughly

$$g \sim 0.07\%. \tag{4.12}$$

There is no recoil because of symmetry under parity reversal. If two nonrotating black holes of unequal masses m_1 and m_2 collide head-on, the efficiency is probably smaller but the recoil will be finite because the symmetry is broken. In the limit that either mass goes to zero with the other held finite, perturbation theory applies; Eqs. (4.8a) and (4.9) then give the results.

It is tempting to extrapolate the perturbation theory results. Smarr (1979a and references cited therein) suggested an extrapolation scheme whereby the black hole mass M in perturbation theory should be replaced by the total mass in the two black hole problem, and the particle mass μ should be replaced by the reduced mass in this problem:

$$M = m_1 + m_2 \tag{4.13a}$$
$$\mu = m_1 m_2/(m_1 + m_2) \tag{4.13b}$$

These equations are motivated by the special case of Newtonian orbits for the masses and quadrupole formula for gravitational wave emission; in this case they give the correct extrapolation.

This extrapolation has been used by Smarr (1979a) and Detweiler (1979) to guess energy efficiencies g, starting from e.g. Eqs. (4.8) and (4.9). Define a dimensionless mass ratio x,

$$m_1 \equiv xM, \; m_2 \equiv (1-x)M, \; 0 \leq x \leq 1. \qquad (4.14abc)$$

Then Eq. (4.6) becomes

? $$g = x^2(1-x)^2 \; f(\text{rotation of hole, orbit}), \qquad (4.15)$$

while Eqs. (4.8ab) become estimates for coalescence of nonrotating black holes,

? $$g = (0.0007)[16x^2(1-x)^2], \text{ head-on collision}, \qquad (4.16a)$$

? $$g = (0.03)[16x^2(1-x)^2], \text{ nearly enough orbital angular momentum to go into orbit before coalescing.} \qquad (4.16b)$$

The polynomial $x^2(1-x)^2$ is symmetric about $x = 1/2$ (equal masses) as it ought to be by inversion symmetry; it has its maximum value at $x = 1/2$, there taking the value 1/16. The quantity in square brackets [] is normalized to have maximum value 1.

As Smarr (1979a) pointed out, Eq. (4.16a) predicts g = 0.0625%, in good agreement with Eq. (4.12) as determined by numerical relativity; this agreement encourages belief in the extrapolation. Eq. (4.16b) then predicts g = 3% for the once-around coalescence of two equally massive black holes (Detweiler 1979).

Recently, Fitchett (1982) has applied a similar extrapolation to gravitational wave recoil estimates. In the case of Newtonian orbits for the masses and lowest order multipoles for the gravitational wave recoil (cf. Eq. 3.54) he finds for the recoil

$$v = x^2(1-x)^2(1-2x) \; f'(\text{orbit}) \qquad (4.17)$$

where f′ is another dimensionless function. He therefore suggests that this formula can be extrapolated to compact object encounters, with f′ being evaluated by black hole perturbation theory, in the same spirit as Eq. (4.15) for energy. As a function of x, this formula is antisymmetric about $x = 1/2$, as it should by inversion symmetry. The polynomial $x^2(1-x)^2(1-2x)$ has its extrema at $x = 0.28$, $x = 0.72$ where it takes the values ±0.018. Here the results from perturbation theory are not known (see Sect. 4.2) but a crude guess, parallel to Eqs. (4.16), would be

??? $$v \sim (2\times10^{-5})[x^2(1-x)^2(1-2x)/0.018], \text{ head-on} \qquad (4.18a)$$

??? $$v \sim (10^{-3})[x^2(1-x)^2(1-2x)/0.018], \text{ nearly orbit}, \qquad (4.18b)$$

for coalescences of nonrotating black holes. Again the quantity [] is normalized to have absolute value 1 at its extrema.

The orbital decay of two nonrotating black holes from a distant circular orbit is harder to approximate in perturbation theory, because no simple way exists to judge how fast the orbit shrinks and when it loses stability. Clark and Eardley (1977) gave a crude estimate of the binding energy at the last stable orbit for two objects (for instance black holes) of comparable masses; they suggest 2% for maximum binding of equally massive object before loss of orbital stability. This 2% must come out in gravitational waves while the orbit is stably decaying. Another few % might come out in the final plunge and coalescence (cf. Eq. 4.16b). The recoil might be the same as Eq. (4.18b). These considerations suggest for the orbital decay and coalescence of two nonrotating black holes of comparable masses,

$$? \quad g \sim (2\%)[2\min(x,1-x)] + (3\%)[16x^2(1-x)^2], \tag{4.19a}$$

$$??? \quad v \sim (10^{-3})[x^2(1-x)^2(1-2x)/0.018]. \tag{4.19b}$$

For coalescences of rapidly rotating holes, spin-orbit and spin-spin couplings come into play. Since results in perturbation theory tend to give higher efficiencies for rapidly rotating holes than nonrotating ones, there is reason to hope that efficiencies will be higher here too (Detweiler 1979).

5. BINARY SYSTEMS

In Newtonian gravity, the two body system is exactly soluble. Bound orbits are ellipses of semimajor axis $\underline{a}$ and eccentricity e; these are related to the conserved energy E and conserved angular momentum J by

$$E = GM\mu/2a, \tag{5.1a}$$

$$J = \mu[GMa(1-e^2)]^{1/2}, \tag{5.1b}$$

where M and μ are total and reduced mass (Eqs. 4.13). The orbital period is

$$P_b = 2\ (GM/a^3)^{-1/2}. \tag{5.1c}$$

5.1 DECAY OF THE ORBIT DUE TO GRAVITATIONAL WAVES IN GENERAL RELATIVITY

In his lectures, Thorne reviewed the formulas for energy and angular momentum loss from an isolated system due to gravitational waves. For a binary system in which the orbital velocities are much less than the speed of light, only the lowest radiatable multipoles contribute. In particular, the energy loss is dominated by the even-parity quadrupole, which is given by the famous quadrupole formula. Damour summarized the equations of motion in general relativity, and described the recent results of Deruelle and Damour which give a complete account of all terms in the equations of motion up to third order in G for slow motion problems, including explicit expressions for energy and angular momentum. This author is not an expert on equations of motion, but he hopes that the controversy about the validity of the quadrupole formula as applied to slow motion binary systems is coming to and end, with the answer being, as most physicists have been willing to believe all along, that the formula is valid.

Applying these results to a binary system gives rates of change of orbital period and orbital eccentricity as (Peters and Mathews 1963)

$$P_b^{-1}\, dP_b/dt = -\,(96G^3/5c^5)\ \mu M^2/a^4\ (1+73e^2/24+37e^4/96)(1-e^2)^{-7/2}, \qquad (5.2a)$$

$$e^{-1}\, de/dt = -\,(304G^3/15c^5)\ \mu M^2/a^4\ (1+121e^2/304)(1-e^2)^{-5/2}. \qquad (5.2b)$$

In astrophysical units, the period decay is

$$P_b^{-1}\, dP_b/dt = -(1/2.62\text{x}10^7\ \text{yr})(\mu/M_\odot)(M/M_\odot)^{2/3}(P_b/1^h)^{-8/3} \cdot(1+73e^2/24+37e^4/96)(1-e^2)^{-7/2}. \qquad (5.3)$$

If the orbit is circular ($e = 0$), the gravitational wave signal is at a frequency $2/P_b$ (2 because the wave is quadrupole), and the amplitude at a detector is

$$h = 7\text{x}10^{-21}(\mu/M_\odot)(M/M_\odot)^{2/3}(P_b/1^h)^{-2/3}(100\ \text{pc}/D), \qquad (5.4)$$

where D is distance. Of known binaries with periods from 1^h to 10^h, several exist giving amplitudes

$$h \sim 10^{-22}\ \text{to}\ 10^{-20}\quad \text{at frequencies}\ f \sim 10^{-4}\ \text{Hz}; \qquad (5.5)$$

see Douglass and Braginsky (1979).

The final decay of hypothetical neutron star/neutron star binaries forms a possible source of detectable gravitational wave sources at higher frequencies (CLark and Eardley 1977; Sect. 4.3 above). One day before final decay, the frequency f would be about 1 Hz, the amplitude h about 10^{-23} at D = 10Mpc, and the Q about 1000. One second before decay, $f \sim 100$ Hz, $h \sim 10^{-21}$, and $Q \sim 100$. The source has an efficiency $\varepsilon \sim 1\%$ and a maximum frequency of 1 or 2 kHz. Similar comments apply to binaries containing black holes. White dwarfs will be disrupted or begin to lose mass at periods of about a second in such a binary; main sequence stars at periods of 1 hour or more.

5.2 THE BINARY PULSAR PSR 1913+16

The first radio pulsar to be found in a binary system was discovered by Hulse and Taylor (1975). Two others have since been discovered, but these two have longer periods and seem much less interesting for tests of relativity, although they raise some interesting astrophysical problems.

The binary system containing PSR 1913+16 is tight, although not nearly the tightest known. It is an extremely clean system, in that there are no signs of any forces acting except gravity. Other tight binaries often have mass exchange, accretion and tidal coupling going on, accompanied by messy forces which swamp the very small relativistic effects that are observed in PSR 1913+16. The system can be treated as a classical single-line spectroscopic binary, with doppler shift of the pulsar pulse period (~59 msec) playing the role of spectral line doppler shift in optical astronomy. The latest reported observations from Taylor and Weisberg (1982) give fantastically accurate values for parameters of the system determined from Newtonian gravity, for example,

$$e = 0.617139 \pm 0.000005, \tag{5.6a}$$

$$P_b = 27906.98161 \pm 0.00003 \text{ sec (at a specified epoch).} \tag{5.6b}$$

From the Newtonian reductions, one is missing two parameters to determine the system completely; these can be taken as the pulsar mass m_1 and the companion mass m_2. (The companion has never been observed.)

Three relativistic effects have been measured to useful accuracy (Taylor and Weisberg 1982); assuming that no nongravitational forces act, an assumption which has been discussed at length by a number of authors and seems reasonable although it cannot be proven, their interpretations are

$$\dot{\omega} = 4.2261 \pm 0.0007 \text{ deg/yr, periastron precession,} \tag{5.7a}$$

$$\gamma = 0.00438 \pm 0.00024 \text{ sec, gravitational redshift together with second order doppler shift,} \tag{5.7b}$$

$$dP_b/dt = -(2.30 \pm 0.22)\text{x}10^{-12} \text{ sec/sec, decay of binary period due to gravitational wave damping.} \tag{5.7c}$$

The first two effects are consistently interpreted as $O(c^{-2})$ relativistic effects; using formulas for theoretical prediction of these effects then allows the orbital parameters and masses of the system to be determined completely (Taylor and Weisberg 1982), e.g.

$$m_1 = 1.42 \pm 0.06\ M_\odot, \tag{5.8a}$$

$$m_2 = 1.41 \pm 0.06\ M_\odot. \tag{5.8b}$$

Using the values given by Eqs. (5.8) and (5.6) in the theoretical formula for gravitational wave damping, Eqs. (5.2a,3), gives a prediction for orbital decay (Taylor, Fowler, and McCulloch 1979, Taylor and Weisberg 1982)

$$dP_b/dt = -(2.403 \pm 0.005)\text{x}10^{-12} \text{ sec/sec.} \tag{5.9}$$

The observations of orbital decay, Eq. (5.7c), are wonderfully consistent with the prediction of the quadrupole formula for gravitational wave damping of the orbit in general relativity theory. The observational errors should decrease steadily with time, with marked improvements over several years. Furthermore, a separate group of radio astronomers, based at Cornell University, is setting out to observe and determine the parameters of the system in order to confirm independently this important result. See footnote 3.

5.3 DECAY OF THE ORBIT DUE TO GRAVITATIONAL WAVES IN OTHER THEORIES OF GRAVITY

Tests of theories of gravity have been reviewed extensively in the recent book by Will (1982), including tests by means of gravitational radiation and the binary pulsar; the reader should consult this book for a complete discussion. This Section will make some brief comments on the subject, in light of the topics at this Summer School.

In Damour's lectures, the nature of relativistic corrections to the Newtonian approximation for the motion of two compact bodies in general relativity was discussed. Since the bodies are compact, e.g. neutron stars, we must keep a full strong field but quasi-static description of the bodies, up to "all powers of c". Only the orbit may be expanded in an inverse power series of rapidly decreasing terms in 1/c. Relativistic effects first appear at $O(c^{-2})$, such as periastron precession and gravitational redshift. Gravitational wave damping of the orbit first appears at $O(G^3c^{-5})$ (cf. Eqs. 5.2 above).

In other theories of gravity, perhaps in all other theories of gravity than general relativity, the story is completely different. Corrections to Newtonian theory first appear at $O(Gc^0)$ (!) in the orbit, and thus represent an order-unity correction to Newton's law of gravity between neutron stars (or black holes, when the theory admits them). The effect that appears is a violation of the equivalence principle for strongly self-gravitating bodies, which is called the Nordtvedt (1968) effect; this effect is $O(G/c^2)$ and $O(G^2/c^4)$ in the internal structure of the individual bodies; but as emphasized above, these orders are O(1) in the problem at hand. The Nordtvedt effect has been searched for, and not found at a level of 1% agreement with general relativity, by lunar laser ranging (see Will 1982). However, lunar laser ranging, like all presently feasible solar-system tests of gravity theory, only probes the $O(G/c^2)$ terms here; the $O(G^2/c^4)$ terms are far too small to measure. Both these terms are order unity in a neutron star binary, even a very distant one. Therefore it is necessary to carry out the reduction of system parameters in the binary pulsar, even the Newtonian ones, in a different way for other theories of gravity; the general relativistic or PPN formulas are not correct, although in individual cases they may be rather good approximations numerically.

Gravitational waves are also very different in other theories. Monopole and dipole waves can appear as well as quadrupole, and for neutron star binaries the dipole wave, which appears at $O(c^{-3})$ in the orbit, generally dominates the quadrupole wave (Eardley 1975, Will 1982, Taylor and Weisberg 1982). Therefore other theories of gravity tend to predict a rate of orbital decay several orders of magnitude larger than that observed for PSR 1913+16 (Eq. 5.7c), although the dipole wave vanishes by symmetry if the two bodies are identical. Even though the observed masses are equal in general relativity (Eqs. 5.8), they generally cannot be equal in other theories because of Nordtvedt-effect corrections to the reductions. Even for hypothesized equal masses, the quadrupole wave in other theories is different for neutron star binaries. At present, all other theories of gravity which are consistent with all solar system tests flunk the binary pulsar test.

5.4 SUMMARY

General relativity is beautifully consistent with observations of the binary pulsar by Taylor and collaborators. This test is not at conclusive as solar-system tests, simply because the system is very far away and in certain respects the experiment cannot be controlled completely. Some astrophysical assumptions have to be made about the system; while some are compelling and all are at least plausible, these assumptions cannot be independently checked. These limitations are simply part of the human condition as it applies to astronomers.

However, this test opens an entirely new regime of the theory of general relativity. It amounts to the indirect discovery of gravitational radiation; indirect, because the waves themselves are not detected, but their physical effect in removing energy from a system is observed. The direct discovery, observation, and astronomical exploitation of gravitational radiation remains by far the most important problem in experimental gravitation.

ACKNOWLEDGEMENTS

I thank the organizers of this summer school, N. Deruelle and T. Piran, for planning and running such an excellent meeting. For helpful comments and conversations I am very grateful to A. Ashtekar, J. Bardeen, D. Blair, C. Caves, T. Damour, R. Drever, M. Fitchett, M. Haugen, R. Hellings, R. Kates, P. Michelson, T. Nakamura, T. Piran, M. Rees, K. Thorne, M. Walker, and J.York. This work was supported in part by the National Science Foundation through Grant No. PHY80-07351 to Harvard University.

REFERENCES

Abraham, R. and Marsden, J. 1967, Fundamentals of Mechanics (New York: Benjamin).
Abramowitz, M. and Stegun, I. A. 1964, Handbook of Mathematical Functions (Washington: U. S. Government Printing Office).
Arnett, W. D. 1979, "Gravitational Collapse of Evolved Stars as a Problem in Physics", in: Smarr, L. L. (ed.), Sources of Gravitational Radiation (London: Cambridge University Press, 1979).
Arnol'd, V. I. 1980, Mathematical Methods of Classical Mechanics (New York: Springer).
Arnol'd, V. I. and Avez, A. 1968, Ergodic Problems of Classical Mechanics (New York: Benjamin), Appendix 29.
Bardeen, J. M., Carter, B. and Hawking, S. W. 1973, Commun. Math. Phys. 31, 181.
Begelman, M. C., Blandford, R. D. and Rees, M. J. 1980, Nature 287, 307.
Bekenstein. J. 1973, Astrophys. J. 183, 657.
Braginsky, V. B. and Douglass, D. H. 1979, "Gravitational Radiation Experiments", in: Hawking, S. W. and Israel, W. (eds.), General Relativity: An Einstein Centenary Survey (London: Cambridge University Press, 1979).
Brown, G. E., Bethe, H. A. and Baym, G. 1982, Physica Scripta
Chandrasekhar, S. 1939, Stellar Structure (Chicago: University of Chicago Press).
Clark, J. P. A. 1979, "The Role of Binaries in Gravitational Wave Production", in: Smarr, L. L. (ed.), Sources of Gravitational Radiation (London: Cambridge University Press, 1979).
Clark, J. P. A. 1979, unpublished work toward a Ph. D. thesis, Yale University.
Clark, J. P. A. 1980, unpublished work toward a Ph. D. thesis, Yale University.
Clark, J. P. A. and Eardley, D. M. 1977, Astrophys. J. 215, 311.
Cox, J. 1980, Theory of Stellar Pulsation (Princeton: Princeton University Press).
Cunningham, C. T., Price, R. H. and Moncrief, V. 1978, Astrophys. J. 224, 643.
Cunningham, C. T., Price, R. H. and Moncrief, V. 1979, Astrophys. J. 230, 870.
Davis, M., Ruffini R., Press, W. H. and Price, R. H. 1971, Phys. Rev. Lett. 27, 1466.
Davis, M., Ruffini, R. and Tiomno, J. 1972, Phys. Rev. D5, 2932.
Detweiler, S. L. 1979, "Black Holes and Gravitational Waves: Perturbation Analysis", in: Smarr, L. L. (ed.), Sources of Gravitational Radiation (London: Cambridge University Press, 1979).
Detweiler, S. and Lindblom, L. 1981, Astrophys. J. 250, 739.
Douglass, D. H. and Braginsky, V. B. 1979, "Gravitational Radiation Experiments", in: Hawking, S. W. and Israel, W. (eds.), General Relativity: An Einstein Centenary Survey (London: Cambridge University Press, 1979).
Eardley, D. M. 1975, Astrophys. J. Lett. 196, L59.
Fitchett, M. 1982, preprint, Institute of Astronomy, Cambridge University.
Goldreich, P. and Weber, S. V. 1980, Astrophys. J. 238, 991.
Haugen, M. P., Shapiro, S. L. and Wasserman, I. 1981, "The Suppression of Gravitational Radiation from Finite-Size Stars Falling into Black Holes", Cornell University preprint CRSR 781.
Hawking, S. W. 1973, "The Event Horizon", in: DeWitt, B. and DeWitt, C. (eds.), Black Holes: Les Houches 1972 (New York: Gordon and Breach, 1973).
Hillebrandt, W. and Müller, E. 1981, Astron. Astrophys. 103, 147.

Hulse, R. A. and Taylor, J. H. 1975, Astrophys. J. Lett. 195, L51.
Katz, J. I. 1980, Nature 283, 551.
Kazanas, D. and Schramm, D. N. 1979, "Neutrino Competition with Gravitational Radiation during Collapse", in: Smarr, L. L. (ed.), Sources of Gravitational Radiation (London: Cambridge University Press, 1979).
Landau, L. D. and Lifshitz, E. M. 1975, The Classical Theory of Fields (Cambridge, MA: Addison-Wesley).
Landau, L. D. and Lifshitz, E. M. 1960, Mechanics (Oxford: Pergamon), Sect. 27.
Lattimer, J. M. and Schramm, D. N. 1974, Astrophys. J. Lett. 192, L145.
Manchester, R. N. and Taylor, J. H. 1977, Pulsars (San Francisco: Freeman).
Misner, C. W., Thorne, K. S. and Wheeler, J. A. 1973, Gravitation (San Francisco: Freeman).
Moncrief, V. 1979, Astrophys. J. 234, 628.
Moncrief, V., Cunningham, C. T. and Price, R. H. 1979, "Radiation from Slightly Nonspherical Models of Gravitational Collapse", in: Smarr, L. L. (ed.), Sources of Gravitational Radiation (London: Cambridge University Press, 1979).
Müller, E. and Hillebrandt, W. 1981, Astron. Astrophys. 103, 358.
Nakamura, T. and Sasaki, M. 1981, "Is Collapse of a Deformed Star Always Effectual for the Gravitational Radiation?" Kyoto University preprint RIFP-443.
Nakamura, T. and Sato, H. 1981, "General Relativistic Collapse of Rotating Supermassive Stars", Kyoto University preprint RIFP-441.
Nordtvedt, K. 1968, Phys. Rev. 169, 1014 and 169, 1017.
Oppenheimer, J. R. and Snyder, H. 1939, Phys. Rev. 56, 455.
Peters, P. C. and Mathews, J. 1963, Phys. Rev. 131, 435.
Press, W. H., and Thorne, K. S. 1972, Ann Rev. Astron. Astrophys. 10, 335.
Ramaty, R., Bonazzola, S., Cline, T. L., Kazanas, D., Mészáros, P., and Lingenfelter, R. E. 1980, Nature 287, 122.
Ruderman, M. L. 1972, Ann. Rev. Astron. Astrophys. 10, 427.
Saenz, R. A. and Shapiro, S. L. 1978, Astrophys. J. 221, 286.
Saenz, R. A. and Shapiro, S. L. 1979, Astrophys. J. 229, 1107.
Saenz, R. A. and Shapiro, S. L. 1981, Astrophys. J. 244, 1033.
Saenz, R. A. 1982, preprint.
Schumaker, B. L. and Thorne, K. S. 1982, "Torsional Oscillations of Neutron Stars", Caltech preprint OAP-640.
Schoen, R. and Yau, S.-T. 1979, Commun. Math. Phys. 65, 45.
Shapiro, S. L. 1980, Astrophys. J. 240, 246.
Shapiro, S. L. and Wasserman, I. 1981, "Gravitational Radiation from Nonspherical Infall into Black Holes", Cornell University preprint CRSR 783.
Smarr, L. L. 1979, Sources of Gravitational Radiation (London: Cambridge University Press).
Smarr, L. L. 1979a, "Gauge Conditions, Radiation Formulae, and the Two Black Hole Collision", in: Smarr, L. L. (ed.), Sources of Gravitational Radiation (London: Cambridge University Press, 1979).
Stellingwerf, R. F. 1974, Astrophys. J. 192, 139.
Taylor, J. H., Fowler, L. A. and McCulloch, P. M. 1979, Nature 277, 437.
Taylor, J. H. and Weisberg,J. M. 1982, Astrophys. J. 253, 908.
Thorne, K. S. 1975, "General Relativistic Astrophysics", in: Lebovitz, N. R., Reid, W. H. and Vandervoort P. O. (eds.), Theoretical Principles in Astrophysics and Relativity (Chicago: University of Chicago Press, 1978).
Thorne, K. S. 1977, "The Generation of Gravitational Waves: A Review of Computational Techniques", in: de Sabbata, V. and Weber, J. (eds.), Topics in Theoretical and Experimental Gravitation Physics (London: Plenum, 1977).
Thorne, K. S. 1980, Rev. Mod. Phys., 52, 285.
Van Riper, K. 1979, private communication.
Weinberg, S. L. 1972, Gravitation and Cosmology (New York: John Wiley).
Wiita, P. J. and Press, W. H. 1976, Astrophys. J. 208, 525.
Will, C. M. 1982, Theory and Experiment in Gravitation Physics (London: Cambridge University Press).

Wilson, J. R. 1979, "A Numerical Method for Relativistic Hydrodynamics" in: Smarr, L. L. (ed.), Sources of Gravitational Radiation (London: Cambridge University Press, 1979).
Wilson, J. R. 1980, Ann. N. Y. Acad. Sci. 336, 358.
Zel'dovich, Ya. B. and Novikov, I. D. 1971, Relativistic Astrophysics: Vol. I, Stars and Relativity (Chicago, University of Chicago Press), pp. 249 - 254.

FOOTNOTES ADDED IN PROOF

1. A discussion of rates of stellar collapse in our galaxy, and their observability by presently operating gravitational wave and neutrino detectors, is given by Bahcall and Piran (1982). On the issue of whether the collapse of a non-rotating, nonmagnetized massive stellar core will succeed in producing a supernova explosion, or whether the shock will die out before ejecting the envelope: This question is still open as of October 1982. A workshop at Aspen in August 1982 brought together many of the experts on core collapse, and differences of physics input and numerical method between codes are better understood; but some codes show explosions (albeit weak ones) while others show no explosions. Clearly the question is a very delciate one.

2. Rotating neutron stars, e.g. radiopulsars, will emit continuous but weak gravitational radiation as long as they are deformed to some extent away from axial symmetry. Tuned detectors could detect such radiation. For source models, further discussion, and references to previous literature, see Zimmerman and Szedenits (1980), Zimmerman (1980). A notable feature is that the spectral power may be concentrated not at exactly twice the pulsar frequency, or even exactly at the pulsar frequency, but at nearby frequencies, due to aliasing from rigid-body rotation effects.

3. For the observations of the Cornell group, see Boriakoff et al. (1982). Detweiler (1979b) discusses the use of pulsars as detectors of low frequency (microHz) gravitational radiation, taking advantage of the constancy of their clock. Bertotti, Carr and Rees (1982) propose a similar use of the orbital clock of PSR 1913+16, since the rate of the orbital clock can be predicted from general relativity theory; within a few years it should be possible to rule out (or detect) a cosmological density of 10^{-4} of the closure density, for wave periods up to 10^4 years.

REFERENCES ADDED IN PROOF

Bahcall, J. N. and Piran, T. 1982, "Stellar Collapse in the Galaxy", preprint, Institute for Advanced Study, Princeton.
Bertotti, B., Carr, B. J. and Rees, M. J. 1982, "Limits from the Timing of Pulsars on the Cosmic Gravitational Wave Background", preprint, Institute of Astronomy, Cambridge (submitted to Monthly Not. Roy. Astron. Soc.).
Boriakoff, V., Ferguson, D. C., Haugen, M. H., Terzian, Y. and Teukolsky, S. 1982, Astrophys. J. (in press).
Detweiler, S. 1979b, Astrophys. J. 234, 1100.
Zimmerman, M. and Szedenitz, E., Jr. 1980, Phys. Rev. D20, 351.
Zimmerman, M. 1980, Phys. Rev. D21, 891.

EXTRAGALACTIC SOURCES OF GRAVITATIONAL WAVES

Martin J. Rees

Institute of Astronomy
Madingley Road
Cambridge CB3 OHA, U.K.

The prospects of detecting gravitational waves from galactic nuclei are shown to be bleak: although some "scenarios", such as those involving black hole coalescence, would emit a pulse with ~ 0.1 efficiency, the predicted event rate is discouragingly low (§ 2). If most of the "unseen" mass in the Universe were in the remnants of massive "Population III" stars - a possibility discussed in §3 - then the overlapping bursts from the collapse of such objects in early epochs would yield a stochastic background that could amount to $\sim 10^{-3}$ (or even more) of the critical cosmological density. Such a background may be above the detectability threshold for future experiments, and can be probed by studying the timing noise of pulsars, and the secular behaviour of the binary pulsar (§ 4). General constraints on stochastic backgrounds, including "primordial" gravitational radiation, are summarised in § 5.

1. INTRODUCTION

These lectures deal with the production of gravitational waves by galactic nuclei and by pregalactic processes. The emphasis, in this written version, is on topics which have not been adequately covered in earlier literature, or where there have been some new ideas. These lectures should therefore be regarded as a supplement to the articles by Blandford, Clark and Ostriker (all in the book edited by Smarr (1979)) and to those by Rosi and Zimmerman (1976), Thorne (1978) and Carr (1980); they are complementary to the lectures by Eardley in this volume, which deal with gravitational waves from supernovae and pulsars.

In § 2, gravitational waves from active galactic nuclei are considered. Most modes for the formation and evolution of these systems turn out to yield pessimistic estimates for the efficiency of gravitational energy release and the event rate. The only related events that are guaranteed to be efficient are coalescence of black hole binaries; I summarise the physics of this process and the reasons for expecting at least occasional events of this type ($\lesssim 1$ per century!).

Even if galactic nuclei generate occasional detectable bursts, their integrated output of waves cannot amount to more than 10^{-6} of the "critical" cosmological density. Among the possible ingredients of "unseen mass" in the Universe are massive black holes - perhaps the remnants of a pregalactic "Population III". In § 3, the arguments for "unseen" mass and the constraints on its form are summarised; the possible stochastic background of gravitational waves associated with population III is estimated.

§ 4 deals with the techniques for detecting a stochastic background at low frequencies, with particular emphasis on the potential of pulsar tuming data for probing periods $\gtrsim 1$ year. In § 5 the constraints on a primordial background are summarised.

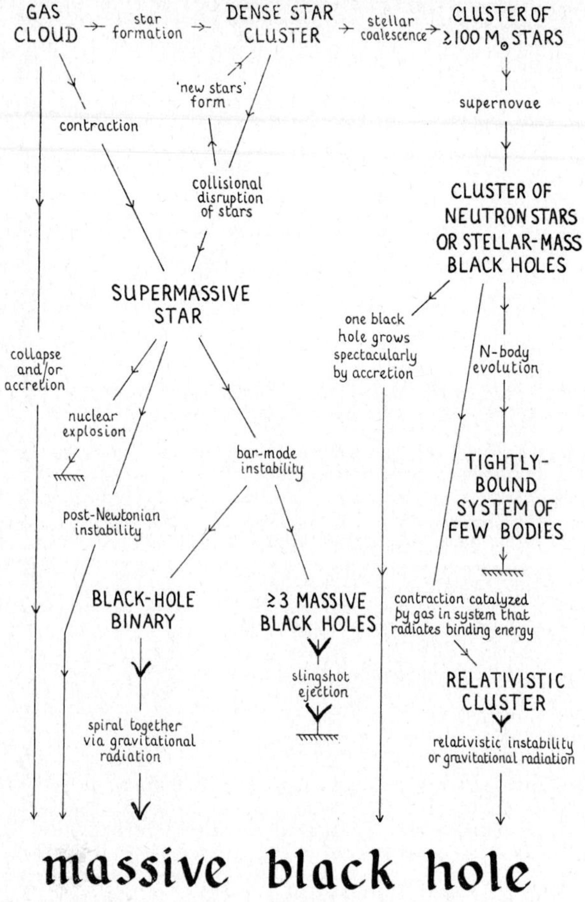

Figure 1. Possible evolutionary pathways for active galactic nuclei (from Rees 1978). The routes likely to be most "efficient" in generating gravitational waves are marked by the larger arrows.

2. ACTIVE GALACTIC NUCLEI

2.1 Possible evolutionary pathways

Figure 1 (reproduced from Rees 1978) illustrates the various evolutionary pathways whereby a galactic nucleus may run away towards gravitational collapse. It is unclear which route is the more common one; nor do we know how (nor, indeed, whether) specific stages or routes can be associated with particular types of violent activity in galactic nuclei. Two things only seem clear:

(i) Most evolutionary pathways involve an inexorably deepening potential well, and it is hard to avoid concluding that much of the material ends up by collapsing into a black hole.

(ii) Some forms of activity are better explained by processes involving accretion onto an already-formed black hole, or energy extraction from a spinning hole, than in terms of any "precusor" stage. (See, for instance, Rees et al. 1982, and references cited therein.)

It is therefore interesting to consider the gravitational wave production by any processes involving massive black holes or their formation.

2.2 Dense (relativistic?) star clusters

A "relativistic star cluster" - i.e. a cluster of compact objects in which the virial velocity is relativistic (or almost so) - would be a prolific source of gravitational waves. Although dense star clusters have been proposed as models for active galactic nuclei, it is difficult to see how they can evolve into the relativistic domain from realistic initial conditions.

If the cluster evolved under purely stellar-dynamical processes (as would be so if it were composed of stellar-mass black holes, or neutron stars) then the number N of stars in the core, and the core radius R , would evolve with approximately constant binding energy according to the relationship

$$R \propto N^2, \; v^2 \propto N^{-1},$$

with N decreasing on a timescale $t_{evo} \sim N(R/v)$. (t_{evo} is the time a typical star has to wait before it passes close enough to another to suffer a 90° deflection.) Thus, if the initial velocity dispersion were (say) 100 km s^{-1}, only 10^{-6} of the original stars would remain by the time v had increased to $\sim 10^5$ km s^{-1}. Only if there were some dissipative process (whereby, for instance, the stars suffered drag on gas which then radiated efficiently), could the gravitational binding energy ($\propto N^2/R$) be enhanced so that R could decrease (and v rise) without a drastic reduction in N. Gravitational radiation does not itself influence the evolution until the cluster is already relativistic.

A cluster of real stars cannot evolve beyond the stage when v is comparable with $(Gm^*/r^*)^{\frac{1}{2}}$, the escape velocity from a single star. This is $\sim 10^3$ km s^{-1} for main sequence stars. If the stars are not compact remnants, stellar collisions become important long before dynamical evolution can approach the relativistic regime, leading to complicated scenarios (cf. Begelman and Rees 1978) whose endpoint may be a single supermassive object (see §2.3).

A surprising feature of star clusters – though it is perhaps no more than a curiosity – has been remarked on by Ostriker (1979): even though gravitational radiation is unimportant in influencing the dynamical evolution of star clusters when v << c, it turns out that, at least in an "ensemble average" sense, any cluster of compact objects (even one with v << c) radiates as much gravitational wave energy as its entire binding energy ($\sim G(Nm^*)^2/R$) on a timescale t_{evo}. In a typical close encounter, leading to a $\pi/2$ deflection, the gravitational radiation energy emitted amounts to only $\sim m_* v^2 (v/c)^5$. However in a time t_{evo} a fraction $\sim (v/c)^2$ of the stars will pass as close as $\sim Gm_*/c^2$ and will radiate $\sim \varepsilon m_* c^2$ (where ε is the efficiency factor for encounters with periastron of order the gravitational radius). This power is $\sim (c/v)^2$ larger than the kinetic energy of the typical star, a factor which makes up for the rareness of the encounters with such small periastron.

Actually, even a less extreme encounter, involving passage within a distance $\sim (c/v)^{4/7}$ larger than the gravitational radius, is sufficient to radiate more than $m_* v^2$, and thus lead to a bound binary which then spirals together, so the conclusion can be made even stronger. Note, nevertheless, that the gravitational wave energy radiated comes from the binding energy of the close binaries which are formed, and not from the binding energy of the cluster as a whole.

2.3 Collapse of supermassive objects

A central black hole may grow gradually via capture of gas or stars (in which case the production of gravitational waves is certainly inefficient). Alternatively, it may form in one go from a super-massive object. A key question is obviously the likely value of ε_g - the fraction of rest mass emitted as gravitational waves - when a supermassive object collapses. For stellar-mass collapses, this is discussed in Eardley's lectures. A supermassive object, however, may go dynamically unstable when its radius is still much larger than GM/c^2. This raises the possibility (see Rees 1977) that ε_g may be very low, because the collapse will then occupy a time of order the free-fall time from the radius where instability sets in (i.e. be spread over an interval $\gg GM/c^3$). Calculations by Shapiro and Teukolsky (1979) show, however, that the collapse does not proceed via formation of a black hole into which surrounding material drains, but that the dynamical phase of the collapse proceeds in an almost self-similar way. Consequently, the effective timescale for formation of the hole is $\lesssim 30(GM/c^3)$, a conclusion that favours more optimistic estimates of ε_g. Some deviation from spherical symmetry is of course required, and the effects of rotation are hard to quantify.

The maximally-efficient collapse mode, from the point of view of gravitational wave production, would be one in which rotation caused the collapsing object to bifurcate into a binary: the two components each evolve into black holes, unimpeded by rotation; the resultant binary then spirals together via the energy loss due to gravitational radiation. Such a scenario would yield $\varepsilon_g \simeq 0.1$.

The value of ε_g is therefore very uncertain. Moreover, the prospects of calculating it are bleaker than for non-spherical supernova collapse, because a supermassive object is inherently more fragile and less homogeneous than the core of a collapsing star.

2.4 The space-density of "dead" quasars

Even though we do not yet understand the power source of active quasars in detail, it is hard to escape the conclusion that "dead" quasars would be massive black holes (see Figure 1). These holes may lurk in the centres of many galaxies; they would be inconspicuous if they were now "starved" of fuel owing to the depletion of gas around them. Estimates of how many "dead" quasars exist are bedevilled by uncertainty about the lifetime of individual quasars and the evolutionary properties of the quasar population.

An interesting argument bypassing the uncertainty in quasar lifetimes was recently presented by Soltan (1982). He points out that quasars contribute integrated background light amounting to $\gtrsim 8\times10^{66}$ ergs Gpc^{-3}. This is a lower limit: the actual value would be higher because of the contribution from faint quasars (Soltan assumed 200 quasars per square degree down to magnitude 22.5); also, there may be more luminosity in X-rays than in the optical band. A lower limit of

$$8\times10^{13} \left(\frac{\varepsilon_e}{0.1} \right)^{-1} M_o \ \mathrm{Gpc}^{-3} \qquad (2.1)$$

can then be placed on the total mass of the remnants, where ε_e is the overall efficiency with which rest mass is converted into electromagnetic energy over a typical quasar's active lifetime. The limit (2.1) is independent of the individual quasar lifetime - it makes no difference whether 10 or 10^3 generations of quasars are born during a Hubble time. Relation (2.1) does however imply the following:

(1) If the remnant masses were $10^8 - 10^9$ $M_\odot$, there would be $10^5 - 10^6$ of them per Gpc^3.

(2) If all quasars were associated with "bright" galaxies ($M_B \lesssim -21.3$) whose space density is known, the mean hole mass would be > $2 \times 10^7 (\varepsilon_e/0.1)^{-1}$ $M_\odot$.

2.5 Black hole binaries formed via galactic mergers

None of the formation routes for massive black holes is guaranteed to yield highly efficient gravitational wave emission (though see Thorne and Braginsky (1975) for some relatively optimistic estimates, the event rates being sensitive to the uncertain quasar lifetimes). However, one can pinpoint a class of events which would generate low frequency pulses with an ε_g which would certainly be high: these involve coalescence of binary black holes, the binaries being formed from mergers of galaxies which each contain black holes. Soltan's (1982) argument tells us that there may indeed be black holes in most large galaxies. Moreover, "mergers" of galaxies are frequent enough that $\gtrsim$ 10% of all galaxies may have experienced such an event during the Hubble time. It has in fact been suggested that all elliptical galaxies may result from mergers between disc systems, though there are problems with such an extreme view (Efstathiou and Jones, 1980; Ostriker, 1980).

When two galaxies merge, they relax after a few dynamical times into an amorphous elliptical-like system. Any massive black holes would gravitate via dynamical friction into the central region of the merged galaxy.

Begelman, Blandford and I (1980) have explored how a pair of massive black holes in the core of a galaxy would evolve towards coalescence. Thus evolution proceeds through several stages:

(1) If the black holes were in the centres of two galaxies which underwent a merger, they would probably be surrounded by dense stellar clusters; that within the less massive galaxy should be denser and will survive intact until the nuclei merge. Dynamical friction (Ostriker and Tremaine, 1975) is extremely efficient and the cores merge and undergo violent relaxation in a characteristic galactic dynamical time $t_{gal} \sim 10^8$ yr.

(2) The captured hole sinks toward the centre of the stellar distribution on the dynamical friction time scale:

$$t_{df} \sim \frac{6 \times 10^6}{\log N} \left(\frac{v_c}{300 \text{ km s}^{-1}} \right) \left(\frac{r_c}{100 \text{ pc}} \right)^2 M_8^{-1} x^{-1} \text{ yr} \quad (2.2)$$

where the core is presumed to have a central velocity dispersion v_c, a core radius r_c and contain N stars, mass m*. M_8 is the mass M_h of the larger black hole, in units of 10^8 $M_\odot$, which is assumed to be less than Nm* (the mass of the core). The smaller black hole, presumed to be associated with the smaller galaxy, has a mass xM_h.

(3) When the black holes approach closer than $r_B \sim (M_h/Nm_*)^{1/3} r_c$, they will become bound to each other with an orbital velocity that is initially smaller than the velocity dispersion of the stars by a factor $(M_h/Nm_*)^{1/3}$.

(4) The holes continue to spiral together under dynamical friction. As the binary becomes 'harder', the maximum impact parameter for effective energy transfer diminishes as $(r/r_B)^{3/2} r_c$ because a binary cannot lose energy effectively to a field star during an encounter which lasts longer than one orbital period. For longer encounter times, the orbital energy is adiabatically invariant and the energy transfer diminishes exponentially (Heggie, 1975). This affects t_{df} only through the logarithm as long as the binding energy of the binary is small compared with the

total kinetic energy of all the stars whose orbits pass sufficiently close to interact effectively.

(5) When $r \lesssim r_{1c} = (m/M)^{1/4}(r_B/r_c)^{9/4} r_c$, this condition is violated and further stellar dynamical evolution is controlled by the rate at which stars whose orbits do not come close to the binary can diffuse into more radial 'loss cone' orbits (Frank and Rees, 1976) that pass within a radius $\sim r$. Two-body 'star-star' relaxation will repopulate the loss cone in a time $\sim$ (solid angle of loss cone) x (two-body relaxation time t_{evo}). The loss cone must be repopulated $(r_{1c}/r)^4$ times to halve the binary orbit. The relevant binary evolution time is then:

$$t_{1c} \sim t_{df} \max\left[1,\ x^{7/4} N\left(\frac{r_B}{r_c}\right)^{27/4}\left(\frac{r_{1c}}{r}\right)\right] \qquad (2.3)$$

Collective effects may, however, lead to a more rapid repopulation of the loss cone and evolution on a time closer to t_{df}.

(6) The binary becomes 'hard' when its orbital speed reaches v_c, at a separation $r_h \sim (r_B/r_c)^3 r_c$. The maximum impact parameter for dynamical friction is now $(rr_h)^{\frac{1}{2}}$. Each interacting star on average carries off a fraction $\sim m_* x/M$ of the binary's binding energy. The binary evolution time scale is now

$$t_h \sim t_{df} \max\left[(r_h/r)\ \ln N,\ (M_h/Nm^*)^2\ N\right] \qquad (2.4)$$

(7) When the binary becomes sufficiently tightly bound, gravitational radiation shrinks the orbit on a time scale $|r/\dot{r}|$ given by

$$t_{GR} \sim 3 \times 10^5\ x^{-1}\ M_8^{-3}\ r_{16}^4\ \text{yr} \qquad (2.5)$$

(8) The evolution now proceeds quite rapidly to coalescence. This may be accompanied by a powerful burst of electromagnetic radiation, depending on the local gas density and magnetic field strength, as well as a pulse of gravitational radiation (Thorne and Braginsky, 1976; Blandford, 1979). Indeed, the final plunge will lead to the emission of net linear momentum; the recoil could in principle be sufficient to eject the combined hole from the core and hence from the galaxy. Estimates of the recoil for a binary collapse (Bekenstein, 1973; Fitchett, 1982) suggest that the degree of asymmetry is unlikely to be bigger than a fraction of one percent, leading to recoil speeds only $\sim$ 100 km s^{-1} even for $\varepsilon_g \approx 0.1$. The hole is therefore less likely to escape entirely than to oscillate around the centre of the galaxy until dynamical friction restores it to rest.

The timescales for the various stages leading to coalescence are plotted in Figure 2. We note the possibility that a binary can become "hung up" at a separation of $(10^4 - 10^5)(G\ M_h/c^2)$ because stellar-dynamical extraction of energy from a "hard" binary is very slow. However, infall of gas into the system could drive the binary closer. (This gas would reactivate the nuclear source, and some "precessing" radio sources could be interpreted as jets from a precessing black hole in just such a binary.) However when the separation is sufficiently small, gravitational radiation is the dominant effect that drives the holes closer. The timescale for this is $< 10^8$ yrs for

$$r < r_{GR} = 5 \times 10^{16}\ x^{1/4}\ M_{h8}^{3/4}\ \text{cm} \qquad (2.6)$$

Of course the evolutionary properties of black hole binaries could be far richer than we have described. For example, drawing an analogy with stellar evolution, if one of the holes possessed a massive extended disk or envelope then mass and angular momentum transfer between the components could be important. Also, merging may occur more rapidly than evolution of the binary and three or more black holes may collect in the core. This would lead to a gravitational sling-shot (Saslaw, Valtonen and Aarseth, 1974) rather than coalescence; this would still leave a coalescing binary (leading to a gravitational wave pulse) even though the resulting single hole might have escaped from its host galaxy with almost relativistic speed.

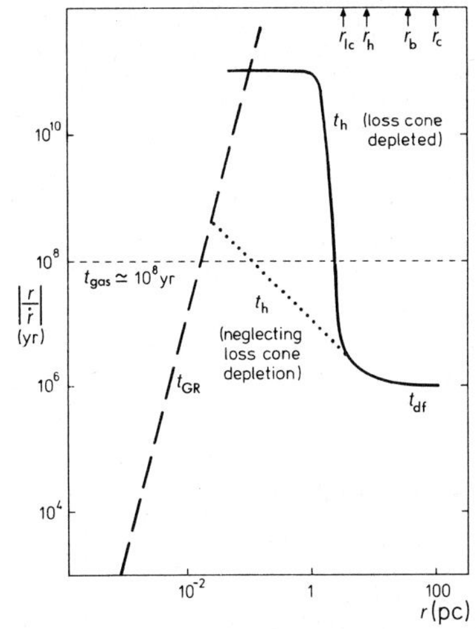

Figure 2. The time scales involved in the approach, and eventual coalescence, of a supermassive binary (after Begelman, Blandford and Rees, 1980). The core parameters chosen are those that might be appropriate to a giant elliptical: $r_c \sim 100$pc, $v_c \sim 300$ km s^{-1}, $N \sim 2x10^9$ and $m_* \sim 1$. The members of the binary are taken to have masses $M_8 = 1$ and $m_8 = 0.3$. For this system the dynamical friction time is $t_{df} \sim 10^6$ yr. Within r_h the evolution time scale would be $(r_h/r)t_{df}$ if loss cone depletion could be ignored; however, unless collective effects permit replenishment of the loss cone on much less than the ordinary stellar relaxation time, the evolution within r_{lc} proceeds on a very much longer time scale $\gtrsim 10^{11}$ yr. Influx of gas into the system at a rate $M \sim 1\ M_\odot\ yr^{-1}$ would however yield a time scale $t_{gas} \simeq 10^8$yr. Gravitational radiation would take over as the dominant mechanism within $1.3x10^{-2}(t_{gas}/10^8 yr)^{1/4}$pc, and the binary would then evolve towards coalescence. The recoil in the final burst may be enough to eject the newly-merged hole from the core of the galaxy.

The energy radiated in the final coalescence is $\varepsilon_g(xMc^2)$, where $\varepsilon_g \simeq 0.1$. The power will be concentrated in a single pulse if the mass ratio x is of order unity; it will constitute a quasi-periodic wave of x^{-1} cycles if $x \ll 1$. The maximum dimensionless amplitude, for the coalescence of two massive black holes of comparable mass ($x \simeq 1$), is (see, for instance Thorne 1978, Carr 1980)

$$h = (2\varepsilon_g)^{\frac{1}{2}}\ x\ \{\text{angle subtended by gravitational radius of each object}\}\ ,$$

$$\text{i.e. } h \simeq 4x10^{-16}\ (\varepsilon_g/0.1)^{\frac{1}{2}}\ (M_h/10^8 M_\odot)\ \left[\frac{1-q_o+q_o z-(1-q_o)(1+2q_o{}^2)^{\frac{1}{2}}}{q_o{}^2(1+z)}\right] \qquad (2.7)$$

The expression in the square brackets, a function of the redshift z and the cosmological deceleration parameter q_o, is of order unity for an event at $z \simeq 1$.

We are therefore led by the foregoing discussion to conclude that active galactic nuclei are not likely to be strong sources of gravitational wave pulses - moreover, it is not obvious that a typical galactic nucleus, evolving along one of the tracks in Figure 1, need ever emit a significant fraction of its binding energy as gravitational radiation. The only predictable events leading to strong pulses ($h \gtrsim 10^{-15}$) would be the coalescence of binaries resulting from galactic mergers. But the rate of these events is unlikely to exceed one per century - depressing even for those experimenters willing to dedicate their entire lives to the quest!

3. STOCHASTIC BACKGROUND FROM THE FORMATION OF POPULATION III: "UNSEEN" MASS

3.1 Possible forms of "unseen mass"

One reason why galactic nuclei offer such a poor prospect as sources of gravitational waves is that they contribute, in toto, such a small fraction of the mass of the Universe. Even if every galaxy harbours a central black hole, these holes cannot collectively amount to more than 10^{-3}-10^{-4} of the mass of the visible content of galaxies. Moreover, the entire luminous content of galaxies may be only a "trace" constituent of the Universe, in terms of mass: other forms of "unseen" material, in galactic halos or intergalactic space, may be dynamically dominant (see Peebles 1980, for a comprehensive review). I shall briefly summarise the various lines of evidence on this subject, and then discuss the possibility that the "unseen" mass is composed of collapsed remnants of supermassive stars. This is particularly interesting in the present context, because it opens up the possibility that most of the universe (mass-wise) may comprise - or may have been in the past - efficient sources of gravitational waves. It is usual in such discussions to define the "critical" cosmological density as

$$\rho_c = \left(\frac{8}{3}\pi G\, t_{Hubble}^{2}\right)^{-1},$$

and to define a density parameter $\Omega = \rho/\rho_c$.

The arguments for "unseen mass", and the evidence on its distribution, are still somewhat controversial as far as the details are concerned, but the following four statements would be widely accepted:

(i) Baryons cannot contribute much less than 1% of the critical density - i.e. Ω baryon $\gtrsim 0.01$. This limit comes from the "luminous" content of galaxies, and from the inferred amount of X-ray emitting gas in clusters.

(ii) (M/L) values in the range around 100 are derived from studies of virialised clusters and from the cosmic virial theorem. These refer to length studies of (2 - 4) Mpc. (For a Hubble constant H_o of 50 km sec^{-1} Mpc^{-1}.)

(iii) (M/L) appears to be a non-decreasing function of length scale

(iv) If $\Omega \simeq 1$ - the value favoured by some theorists, especially the advocates of "inflationary" cosmology - then (M/L) must continue to increase out to at least $\sim$ 20 Mpc. Otherwise, a high density Universe would be incompatible with the low random velocities which lead to conclusion (ii) above.

The straightforward relationship

$$\langle M/L\rangle \simeq 1100\ \Omega\ (H_o/50 \text{ km sec}^{-1} \text{ Mpc}^{-1}) \qquad (3.1)$$

shows that 90% (or even, if $\Omega \simeq 1$, as much as 99%) of the mass-energy in the Universe must be in some form with much greater M/L than the objects that astronomers normally investigate.

The acceptable forms for "unseen" mass include:

Non-baryonic $\sim$ 10 ev neutrinos
Other elementary particles (photinos, gravitinos, etc.)

<u>Baryonic</u> "Jupiters" of < 0.1 $M_\odot$
$10^3 - 10^6$ $M_\odot$ black holes
Diffuse gas in "voids"

Observations may soon reduce the range of options. Alternatively, they may show that more than one type of unseen mass exists; there may, for instance, be a widely-diffused non-baryonic component, as well as a large number of Population III remnants concentrated in the halos of individual galaxies. The non-baryonic options are of course interesting both for cosmology and for particle physics. However, for the present discussion it is more relevant to focus on the possibility that the unseen mass may be in the form of stars or compact remnants, and explore whether these could cumulatively have generated an interesting background level of gravitational waves.

3.2 Baryonic "unseen mass": what mass range is permitted by present evidence?

If galaxies and clusters evolved hierarchically from sub-units that condensed earlier (cf. White and Rees, 1978), most of the initial baryons might have been incorporated in a pregalactic Population III. Ideally, one would like to be able to calculate what happens when a cloud of 10^6-10^8 $M_\odot$ condenses out soon after recombination - does it form one (or a few) supermassive objects, or does fragmentation proceed efficiently down to low-mass stars? Our poor understanding of the initial mass function (IMF) for stars forming now in our own Galaxy gives us little confidence that we can predict the nature of pregalactic stars, forming in an environment differing from our (present-day) Galaxy in at least four significant ways:

(i) The initial cloud masses may be larger than any dense clouds in our Galaxy - the maximum scale on which $\delta\rho/\rho \simeq 1$ at recombination depends on the initial fluctuation spectrum, but may be as high as 10^8 $M_\odot$.

(ii) There may be no coolants apart from H and He.

(iii) The microwave background prevents cooling below $\sim 3(1+z)^\circ K$.

(iv) The energy density in background radiation ($\propto (1+z)^4$) is so high that "Compton drag" may inhibit free-fall collapse if the material is partially ionized.

Kashlinsky and I have (1982) tried to investigate these processes in some detail, but we reach the depressing conclusion that one cannot yet confidently pin down the masses within even ten order of magnitude (10^{-2} - 10^8 $M_\odot$)! Starting with a post-recombination bound cloud of 10^6 - 10^8 $M_\odot$, there are two extreme possibilities. Fragmentation may be so ineffectual that a single supermassive object results; on the other hand, if fragmentation were maximally efficient, we could end up with 10^{-2} $M_\odot$ stars, this being the Jeans mass if the material were compressed to the highest density ($\sim 10^{10}$ cm^{-3}) permitted by the clouds' likely initial rotation, and turned into H_2 at $\sim 10^3$ $^\circ K$.

Despite our inability to "predict" what Population III should be like, there are several constraints which together allow us to conclude that the masses must either be $\lesssim 0.1$ $M_\odot$ or else in the range 10^3-10^6 $M_\odot$.

<u>The (M/L) ratio</u>. Relation (3.1) obviously rules out masses above 0.1 $M_\odot$ unless the stars have all evolved and died, leaving dark remnants.

<u>Nucleosynthesis, background light etc</u>. A severe constraint comes from the requirement that Population III should not overproduce heavy elements. If this population predates all Population II, the fraction of heavy elements produced must be $\lesssim 10^{-4}$; if Population II and Population III are coeval, maybe up to 10^{-3} is permissible. This sets strict limits on the mass fraction going into the upper mass range for "ordinary" stars (15 - 100 $M_\odot$). Limits on the range 100 - 400 $M_\odot$ are uncertain because only ^4He may be ejected, the "heavies" in the core collapsing into a black hole remnant. An uncertainty in the evolution of massive or supermassive stars is

the amount of mass loss during H-burning; however an IMF such that most mass goes into very massive objects (VMOs) of $\gtrsim 10^4\ M_\odot$ is compatible with the nucleosynthesis constraints. A further consideration favouring these high masses is that they are likely to terminate their evolution by a collapse which swallows most of the mass - if most of the material were ejected we would need to evoke "recycling" through several generations in order to end up with most of the material in black holes rather than gas.

The background light constraint depends on the redshift at which the VMOs form. If z_F were small, the background light would be concentrated in the optical or near infrared; if z_F were large, it would not only be more redshifted, and diluted by a $(1+z_F)$ factor, but may have been thermalised so that it is manifested only as a possible distortion of the microwave background. Detailed discussions of Population III are given by Carr, Bond and Arnett (1982) from whose work Figure 3 is adapted, and by Tarbet and Rowan-Robinson (1982).

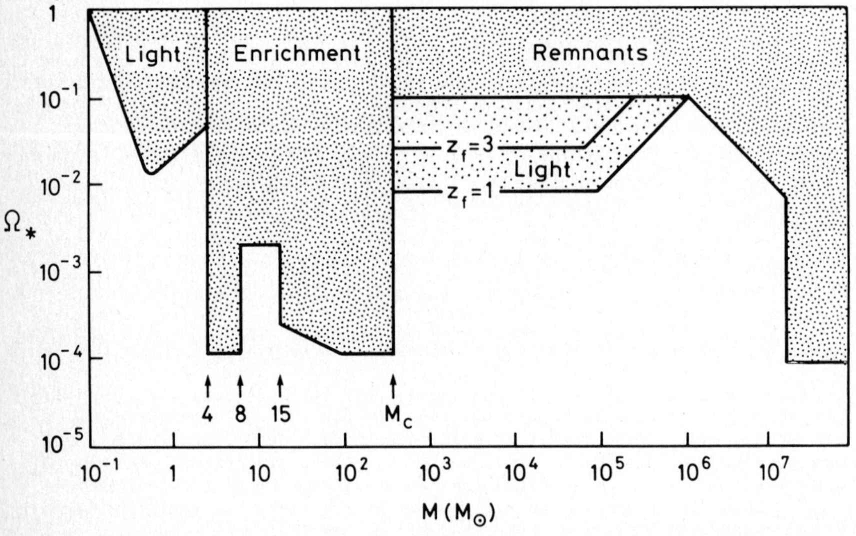

Figure 3. This diagram, from Carr, Bond and Arnett (1982) shows various constraints on the contribution to Ω that can be made by Population III stars (or remnants) in different mass ranges.

Dynamical friction, etc. Carr (1978) has reviewed the effects of massive black holes on the dynamics of our galactic disc and the effects of accretion, showing that our Galactic halo cannot be composed of objects whose individual masses exceed $\sim 10^6\ M_\odot$. This limit cannot however be applied to the more diffusely-distributed objects that might contribute $\Omega \simeq 1$.

Gravitational Lenses. If a remote source (e.g. a quasar) is sufficiently compact, the probability that our line of sight passes close enough to one of the Population III objects for significant lensing to occur is $\sim \Omega$. Note that the individual lensing masses do not affect this probability, only their total contribution to Ω.

The characteristic scale of the images is

$$\theta \simeq 10^{-6} \; (M_{lens}/M_{\odot})^{\frac{1}{2}} \text{ arc sec.} \tag{3.2}$$

The precise coefficient in (3.2) is, of course, a function of the source and lens redshift and of the cosmological model, but is ~ 1 for sources with $z \gtrsim 1$ and lenses $\sim \frac{1}{2}$ way along the line of sight. The structure on milli-arc second scales predicted by (3.2) for 10^6 $M_{\odot}$ holes could be resolved by intercontinental baseline radio interferometry. For "Jupiters" of $\lesssim 0.1$ $M_{\odot}$ there is no short-term hope of achieving the angular resolution required ($< 10^{-6}$ arc seconds); however there is then a chance of detecting variability on timescales of years due to transverse motions of the sources themselves (Gott, 1981; Young, 1981). Such variability would be found only in source components whose intrinsic angular size was less than the θ given by (3.2). For $z \simeq 1$ this requires linear dimensions of around a light day or less. The region emitting the quasar optical and X-ray continuum probably fulfils this requirement, but its rapid intrinsic variability would be hard to disentangle from effects due to lensing. Canizares (1982) argues that one can already exclude $\Omega \gtrsim 1$ in "Jupiters" because the apparent magnitude of the typical quasar continuum region would then be altered by a factor ~ 2 relative to that of the (larger) line-emitting component, thereby introducing an unacceptably large scatter in the equivalent widths of quasar emission lines. Gravitational lens effects may in the next few years allow us to discriminate between the low-mass and high-mass options for Population III.

Even if we knew the mass-range of Population III, and the epoch at which it formed, the gravitational wave output would still be uncertain because the efficiency ε_g is hard to pin down (for the reasons discussed in § 2.3). So ε_g must be left as a parameter. It may be as high as 0.1; but it could be orders-of-magnitude lower, particularly if the masses lie at the upper end of the permitted range (10^5–10^6 $M_{\odot}$).

If most of the energy were radiated in a burst with wavelength $\sim 10(G\,M/c^2)$, the present frequency of the radiation from massive objects of mass M collapsing at redshift z_F would be

$$\nu \simeq \left(\frac{M}{10^4 M_{\odot}}\right)^{-1} (1 + z_F)^{-1} \text{ Hz} \tag{3.3}$$

If the number of objects which collapsed suffices to contribute Ω_{BH} to the unseen mass, then the bursts would be overlapping if

$$\Omega_{BH} > 10^{-2} \; z_F^{-1} \; q_o^{2} \qquad (\text{for } z_F >> q_o^{-1}) \tag{3.4}$$

This is certain to be satisfied whenever the black hole remnants make a substantial contribution to Ω (provided that they formed "in one go" rather than growing via accretion). If each burst lasted much longer than $\sim \nu^{-1}$ (as it would in, for instance, the case of two very unequal masses spiralling together) the overlap condition is even weaker than (3.4). The overlapping bursts would then constitute a stochastic background, with h larger than that for an individual collapse by the square root of the overlap factor.

If $\rho_g(\omega)$ is defined as the spectral energy density of the waves (cf. Isaacson, 1968), then we define Ω_g as $\omega\rho_g/\rho_c$: in other words, Ω_g is the fraction of the critical density in broad-band gravitational waves in a bandwidth around $\omega(= 2\pi\nu)$ with $\delta\omega \simeq \omega$. We then of course can write

$$\Omega_g = \Omega_{BH} \; (1 + z_F)^{-1} \; \varepsilon_g . \tag{3.5}$$

Carr, Bond and Arnett (1982) discuss various other consequences of the formation of VMOs. The (electromagnetic) background constraint would preclude $\Omega_{BH} \simeq 1$ if the formation era were at $z_F \lesssim 10$, because the optical output would exceed the observed background. These constraints are eased if $z_F \simeq 100$, both because of the $(1+z_F)^{-1}$ factor and also because the radiation could have been reprocessed and thermalised by dust. Thus the idea that the unseen dark matter is mainly in black hole remnants of VMOs in the range $10^4 - 10^6\ M_\odot$ would be compatible with $\Omega_g \simeq 10^{-3}\ \Omega_{BH}$, taking ε_g to be ~ 0.1, the highest plausible value (Ω_{BH} would then be in the range 0.1 - 1).

Clustering of black holes (VMO remnants) plays a role in some models for galaxy formation (e.g. Carr and Rees, 1982). The quantitative details of this clustering depend on the nature of the initial "random" distribution of the holes and on their random velocities; the recoil effect (Bekenstein, 1973; Moncrief, 1979) expected of ε_g were indeed as high as 0.1 would be very important in this context.

Equation (3.5) gives the highest level of stochastic background that could arise quite naturally in the context of Population III. But a still higher background could be generated if the black hole remnants were themselves in binaries that were close enough for them to spiral together in less than the Hubble time. The resulting burst would be similar to that associated with the formation of the original hole; however a high efficiency ($\varepsilon_g \simeq 0.1$) would be guaranteed, and the coalescence would occur at a smaller redshift than the formation of the original holes. The optimal case, of course, occurs if the binaries are all coalescing now (i.e. $z \simeq 1$ in (2.7)). This requires an initial separation of $\sim 10^2 (M/10^2\ M_\odot)^{3/4}$ solar radii (Bond and Carr, 1982). In this rather contrived case, the strength of the background would approach the "cherished belief" upper limit of $\Omega_g \simeq 1$. Bond and Carr (1982) note further that one might then detect individual burst events due to coalescence of Population III binaries within our own Galactic Halo. Such bursts would have an amplitude

$$h_{burst} \simeq 10^{-16}\ (M/10^2 M_\odot)\ (R_{Halo}/60\ \mathrm{kpc})^{-1} \qquad (3.6)$$

and would occur at intervals

$$t_{burst} \lesssim 10\ (M/10^2 M_\odot)^{-1} (M_{halo}/10^{12} M_\odot)\ \mathrm{yr}^{-1} \qquad (3.7)$$

Approximate equality in (3.7) would be attained only in the very artificial case where all the binaries formed with the optimal initial separation, corresponding to a coalescence time of $\sim 10^{10}$ yrs. On such a hypothesis, there would also be a background contribution due to superposition of the (discrete-frequency) radiation from binaries which have not yet coalesced. The nearest such binary in our galactic halo would be only $\sim 20 (M/10^2 M_\odot)^{1/3}$ parsecs away; if it were radiating its binding energy on a timescale $\sim 10^{10}$yrs it would emit monochromatic waves with

$$h = 10^{-18}\ (M/10^2 M_\odot)^{11/12} \text{ at a frequency } 4 \times 10^5\ (M/10^2 M_\odot)^{5/8}\ \mathrm{sec.}$$

One cannot yet venture any quantitative assessment of how many Population III objects should be in binaries. This depends on how they form - one can readily show that, if none were born in binaries, the chances of forming binaries subsequently by 3-body processes, or by 2-body dissipative effects, would be negligible.

4. PROSPECTS FOR PROBING A STOCHASTIC BACKGROUND OF LONG-WAVELENGTH GRAVITATIONAL WAVES

4.1 The "target" sensitivity level

To put into perspective the problems of detecting a low-frequency background, it is convenient to think in terms of the order-of-magnitude relationship for the dimensionless amplitude:

$$h = (\nu t_{Hubble})^{-1} \Omega_g^{\frac{1}{2}} . \tag{4.1}$$

Observational techniques are, of course, only of interest if they are sensitive enough to reveal a wave background with $\Omega_g \lesssim 1$. In terms of wave frequency ν, we can express relation (4.1) as

$$h = 5 \times 10^{-19} \Omega_g^{\frac{1}{2}} \nu_{Hz} \tag{4.2}$$

(assuming a Hubble constant of 2×10^{10} yr^{-1}). This gives a "target" level of sensitivity for detectors aiming to detect a possible broad-band stochastic background. Note that (4.1), which applies only when $\ell \ll \ell_H$, implies that a wave background contributing $\Omega_g \simeq 1$ generates an apparent shear which is comparable to that induced by the Hubble flow on scales $\lesssim \ell$.

4.2 Experimental techniques

Experiments are primarily aimed at detecting discrete sources or bursts. However a stochastic background of the kind expected from VMOs could be detectable. If the VMO masses are at the lower end of the likely range, then the frequencies are $\gtrsim$ 1 Hz if $z_F < 100$. Drever (private communication; see also these proceedings) claims that it may be feasible to detect a broad-band background ($\Delta\nu/\nu \simeq 1$) at $\nu \simeq 100$ Hz, with a value of h as small as 5×10^{-22}. This would correspond (cf. (4.2)) to $\Omega_g \simeq 10^{-2}$. Though the most likely frequency range of the stochastic backgrounds discussed in § 3 would be well below 100 Hz, this indicates that ground-based experiments may do more than just detect isolated strong pulses.

The stochastic background from VMOs is more likely to lie in the lower frequency range where doppler-tracking of spacecraft offer the optimal technique (Estabrook et al., 1979; Bertotti and Carr, 1980; Hellings, 1981). Limitations on the stability of hydrogen-maser clocks prevent these techniques from attaining an interesting level of sensitivity - i.e. $\Omega_g < 1$ in (4.2) - for $\nu > 10^{-2}$ Hz. However the sensitivity improves rapidly for lower frequencies. If observations continued for a year, and if ϵ_g and Ω_{BH} had their maximum likely values of 0.1 and 1 respectively (equation (3.5)), then the background would be detectable if $M_{BH} > 3000\, z_F\, M_\odot$. If dual-frequency tracking could eliminate the plasma noise (which, even for X-band, is the main limitation at the lowest frequencies), then this technique would reach a sensitivity of $\Omega_g = 10^{-5}$ for $\nu \simeq 10^{-6}$ Hz - in other words, if $M_{BH}\, z_F \simeq 10^7\, M_\odot$ and $\Omega_{BH} = 1$, the background would be detectable even for $\epsilon_g \simeq 10^{-5}\, z_F^{-1}$.

4.3 Orbits in the Solar System

Mashhoon, Carr and Hu (1981) discuss how a gravitational wave background would induce small perturbation in the orbits of bodies in the Solar System. The most interesting limit that these authors claim, implying $\Omega_g < 0.1$ at periods $\sim$ 1 year, comes from the precision with which the orbit of Mars is now known. However, the Earth-Moon system would eventually be sensitive to waves of one-month period at a level $\Omega_g \simeq 0.1$ (even for $\Delta\nu/\nu \simeq 1$), if the determination of the Moon's orbit could be refined to the limiting precision ($\sim$ 3 cm) of the laser ranging technique.

4.4 Pulsar "timing noise"

As we consider lower frequencies, the demands on the timing precision required in order to detect a given Ω_g become less stringent: the value of h corresponding to a given Ω_g scales as ν^{-1} (cf. equation (4.1)), and the apparent time delay built up during a half-cycle, for a given h, also obviously grows as ν^{-1}. This means that the "clocks" provided by the spin of pulsars, even though they may be less good than H-masers, can be used to probe the wave background at lower frequencies. The principles are similar to those of the doppler-tracking method. The timing data now extend over 10 years, and are precise enough to reveal effects in pulse arrival time at the level of tens of microseconds. In other words, fractional deviations in clock rate are in principle detectable at the level of 10^{-11} - 10^{-12}. Since waves of 1 - 10 yr period would induce changes at the level of $h \simeq 10^{-10}\Omega_g^{\frac{1}{2}}$ x (period in years) we immediately see that, if other kinds of "timing noise" are not too severe, an interesting degree of sensitivity can be attained at these periods. This topic was discussed by Detweiler (1979); recently it has been studied in more detail by Bertotti, Carr and myself (1982) and in what follows I shall paraphrase our treatment and conclusions.

Following Mashhoon (1982) and Mashhoon and Grishchuk (1980), we choose a coordinate gauge in which the only metric component we need reads

$$h_{zz}(t,\underline{x}) = -\frac{1}{2}\Sigma_{\underline{k}} \sin^2\theta \ \mathrm{Re}\ (H(\underline{k}) \exp i(\omega t + \underline{k}.\underline{x})). \qquad (4.3)$$

Here, θ is the angle between $k = \omega\hat{k}$ and the pulsar, which is placed on the z-axis at distance L. $H = H_+ + H_x$ is the sum of the complex amplitudes of the two polarisation modes; the experiment does not distinguish between them. The factor $\sin^2\theta$ arises from the transverse character of the waves. The energy flux in each mode is

$$\mathfrak{F}(\underline{k}) = \frac{\omega^2}{64} (|H_+|^2 + |H_x|^2) \qquad (4.4)$$

(taking units with G = c = 1); the spectral energy density is defined by

$$\rho_g(\omega)\ d\omega = \sum_{\omega<k<\omega+d\omega} \mathfrak{F}(k) = \Omega_g(\omega)\ \rho_c\ d\omega. \qquad (4.5)$$

Integrating $-\frac{1}{2}\ \partial h_{zz}/\partial t$ along the electromagnetic path, one readily obtains the redshift

$$z_g(t) = \tfrac{1}{2}\ \Sigma_k\ \mathrm{Re} \left[H(k) \sin^2\theta \left(\frac{1-e^{-i\omega uL}}{u} \right) e^{i\omega t} \right], \qquad (4.6)$$

where $u \equiv 1 + \cos\theta$.

The gravitational background has a random phase distribution; we also assume an isotropic spectrum. The spectrum of z_g is the Fourier transform of the correlation function:

$$<z_g(t)\ z_g(t+\tau)> = Z \int_0^\infty d\omega \cos\omega\tau\ S_{z_g}(\omega). \qquad (4.7)$$

One obtains

$$S_{z_g}(\omega) = \frac{8\pi}{3} \frac{\rho_g(\omega)}{\omega^2} B(\omega L) \qquad (4.8)$$

where the distance-dependence is contained in the function

$$B(x) = \frac{3}{4}\int_0^\pi d\theta \frac{\sin^5\theta}{u^2} \sin^2\left(\frac{xu}{2}\right) = 1 - \frac{3}{4}\left(\frac{2x-\sin 2x}{x^3}\right) \qquad (4.9)$$

For $x \ll 1$, $B(x) = O(x^2)$.

The isotropic background we are looking for is determined statistically by its energy spectrum $\rho_g(\omega)$, the phases and polarization of each mode being random. Consequently the theory enables us to calculate only the expectation value of any physical quantity over the randon phase ensemble. Note that the ergodic theorem ensures equality of the ensemble and time averages only if T exceeds the characteristic timescale of the phenomenon (which is $\sim$ L/c because the convergence of the spectrum (4.8) is ensured by $\omega L << 1$).

It is worth pointing out that, for $\omega L >> 1$, the frequency shift is independent of L: equation (4.8) shows that there is no secular effect ($B \to 1$ when $L \to \infty$). This is a consequence of the transverse character of the gravitational waves. A secular term can arise only from waves with $\omega uL << 1$, from (4.6), which requires $|\theta - \pi| < (\omega L)^{\frac{1}{2}}$. On the other hand, these waves have a negligible effect because of the transversality factor $\sin^2\theta$ appearing in equation (4.6). Were purely longitudinal modes present, the function B(x) would be proportional to L, as naively expected. Secular terms in the electromagnetic effects of gravitational waves are also absent, for essentially the same reason, in the scintillation of a distant source (Zipoy and Bertotti, 1968; Bertotti and Trevese, 1972).

In all pulsars except for the binary pulsar (Taylor and Weisberg, 1982) the phase residuals $\phi_R(t)$ are apparently dominated not by measurement noise, but by the effects of intrinsic fluctuations in the rotation rate. It is found that $\phi_R(t)$ is not a stationary stochastic variable, but it can be modelled as a random walk in the phase (PN) the frequency (FN), or the time derivative of the frequency (SN) (Helfand et al., 1980; Cordes, 1980). For these three cases, the quantity

$$\sigma^2(T) \equiv \frac{1}{T} \int_0^T dt\, \phi_R(t)^2 \qquad (4.10)$$

grows with integration time (on the average) like T, T^3 and T^5 respectively:

$$<\sigma^2(T) = \begin{cases} \frac{1}{2} S_{PN}\, T & (PN) \\ \frac{1}{12} S_{FN}\, T^3 & (FN) \\ \frac{1}{20} S_{SN}\, T^5 & (SN) \end{cases} \qquad (4.11)$$

(Cordes and Greenstein, 1981).

The actual phase residuals $\phi_R(t)$ for a given pulsar are obtained from the observed phase by applying the appropriate astrometric correction due to the motion of the receiver and the source, and by subtracting the systematic component due to the spin-down. A polynomial fitting method, described in detail by Cordes and Greenstein (1981) then yields "timing residuals" - i.e. the quantities $\sigma(T)$ (equation 4.10) where an additive constant, and any linear or quadratic trend have been subtracted out. This is, of course, equivalent to cutting off the Fourier transform of the phase at a frequency α/T (where $\alpha \simeq 1$). The actual value of the numerical constant α (or, more precisely, the shape of the cut-off) would need to be computed separately for different assumptions about the low frequency spectrum. Such precision does not seem worthwhile at present, so we take $\alpha = 2\pi$: we know that a full sine-wave cannot be fitted by a quadratic form, whereas up to a half-period of a sine-wave is filled reasonably well.

We can now compute the average of the quantity (4.10) for an arbitrary gravitational wave spectrum:

$$<\sigma^2(T)> = \left(\frac{2\pi}{P}\right)^2 \frac{1}{T} \int_0^T dt \int_0^t dt_1 \int_0^t dt_2 <z_g(t_1)\, z_h(t_2)> . \qquad (4.12)$$

Using the definition (4.7), we get

$$\langle\sigma^2(T)\rangle = \frac{2}{T}\left(\frac{2\pi}{P}\right)^2 \int_{\frac{\alpha}{T}}^{\infty} d\omega\, S_z(\omega) \int_o^T dt \int^t dt_1 \int_o^t dt_2 \cos\omega\,(t_1-t_2)$$

$$\left(\frac{2\pi}{P}\right)^2\left(\frac{32\pi}{3}\right) \int_{\frac{\alpha}{T}}^{\infty} d\omega \frac{\rho_g(\omega)}{\omega^4} \left(1 - \frac{\sin\omega T}{\omega T}\right) . \qquad (4.13)$$

An appropriate power-law spectrum for the gravitational waves can lead to $\sigma(T)$ growing with any positive power of T. If $\rho_g(\omega) = \rho_n\omega^n$, then from equation (4.13) we have (writing $x = \omega T$),

$$\langle\sigma^2(T)\rangle = \frac{32\pi}{3}\left(\frac{2\pi}{P}\right)^2 \rho_n\, T^{3-n} \int_\alpha^\infty dx\, x^{n-4} \left(1 - \frac{\sin x}{x}\right) . \qquad (4.14)$$

Denoting the integral as

$$f_n(\alpha) \equiv \int_\alpha^\infty dx\, x^{n-4} \left(1 - \frac{\sin x}{x}\right) , \qquad (4.15)$$

we get phase-noise for $n = 2$,

$$S_{PN} = 64\pi \left(\frac{2\pi}{P}\right)^2 \rho_2 \quad f_2(\alpha); \qquad (4.16)$$

frequency noise for $n = 0$,

$$S_{FN} = 128\pi\left(\frac{2\pi}{P}\right)^2 \rho_0 \; f_0(\alpha); \qquad (4.17)$$

slowing-down (torque) noise for $n = -2$,

$$S_{SN} = 1280\pi \left(\frac{2\pi}{P}\right)^2 \rho_{-2} \quad f_{-2}(\alpha). \qquad (4.18)$$

The number $f_2(2\pi)$ is easily evaluated in terms of the sine integral and gives $64\pi\; f_2(2\pi)/3 \simeq 10$. However, $f_0(2\pi) \simeq 1.2 \times 10^{-4}$ and $f_{-2}(2\pi) \simeq 1.5 \times 10^{-5}$ are much smaller, making FN and SN spectra less powerful.

Bertotti, Carr, and I have used the data given by Cordes and Helfand (1980) to set limits to $\rho_g(\omega)$. These latter authors have studied 11 pulsars, determining the form of random walk and the corresponding strength for each of them (cf. equation 4.11). PSR 2217+47 and PSR 1133+16 are particularly interesting because their PN spectra penetrate deeply into the 'closure line' defined by $\Omega_g(\omega) = 1$, yielding a limit on $\Omega_g(\omega)$ at $\omega = 2.6 \times 10^{-8}$ sec^{-1} almost three orders of magnitude below the closure line. (See Figure 4.) In the figure we also plot the limits from PSR 2016+28, found by Cordes and Helfand to have a FN spectrum. Cordes and Greenstein (1981) quote limits to the contributions of the other (non-dominant) forms of noise, but these do not modify the gravitational wave limits drawn in Figure 4. With the lengthening of the time record, the limits will improve, not only because of the higher accuracy, but also because the frequency cut-off $2\pi/T$ will become lower.

For most pulsars, we have no definite information about the spectrum of the timing residuals, and their amplitude is measured by a single parameter, the 'activity' of the pulsar (Cordes and Helfand, 1980). This is essentially the quantity $\sigma^2(T)$ for a timespan of length from a third to the full available record, and it provides a relevant time to the dimensionless integral (cf. equation 4.13).

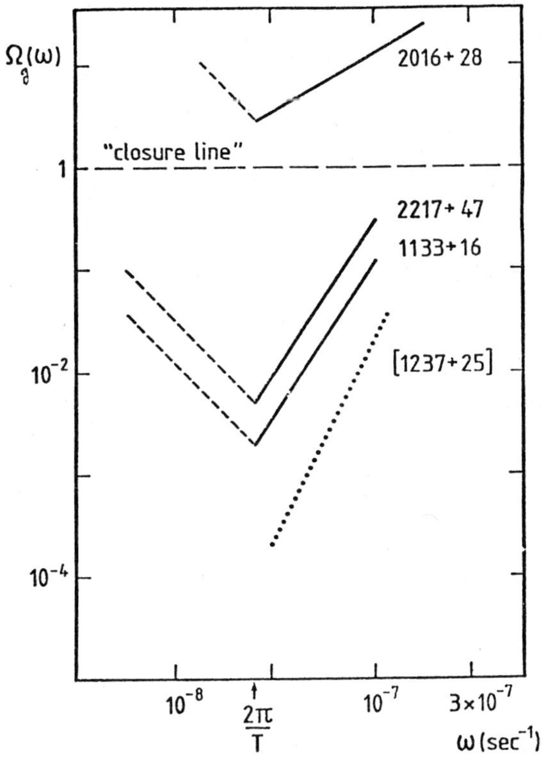

Figure 4, from Bertotti, Carr and Rees (1982) shows the upper limits on a stochastic gravitational background, in terms of the density parameter $\Omega_g(\omega)$, defined as the fraction of the critical density in gravitational waves in the waveband ω to 2ω (where $\omega = 2\pi\nu$). The limits are drawn for $t_{Hubble} = 2 \times 10^{10}$ yrs and are proportional to t_{Hubble}^{-2}. The two pulsars 1133+16 and 2217+47 display 'phase noise' (PN); 2016+28 displays 'frequency noise' (FN). The limits are strongest for frequencies of (length of available record)$^{-1} = T^{-1} \simeq 2.6 \times 10^{-8}$ sec^{-1}. We also plot as a dotted line the limit ($\Omega_g \propto \omega^4$) that can be set from the 'activity parameter' of a typical quiet pulsar, 1237+25; this limit is, however, less reliable than the other except when $\nu >> 1/T$ (see text). The limits can be extended to $\nu < 1/T$ (i.e. to wave periods exceeding the timespan of the data) because intense slow waves would contribute a large second derivative to the observed period. These limits, shown by the dashed lines, weaken as ω^{-2} at lower frequencies. Potentially much better limits down to $\omega \simeq 10^{-4}$ yr^{-1} come from a different argument involving the orbital behaviour of the binary pulsar, discussed in §4.5 of the text.

$$K \equiv \frac{1}{T^4} \int_{\frac{\alpha}{T}}^{\infty} d\omega \, \frac{\Omega_g(\omega)}{\omega^5} \left(1 - \frac{\sin \omega T}{\omega T}\right) . \tag{4.19}$$

(The upper limit is really the reciprocal of the resolution time.) The 'activity parameter' then provides an upper limit $\propto \omega^4$ to the value of $\Omega_g(\omega)$ in any waveband with $\omega \gg 1/T$:

$$\Omega_g(\omega) < K(\omega T)^4 \quad . \tag{4.20}$$

This is essentially the argument first given by Detweiler (1979).

The timespan T is typically $\sim$ 1000 days. Inserting these values into (4.20) seems to yield impressively low limits. However, we can only apply (4.20) with confidence when $\omega T \gg \alpha \simeq 2\pi$ and the sensitivity diminishes rapidly towards higher frequencies. A representative limit derived from the 'activity parameter' of 1237+25 is plotted in Figure 4. These limits are comparable to those for the more carefully-studied pulsars for periods $\sim$ 1 year; but the limits on $\Omega_g(\omega)$ worsen more steeply at higher frequency. This is because the activity parameter does not tell us how $\sigma(T)$ diminishes as we consider shorter spans of data, whereas for PN we get a $T^{\frac{1}{2}}$ dependence.

The contribution to $\sigma(T)$ from waves with $\omega T \ll 1$ is truncated owing to the $(1 - (\sin \omega T)/\omega T)$ term in the integrals (4.13) and (4.19); it is essentially absorbed in the polynomial fit. Nevertheless, one can set <u>some</u> limits to $\Omega_g(\omega)$ at low frequencies - albeit with poorer sensitivity - from the nature of the polynomial fit itself. This is because a large-amplitude contribution to $\sigma(T)$ from a wave with $\omega \ll T^{-1}$ would yield a quadratic term (i.e. a second derivative) in the timing residuals. Cordes and Helfand (1980) show that there is no evidence for a significant second derivative except in the Crab pulsar (they do this by comparing the size of the residuals after subtracting a second order polynomial with those obtained by a third-order fit). This limit to the quadratic term yields a limit on $\Omega_g(\omega)$ proportional to ω^{-2} (for $T^{-1} \gg \omega > L^{-1}$). By matching this limit onto the results plotted in Figure 4, we can rule out $\Omega_g(\omega) = 1$ for periods between $\sim$ 1 month and $\sim$ 100 years.

These (already significant) limits have been derived from data collected and analysed for other purposes. Substantial improvements could be made by concentrating efforts on pulsars with the 'quietest' spin-rates (e.g. the binary pulsar). Furthermore, one can distinguish between 'noise' intrinsic to the pulsar and the effects of gravitational waves by <u>correlating</u> data from different pulsars. The gravitational wave contribution to $\sigma(T)$ arises half from the metric variations at the pulsar and half from variations at the Earth; the latter would yield correlations between the timing data of different pulsars. If this were found, it would be positive evidence for a stochastic gravitational wave background.

4.5 The binary pulsar as a probe for periods $10 - 10^6$ yrs

The reason why the pulsar timing residuals do not provide useful information about the background at frequencies $\ll T^{-1}$ is that they are not predictable enough clocks. As we show below, we are looking for fractional period changes of order 10^{-10} yr^{-1} (the Hubble constant); for typical pulsars, $\dot{P}/P$ is 10^{-8} yr^{-1} - two orders of magnitude larger - and we have no independent way of calculating what $\dot{P}$ should be. Things are better if one considers the gravitational clock provided by the binary pulsar PSR 1913-16. The work by Taylor <u>et al.</u> (Taylor <u>et al.</u>, 1976; McCulloch, Taylor and Weisberg, 1979; Taylor, Fowler and McCulloch, 1979; Boriakoff <u>et al.</u> 1982; and especially Taylor and Weisberg, 1982) has pinned down the parameters of the system so well that the general relativistic secular speed-up of the orbital period due to gravitational radiation is predicted to be $|\dot{P}_K/P_K| \simeq (3 \times 10^8 \text{ yr})^{-1}$ with an uncertainty of only 0.2 per cent (i.e. we have a 'clock' whose behaviour is known with precision better than 10^{-11} yr^{-1}). The observations have a precision of $(5 \times 10^9 \text{ yr})^{-1}$ and agree with this prediction; moreover, there will be a rapid improvement in the measurement of $|\dot{P}_K/P_K|$ as the data accumulate over a longer timebase. See the lectures by Eardley for a full discussion of the binary pulsar.

To see the potentialities of these observations for probing the gravitational wave background, we must compute the expectation value of the square of the frequency change, $\Delta z_g(t) \equiv z_g(t) - z_g(0)$, which these waves would induce. Equations (4.7) and (4.8) give

$$<(\Delta z_g(T))^2> = 4 \int_0^\infty d\omega\, S_{z_g}(\omega)\,(1 - \cos\omega T) = \frac{64\pi}{3} \int_0^\infty \frac{d\omega}{\omega^2}\, \rho_g(\omega)\, \sin^2 \frac{\omega T}{2}\, B(\omega L). \tag{4.21}$$

The integral is effectively cut off below $\omega \simeq L^{-1}$, unless $\rho_g(\omega)$ falls off faster than ω^{-1}, by the function $B(\omega L)$; the function

$$\frac{4}{\omega^2 T^2} \sin^2 \frac{\omega T}{2}$$

provides the upper cut-off at $\omega \sim T^{-1} >> L^{-1}$, unless $\rho_g(\omega)$ rises faster than ω. Since these two functions are equal to unity far from their respective cut-offs, the integral (4.21) is approximated by

$$<(\Delta z_g(T))^2> = \frac{16\pi}{3} T^2 \int_{L^{-1}}^{T^{-1}} d\omega\, \rho_g(\omega), \tag{4.22}$$

thus providing the precise upper limit

$$\frac{3}{16\pi T^2} <(\Delta z_g(T))^2>$$

to the energy of the background between L^{-1} and T^{-1}. For wavelengths > L, equation (4.21) still yields a limit, but one which weakens as ω^{-2}. Therefore, assuming that relativity describes the orbital behaviour of the binary pulsar correctly, we get for this frequency interval

$$\Omega_g < \frac{1}{2} \left(\frac{\delta \dot{P}_K}{P}\, t_{Hubble} \right)^2 \tag{4.23}$$

where $\delta\dot{P}_K$ is the part of $\dot{P}_K$ that could be due to gravitational waves (cf. equation 4.22). Contributions to $\delta\dot{P}_K$ come from (a) observational uncertainties and (b) uncertainties in the $\dot{P}_K$ given by the Landau-Lifshitz formula. The latter arise because the parameters of the system (masses, eccentricity etc.) are imperfectly known. At present, the measurement uncertainties (a) are dominant, and (4.23) yields a limit no better than $\Omega_g \lesssim 2$. However, we now assess the various errors in order to show that there are excellent chances of pushing this limit down by several powers of ten.

Observational errors. If all observations were of similar quality, we would expect the measured uncertainty in $\dot{P}_K$ to decrease as the 5/2 - power of the time-base of the observations, since we are measuring a phase which increases quadratically with time. Since the present time-base is 6 years, this would imply an improvement in the next 6 years of $2^{5/2} \simeq 5.6$. Since the newer data have higher weight, the observational errors may fall still more rapidly.

The predicted $\dot{P}_K$ from the Landau-Lifshitz formula. Gravitational radiation causes the binary orbit to contract, and the orbital period P_K to decrease, at a rate

$$\dot{P}_K/P_K = (\text{constant}) \times P_K^{-8/3}\, f(e)\, m_1 m_2 (m_1 + m_2)^{-1/3}, \tag{4.24}$$

where e is the orbital eccentricity and m_1 and m_2 are the component masses. The periastron precession, which is known with high accuracy, determines $(m_1 + m_2)^{2/3}$; the main uncertainty in the mass function comes from the mass ratio, which has to be inferred from the gravitational redshift and second-order Doppler effect (Taylor & Weisberg, 1982) and is 1 ± 0.04. However, equation (4.24) shows that $\dot{P}_K$ depends only quadratically on the error in the mass ratio when this ratio is close to unity; it is for this reason that the predicted $\dot{P}_K$ is only uncertain by 0.002. The determination of m_1/m_2 will improve as $T^{5/2}$ (since this is a secular observable, at least for timespan smaller than the periastron precession period). The uncertainty in $\dot{P}_K$ will therefore reduce as T^{-5} (quadratically with the error in m_1/m_2) until m_1/m_2 is found to differ significantly from unity, and thereafter as $T^{-5/2}$. The uncertainty in eccentricity e will diminish only as $T^{-\frac{1}{2}}$; but since this is already known with 10^{-5} precision, it will be a long time before it becomes the dominant uncertainty in (4.24).

Motion of the binary pulsar system in the Galaxy. Another limiting factor is the contribution to $\dot{P}_K$ as the pulsar's Doppler shift changes due to its motion in the Galaxy. The acceleration due to the mean gravitational field of the Galaxy contributes only 2×10^{-13} yr^{-1}, and perturbations due to interstellar clouds, etc. are of the same order. However, if the binary pulsar system has a large peculiar velocity V, there is a changing Doppler effect as it moves (even with constant velocity) transverse to the line of sight. This yields $|\dot{P}_K/P_K| = V^2/cD \sin^2\theta$ (where D is the distance and θ the angle between the velocity and the line of sight). For D = 5 kpc, this contribution is at the level of 10^{-11} yr^{-1} if V has the high value ~ 200 km sec^{-1} typical of ordinary pulsars. The proper motion $V \sin\theta/D$ may eventually be measurable. If this proves to be anomalously small, the associated $\dot{P}_K$ may be negligible. However, if the proper motion were (say) ~ 5 milliarcsecs per year (corresponding to $V \simeq 200$ km s^{-1}, $\theta = 45^{\circ}$), then, even if it were known exactly, there would still be an uncertainty $\sim 10^{-11}\ \delta D/D$ yr^{-1} in the contribution to $\dot{P}_K$ resulting from the changing Doppler effect. It seems most unlikely that the fractional error $\Delta D/D$ in the distance can be reduced below 0.1, so it may never be possible to discuss effects at the level below 10^{-12} yr^{-1} (unless other binary pulsars are discovered).

The precision with which we know the orbital parameters and masses is improving so fast that we will, within a few years, be able to calculate $\dot{P}_K$ with a precision better than 10^{-12} yr^{-1}. Within 10 years the observations could also have achieved this same precision; we may then (if no discrepancy appears) be able to use (4.23) to set limits $\Omega_g \lesssim 10^{-4}$ to any wave background at wavelengths 10 - 10^4 light-years. Improvements beyond this level may be bedevilled by our ignorance of how the binary pulsar is moving through the Galaxy.

5. PRIMORDIAL WAVES

Quite apart from the possible stochastic background from (for instance) Population III objects, gravitational waves may pervade the Universe which were due to initial cosmic inhomogeneities imprinted when their comoving wavelength was $\gtrsim$ the horizon scale - perhaps even as early as the Planck time. These may be termed primordial waves (see Carr, 1980 for a full review).

The expected intensity of the primordial wave background has been considered by - among others - Grishchuk (1977) and Starobinsky (1979). The waves are related to the fluctuations, and need not be restricted to the 'thermal' graviton background which would be at wavelengths of a few millimetres. According to Starobinsky (1979) who envisages that the Universe experienced a de Sitter 'inflationary' phase close to the Planck time, the waves may have a spectrum such that there is a comparable contribution to Ω_g from all (logarithmic) wavebands. A similar spectrum has been proposed in a model where the fluctuations are induced by macroscopic 'strings' (Vilenkin, 1981). The techniques discussed in §4 set limits over a broad range of wavelengths relevant to primordial waves as well as on those from (e.g.) Population III. However, the spectrum of primordial waves (unlike those generated by discrete objects) may extend up to wavelengths of millions of light years, or even the Hubble radius. In this band, the values of h corresponding to $\Omega_g \simeq 1$ are (from (4.1)) large enough that even relatively crude observations can set significant constraints.

As the Universe expands, with scale factor $R(t) = R_o(1+z)^{-1}$, the parameters of waves of wavelength ℓ vary as

$$\nu \propto R^{-1}$$

$$\left.\begin{aligned} h &\propto R^{-1} \\ \rho_g &\propto R^{-4} \end{aligned}\right\} \quad \text{for } \nu^{-1} << t_{\text{Hubble}} \text{ or } \ell < \ell_{\text{Hubble}} \qquad (5.1)$$

In a Friedmann Universe $R \propto t^n$ ($n \lesssim 2/3$), so at early times ℓ/ℓ_H (for a given wave) would have exceeded unity. The Isaacson (1968) approximation on which (5.1) is based would then break down. When the waves contribute $\Omega_g \simeq 1$ tracing the behaviour back to these early times involves considering not merely anisotropic but strongly inhomogeneous models.

Carr (1980) gives a thorough discussion of the observational limits on primordial waves; I will merely summarise them here.

(i) The primordial ^{4}He abundance is sensitive to the expansion rate. Consequently, one can exclude a gravitational wave background whose energy density exceeds that of the thermal radiation i.e. $\Omega_g < \Omega_{rad} \simeq 10^{-4}$. This limit applies straightforwardly to wavelengths less than the comoving horizon scale at the epoch of helium synthesis ($t \simeq 1$ sec), i.e. $\ell < 10^{19}$ cm, since it is only in this range that the scaling laws (5.1) apply. On larger scales the limits may actually be stronger, because the 'anisotropy energy' density in some cosmologies varies as R^{-6}; however we cannot be so confident about this wavelength range until more is known about inhomogeneous cosmologies (cf. Adams et al., 1982). This limit of course does not apply to waves generated by 'astrophysical' processes such as those discussed in §3.

(ii) A range of strong limits to Ω_g on longer wavelengths comes from the microwave background isotropy on angular scales of minutes or degrees, which constrains the metric fluctuations at the epoch of last scattering (redshift $z_* \lesssim 10^3$). For scales of order the horizon size at z_*, $\Delta T/T < 10^{-4}$ at z_*, equivalent to $h < 10^{-7}$ now, for $z_* \simeq 10^3$. (Limits are weaker for smaller scales, and sensitive to the thermal history of the intergalactic medium.)

(iii) Related limits at long wavelengths come from the 24h anisotropy of the microwave background (this yields $h < 10^{-4}$ independently of z_*). Another constraint comes from the precision with which the Hubble law is obeyed. Equation (4.1) implies that the waves induce an apparent shear of $\Omega_g^{\frac{1}{2}}$ x (Hubble expansion) on scales $\lesssim \ell$. Though these latter limits are less sensitive, they are more 'robust' in that they do not involve any extrapolation back to early (and very different) eras in the Universe.

Figure 5 collects together various limits on a stochastic background. Doppler tracking of spacecraft could be very sensitive for $\nu \simeq 10^{-7}$ Hz, and pulsar timing holds prospects of great improvement at still lower frequencies. In assessing how significant these are, one should bear in mind that there is a plausible class of models for galaxy formation (discussed in §3), involving collapsing massive objects of mass M which could yield $\Omega_g \simeq 10^{-3}$ at periods up to $\gtrsim 10^2\ (M/10^4 M_\odot)$ seconds (equation 3.3), but that the only non-primordial sources at still longer periods

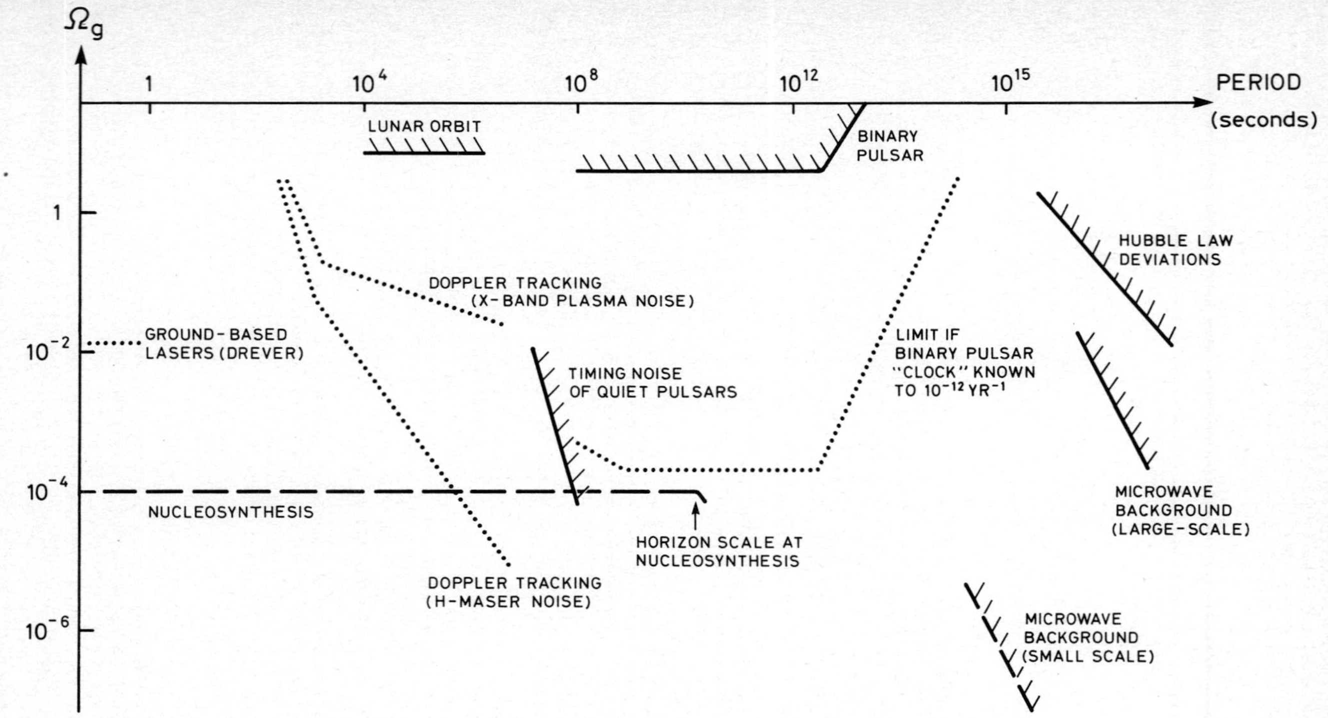

Figure 5. A schematic compilation of the various limits to a low-frequency stochastic background. The 'shaded' lines indicate limits that can already be set. The dotted lines show the levels of sensitivity that can feasibly be attained within a decade; the pulsar timing limits also are capable of substantial refinement. The long dashes denote limits which depend on assumptions about early cosmological epochs.

(e.g. wide binaries) are likely to be very much weaker. The cosmological observations yield worthwhile limits only at ultra-low frequencies where there is no possibility of there being any significant 'astrophysical' sources; the cosmological limits are nevertheless important in that they provide the strongest constraints we have on cosmological models which predict comparable contributions to Ω_g from every 'octave' of frequency.

I am grateful for helpful discussions with many people, and would particularly like to thank Mitch Begelman, Bruno Bertotti, Roger Blandford, Dick Bond, Bernard Carr, Doug Eardley, Ron Hellings and Bahram Mashhoon for advice and/or collaborative work on the topics summarised in these lectures.

REFERENCES

Adams, P.J., Hellings, R.W., Zimmerman, R.L., Farhoosh, H., Levine, D.I. and Zeldich, S. 1982. Astrophys.J., 253, 1.

Begelman, M.C., Blandford, R.D. and Rees, M.J. 1980. Nature, 287, 307.

Begelman, M.C. and Rees, M.J. 1978. MNRAS, 185, 847.

Bekenstein, J.D. 1973. Astrophys.J., 183, 657.

Bertotti, B. and Carr, B.J. 1980. Astrophys.J., 236, 1000.

Bertotti, B., Carr, B.J. and Rees, M.J. 1982. MNRAS (in press).

Bertotti, B. and Trevese, D. 1972. Nuovo Cim. 2B, 223.

Blandford, R.D. 1979. in Smarr (1979).

Bond, J.R. and Carr, B.J. 1982 in preparation.

Boriakoff, V., Ferguson, D.C., Haugan, M.H., Terzian, Y. and Teukolsky, S. 1982. Astrophys.J. (in press).

Canizares, C. 1982. Astrophys.J. (in press).

Carr, B.J. 1978. Comments Astrophys., 7, 161.

Carr, B.J. 1980. Astron.Astrophys., 89, 6.

Carr, B.J., Bond, J.R. and Arnett, W.D. 1982. Astrophys.J. (in press).

Carr, B.J. and Rees, M.J. 1982. MNRAS (submitted).

Cordes, J.M. 1980. Astrophys.J., 237, 216.

Cordes, J.M. and Greenstein, G. 1981. Astrophys.J., 234, 640.

Cordes, J.M. and Helfand, D.J. 1980. Astrophys.J., 234, 640.

Detweiler, S. 1979. Astrophys.J., 234, 1100.

Efstathiou, G. and Jones, B.J.T. 1980. Comments Astrophys., 8, 169.

Estabrook, F.B., Hellings, R.W., Wahlquist, H.D. and Woolf, R.S. 1979. in Smarr (1979), p. 37.

Fitchett, M. 1982. MNRAS (in press).

Frank, J. and Rees, M.J. 1976. MNRAS, 176, 633.

Gott, J.R. 1981. Astrophys.J., 243, 140.

Grishchuk, L. 1977. Ann. N.Y.Acad.Sci., 302, 439.

Heggie, D.C. 1975. MNRAS, 173, 729.

Helfand, D.J., Taylor, J.H., Backus, P.R. and Cordes, J.M. 1980. Astrophys.J., 237, 206.

Hellings, R.W. 1981. Phys.Rev., D23, 832.

Isaacson, R.A. 1968. Phys.Rev., 166, 1263.

Kashlinsky, A. and Rees, M.J. 1982. MNRAS (submitted).

Mashhoon, B. 1982. MNRAS, 199, 659.

Mashhoon, B., Carr, B.J. and Hu, B.L. 1981. Astrophys.J., 246, 569.

Mashhoon, B. and Grishchuk, L.P. 1980. Astrophys.J., 236, 990.

Moncrief, V. 1979. Astrophys.J., 238, 333.

Ostriker, J.P. 1979 in Smarr (1979).

Ostriker, J.P. 1980. Comments Astrophys., 8, 177.

Ostriker, J.P. and Tremaine, S.D. 1975. Astrophys.J.(Lett.), 202, 113.

Peebles, P.J.E. 1980. in "Physical Cosmology", ed. R. Balian, J. Audouze and D.N. Schramm (North-Holland, Amsterdam), p. 213.

Rees, M.J. 1977. Proc. Pavia Symposium on "Experimental Gravitation", ed. B. Bertotti, p. 423.
Rees, M.J. 1978. Observatory, 98, 210.
Rees, M.J., Begelman, M.C., Blandford and Phinney, E.S. 1982. Nature, 295, 17.
Rosi, L.A. and Zimmerman, R.L. 1976. Ap.Space Sci., 45, 447.
Saslaw, W.C., Valtonen, M. and Aarseth, S.J. 1974. Astrophys.J., 190, 253.
Shapiro, S.L. and Teukowsky, S. 1979. Astrophys.J.(Lett.), 234, L177.
Smarr, L. 1979 (editor) "Sources of Gravitational Radiation", (Cambridge U.P.)
Soltan, A. 1982. MNRAS (in press).
Starobinsky, A.A. 1979. Pis'ma JETP, 30, 719.
Tarbet, P.W. and Rowan-Robinson, M. 1982. Nature, 298, 711.
Taylor, J.H., Hulse, R.A., Fowler, L.A., Gullahorn, G.E. and Rankin, J.M. 1976. Astrophys.J.(Lett.), 206, L63.
Taylor, J.H., Fowler, L.A. and McCulloch, P.M. 1979. Nature, 277, 437.
Taylor, J.H. and Weisberg, J.M. 1982. Astrophys.J., 253, 908.
Thorne, K.S. 1978 in "Theoretical Principles in Astrophysics and Relativity" ed. N.R. Lebovitz et al. (Univ. of Chicago Press).
Thorne, K.S. and Braginsky, V.B. 1975. Astrophys.J.(Lett.), 204, L1.
Vilenkin, A. 1981. Phys.Rev., D24, 2082.
White, S.D.M. and Rees, M.J. 1978. MNRAS, 183, 341.
Young, P.J. 1981. Astrophys.J., 244, 756.
Zipoy, D.M. and Bertotti, B. 1968. Nueovo Cim., 56B, 195.

INTERFEROMETRIC DETECTORS FOR GRAVITATIONAL RADIATION

R.W.P. Drever

California Institute of Technology, Pasadena
and
University of Glasgow, Glasgow, Scotland

1. INTRODUCTION

Most of the experiments aimed at the detection of gravitational radiation carried out to date have employed resonant bar gravity wave detectors, in which changes in longitudinal vibration of a suspended metal bar, due to the apparent differential action of the gravity wave on the material towards the ends of the bar, are sought. An alternative approach, in which changes in the relative motions of two or more widely separated and nearly free test masses are monitored using laser interferometry, is now being developed in several laboratories. We shall outline here some of the principles and ideas behind these laser interferometer gravitational wave detectors, and also some possibilities for further development of these techniques which seem interesting for future experiments.

An obvious way one might consider detecting gravity waves is through the changes in separation of free test particles, and the idea of using optical interferometers for observing this has certainly occurred to many physicists: indeed one might wonder why so few searches for gravity waves have been made this way. The smallness of the expected effects provides the main answer: for even the relatively strong signal from a supernova in our galaxy would give a relative motion in a pair of test masses 10 meters apart of only 10^{-16} m, and the idea of measuring this in a time of order of a millisecond using light of wavelength nearly 10^{10} times larger than this is not initially attractive. With the resonant bar technique, however, the test masses are linked together by the elasticity of a metal bar chosen to resonate near the frequency of interest, extending the time available for the measurement up to the damping time of the bar, and enabling piezo-electric or capacitative transducers to be used which approach this order of sensitivity. These resonant bar detectors, pioneered by Joseph Weber, have been, and are being, successfully developed in many laboratories.

If one looks for much higher sensitivity, however, as may be required for detection of supernova signals from the distance of the Virgo cluster, the very small energy changes to be sensed in a resonant bar detector do impose serious practical difficulties. Thermal noise in the bar, and transducer sensitivity,are both severe problems, even in a low temperature system. It used to be thought that quantum limits would set a fundamental barrier, but there now appear to be ways of avoiding these in principle and the thermal noise seems to be the dominant problem. In this region of gravity wave sensitivity, there are of course severe problems with free mass detectors too; but with these, there is the important advantage that the displacements to be observed may be increased considerably by increasing the distance between the masses - in principle till the distance becomes comparable to half the wavelength of the gravity wave, typically many tens of kilometers. Thermal noise is made even less important by the fact that there is no need for any material connection between the test masses to resonate near the frequencies of interest. A free mass detector also looks likely to operate over a wider range of frequencies than resonant bar instruments. These considerations have made it seem worth while to investigate and develop possibilities for free-mass gravity wave detectors with optical displacement sensing.

2. SENSITIVITY DESIRABLE

The wide spectrum of gravitational radiation signals expected from astronomical phenomena of various types presents a considerable range of possible targets for experimental searches, if adequate sensitivity can be achieved. Much effort has gone into estimating radiation fluxes, and recent work in this area is reviewed elsewhere in this volume. Several summaries of spectra of gravitational radiation anticipated at the earth have also been published.[1] A part of the spectrum relatively accessible to earth-bound experiments is that in the region between a few tens of hertz and a few kilohertz and here signals from stellar collapse in our galaxy may give amplitudes of order 10^{-17}, but probably occurring at a rate less than one per year. For a pulse rate of order one per month a sensitivity of order 10^{-21} or better in gravity wave amplitude may be required. Indeed at sensitivities around this several types of sources may become detectable and this might be an interesting target to consider for future pulse experiments- at least in the long term. Other types of signals are also possible targets, such as the continuous gravitational radiation from pulsars, or a stochastic background from the big bang or from stellar collapse processes occurring at an early epoch. In these cases the gravity wave amplitudes expected are even smaller than from impulsive events, but the continuous nature of the signal may in principle enable higher sensitivity to be achieved with an appropriate detector and suitable mode of operation, as we will consider later.

3. BASIC ARRANGEMENT

To attempt to measure by optical means a change in distance between a pair of masses of order one part in 10^{21} would require an exceptionally stable wavelength standard; and there are obvious advantages in making a differential measurement of two almost equal baselines perpendicular to one another, which may be oppositely affected by a gravitational wave of suitable polarisation and direction of propagation. In principle this might be done using a Michelson interferometer to compare distances between mirrors attached to three test masses suspended like pendulums, as schematically indicated in Figure 1. Monochromatic light is not

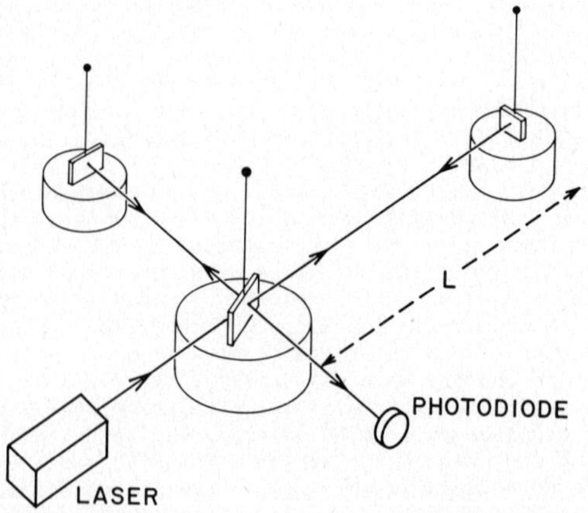

Figure 1

essential for such a measurement, but a laser is a convenient source because of the intensity and directional properties of its output. Let us assume that the gravitational waves of interest have a period short compared with the period of the pendulum suspensions, so that the test masses may be regarded as effectively free for small horizontal motions, and consider some of the more basic noise sources expected in a measurement of a short gravitational wave pulse.

3.1 Quantum Limit.

One limit to the sensitivity of a pulse measurement would be set by the quantum uncertainty in the position of each of the free masses. For detection of change in position over a time τ, the duration of the gravity wave pulse, the smallest displacement detectable is approximately $(2\hbar\tau/m)^{\frac{1}{2}}$, where m is the mass and $2\pi\hbar$ is Planck's Constant. If the baseline L between the masses is 40 m, the pulse duration τ is one millisecond, and test mass m = 100 kg, this quantum uncertainty would set a limit to gravity wave amplitude, h, detectable at unity signal to noise ratio, of order $h = 10^{-21}$. Thus for a 40 m detector, the quantum limit is of the same order as our target sensitivity for short pulses, and it could be reduced further by increasing the baseline. In fact the quantum limit is not likely to be a serious difficulty in searches for short pulses with this type of detector, although it may become important in measurements of long pulses or continuous signals. In practice, photon counting error is more likely to be a problem.

3.2 Photon Counting Error.

As the motions expected are small compared with the wavelength of the light, only a small change in output light intensity can be anticipated, and in a simple system this must be detected in the presence of intensity fluctuations due to photon counting statistics, at the least.[2] In the arrangement in Figure 1, a single photodetector is indicated receiving light from one side of the beamsplitter. In this situation, it may be shown that the displacement sensitivity set by photon counting error depends on the initial phase difference between the two components making up the output light, and optimum photon-shot-noise-limited sensitivity is obtained when the phase difference tends to π, that is near a dark fringe in the output light. If it is assumed that the photodiode has unity quantum efficiency, then the corresponding limit to the amplitude of gravitational wave detectable is $h = (\lambda\hbar c/ 8\pi L^2 I \tau)^{\frac{1}{2}}$, where I is the laser power, λ is the wavelength of the light, and c is the velocity of light. An alternative mode of operation would be to use two photodiodes, one detecting light from each side of the beamsplitter; and in this case the same overall sensitivity may be obtained anywhere in the fringe pattern. In either case, if we take a laser power of 1 watt at a wavelength of 500 nm, a baseline L = 40 m and measuring time τ of one millisecond as before, the gravity wave amplitude giving unity signal to noise ratio against the photon counting error is $h = 2 \times 10^{-17}$. This is far from our target sensitivity; and if we were to attempt to approach the quantum limit by merely increasing the laser power in this simple configuration we would require many megawatts of light.

It may be noted that some pioneering experiments with this type of gravity wave detector have been carried out using a configuration essentially similar to this by Moss and Forward[3], who showed that performance near the photon noise limit for a low power laser could be achieved.

An ingenious proposal for reducing photon counting error was recently made by C. M. Caves[4], who suggested use of squeezed photon states. By altering the distribution of vacuum fluctuations between two orthogonal phases, the photon counting fluctuations may be decreased at the expense of increased but less significant fluctuations in differential radiation pressure on the test masses. Practical application looks difficult at present, due partly to losses in the non-linear optical elements required; but the idea is in principle an extremely interesting one.

An important practical method for improving photon-noise limited sensitivity was suggested by R. Weiss[5]: the use of optical delay lines to reflect the light beam many times between the test masses, and thus increase the optical phase shift resulting from relative motion. Experimental work on this type of multiple-reflection Michelson interferometer has been, or is being, carried out at several laboratories including M.I.T., the Max Planck Institute at Munich[6], and the University of Glasgow.[7]

4. MULTIREFLECTION MICHELSON INTERFEROMETERS

A simplified schematic arrangement for a multireflection Michelson interferometer gravity wave detector is shown in Figure 2. Here the light is made to traverse the distance between the test masses many times by a suitable optical system, such as a Herriott delay line, before it recombines at the beamsplitter. This increases the total phase shift experienced by the light for a given movement of the masses by the number of round trips in each arm: and by using a suitable concave mirror configuration to minimize diffraction losses this number can be made large. In practice the useful number of reflections may be limited by one of two factors: the reflection losses at the mirror, or the total light travel time within each arm of the interferometer. In the first case, with mirror losses important, it may be shown that optimum photon-noise-limited sensitivity is obtained with a number of reflections in each arm equal to $2/(1-R)$, where R is the mirror reflectivity. The sensitivity achieved is then better than that of a simple Michelson interferometer by a factor of $e(1-R)$, where $e = 2.72...$ In a system with baseline $L = 40m$, mirror reflectivity $R = 0.997$, and other parameters as before, this would give a gravity wave sensitivity of order $h = 10^{-19}$.

If, however, the baseline were large enough, and the mirror reflectivity high enough to cause light making $2/(1-R)$ reflections to spend a time within the system longer than the time scale in which the gravity wave reverses its sign, then

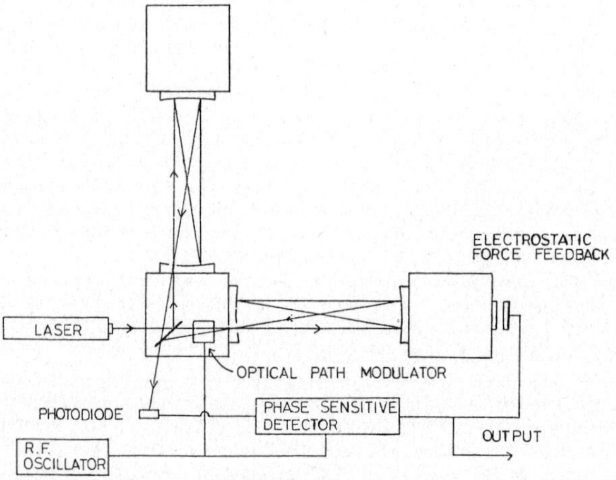

Figure 2

some cancellation of signal could occur. In this case it would be nearer optimum to choose the number of reflections to make the light spend a time in each arm equal to the time scale of the gravity wave. The sensitivity then becomes independent of arm length; and for a storage time of one millisecond and a laser power of 1 W, this could correspond to $h = 2 \times 10^{-21}$ for either a 40 m armlength system with 8000 reflections or a 4 km armlength system with 80 reflections.

These examples are idealised, of course, but they do suggest that interesting sensitivities might be achieved with this type of gravity wave detector if the many practical problems could be overcome. Also, there are some new ideas for improving the photon-noise-limited sensitivity even further, as we shall discuss later.

One practical difficulty in the optical sensing system just described became apparent in early experiments at Munich and at Glasgow - the potentially serious effect of incoherent scattering of light at the multireflection mirrors or elsewhere in the system. If scattered light reaches the photodetector having traversed a path different from that of the main beam, it will differ in phase from it by an amount dependent both on the path difference and the instantaneous wavelength of the light. The path difference involved can be very long - comparable to the total travel distance through the system - so small fluctuations in wavelength may give relatively large phase fluctuations in the output, particularly as the phase fluctuation in the resultant beam is proportional to the relative amplitude of the scattered light and not its relative intensity. The effect may be reduced by precise stabilisation of the wavelength of the laser, and also by arranging that the spots on the multireflection mirrors where successively reflections take place do not overlap, but it may still be important in a large system. The Munich group suggested[8] that the effect might be reduced further by modulating the wavelength of the laser light through an amount chosen to make the phase difference of the major components of the scattered light average to zero over the integration time of the measurement. Another approach would be to make the path traveled by scattered light equal to that of the main beam, and this may in fact be achieved if another type of optical system, a Fabry-Perot cavity, is used instead of a Michelson interferometer with many discrete reflections in each arm.

5. OPTICAL CAVITY INTERFEROMETERS

5.1 Principle.

The idea of using changes in the resonant frequency of an optical (or microwave) cavity to detect small motions is an old one, but one practical method of using optical cavities in gravity wave detectors was outlined only relatively recently.[9] The principle is indicated in Figure 3. Light from a laser passes through a beamsplitter to a pair of Fabry-Perot cavities formed between mirrors attached to the three test masses. If the lengths of the two cavities are adjusted to give resonance with the light from the laser, then differential changes in length may be sensed by changes in the resonance conditions and small changes near resonance may be detected by measuring phase changes between light within each cavity and the input beam, or directly between one cavity and another. The phase difference might be detected by interference between light emerging from each of the cavities back through its input mirror, possibly by using the high frequency phase modulation technique shown in Fig. 2 in connection with the multireflection Michelson interferometer. One way of carrying this out is indicated schematically in Figure 4. Here light from the cavities is phase modulated by two Pockels cells, P1 and P2, driven in antiphase at a suitable radiofrequency, and is detected by photodiode D1. The output from this photodiode, when synchronously demodulated, can give a measure of the phase difference between the light in the cavities. An optical isolator I is used to prevent reflected light affecting the operation of the laser. The additional photodetectors D2 and D3

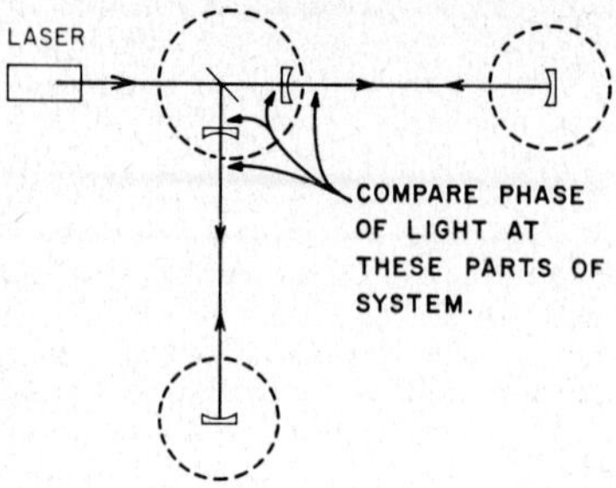

Figure 3

are for auxiliary functions which will be described later.

The maximum sensitivity in this arrangement is obtained when the second mirror in each cavity has the highest reflectivity available, R, say, and the reflectivity of the input mirror for each cavity is chosen either to give optimum photon-noise-limited displacement measurement or to give a light storage time equal to the time scale of the gravity wave, whichever is appropriate. In the former case it may be shown that the gravity wave sensitivity is given approximately by $h = (1-R)\ (\lambda\ \hbar\ c/\ 8\pi\ L^2\ I\ \tau)^{\frac{1}{2}}$, where it is assumed that absorption and scattering losses in the transmission of light by the input mirrors of the cavities are negligible (that is, transmission coefficient = 1-R). This expected

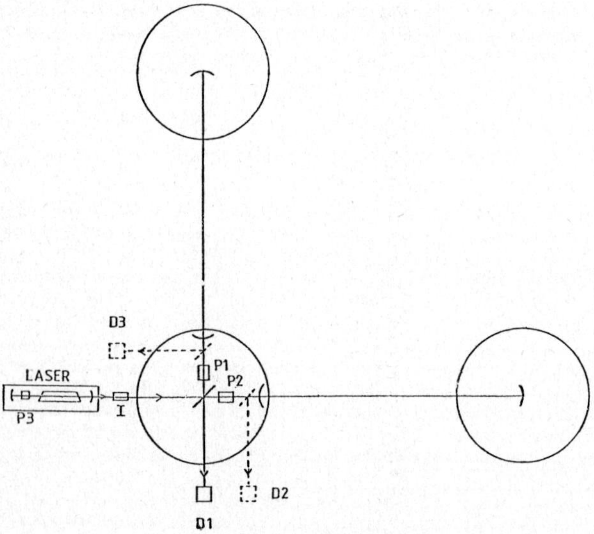

Figure 4

sensitivity is better by a factor of about 2 than the sensitivity obtainable by a multireflection Michelson interferometer using mirrors of the same reflectivity, but transmission losses may degrade this so that in practice the photon noise limit to sensitivity of the two types of optical system is likely to be roughly equal.

There are several advantages of this type of cavity interferometer over the delay-line Michelson system, apart from the possibility of reduced phase noise from scattered light. The diameter of the cavity mirrors can be considerably smaller than that of delay-line mirrors; and for example, even with cavities 10 km long, a mirror diameter of 18 cm is sufficient to make diffraction losses less than 1 part in 10^5 for light of wavelength 500 nm. This reduces the diameter of vacuum pipe required, and also may make it easier to keep mechanical resonances in the mirrors and their mountings high compared with the frequency of the gravity waves, thus minimizing thermal noise. The Fabry-Perot system has, however, some obvious disadvantages too- particularly the requirement for very precise control of the wavelength of the laser and of the lengths of the cavities. Indeed with long cavities of the high finesse desirable here exceptional short-term wavelength stability is required from the laser. A special laser stabilisation technique has been developed to provide this.

5.2 Laser wavelength stabilisation.

The principle of the laser wavelength control system being used is shown in Figure 5. Plane polarised light from the laser is phase modulated by passage through a Pockels cell, at a frequency in the range of 10 to 40 MHz, and then enters one of the Fabry-Perot cavities through a polarising beamsplitter and a quarter-wave plate. The axes of the quarter-wave plate are oriented at $\pm 45^{\circ}$ to the polarisation of the input light, so that circularly polarised light enters the cavity. Light coming back from the input mirror of the cavity is circularly polarised in the opposite sense, is transformed into plane polarised light with polarisation orthogonal to that of the input beam, and is reflected by the polarising beamsplitter to the photodetector. The light arriving at the photodiode can be considered to have two components: the

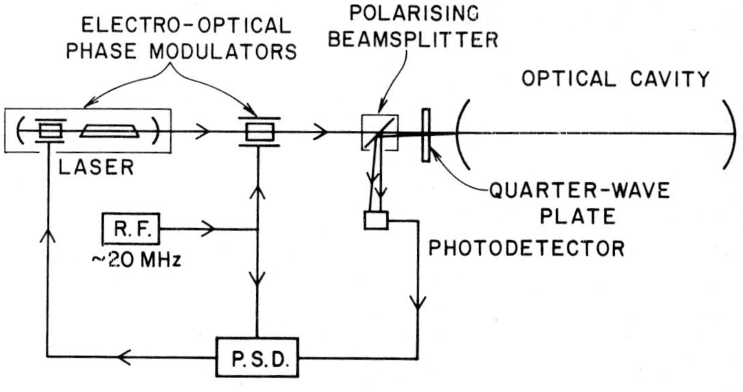

Figure 5

phase-modulated laser light directly reflected by the input cavity mirror, and light emerging from within the cavity - which has built up over the cavity storage time and thus has had its modulation sidebands removed. In the figure, these components are drawn as diverging rays to make the operation clearer, although they are of course coincident in reality. If the laser light is precisely in resonance with the cavity these two components have opposite average phase, and the photodiode output has no component at the modulation frequency. If the laser is slightly off resonance, the photodiode gives a signal at the modulation frequency whose amplitude and phase indicates the magnitude and sign of the error. Demodulation of the photodiode signal by a phase sensitive detector (P.S.D.) gives a voltage signal which may be applied to a second Pockels cell within the laser cavity itself, so that the wavelength of the light from the laser is driven closer to the cavity resonance, and the laser becomes locked in wavelength to the cavity. To achieve a high degree of stabilisation at the gravity-wave frequency it is important that the control system has a wide bandwidth, and a useful feature of the arrangement is that the rise time of the phase error signal is not affected by the fact that the cavity may have a very long storage time.

Early experimental work on this laser-cavity stabilisation technique has been done at the Joint Institute for Laboratory Astrophysics, Boulder, using dye and helium-neon lasers* and at Glasgow, and subsequently Caltech, with argon ion lasers[10,11], and has shown that adequate stabilisation for at least the current stage of development of the Fabry-Perot interferometers can be achieved.

A considerable amount of experimental work relating to gravity wave detectors using Fabry-Perot interferometers has been carried out at Glasgow and at Caltech, much of the earlier work being done with a slightly different arrangement, shown in simplified form in Figure 6. Here triangular cavities are used instead of 2-mirror cavities so that optical feedback to the laser is avoided without use of

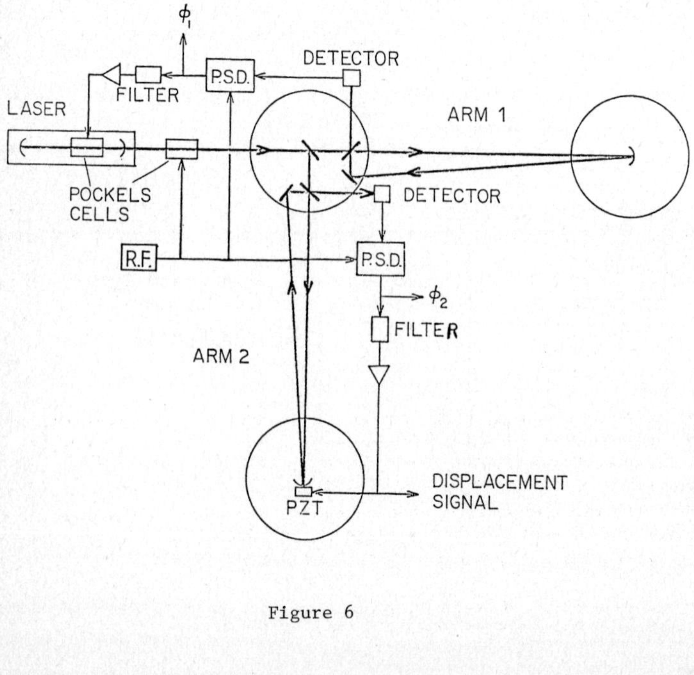

Figure 6

isolators, and separate detection of signals from the two cavities is used to simplify the optical system. The laser is shown arranged to be locked in wavelength to the right-hand cavity (arm 1) in the figure by the method described above; and a similar phase measuring system is then used to give a fine adjustment to the length of the lower cavity (arm 2) by a piezoelectric transducer (PZT) on which one of the cavity mirrors is mounted, so that this cavity becomes locked into resonance with the wavelength of the light. With this arrangement, a signal corresponding to a gravity wave disturbance may be obtained, approximately, from the feedback voltage applied to the piezoelectric transducer, or, more precisely, from a suitable combination of this signal with the phase error signals ϕ_1 and ϕ_2 from the two feedback loops.

It may be noted that separate detection of resonance in the two cavities, as indicated here, does in principle degrade the photon-noise-limited sensitivity by a factor of 2, but it is convenient for initial experiments since it avoids need for Pockels cells on any of the test masses, or matching of cavity finesse. Optical systems more like that shown in Figure 4 are now being developed. Here the auxiliary photodiodes D2 and D3 shown dotted are intended for laser stabilisation and to facilitate monitoring of the two cavities, and would be arranged to use only a small sample of the total available light.

The experimental development of laser interferometer gravity wave detectors based on either the multireflection Michelson or the optical cavity system outlined has led to overall arrangements which are in practice considerably more complex than suggested by the diagrams here, for additional feedback systems have to be incorporated to control orientation and position of the test masses in the presence of seismic disturbances, and fluctuations in direction and position of the laser beam have to be reduced by passive or active optical systems. Although many problems remain to be overcome, the experimental work has gone far enough to make it seem likely that optical sensing performance close to that indicated by the simple theoretical estimates given above may indeed be achievable by either of the techniques we have outlined. It may be useful to consider some other basic noise sources at this point, and in particular thermal noise - for this is a limiting factor in current resonant bar gravity wave detectors, and is not negligible here.

6. THERMAL NOISE IN LASER INTERFEROMETERS

The real or apparent fluctuations in motion of test masses have to be carefully considered in any gravity wave experiment, for the displacements to be observed are usually small compared with the mean amplitudes of thermal motion. In the type of nearly free mass detector discussed here the mechanical thermal noise may be conveniently divided into two parts - that associated with the low frequency pendulum mode of oscillation of the test masses, and that associated with internal degrees of freedom of the test mass and mirror structure itself. Relevant analyses of thermal noise fluctuations have been given by Weiss[5], Braginsky and Manukin[12], and others; we will just summarise some results here.

6.1 Thermal noise - pendulum mode.

With a simple pendulum suspension of convenient length, the resonant frequency for the pendulum mode of a test mass is of order 1 Hz or lower, well below the frequency of interest for initial gravity wave searches. The power spectral density of displacement is given approximately by $(\delta x)^2/\delta f = 4\ kT\ \omega_o/m\ Q\ \omega^4$, where ω_o is the angular frequency of the pendulum resonance, Q the quality factor of the resonance, m the test mass, ω the angular frequency of interest, k = Boltzman's Constant, and T the temperature. Some early tests at Glasgow suggest that construction of a simple pendulum with Q near 10^6 is quite practicable;and if we take this value for Q, a mass m=10 kg, $\omega_o=2\pi$, $\omega=2\pi.1000$,and T=300 we find that in a system with a 40 m baseline, thermal noise would set a limit to sensitivity of the order of $h = 3 \times 10^{-22}$ in a bandwidth of 1 kHz. This component of thermal noise is therefore not expected to be very serious at these frequencies, if an effective high Q can be maintained in a practical suspension system ;and a longer baseline will reduce the noise further. However thermal noise may well become important at lower frequencies.

6.2 Thermal noise - internal modes.

Internal vibrations of the test mass structure can be very complex and there may be many modes near the frequency of interest when the test mass incorporates several mirrors and other components. To minimize the thermal noise in the frequency region of interest, it is desirable to keep the resonant frequency of all modes as high as possible, and certainly high compared with the gravity wave frequency - which may not be easy. In this case, for a single mode of angular resonant frequency ω_0 , the power spectrum of displacement is given approximately by $(\delta x)^2/\delta f = 4\,kT/m\,Q\,\omega_0^{\,3}$. If we take as example m = 10 kg, T = 300, $\omega_0 = 2\pi.5000$ and $Q = 10^6$, we find that this sets a limit of about $h = 6 \times 10^{-21}$ in a bandwidth of 1 kHz with a system of baseline 40 m. These values for Q and ω_0 are however not easy to achieve in a complex structure. Increase of baseline makes this component of thermal noise less significant, but it is evident that careful design of the test mass structure is required.

It may be noted that the Fabry-Perot cavity type of interferometer may have a disadvantage here in that it is likely to require more precise mirror adjustment than a Michelson system, and thus lead to a more complex structure for at least one of the test masses. One arrangement which we suggest may ameliorate this problem involves use of two separate and very simple test masses at the junction of the two baselines, each containing merely a single cavity mirror,with a separate and more complex suspended structure incorporating the rest of the optical components. In this way, the thermal noise may be minimized in the parts where it is most significant, although the system as a whole does become more complex. At the present stage these problems have not been fully investigated, although considerable advances in reducing thermal noise in a Michelson interferometer system have been made by the Munich group. At present, it appears that to keep internal thermal noise sufficiently small does require careful design of the test masses, but we feel that the problems involved are by no means insoluble ones.

Some notes on the question of seismic isolation of an interferometer gravity wave detector may be appropriate at this point.

7. SEISMIC ISOLATION

Isolation from seismic disturbance is an important practical problem for any type of gravitational wave detector. In the region of the spectrum around 1 kHz, however, it has been tackled very successfully in work with resonant bar gravity wave detectors. At these frequencies good vibration attenuation can be obtained by simple stacks of lead or steel masses alternating with layers of rubber, of the general type developed and widely used since the initial experiments of Joseph Weber. These same methods are applicable for interferometer detectors, and indeed in some ways the problems are simpler than for resonant bar detectors of the same sensitivity, for the displacements to be observed are larger with the laser detectors due to the much longer baselines involved. The seismic motions at the ends of a long baseline are of course less correlated than the motions at the two ends of a resonant bar, but the isolation of the simple pendulum suspension of a single test mass is sufficient on its own to give good attentuation at 1 kHz. Overall, it seems that seismic isolation is unlikely to be a very serious problem for gravity wave frequencies near 1 kHz, although it becomes rapidly more difficult at lower frequencies. It may be noted that low frequency motions of the suspended test masses can give dynamic range problems in optical interferometer systems, and active feedback systems are necessary to damp and restrain the low frequency movements of the masses. The masses may be controlled by applying magnetic or electrostatic forces, or by mechanical motion of the points from which the suspension wires are supported, and all of these methods have proved satisfactory to some degree. The problems involved are technically quite challenging ones, and the solutions are interesting, but it is not appropriate to discuss these in detail here in this article which relates more to basic limitations to the interferometer techniques.

We have now discussed many aspects of laser interferometer gravity wave detectors and have indicated how there may be real possibilities for achieving gravity wave amplitude sensitivities of the order of 10^{-21} for 1 millisecond pulses, with large scale instruments of this type. The most serious limitation to sensitivity in this part of the spectrum looks likely to come from photon counting noise, and although this may possibly be reduced by increases in laser power, or use of multiple lasers, there would seem to be practical limits to these solutions. It may be useful to briefly discuss here some relatively new ideas which suggest alternative ways of improving sensitivity, although it should be emphasized that these suggestions relate more to future possibilities than to the current stage in the experimental development of the techniques.

8. POSSIBILITIES FOR FUTURE ENHANCEMENT IN SENSITIVITY

8.1 Possibility for more efficient use of the light.

It has been mentioned in Section 3.2 that in a Michelson interferometer using a single photodetector maximum sensitivity is obtained when the detector is near a dark fringe; and if the system is efficient and adjusted so that one fringe extends over the whole width of the output beam this implies that most of the light leaves the interferometer through the other side of the beamsplitter. It has occurred to us that this light may be fed back into the interferometer by making it add coherently to the initial laser beam by means of an additional mirror of suitably chosen reflectivity, as indicated in Figure 7. Accurate adjustment of path lengths or of laser wavelength would, of course, be necessary to insure that maximum enhancement of light is achieved, and one way of doing this might be with the phase modulation laser-cavity locking system described in Section 5, using a phase modulating Pockels cell P3 and additional photodetector D2, with the system arranged to minimise the light intensity at D2. The whole optical system then

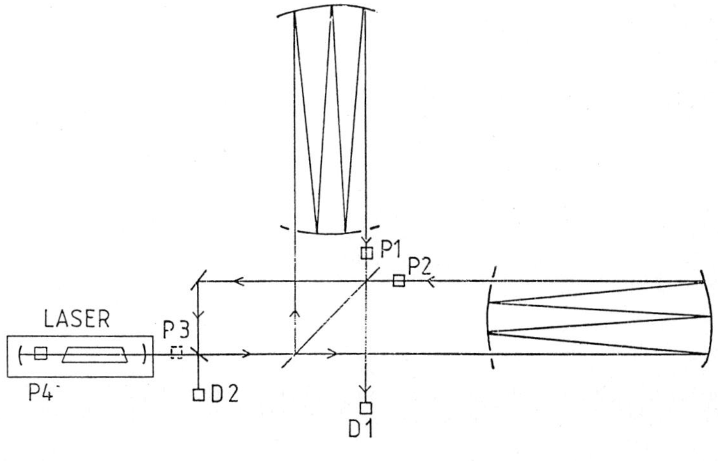

Figure 7

functions like a large Fabry-Perot cavity , and if losses are small and the input mirror reflectivity is suitably chosen there can be considerable enhancement of internal light flux. This arrangement is only useful if the combination of arm length and reflectivity of the delay line mirrors is such that the maximum achievable storage time of the light within each delay line is longer than the time-scale of the gravity waves of interest. The number of reflections in each arm would then be chosen to give a storage time which matches the gravity wave time-scale, and the light intensity within the whole system can then build up over a time approaching the maximum storage time permitted by the losses in the mirrors and other components. If the system is such that the dominant losses are those associated with delay line mirrors of reflectivity R, and the reflectivity of the feedback mirror is chosen for maximum light buildup, then the sensitivity is given approximately by $h = \{ \lambda \hbar (1-R)/2 \pi L I \tau^2 \}^{\frac{1}{2}}$, where I= output power of laser. If one considers a large system, with baseline L = 10km, and $(1-R) = 10^{-4}$, then the sensitivity would be of order 10^{-22} for 1 millisecond gravity wave pulses, with a laser power of 10 watts. These parameters are not impossible ones for future experiments.

The same method may be applied to optical cavity interferometers also, as shown, for example in Figure 8. Again, the system is only useful if achievable storage times exceed the time-scale of the gravity waves of interest. The reflectivity of the input mirror of each cavity is chosen to give a storage time within the cavity which matches the time-scale of the gravity wave, which under these conditions would lead to reflection of a large fraction of the light incident on each cavity input mirror back towards the laser. An additional mirror is added in front of the laser to return most of this light back to the interferometer, with phase adjusted to enhance the input light from the laser. If the reflectivity of the input mirror is suitably chosen for maximum light buildup, then the

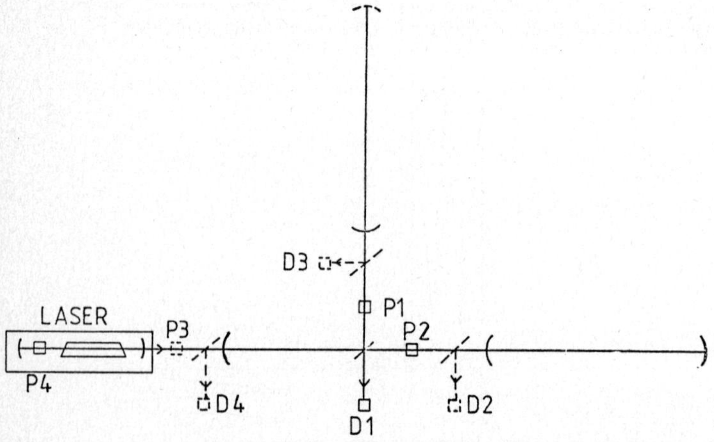

Figure 8

photon-noise-limited sensitivity of this system becomes essentially equal to that of the Michelson interferometer system just described. Precise adjustment of optical paths as well as laser wavelength is required to achieve correct phasing within this system, and auxiliary photodiodes D2, D3 and D4 along with phase modulators P1, P2 and P3 are indicated as means of achieving this. As the internal phase adjustment requires only a narrow bandwidth the photodiodes D2 and D3 need only remove a very small fraction of the light circulating within the system.

With these proposed techniques for re-use of light within an interferometer,[13] the optical system as a whole may be regarded as a large cavity which stores up light to an extent limited in principle only by the losses in the components. When a gravity wave pulse arrives, the resultant phase changes allow a part of this stored energy to pass out quickly to the output photodiode. The system may thus be quite energy-efficient, and it looks a promising one for future experiments.

8.2 A possibility for enhancing sensitivity for periodic signals.

Our discussion so far has concerned principally the detection of short gravity wave pulses, but it is evident that the same kind of apparatus could be used for searching for periodic gravity wave signals, such as those expected from pulsars, from rapidly rotating neutron star binaries, or possibly from vibrations of neutron stars or other objects. By use of appropriate data processing and integration over many periods of the gravity wave it is clear that better amplitude sensitivity may be obtained with periodic signals than with single pulses. Consideration of expected signal strengths from known sources, such as the Crab or Vela pulsar, does however suggest that it would be useful to have a sensitivity higher than obtainable in this way. We propose now a possible method for further enhancing the sensitivity of a laser interferometer detector for periodic signals. This technique, like the ones described in the previous section, depends on use of an optical system capable of giving very long light storage times - the condition in this case being that the combination of baseline length and mirror losses should enable light to be kept in the system for times long compared with the period of the expected signal.

The idea is most easily explained for a multireflection Michelson interferometer which in this application might have its optical system re-arranged as shown in Figure 9. Light from the laser enters the system through a beamsplitter, M1,

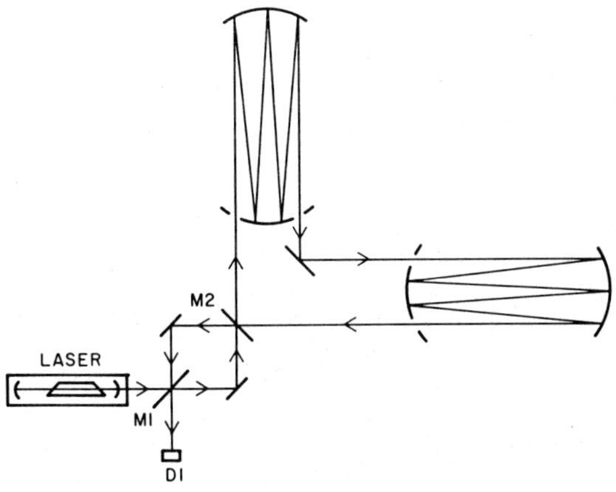

Figure 9

which divides it into two equal parts which pass through a mirror, M2, of suitably chosen high reflectivity and then traverse the delay lines in opposite directions. It is arranged that each delay line introduces a delay equal to half of the gravity wave period. Light travelling in the direction of the arrows which enters the upper delay line at a time when the gravity-wave-induced displacement of the test masses is changing its sign will have its phase shifted in one direction while it is within this delay line. It then leaves this delay line and enters the right-hand one just as the gravity-wave displacement is reversing, so that this light experiences a further shift of phase in the same direction in the second delay line. Most of the light then retraverses the first delay line where further phase shift takes place. Light passing through the delay lines in the opposite direction experiences a buildup of the opposite phase shift, and the phase differences generated over the total storage time of the system may eventually be detected at photodiode D1, possibly using a radiofrequency phase modulation system (omitted from the diagram for simplicity).

An optical cavity gravity wave detector can also be arranged in a similar way to have enhanced sensitivity for periodic signals, as indicated in Figure 10. Here the storage time of each cavity is made to equal half of the period of the expected signal by suitably choosing the reflectivity of mirrors M3 and M3';and by use of polarising beamsplitters (labelled POL. in the figure) and quarter-wave plates (labelled λ/4)the light is made to circulate from one cavity to the other, building up phase shift from a gravity wave signal over the total storage time of the system.

The buildup of phase differences over a long storage time can give a considerable improvement in the photon counting limit to the sensitivity of both these types of interferometers. In essence the sensitivity is improved over that obtainable in one period of the signal with a conventional multireflection system by a factor approximately equal to the ratio of the storage time to the period of the signal, with a further improvement by the square root of the number of periods integrated over. The photon counting limit to sensitivity becomes approximately

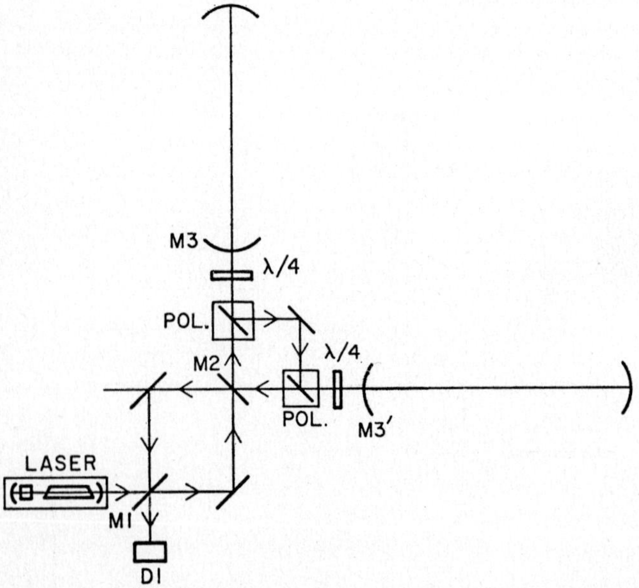

Figure 10

$h = \{ \lambda \hbar c (1-R)^2 / 2\pi I \tau' L^2 \}^{\frac{1}{2}}$, where R is the maximum mirror reflectivity available, and τ' is the total duration of the measurement. This arrangement can in principle give such a good photon counting limit to sensitivity that substitution of parameters for a large low-loss interferometer might make it seem straightforward to detect the expected gravity wave flux from the Crab or Vela pulsars. This is misleading, however, since other noise sources have to be considered also, and in this case thermal noise from the suspension and even the quantum limit for the test masses are likely to be serious problems. This type of interferometer will probably be more useful at slightly higher frequencies, perhaps for the more intense periodic signals which may follow some collapse processes.

Having now discussed techniques for detection of pulses and of periodic signals using laser interferometer gravity wave detectors, it might be worth mentioning briefly how these same instruments might be used to detect a stochastic background of gravitational radiation.

9. DETECTION OF A STOCHASTIC BACKGROUND

Laser interferometer detectors seem quite promising instruments for searches for a stochastic background of gravitational radiation, as might arise for example, from collapse of black holes at an early epoch. In a search of this type, the signal has the form of noise itself, and a considerable improvement in effective sensitivity can be obtained by use of a pair of detectors in a correlation mode to provide discrimination against internal noise from either instrument. Early experiments of this type have been carried out using resonant bar gravity wave detectors at Glasgow[14] and similar experiments have also been performed at Tokyo[15]. There is, however, a real possibility of achieving a much more interesting sensitivity with laser interferometers due to their higher expected intrinsic sensitivity together with wide bandwidth.

The principle of such an experiment is indicated in Figure 11 where the outputs

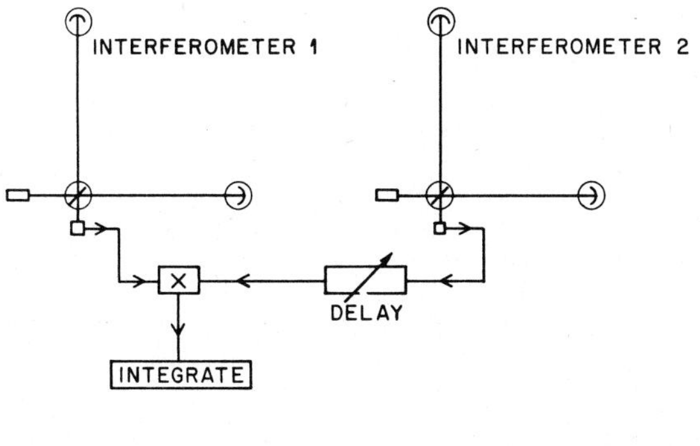

Figure 11

from two laser interferometric gravity wave detectors are multiplied together and integrated over a suitable observing time τ'. If the distance between the detectors is small compared with the wavelength of the gravitational radiation of interest, any common signal will give a correlated output and the power sensitivity obtained in the measurement becomes better than that achievable with a single detector alone by a factor of $(\pi B\tau')^{-\frac{1}{2}}$, where B is the bandwidth of each instrument by itself. If we take as example, a pair of optical cavity detectors with armlengths of 40 m, mirrors having reflectivity corresponding to $(1-R)=10^{-3}$ operating at a frequency centered on 100 Hz with a bandwidth of 100 Hz, and with other parameters as before, we might expect a gravity wave amplitude sensitivity for the individual detectors of the order of $2 \times 10^{-21}/\sqrt{Hz}$. An experiment involving correlation over 10^5 seconds could then set a limit of about $3 \times 10^{-23}/\sqrt{Hz}$ for radiation with the most favorable polarisation and flux direction. If it were assumed that gravitational radiation flux is concentrated in a frequency region near the frequency investigated, then an experiment of this type might set a limit to this gravity wave energy corresponding to a few percent of the closure density for the universe. With larger and more sensitive detectors such as those discussed earlier, correlation searches become feasible at a quite interesting level, and such experiments could form a very useful part of a general search for gravitational radiation of all types. They might, for example, provide the best sensitivity achievable for a wide range of unpredicted kinds of signals, such as large numbers of very small pulses, or nearly periodic signals of various types.

10. GENERAL REMARKS

It is hoped that the account given here of some current developments and ideas relating to laser interferometer gravity wave detectors gives a fair picture of the present state of this type of research. These instruments are complex and difficult ones, and their development presents a real challenge to the experimental physicist. It is too early yet to know which experimental approaches will prove most successful for the eventual unambiguous detection and investigation of gravitational wave signals, but the detectors discussed here seem at least as promising as other instruments of comparable cost and difficulty and the possibility of tailoring a single detector for several different types of experiment, suggested by some of the ideas outlined here, seems an interesting one. A considerable amount of difficult experimental work will still be necessary before experiments near the limits of sensitivity discussed here are likely to be made, but the prospects look good and the possibilities for real development of gravitational wave astronomy look interesting and exciting.

ACKNOWLEDGMENTS

The author would like to acknowledge the essential contributions of his colleagues at the California Institute of Technology and the University of Glasgow both in relation to discussions of principles and ideas and to underlying experimental work. The research in the USA is supported by the National Science Foundation (Grant NSF PHY82 04056) and in the UK by the Science and Engineering Research Council.

REFERENCES

(1) Thorne, K.S., Rev. Mod. Phys. 52 (1980) 285.
Smarr, L. Sources of Gravitational Radiation (Cambridge University Press, 1979).
Epstein, R. and Clark, J.P.A. in: Smarr, L. (ed.) Sources of Gravitational Radiation (Cambridge University Press, 1979).
Thorne, K.S. in: Lebovitz, N.R., Reid, W.H. and Vandervoort, P.O. (eds.) Theoretical Principles in Astrophysics and Relativity (University of Chicago Press, 1978) 149.
Douglass, D.H. and Braginsky,V.B., in:Hawking,S.W. and Israel, W.(eds.), General Relativity: An Einstein Centenary Survey (Cambridge University Press, 1979).
Tyson, J.A. and Giffard, R.P., Ann Rev. of Astro. Astrophys. 16 (1978) 521.
Press, W.H. and Thorne, K.S., Ann. Rev. of Astro. Astrophys. 10 (1972) 335.

(2) Edelstein, W.A., Hough, J., Pugh, J.R., and Martin, W., J. Phys. E. Sci. Instrum., 11 (1978) 710.
Caves, C.M., Phys. Rev. Letters 45 (1980) 75.

(3) Moss, G.E., Miller, L.R. and Forward, R.L., Appl.Opt. 10 (1971) 2495.
Forward, R.L., Phys. Rev. D17 (1978) 379.

(4) Caves, C.M., Phys. Rev. D23 (1981) 1693.

(5) Weiss,R., Progress Report 105, Res. Lab Electronics, MIT (1972) 54.

(6) Billing, H., Maischberger, K., Rudiger, A., Schilling, S., Schnupp, L. and Winkler, W., J. Phys. E12 (1979) 1043.

(7) Drever, R.W.P., Hough, J., Edelstein, W.A., Pugh, J.R., Martin, W., Proc. of the Intern. Sympos. on Experimental Gravitation, Pavia 1976, B. Bertotti (ed.) (Accad. Nazionale dei Lincei, 1977).

(8) Schilling, R., Schnupp, L., Winkler, W., Billing, H., Maischberger, K. and Rudiger, A., J. Phys. E. Sci. Instrum., 14 (1981) 65.

(9) Drever, R.W.P., Ford, G.M., Hough, J., Kerr, I., Munley, A.J., Pugh, J.R., Robertson, N.A. and Ward, H., 9th International Conference on General Relativity and Gravitation, GR9, Jena (1980), (in press).

(10) Drever, R.W.P., Hough, J., Munley, A.J., Lee, S-A., Spero, R., Whitcomb, S.E., Ward, H., Ford, G.M., Hereld, M., Robertson, N.A., Kerr , I., Pugh, J.R., Newton, G.P., Meers, B., Brooks III, E.D. and Gursel, Y., Proc. of the 5th International Conference on Laser Spectroscopy (Springer-Verlag, 1981) 33.

(11) Hough, J., Drever, R.W.P., Munley, A.J., Lee, S-A., Spero, R., Whitcomb, S.E., Ward, H., Ford, G.M., Hereld, M., Robertson, N.A., Kerr, I., Pugh, J.R., Newton, G.P., Meers, B., Brooks III, E.D. and Gursel, Y. Proc. of the NATO Advanced Study Institute, Bad Windsheim, West Germany 1981 (in press).

(12) Braginsky, V.B. and Manukin, A.B., Measurement of Small Forces in Physical Experiments (Nauka, Moscow, 1974; University of Chicago Press, 1977).

(13) Drever, R.W.P., Hough, J., Munley, A.J., Lee, S-A., Spero, R., Whitcomb, S.E., Ward, H., Ford, G.M., Hereld, M., Robertson, N.A., Kerr, I., Pugh, J.R., Newton, G.P., Meers, B., Brooks III, E.D. and Gursel, Y. Proc. of the NATO Advanced Study Institute, Bad Windsheim, West Germany 1981 (in press).

(14) Hough, J., Pugh, J.R., Bland, R. and Drever, R.W.P. Nature 254 (1975) 498.

(15) Hirakawa, H. and Narihara, K., Phys. Rev. Lett. 35 (1975) 330.

FOOTNOTE

*Some of the initial development and testing of this stabilisation technique was done in collaborative work by J.L. Hall and F.W. Kowalski of the Joint Institute for Laboratory Astrophysics, University of Colorado, and the University of Glasgow gravity wave group.[9]

RESONANT BAR DETECTORS FOR GRAVITATIONAL WAVES

David G. Blair

Department of Physics
University of Western Australia
Nedlands
Western Australia

CONTENTS

I INTRODUCTION

In 1960 Joseph Weber[1] published a paper setting out experimental techniques which could be used to detect the gravitational radiation which might originate from astrophysical sources. He showed that a mechanical mass quadrupole harmonic oscillator will be excited by gravitational waves. The harmonic oscillator, idealised as shown in Figure 1, could be a block of piezoelectric crystal, and a gravitational wave would induce a voltage across it, which could be measured with a sensitive amplifier. Equally, if the harmonic oscillator was a metal bar, vibrations induced in the bar could be detected by a capacitive transducer.

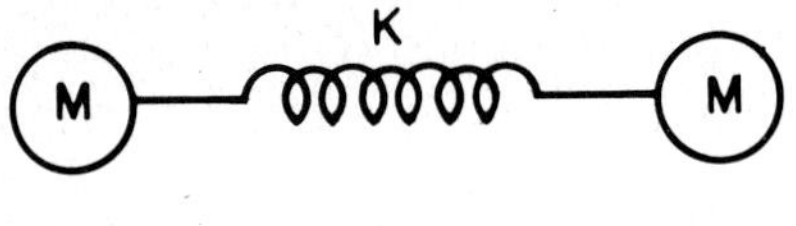

Figure 1. Harmonic oscillator excited by gravitational waves

Weber considered a range of possible detectors, from the earth itself whose ~ 1 cycle/hour normal modes would be excited by low frequency gravitational waves, to small piezoelectric crystals resonant at 10^7Hz. He particularly mentioned planned experimental searches at ~ 1 kHz and he suggested that gravitational wave spectral densities of 10^{-4} ergs - $(cm^2 \text{ sec Hz})^{-1}$ should be detectable.

The difference between the idealised quadrupole mass harmonic oscillator of Figure 1, and the practical distributed mass oscillator such as the earth or a cylindrical bar is, of course, that the distributed mass oscillator has a set of normal modes. The fundamental longitudinal mode is analogous to the mode of the idealised oscillator. All higher modes have reduced sensitivity to gravitational waves due to their reduced time varying quadrupole moment: even modes are not excited at all, while the effective cross section for odd modes falls as $1/n^2$. (n is the mode number). Thus follows the well known result that there is no advantage in making an antenna longer unless it is desired to use it at a lower frequency.

The problem of detecting gravitational radiation can be loosely understood as an impedance matching problem. Starting from Einstein's equations $\underline{T} = (c^4/8\pi G).\underline{G}$ we consider the coupling constant $c^4/8\pi G$ as a sort of metrical stiffness[2] or modulus of elasticity for space-time, with the dimensions of energy density per unit curvature. A gravitational wave is a wave in a medium with this extremely large stiffness. Since the propagation velocity is c, we can, by analogy with acoustic waves, identify the quantity c^3/G with the characteristic impedance of the medium. The material of the antenna on the other hand has an impedance ρv_s per unit area, where ρ is the density, and v_s is the sound velocity. For an antenna made of a molecular solid the impedance is ~ 10^8 kg sec^{-1}, whereas c^3/G is 4.5×10^{35} kg sec^{-1}. Thus on entering a molecular solid the total impedance to a gravitational wave increases fractionally: by a multiplicative factor of $(1 + 4.5 \times 10^{-27})$. The solid therefore has a tiny effect on the wave motion, and the interaction is very weak.

Large objects made of nuclear matter (neutron stars) with v_s comparable to c are much more closely impedance matched to gravitational waves so that significant absorption, refraction or diffraction can occur. However, the experimentalist who has no nuclear matter available for his use, is faced with a problem comparable to the problem he would have in detecting electromagnetic waves if he could only construct antennae from extremely dilute neutral gases with dielectric constant ~ $1 + 10^{-27}$.

The weak interaction of gravitational waves with matter was also emphasised by Weber. Any form of damping in an antenna can be characterised by a quality factor Q

$$Q = \omega \frac{(\text{maximum stored energy})}{(\text{power dissipated})} \tag{1}$$

One form of damping is by the re-radiation of gravitational waves. The Q-factor associated with this radiation damping Q_R is given by[1]

$$Q_R = 15c^5/2G\omega^3 m\ell^2. \tag{2}$$

Note that the mass m, frequency ω and length ℓ are not independent for practical antennae. The velocity of sound v_s (10^3-10^4 m $\text{sec}^{-1}$for almost all solids) determines ω for a given length ($\omega = \pi v_s/\ell$). The shape of the antenna determines the precise relation between the mass and length, but to assume $m = \rho \ell^3$ will not lead to gross errors. It follows that

$$Q_R = \frac{15\ c^5}{2\pi G^3\ \rho v_s^3 \ell^2} \approx \frac{10^{36}}{\ell^2} \tag{3}$$

Q is extremely large, from 10^{36} if $\ell \sim 1$ metre, to 10^{22} for the Earth. In all cases the decay time is much greater than the age of the universe. In comparison, the internal dissipation in typical solids leads to Q-factors $\sim 10^6$-10^9. Thus, as Weber emphasised, internal losses vastly outweigh gravitational radiation losses. The fluctuation dissipation theorem then tells us that there will be fluctuating forces acting on the antenna that are not of gravitational origin, but are due to the thermal reservoir - the set of modes into which the acoustic energy of the fundamental mode is dissipated.

Realising the significance of thermal fluctuations Weber proposed the use of a pair of detectors with a cross-correlator, such as illustrated in Figure 2(a) He stated: "If radiation is incident it will cause correlated outputs. All sources of internal fluctuations will be uncorrelated."

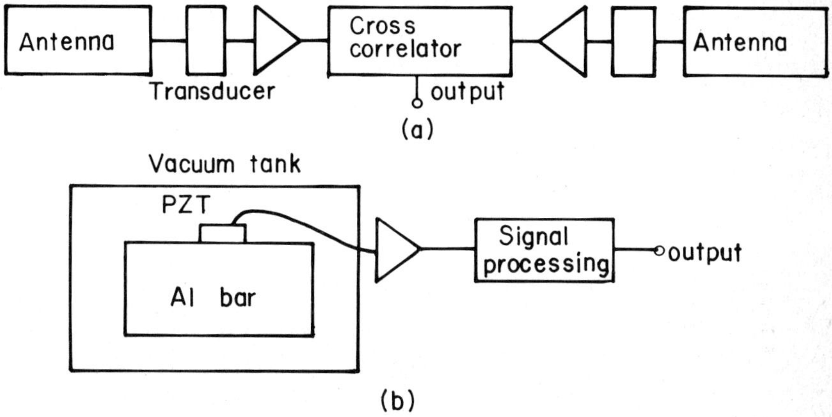

Figure 2(a) Correlated detectors as proposed by Weber.
(b) Schematic diagram of Weber's bar detector.

Weber's 1960 paper preceded a decade of hard work, in which he set up various detectors consisting of aluminium resonators with attached piezoelectric (PZT) crystals to read out their motion. His set up is shown schematically in Fig 3. The bars were carefully vibration isolated in vacuum tanks and the signals from the PZT's were amplified by low noise FET amplifiers. The mean square amplitudes of two antennae, one at Chicago, the other at Maryland 1000 km away were compared for possible coincident excitation. The report of observed coincidences beyond the level expected by chance[3] stimulated world wide interest. Many new antennae were set up, essentially duplicating Weber's apparatus; his techniques came under careful scrutiny and some significant improvements were proposed, as we will see in section III.

The explanation for Weber's results is still not clear. A few examples of coincidences have since been reported, (see for example ref [3(b)]) although the majority of about 10 groups failed to find evidence for coincident excitation of their antennae. Weber's work did confirm the *possibility* of detection of gravitational waves, however, and what has followed is another decade of hard work by groups in Europe, America, Asia and Australia. Their vision, formulated by Fairbank, Hamilton and others in the early 1970's, was to obtain 8 orders of magnitude improvement over Weber's original sensitivity. The work is still in progress. In these lectures we will look at the work so far, the methods, the problems and the prospects, as applied to the present generation of cryogenic "Weber bar" antennae for gravitational waves. The alternative technique, of laser interferometer free mass antennae, are described elsewhere in these proceedings.

II SIGNAL STRENGTHS AND EVENT RATES

Before looking at bar antennae in more detail, I want to look briefly at the signal strengths and event rates expected at the solar system, and in particular to summarise some new results[5]. Bar antennae are best suited to the detection of short broadband gravitational wave pulses expected from the gravitational collapse of stars to form neutron stars or black holes.

The archetypal collapse event is often seen as the Crab nebula - 1054 supernova-Crab pulsar association. Such a collapse in the Milky Way would very likely produce signals detectable at the level of today's technology (see D. Eardley's lectures for more detail on estimated signal strengths). However, at the historically recorded rate, of ~12 supernovae/2000 years, the prospects for detection are not good. The situation is improved somewhat if we assume that obscuration, and inadequate historical records lead to underestimates of the supernova rate. By observing supernovae in external galaxies similar to our own the supernova rate is estimated as 1/10-40 years.[6]

Although both these rates are impractically small for observations of our galaxy, when multiplied up to include several thousand galaxies they become quite acceptable. However, the price paid for increasing this rate is a reduced signal level in the antenna and significant further progress is needed before experimentalists can have confidence in detecting at these reduced levels.

Hence today it is particularly important to have the best possible estimate of the true rate of gravitational collapse in the galaxy. We can ask: Is the supernova rate a good measure of the collapse rate? Is the birthrate for pulsars and x-ray sources consistent with supernova rate? These questions can in principle be answered by a careful statistical analysis of the available data, although we shall see that significant uncertainties still remain.

Table I summarises the approximate total numbers of various astronomical sources, all of which can, with reasonable certainty, be identified as neutron stars or black holes. Based on their observed distributions the total galactic populations can be estimated.

Table I. Observed Collapsed Objects

Type	Radio Pulsars	Bright Steady X-ray Sources	X-ray Pulsars	X-ray Bursters	X-ray Transient Sources
Number	330	73	25	70	40

If the lifetime and total galactic population of each class of object can be estimated it is possible to determine the total rate of gravitational collapse in the galaxy.

The case of pulsars has been best studied to date. The relatively large population, and accurate distance information (obtained by dispersion measure) enabled Manchester to make a reasonably accurate estimate for the total number of *potentially observable* pulsars[7]. To know the true population however, we need to know the average beaming factor f for the population. Clearly the value of f depends on the angle θ between the centre of the emission cone and the pulsar spin axis. If θ is ~90° the observed pulse widths W will be $\lesssim 2\beta$, the aperture of the emission cone. However if $\Theta \rightarrow 0$ the pulse width can approach 360°. If Θ is assumed to be randomly distributed, (relative to the pulsar spin axis) one can try to fit to the observed distribution of pulse widths for a particular value of β (assumed the same size for all pulsars).

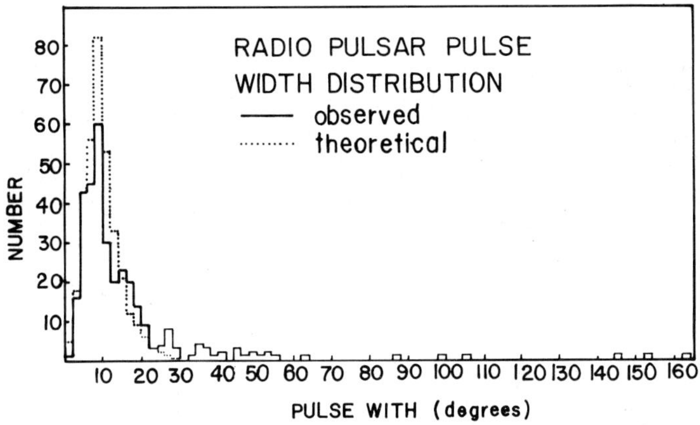

Figure 3. Observed pulse width distribution for radio pulsars compared with a random alignment model.

A surprisingly good fit is obtained for $\beta = 5°$, (as shown in Fig 3), although the long tail of the observed distribution is not reproduced. We could go on and suppose that the long pulse width pulsars are anomalous, and interpret the data as supporting this simple age independent model. However on theoretical grounds one would expect electromagnetic torques to give rise to an evolution of Θ to smaller values[8]. Polar cap emission models also lead to an inverse relationship between β and period P of the form $\beta \propto P^{-\delta}$ with δ in the range 0.3 - 0.7[9,10,11].

In addition Phinney and Blandford[12] have proposed that on the basis of the observed P-$\dot{P}$ distribution the beaming factor f increases by a factor ~5 during the pulsar lifetime.

Combining these results there seems to be strong grounds for accepting the model first proposed by Jones[8] that pulsars are born with large $\Theta \sim 90°$ and large β, that during their evolution $\Theta \rightarrow 0$. This model could well be consistent with the observed pulse width distribution because reducing Θ roughly compensates for the reduced β of the old pulsars to provide an apparent age independent distribution.

The evolutionary model leads to a significantly increased pulsar population, because the mean beaming factor is increased. Dynamical age estimates are also modified (upwards) because fewer old pulsars (with large $|z|$ values) are observed. This compensates somewhat for the increased population in the resulting birthrate estimate. The conclusion of this analysis (see reference (5) for more details) is summarised in Table II in which the horizon H_{85} is the distance within which 85% of the population occurs and τ_d and τ_c refer to the two independent for lifetime estimates, the characteristic and the dynamical lifetime[5]. The pulsar birthperiod appears to be between 5 and 16 years. For comparison the results for the static model are also shown. This gives a birthperiod with more uncertainty due to the lifetime discrepancies.

Table II. Pulsar Statistics

	Nobs.	Horizon H_{85}	Beaming factor	Lifetime (yr) τ_d	τ_c	Birthperiod
Alignment model	330	5.8 kpc	16-23	1.4×10^7	1.6×10^7	5-16 yrs
Static model	330	5.8 kpc	12-18	1.0×10^7	6×10^6	4-28 yrs

The radio pulsars appear to dominate the population of active collapsed objects. However x-ray pulsars and bright steady x-ray sources are thought to have rather short lifetimes, leading to birthrates which are certainly significant as we shall see below. Unfortunately x-ray sources do not have accurate distance indicators, although since all are binary systems of some sort, they have the possibility of distance determination to an optically identified companion. Only the x-ray pulsars are beamed, and the large pulse widths imply that the beaming factor is rather small (1.5 - 2). Horizon estimates for each population are not accurate. They are based partly on optical companions, and partly on the central/anti-central ratio R_{CAC}:

$$R_{CAC} = \frac{\text{number towards galactic centre}}{\text{number towards galactic anticentre}}$$

The results are largely based on data in the catalogues of Amnuel and Guseinov[13,14].

Since the precision of the radio pulsar data is much greater than that for the x-ray sources, one can use the radio pulsar statistics to calibrate for the x-ray source data. This works particularly well for the x-ray pulsars, which like radio pulsars have a wide luminosity range and also a similar observed density distribution and value of R_{CAC} to the radio pulsars. Table III compares R_{CAC}, the beaming factors and the horizons for each population.

Table III. Comparison between radio and X-ray pulsars

	R_{CAC}	H_{85}	Assumed Beaming factor	N_G
Radio pulsars	$3.1 \pm .35$	$5.8 \pm .1$	16	$(1.5 \pm .5) \times 10^6$
X-ray pulsars	4.5 ± 2.4	6 ± 1	1.5 - 2	7500 ± 2000

In the table the total number of x-ray pulsars in the galaxy N_{GX} is obtained simply by scaling relative to the radio pulsar population N_{GR}.

$$N_{GX} = N_{GR} \cdot \frac{\bar{f}_x}{\bar{f}_R} \cdot \frac{N_x}{N_R} \tag{4}$$

The scaling is justified by the insignificant (and presumably fortuitous) differences between the R_{CAC} and H_{85} values for each population, and by the similarities in their number versus distance histograms[5]. Arguments based on R_{CAC} alone have been used previously[13] which give much reduced population estimates for x-ray pulsars. As suggested in reference [5], these may be in error because they do not correctly model the luminosity distributions.

Bright steady x-ray sources have a much more distant horizon: $R_{CAC} \sim 15$, and the horizon is ~10 - 15 kpc. They appear to be unbeamed, and it is probable that we see a large proportion of the entire galactic population. The high luminosity of bright steady x-ray sources indicates a very short lifetime, which based on binary accretion models is generally thought to be in the range 10^4-10^5 years[15]. The x-ray pulsars on the other hand appear to come in 3 separate classes, each with a different lifetime. Of the 19 optically identified x-ray pulsars 8 are associated with massive stars, 8 are associated with Be stars and the remaining three are associated with low mass stars. The lifetime of the massive-companion x-ray pulsars is expected to be comparable to that of bright steady sources 10^4-10^5 years[15]. However the Be-companion pulsars are thought to have a much greater lifetime $\sim 5 \times 10^6$ years, and the low-mass companion pulsars may have even greater lifetimes, $\sim 10^9$ years, before the supernova of the companion. Thus the overall x-ray pulsar birthrate is dominated by the massive-companion subset.

The data for the four classes of x-ray sources is summarised in Table IV. In spite of the uncertain lifetime estimates it is clear that x-ray pulsars contribute strongly to the rate of gravitational collapse, comparable or even greater than radio pulsars. Bright steady x-ray sources contribute at a few percent of the total rate, while x-ray bursters and transient sources contribute negligibly.

Table IV. Birthperiod estimates for X-ray sources.

	N_{obs}	Horizon	N_g	Lifetime	Birth period (yrs)
X-ray Pulsars	25	5	5,500-9,500	a) 10^4-10^5 b) 5×10^6 c) 10^9	1.6-16
Bright steady sources	73	10-15	130-220	10^4-10^5	45-800
X-ray Bursters	70	7-8	300	10^7 10^9	3×10^4-3×10^6
X-ray Transients	40	a) 6-7 b) 10-15	300-600	10^6 10^8	1.5×10^3-3×10^5

Combining the data of Tables II and IV leads to a final mean birthperiod for collapsed objects of 1-10 years. This compares with mean supernova period of 10-40 years[6] and a mean supernova remnant period of 16-40 years[5]. The uncertainties fail to overlap. This can be seen as support for the idea that gravitational collapses occur which are not seen as supernovae. Various discrepancies also tend to support these suggestions:

a) The bright shell type supernova remnant CasA was not observed as a supernova in about 1668 and no collapsed object is detected[16]. If this indicates the presence of non-optically observable supernovae, the above stated supernova period will be too high.

b) The recently reported historical observation of a supernova in the direction of Cygnus X-1 on 24 Oct 1408[17] implies a class of supernovae without long lasting remnants. This implies that the above supernovae remnant period is also too high as a result of omission of short lived remnants.

c) Statement b) above is supported by the fact that whereas nearly half the historical supernova remnants are crablike, less than 10% of presently observed remnants have this structure.

d) Van den Heuvel[18] has suggested that only very massive and very low mass binary systems will become observable as x-ray sources as only these systems provide an appropriate rate of mass transfer. The number of x-ray sources is then an underestimate of the total number of compact objects in binary systems.

e) It is possible that there is an evolutionary link between x-ray sources and radio pulsars. In particular if x-ray sources are precursors of pulsars, and do not require the supernova of the companion, the x-ray sources will be a subset of the already counted pulsar population. Equally, it is possible that x-ray sources are dead pulsars repowered after interacting with a normal companion star.

Clearly there are still significant uncertainties in the estimated total collapse rate, but there is reasonable cause for experimentalists to be optimistic that the total rate of collapse in our galaxy could approach 1 per year.

Settling back now to a more conservative figure, we suppose that the birthrate is 10^{-1} per year for the Milky Way, corresponding roughly to 10^{-12} collapse events/star/year. To obtain a useful rate of gravitational wave pulses, say 100 per year, we need a stellar sample $\sim 10^{14}$ stars. The total stellar population increases only weakly beyond the galaxy, up to the distance of Andromeda, ($\sim$1 Mpc), and only at about 10 Mpc does the population start to scale as R^3. Thus to increase our stellar sample to 10^{14} requires us to sample out to the Virgo cluster, $\sim$19 Mpc. It requires three orders of magnitude in distance to increase the sample by two orders, and this is at the expense of 6 orders of magnitude is signal strength.

Figure 4 shows a plot which combines the above estimates for the rate of gravitational collapse with an estimate for the stellar population, and with a range of conversion efficiencies for gravitational wave production.[19] The lower curve shows the total stellar population as a function of distance. The upper curve shows the range of possible event rates plotted against the range of possible signal amplitudes. To obtain the amplitude range the conversion efficiency to gravitational radiation is assumed to be between 0.1% and 1%. The signal strength scale is also given in equivalent numbers of phonons induced in an optimally aligned 1 tonne resonant bar, using spectral density estimates described in section III. Note the gap at $h \sim 10^{-19}$ which will only be filled by particularly low efficiency events in the Milky Way, or by particularly high efficiency events in more distant galaxies.

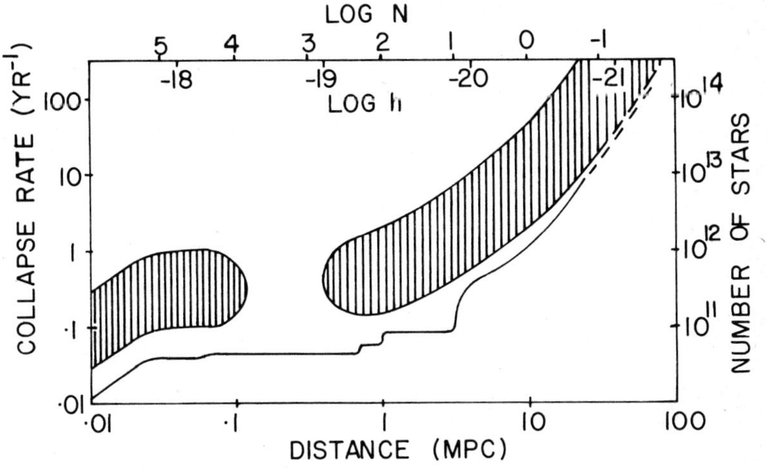

Figure 4. Stellar Population (lower curve), Signal strengths and event rates (shaded curve)

The significant uncertainties in the signal estimates in Fig 4 should again be emphasised. At the present (1982) antenna sensitivities $\sim 10^{-18}$ more than one detectable pulse per year is rather unlikely, although long term operation of antennae at this sensitivity is certainly warranted. Reasonable expectation of a greater event rate does not occur until antenna sensitivities exceed 10^{-20} and only at the technical much more difficult sensitivities $\sim 10^{-22}$ can we be extremely confident of detecting gravitational waves. However only experiment will tell us the truth in these matters.

III INTRINSIC NOISE IN RESONANT MASS ANTENNAE

(1) Brownian Noise, Series Noise, Back Reaction Noise and Quantum Noise

To introduce some of the key concepts in understanding gravitational wave antennae, I will use as a framework a few of the important historical developments of the field, which followed Weber's reported results in 1969 and 1970. I will make no attempt to cover all the valuable contributions of many workers in the last decade. Instead I will concentrate on a few specific papers which themselves contain adequate references for a more detailed study.

In 1971 Gibbons and Hawking published an important paper[20] which lead to improved techniques, and better understanding of the noise sources in resonant bar antennae. They noted that Weber had monitored the *energy* or RMS amplitude of the fundamental mode of his antennae. Since the phase of an incoming gravity wave is random relative to the antenna, and since the energy deposited in the antenna is much smaller than the mean thermal energy of the mode, kT, it follows that the mode energy will only sometimes be increased by a gravity wave. It is equally likely to be reduced in energy and the gravity wave may simply cause a small phase shift.

We will use the symmetrical and quantum mechanically conjugate harmonic oscillator coordinates X_1 and X_2 given by:

$$X_1 = A\cos\phi \qquad X_2 = A\sin\phi \tag{5}$$

to describe the state of the antenna. (A is the antenna amplitude and ϕ is the phase.) Experimentally X_1 and X_2 can be easily measured using two phase sensitive detectors in a configuration shown schematically in Figure 5.

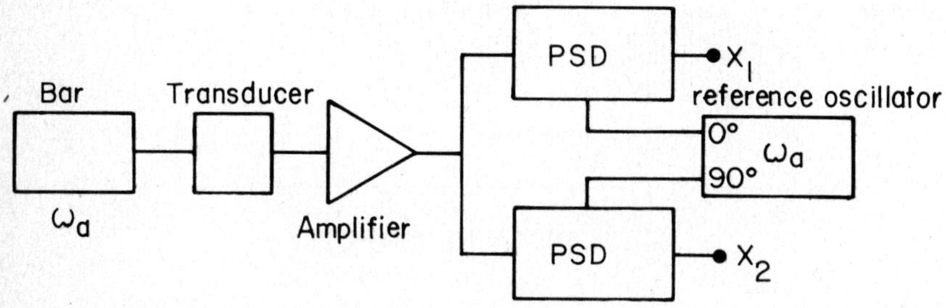

Figure 5. Antenna readout system for obtaining harmonic oscillator coordinates X_1 and X_2

The state of the antenna can be represented by a point P_1 in the (X_1, X_2) plane; the amplitude $A = |P| = (X_1^2 + X_2^2)^{\frac{1}{2}}$ and phase $\phi = \tan^{-1} X_2/X_1$. This is illustrated in Figure 6. A gravity wave causes the antennae to move from P_1 to P_2: the amplitude change is simply $|P_1| - |P_2|$. Clearly $|P_1| - |P_2| \leq |P_1 - P_2|$, and in general a measuring system that monitors $|P_1 - P_2| = |\Delta X_1 - \Delta X_2|$ will be superior to one sensitive to amplitude alone.

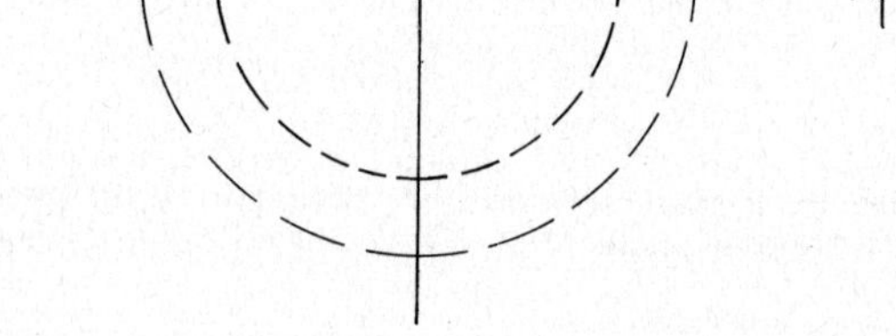

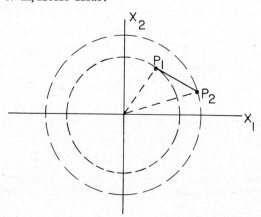

Figure 6. X_1-X_2 representation of the state of the antenna

Thermal fluctuations cause the state vector P to execute a random walk in the X_1X_2 plane. A high Q mode is weakly coupled to the thermal reservoir which is made up of all the higher modes of the system. The antenna loses energy slowly into the reservoir, and equally it is only weakly excited by the reservoir. The relaxation time $\tau_a = 2Q/\omega$ thus characterises both the rate of decay after a high energy excitation, and the rate of amplitude change when the mode is in thermal equilibrium with the reservoir.

Clearly, if τ_a is large and the rate of fluctuation is low, the antenna becomes more deterministic on time scales short compared with τ_a. The mean energy is still kT, but the expected change in energy in a sampling time τ_s is $kT(\tau_s/\tau_a)$. The temperature $T(\tau_s/\tau_a)$ is the effective temperature or noise temperature of the resonator, and quite clearly can be much less than the actual temperature.

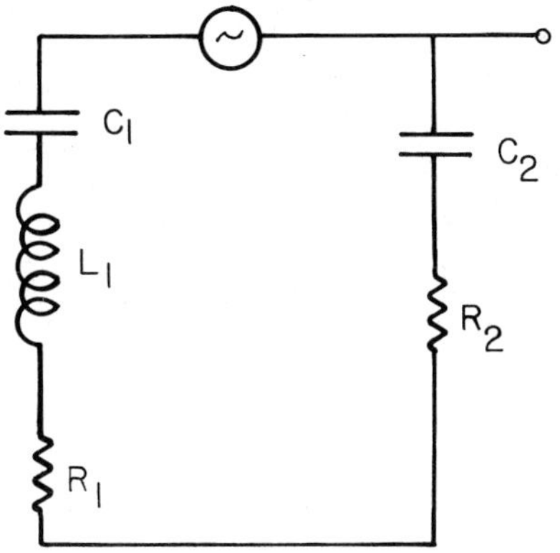

Figure 7. Gibbons & Hawking's equivalent circuit for a resonant antenna with a piezoelectric transducer.

The components L_1, C_1, R_1 represent the bar, with mass L_1 spring constant $1/C_1$, and Q-factor $\omega_a L_1/R_1$. The bar is coupled to a piezoelectric transducer represented by capacitor C_2, and the resistor R represents the losses in the transducer. (Gibbons & Hawking neglected amplifier noise). The resistor R_2 produces noise given by the Nyquist formula

$$V_{R_2}^2 = 4\ kT\ R\ .\frac{1}{\tau_s} \tag{6}$$

where the bandwidth is the reciprocal of the sampling time τ_s.

The system noise with the addition of the transducer noise is then given by

$$V_n^{\ 2} = V_B^{\ 2}\,\tau_s/\tau_a + 4\ kT\ R_2/\tau_s \tag{7}$$

where the first term is the antenna Brownian motion noise as discussed above. The presence of the "series noise" contribution from R_2 completely alters the noise optimisation of the system. No longer can the noise be reduced arbitrarily by reducing τ_s because the series noise blows up as $\tau_s \to 0$. There is an optimum sampling time at which the two noise contributions are equal, and only by increasing τ_a (reducing the losses in the antenna) or decreasing R_2 (improving the transducer) can improvements be made (at any given temperature).

Gibbons and Hawking also introduced a parameter β to characterise the coupling between the bar and the transducer. They defined β as follows:

β = proportion of the elastic energy of the detector that can be extracted electrically through the transducer in one cycle (8)

A bar-transducer system with low β (weak coupling) requires more time for the signal energy to appear in the transducer. The longer the energy transfer takes, the more time there is for fluctuations in the antenna to dominate the noise. This point can be clarified by two alternative viewpoints. One is the thermodynamical model for the system: the antenna is considered as a thermal bath at temperature $T_{eff} = T_a \tau_s/\tau_a$, coupled to a transducer with noise temperature T_T which itself is coupled to an amplifier of noise temperature T_N.

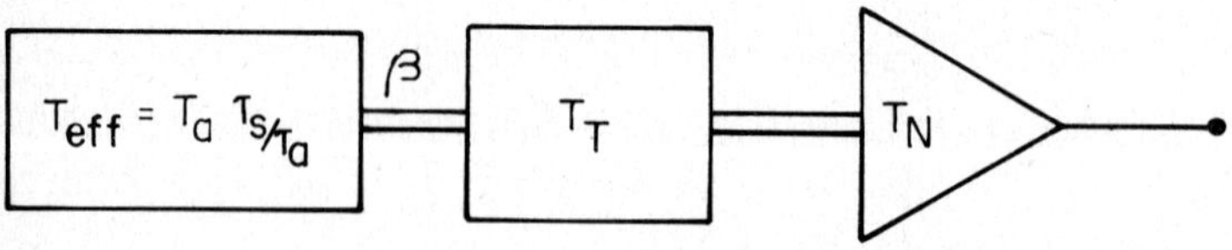

Figure 8. Antenna, transducer and amplifier: thermodynamical model

A gravity wave causes slight "heating" of the fundamental mode and energy flows through the coupling β shown schematically in Figure 8. As long as β > 0 the transducer will eventually come into equilibrium with the bar, but for a rapid response β has to be large. This model emphasises an aspect of the analysis not included by Gibbons and Hawking, which was pointed out by Braginsky[21] in 1975. This is that the coupling is not uni-directional: thermal fluctuations in the amplifier or the transducer act back on the antenna producing *back-reaction noise*. Indeed, it is clear that the transducer is a source of thermal fluctuations comparable to those originating within the bar, and these will produce an additional noise contribution which will diminish as $\tau_s \to 0$ as does the Brownian noise.

The second viewpoint is that the antenna is effectively a transmission line which couples energy into the transducer. One can think in terms of phonons in the bar which may be absorbed by the transducer, with the emission of a photon into the amplifier, or they may be reflected back into the bar, then β determines the proportion of phonons absorbed. In these terms we see β as a measure of the *impedance match* between the bar and the transducer. The bar has a certain mechanical output impedance Z_{out}, which for optimum power flow should be matched to the transducer's mechanical input impedance Z_{11}. The ratio Z_{11}/Z_{out} is simply the coupling coefficient β.

Once we begin to think in terms of phonons and photons we are led to ask: What happens if the induced strain in the antenna is equivalent to less than one quanta $\hbar\omega$? The profound significance of the quantum mechanical limit to macroscopic measurements was realised independently by several groups, particularly by Braginsky[22] and Giffard[23] . Giffard used the much earlier result of Heffner[24] who showed that by the uncertainty principle, a linear amplifier has a fundamental limit to its sensitivity, given approximately by $\hbar\omega$. Similarly Giffard showed that a transducer used with a linear amplifier (an amplifier which preserves amplitude and phase) has a maximum sensitivity corresponding to a gravity wave which produces an equivalent of 2 quanta in the bar. The term *equivalent* is used because the actual energy absorbed by the antenna depends on its instantaneous amplitude. For linear systems the signal-to-noise ratio is independent of the amplitude, and corresponds exactly to the signal produced in an ideal stationary antenna at absolute zero. Giffard's result meant that the maximum achievable sensitivity of an antenna would be limited to about the single phonon level shown in Figure 4.

Meanwhile, at least as early as 1975 Braginsky realised that in principle it was possible to devise "amplifiers" which were able to readout the state of a system without disturbing it. Braginsky, Caves, Thorne, Unruh[25] and others went on to define methods whereby gravitational waves of amplitude less than that required to induce one quanta can in principle be detected using *quantum non-demolition* techniques. These techniques, described by Caves in these proceedings, will not be discussed in detail here, although we will look at practical designs for such QND transducers in the final lecture.

(2) The Signal to Noise Ratio

A gravitational wave carries an energy flux S ($J\,m^{-2}s^{-1}$) given by

$$S = \frac{c^3}{16\pi G} \langle \dot{h}_+^2 + \dot{h}_x^2 \rangle \qquad (9)$$

where h_+ and h_x denote the dimensionless strain amplitudes of the two possible polarisations of the wave. Since the shape of expected gravitational wave pulses from gravitational collapse events is not accurately known, we cannot accurately determine the expected excitation of an antenna even knowing the total pulse energy. We need to know both the spectral distribution of the pulse energy, and the relationship between h and its time derivative. The details of the expected pulses depend not only on the dynamics of the gravitational collapse, but also on the mass of the collapsing object, both of which are uncertain.

If we assume only knowledge of the pulse duration τ_g (expected to be $\sim 10^{-3}$ seconds), and that it is predominantly a single cycle, it is sufficient to assume that $\dot{h} \sim 2h/\tau_g$. Then equation (9) can be rewritten

$$S \approx \frac{c^3}{16\pi G} \cdot \frac{4h^2}{\tau_g^2} \quad J\,m^{-2}s^{-1} \qquad (10)$$

The total pulse energy E is then given by $S.\tau_g$:

$$E \approx \frac{c^3}{16\pi G} \frac{4h^2}{\tau_g} \quad J\,m^{-2} \qquad (11)$$

Now assuming that the spectral distribution of the pulse energy $F(\omega)$ is uniform over a bandwidth $\Delta\omega \sim 1/\tau_g$, it follows that

$$F(\omega) \approx E/\Delta\omega = E\tau_g \approx \frac{c^3h^2}{4\pi G} \quad J\,m^{-2}\,Hz^{-1} \qquad (12)$$

Numerically $F(\omega) \sim 20 \times 10^{34} h^2$.

These results give the estimated signal strengths used in figure 4. However the assumptions used give no more than an order of magnitude estimate of the expected signal spectral densities. Moreover variations in the pulse durations could make any chosen antenna frequency only suitable for a small proportion of actual events. In this light the data in Figure 4 should be interpreted with caution when considering signals at a particular antenna frequency.

The energy deposited in an initially stationary antenna by a signal pulse $F(\omega)$ is given by

$$U_s \approx F(\omega_a)\sin^4\Theta\sin^2 2\phi \cdot \frac{8}{\pi}\left(\frac{G}{c}\right)\left(\frac{V_s}{c}\right)^2 M \tag{13}$$

where Θ and ϕ are coordinates describing the orientation of the bar relative to the incoming wave (as given in Figure 9).

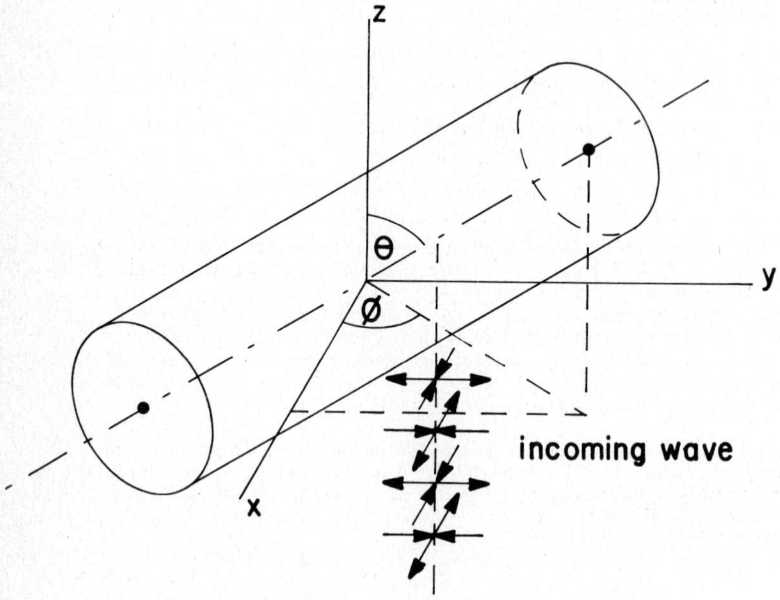

Figure 9. Coordinate system for resonant antenna.

For a short pulse gravitational wave burst the bandwidth of the pulse is roughly the inverse of the pulse duration, and the frequency bandwidth is roughly equal to the peak frequency. Under these circumstances the strain amplitude $\delta\ell/\ell$ induced in the bar is roughly equal to the incoming wave amplitude h; there is no resonant excitation.

For the incoming gravitational wave to be detectable the signal U_s must be greater than the noise in the antenna U_n:

$$U_s \gtrsim U_n \tag{14}$$

To characterise the noise U_n we generalise transducer to a two port device described by a 2 x 2 impedance matrix Z_{ij}.

The transducer accepts force and velocity inputs F and v, and gives current and voltage outputs I and V:

$$\begin{pmatrix} F \\ V \end{pmatrix} = \begin{vmatrix} Z_{11} & Z_{12} \\ Z_{21} & Z_{22} \end{vmatrix} \begin{pmatrix} v \\ I \end{pmatrix} \tag{15}$$

The transducer has input impedance Z_{11}, measured in kg sec^{-1}, and output impedance Z_{22}, measured in ohms. The forward transductance Z_{21} measured in volts/(m sec^{-1}), determines the transducer sensitivity, whereas the reverse transductance Z_{12}, measured in kg/amp determines the back acting force on the antenna due to currents in the output circuit.

All the noise sources in the transducer and the amplifier can be expressed as equivalent spectral densities of current and voltage noise at the input of the amplifier, denoted $S_i(\omega)$ and $S_e(\omega)$ respectively. (see Figure 10)

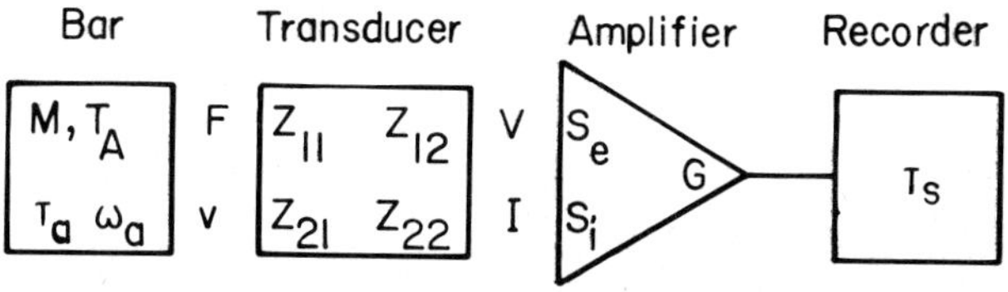

Figure 10. The various quantities used to characterise a gravitational wave antenna system

The current noise S_i is the source of back action noise in the antenna, whereas S_e describes the series noise contribution. In terms of these quantities the total system noise is given by

$$U_n = 2kT_a \, \tau_s/\tau_a + \frac{|Z_{12}|^2}{2M} S_i(\omega)\tau_s + \frac{2M}{|Z_{12}|^2} \frac{S_e(\omega_a)}{\tau_a} \tag{16}$$

The first term in equation (16) is the familiar Brownian motion or thermal noise in the antenna. The second term gives the energy fluctuations arising from the current noise acting back through the reverse transductance, and giving the additional noise contribution proportional to sampling time. The third term is the series electronics noise, which for given S_e is reduced as Z_{21} increases, as well as being proportional to the bandwidth or τ_s^{-1}.

The problem of detecting gravitational waves to a large extent consists of minimising equation (16). The technical means of achieving this requires some or all of the following:

a) reducing the antenna temperature T_A

b) using a transducer with high Z_{21} and low Z_{12}

c) using amplifiers with S_e and S_i as low as possible

d) reducing the acoustic losses in the antenna to obtain highest possible Q or relaxation time

e) obtaining a reasonable impedance match between the bar and the transducer $\beta = Z_{11}/Z_{out} \rightarrow 1$.

It is convenient to scale the noise in the system relative to the "standard quantum limit" of one equivalent quanta induced in the bar. To do this we rewrite the noise equation (16) in terms of noise number A (a quantity first used by Weber to characterise noise in masers):

$$A = U_n/\hbar\omega_a = A_T + A_B + A_S \tag{17}$$

Here A_T, A_B and A_S are the equivalent numbers of noise quanta due to thermal noise, back reaction noise and series noise in the measurement system.

Referring back to figure 4 we see that the experimental goal must be to achieve a total system noise number A approaching 1. To examine the possibility of achieving this we must look in more detail at transducers, antennae material and the problem of isolation against extrinsic sources of noise.

IV TRANSDUCERS FOR RESONANT MASS ANTENNAE

1. Introduction

There are two basic types of transducer for gravitational wave antennae: a) *passive* transducers and b) *active* or *parametric* transducers. Passive transducers have no external power source, and their power gain is less than unity. They must always be used with a high gain, low noise amplifier at the frequency of the antenna ω_a. Parametric transducers on the other hand have an external power source (a pump oscillator) and they have intrinsic power gain. The output of a parametric transducer is generally upconverted to a frequency higher than ω_a. Most parametric transducers use high frequency resonant cavities combined with low noise high frequency amplifiers. Passive transducers use an inductive readout, coupled to a SQUID amplifier. Both types are illustrated schematically in Figure 11.

Fundamentally the difference between passive and active transducers is not very great. Active transducers use a transduction process that is combined with amplification. (Additional amplification of the high frequency signal is still necessary.) Passive transducers have a complete separation between the transduction process and the amplification process. However the amplifier itself (such as a SQUID) makes use of a parametric upconversion process. Thus the difference between passive and active transducers is simply in the choise of whether the parametric upconversion occurs during or after transduction.

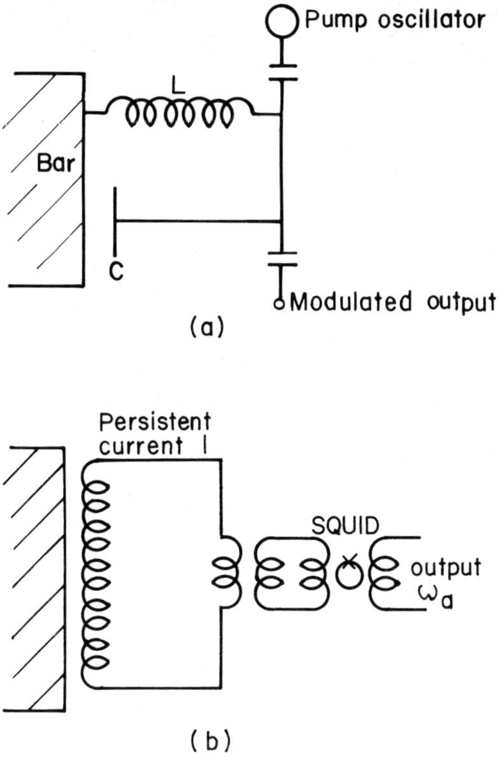

Figure 11. (a) Active or parametric transducer
(b) Passive transducer

Technically, as we shall see, the practical realisation of each type of transducer requires the solution of quite different problems. In principle both types can reach the quantum limit, and in practice it is not obvious which type will ultimately be most successful. Here we will look at parametric transducers in some detail. Then we will go on to look more briefly at passive transducers using SQUID's. The most successful passive transducer is described by Michelson elsewhere in these proceedings.

2. Theory of Parametric Devices

The basic operation of parametric transducers is described by the Manley-Rowe relations[26]. These are equations for the conservation of energy in an ideal lossless non-linear reactance. The non-linear reactance allows frequency conversion to take place, so that essentially the relations describe photon scattering in a classical regime.

In general power can flow at all harmonics of the input frequencies to a device. If there are only two input frequencies ω_1 and ω_2, frequency conversion can allow power to flow at all integral harmonics $\pm|m\omega_1 + n\omega_2|$. Using Pm,n to denote the average power flow at frequency $\pm|m\omega_1 + n\omega_2|$, the Manley-Rowe relations can be expressed

$$\sum_{m=0}^{\infty} \sum_{n=-\infty}^{\infty} \frac{m P_{m,n}}{n\omega_1 + n\omega_2} = 0$$

$$\sum_{n=0} \sum_{m=-\infty} \frac{n P_{m,n}}{m\omega_1 + n\omega_2} = 0 \qquad (18)$$

In practice power flow at *all* harmonics does not occur; the use of filters enables power flow to be restricted to a few chosen harmonics. The simplest cases are generally the most useful. Here we will look at solutions to equations (18) for four technically useful devices, the *single sideband parametric upconverter*, the *double sideband upconverter*, the *double pumped upconverter* and the *negative resistance amplifier*, all of which are relevant to transducers for gravitational wave antennae. They are best described by diagrams analogous to Feynman diagrams.

(a) Single sideband parametric upconverter

The single sideband parametric upconverter is a three frequency device described by Figure 12.

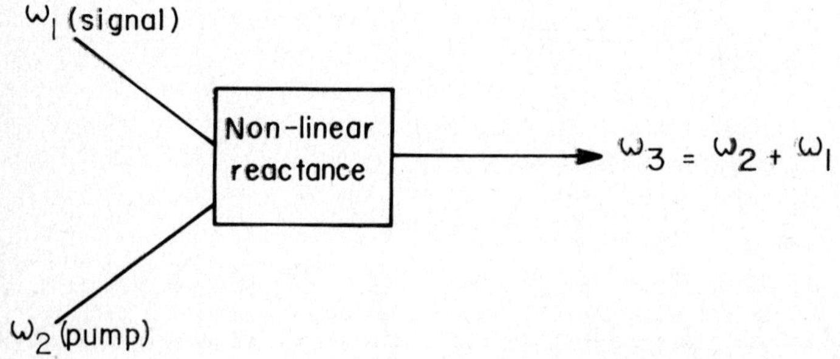

Figure 12. Single sideband parametric upconverter.

Power is allowed to flow only at frequencies ω_1, ω_2 and $\omega_3 = \omega_1 + \omega_2$. Defining positive power as power absorbed, and denoting $P_{1,0} = P_1$, $P_{0,1} = P_2$, $P_{1,1} = P_3$, equations (18) give

$$P_1/\omega_1 + P_3/\omega_3 = 0 \qquad (19)$$

$$P_2/\omega_2 + P_3/\omega_3 = 0 \qquad (20)$$

Now if power is injected by the pump, we have $P_2 > 0$, and from equation (20) $P_3 < 0$: power is emitted at frequency ω_3. Then in equation (19) $P_3 < 0$ implies $P_1 > 0$, and power is absorbed by the signal channel. The power gain G_{13} is then given by P_3/P_1:

$$G_{13} = \frac{P_3}{P_1} = \frac{\omega_3}{\omega_1} \qquad (21)$$

The signal photons have been scattered with pump photons, so that the power gain is simply given by the photon energy ratio. Clearly if the signal frequency is low and the pump frequency is high considerable power gain is possible. There is no increase in the number of photons carrying signal information, however: the device conserves number of quanta. In practice, if the frequency ratio ω_3/ω_1 is large it is difficult to prevent power flow from occurring at frequency $\omega_2 - \omega_1$ since the filter bandwidth required to separate $\omega_2 - \omega_1$ from $\omega_2 + \omega_1$ corresponds to a high filter Q-factor $> \omega_2/\omega_1$. For example if $\omega_1 = 10^3$ Hz and $\omega_2 = 10^{10}$ Hz, the filter Q-factor needed to prevent power flow at $10^{10} - 10^3$ while allowing power flow at $10^{10} \times 10^3$ must exceed 10^7. Thus we go on to consider the device where power flow does occur at the lower sideband frequency.

b) Double Sideband upconverter

The double sideband upconverter is described by Figure 13.

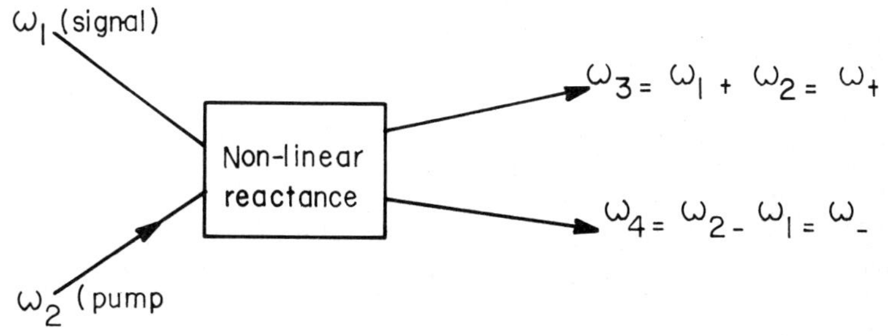

Figure 13. The double sideband parametric upconverter.

Frequencies ω_3 and ω_4, which occur symmetrically on either side of the pump frequency ω_2 are called the upper and lower sideband frequencies, denoted ω_+ and ω_-. The Manley-Rowe relations are

$$\frac{P_+}{\omega_+} + \frac{P_1}{\omega_1} - \frac{P_-}{\omega_-} = 0 \qquad (22)$$

$$\frac{P_-}{\omega_-} + \frac{P_2}{\omega_2} + \frac{P_+}{\omega_+} = 0 \qquad (23)$$

If $\omega_2 \gg \omega_1$, then $\omega_+ \approx \omega_- \approx \omega_2$. Equation (23) then gives

$$P_2 \approx -(P_+ + P_-) \qquad (24)$$

which tells us that the absorbed pump power is approximately equal to the total emitted upconverted signal power. Using this result in equation (22), there are three interesting cases:

(i) When $\frac{P_+}{\omega_+} < \frac{P_-}{\omega_-}$ then $\frac{P_1}{\omega_1} < 0$. (25)

Net power is emitted at the signal port of the parametric device when excess power is extracted from the lower sideband. This can lead to parametric instabilities: a bar with a transducer operating in this mode could be brought into oscillation. The transducer acts like a negative resistance; it reflects more power than is incident on it, so it has reflectivity > 1.

(ii) When $\frac{P_+}{\omega_+} > \frac{P_-}{\omega_-}$ then $\frac{P_1}{\omega_1} > 0$. (26)

Net power is absorbed at the signal port if excess upper sideband power is extracted. The device behaves more like the single sideband upconverter discussed above.

(iii) When $\frac{P_+}{\omega_+} > \frac{P_-}{\omega_-}$ then $\frac{P_1}{\omega_1} = 0$. (27)

Under these circumstances net power flow at the signal frequency is zero. One quanta is emitted from the signal port for each quanta absorbed. In terms of net energy flow the power gain is infinite. This would make the device appear to be a perfect amplifier. In reality it is not perfect because the emitted quanta is not completely coherent with the absorbed quanta. Two amplification process occur simultaneously, in parallel, and the true power gain is given by the frequency ratio ω_2/ω_1 (for $\omega_1 \ll \omega_2$).

c) Double Pumped Upconverter

The double pumped upconverter is described by the same equations as the double sideband upconverter; it differs only in the choice of inputs and output, as shown in Figure 14.

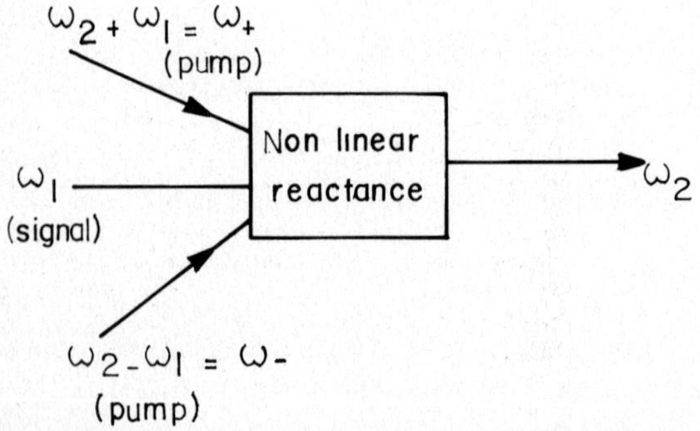

Figure 14. The double pumped parametric upconverter

The device is pumped at the sideband frequencies ω_+ and ω_-, and the input signal ω_1 is upconverted to a high frequency ω_2. If equal photon numbers are absorbed at ω_+ and ω_-, we have $P_+/\omega_+ = P_-/\omega_- > 0$. Then by equation (22) $P_1/\omega_1 = 0$: equal numbers of quanta are emitted and absorbed at the signal frequency. All the absorbed pump power is emitted as amplified signal power at frequency ω_2 (by equation 23).

Double pumped upconverters have important application to the design of quantum non-demolition transducers since when the phases of ω_+ and ω_- are chosen correctly the signal information in the ω_2 channel contains only information on one of the conjugate amplifier coordinates X_1. (See paper by Caves in these proceedings.)

d) Parametric amplifier

The parametric amplifier is described by figure 15.

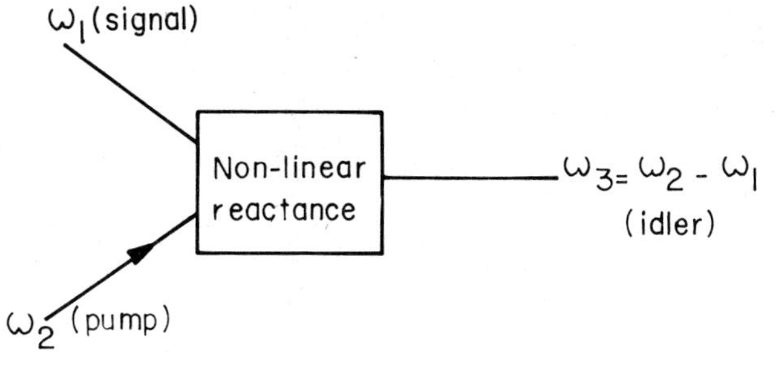

Figure 15. Negative resistance parametric amplifier.

This device is characterised by having a passive "idler circuit" in which power flows, but which plays no external role as an input or output. It operates in the negative resistance regime noted in case (i) of the double sideband upconverter. This is clear from the Manley-Rowe relations

$$P_1/\omega_1 - P_3/\omega_3 = 0 \qquad (28)$$

$$P_3/\omega_3 + P_2/\omega_2 = 0$$

If $P_2 > 0$ then both P_1 and P_3 are negative: more signal is emitted at frequency ω_1 than is absorbed, so an incident signal will be reflected back with gain. Power also flows into the idler circuit where it is dissipated in losses.

The parametric amplifier has a *degenerate* mode, for which $\omega_3 = \omega_2$ and $2\omega_1 = \omega_2$. In this form the device has gain dependent on the *phase* of signal ω_1 relative to the pump frequency ω_2. Such phase dependent gain has important applications to the design of quantum non-demolition devices, as well as leading to useful carrier suppression in linear amplifiers used in conjuction with parametric upconverter transducers.

It should be emphasised that the various devices discussed here are idealisations. All practical non-linear devices have finite losses: thus the filters are not ideal and power flows at unwanted frequencies. In the particular case of the double pumped upconverter its use as a QND transducer is only possible if power flow at frequencies $\omega_2 \pm 2\omega_1$ is sufficiently reduced. Similarly in the case of the conventional double sideband upconverter transducer, minimisation of losses is essential to obtain high sensitivity.

3. Practical Parametric Devices

a) Parametric Upconverter Transducer

The most widely used parametric transducer consists of a re-entrant cavity, which is illustrated in Figure 16. In its simplest form the cylindrically symmetrical cavity is placed near the end face of a resonant bar. The cavity is essentially an LC resonator, with its capacitance (determined by the gap between the end of the centre post and the bar) modulated by the incident low frequency signal, which is the motion of the bar. The inductance, which is basically due to the central post, is fixed.

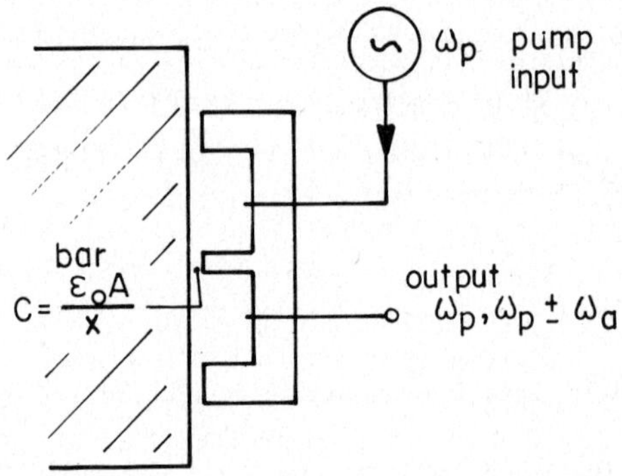

Figure 16. Re-entrant cavity parametric transducer.

The modulation of the resonator parameter C by the input signal provides the necessary non-linear reactance, and by using superconductors the device can have very low loss. The losses are characterised by the electrical Q, Q_e of the cavity.

If the cavity is pumped as shown in figure 15, with the pump frequency $\omega_p = (LC)^{-\frac{1}{2}}$ the device is a good approximation to the double sideband upconverter described above, with a mechanical signal channel, and radio frequency (often microwave or UHF) pump and output frequencies. The signal from the output port consists of a large amplitude carrier frequency, modulated with two sidebands $\omega_p - \omega_a$ and $\omega_p + \omega_a$. In practice several different low frequency acoustic modes will give rise to additional output sidebands, but these need not play a significant role in the device operation.

The high sensitivity of the device to motion signals arises from the high Q_e value, and the small value chosen for the capacitance gap x_o. The device is resonant at frequency ω_p for $x_o = \varepsilon_o A/C$ and the range of gap spacing Δx required for the cavity to cross the electrical resonance is $\Delta x = 2x_o/Q_e$. This quantity Δx, is called the *position bandwidth* of the cavity: clearly if x is small, say 10^{-5} m and $Q_e \sim 10^6$ (achievable with superconductors) the position bandwidth may be extremely small, say 10^{-11} m. To measure a strain amplitude of 10^{-18} with such a transducer would then require resolution of the resonance to $\sim 10^{-7}$ Δx, which is possible if electrical noise does not interfere. We note that the resonance allows the characteristic distance scale to be reduced to less than atomic dimensions, and certainly much less than an optical wavelength.

Re-entrant cavity parametric transducers are under development by the gravitational wave groups at Western Australia, Moscow, Louisiana and Tokyo. Each has a slightly different configuration, which in each case confers various advantages and disadvantages, without changing the fundamental principles. To characterise the transducer in detail it is necessary to solve the equivalent circuit for the antenna-transducer system. Results can be expressed in terms of the transducer impedance matrix described in section III. Full solutions are given in references [27;28] and here we will simply quote the results.

Since output signals occur at both the upper and lower sideband frequencies, the impedance matrix should in general allow for energy transfer into each sideband. In practice one simply has to offset the pump frequency ω_p relative to the resonator frequency $(LC)^{-\frac{1}{2}}$ to vary the relative couplings into the sidebands. Here, for simplicity, we will consider only the symmetrical case, with equal power flow in each sideband. We will also assume that the cavity Q factor Q_e is such that $Q_e < \omega_p/\omega_a$ since this is the usual operating condition. Then the impedance matrix is given by:

$$Z_{11} = \frac{\frac{1}{2} C V_p^2 Q_e}{x_o^2 \omega_p} \quad \text{input impedance} \tag{30}$$

$$Z_{12} = \frac{\frac{1}{2} V_p Q_e}{\omega_p x_o} \quad \text{reverse transductance} \tag{31}$$

$$Z_{21} = \frac{\omega_p}{\omega_a} . Z_{12} \quad \text{forward transductance} \tag{32}$$

$$Z_{22} = \frac{Q_e}{\omega_p C} \quad \text{output impedance} \tag{33}$$

where V_p is the voltage across the capacitor C. The coupling coefficient is given by

$$\beta = \frac{\frac{1}{2} C V_p^2 Q_e}{m\omega^2 x^2} \tag{34}$$

We note some of the main features of the impedance matrix. The input impedance depends on the energy in the capacitor, as one would expect, but it scales with Q_e. However Z_{11} does not increase indefinitely as $Q_e \to \infty$. The low Q approximation breaks down, and Q_e in equation 30 is replaced by ω_p/ω_a in the high Q limit. Compared with a passive transducer, Z_{11} for active transducers is Q_e times greater, enabling some simplification of the problem of impedance matching to the relatively high mechanical impedance of a bar.

The ratio between the forward and reverse transductances is also of interest.

Parametric upconverters are asymmetric devices, with the forward transductance ω_p/ω_a times greater than the reverse transductance. Combined with the possibility of using cryogenic isolators on the transducer output, (see section 4 below) this means that back action forces do not contribute significantly to the antenna noise until one is close to the quantum limit. Note also that Z_{11}, Z_{12} and Z_{21} all scale as x_o^{-1}, so that the capacitance gap must be as small as possible to obtain high sensitivity. This requirement is common to all transducers. However, the use of mechanical transformers to raise the signal displacement amplitude, such as the resonant diaphragm used on the Stanford transducer (see Michelson's paper in these proceedings) allow this requirement to be relaxed.

In contrast to the advantages of high Q resonant upconverter devices, there are undoubtedly disadvantages: The devices are complex, there are a plethora of noise sources which have to be controlled, and there are difficulties with tuning and dynamic range.

b) Degenerate parametric amplifiers

Microwave parametric amplifiers (or paramps) usually make use of the nonlinear capacitance properties of GaAs semiconductor diodes. The degenerate paramp consists of a microwave diode mounted between two transmission lines,

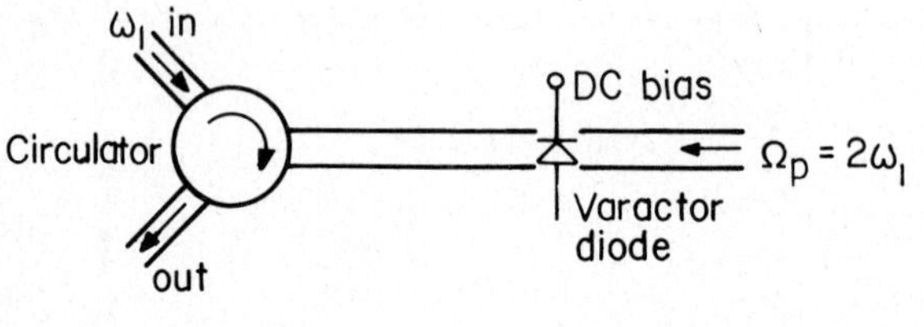

Figure 17. Schematic diagram of a parametric amplifier.

as shown in Figure 17. Both the signal frequency ω_p and the pump fequency $\Omega_p = 2\omega_p$ are applied to a properly biased diode. A circulator enables the incoming signal to be separated from the amplified reflected signal. Because the internal resistance of the diode can be very low, and because the diode can can be cooled to low temperatures, such an amplifier can have a noise level quite close to the quantum limit, and is therefore a promising device for amplification of the signal obtained from a parametric upconverter transducer. For a transducer pumped at a high frequency compared with ω_a, the signal sidebands are also close to the transducer pump frequency. Thus the parametric amplifier need only have a very narrow bandwidth $\sim 2\omega_a/\omega_p$. The amplifier pump frequency can be easily obtained by frequency doubling the transducer pump signal.

The output of the transducer itself contains frequencies ω_p and $\omega_p \pm \omega_a$ (see figure 15) and we must examine the gain of the device for both the carrier ω_p, and the modulation sidebands. Because the amplifier pump Ω_p is phase coherent relative to the carrier ω_p, the device is termed a *phase conerent* degenerate paramp (PCDPA). The phase coherence gives the device phase sensitive gain: under these circumstances it is not a linear amplifier, and has valuable applications to quantum non-demolition. Its phase sensitivity is also manifested in differing gains for AM and FM sidebands. These varying gains are characterised by the following simple relations:

$$G_+ G_- = 1 \tag{35}$$

$$G_{AM} G_{FM} = 1 \tag{36}$$

where G_+ and G_- are the maximum and minimum possible gains for the carrier, and G_{FM} and G_{AM} are the gains for the FM and AM sidebands.

One simply has to vary the phase of the pump to change the gain in one channel from say 10^2, to 10^{-2}. As referred to the amplification of an AM or FM sideband the phase coherent amplifier is still a linear amplifier. It can be operated in such a way that it attenuates the carrier signal, while amplifying the FM sidebands produced by the parametric transducer. In this way the PCDPA helps alleviate the problem of dynamic range which arises when trying to amplify a very small modulation sidebands in the presence of a large carrier. These ideas are illustrated in figure 17 which shows spectra of incident and output signals from a PCDPA compared with a conventional amplifier.

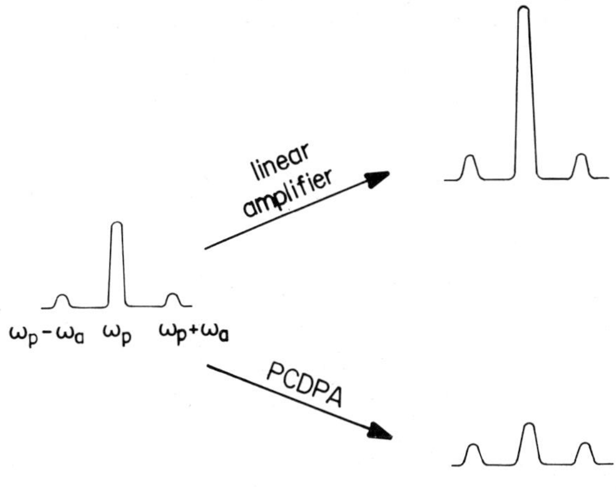

Figure 18. A PCDPA can amplify signal sidebands while attenuating an unwanted carrier, on which a linear amplifier will saturate.

Further details on the QND properties of paramps are given by Caves (these proceedings); a full classical analysis of the PCDPA, including detailed noise analysis, has been performed by R.N. James[29].

4. Practical Parametric Transducer Systems: Noise considerations

To construct a low noise parametric upconverter transducer several precautions must be taken to minimise noise sources. The highest possible stability pump oscillator is needed and this generally means that some sort of high performance frequency stabilisation must be used. The output signal must be amplified by the lowest noise amplifier available, and losses in the signal lines must be minimised to prevent thermal noise from degrading the signal. Seismic noise and other extrinsic noise must be carefully isolated from the system. These requirements are certainly difficult to achieve and so far no transducer has even approached the quantum limit, although transducer noise numbers $\lesssim 10$ appear to be technically achievable.

In the following discussion we will use the transducer developed at UWA as a practical example. The transducer system is illustrated in figure 19. A 10 GHz microwave frequency source is locked to a high Q superconducting cavity so as to minimise oscillator phase noise.

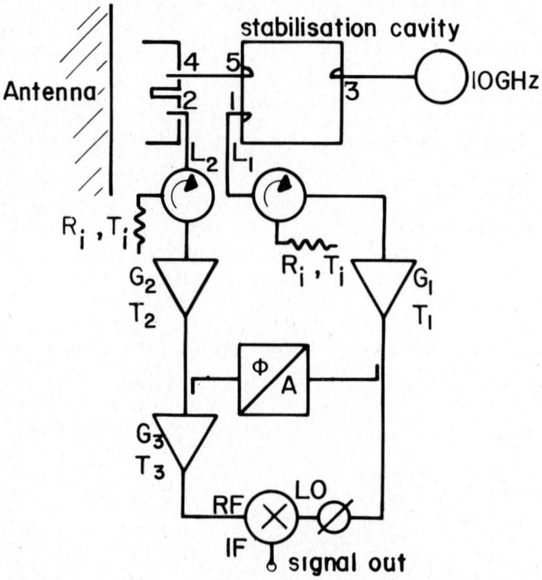

Figure 19. Parametric transducer readout system.

The stabilised and filtered microwave signal is fed to the re-entrant cavity through ports 4 and 5. A filtered local oscillator signal used for demodulation is extracted from port 1 and the modulated microwave signal containing the motion information is extracted from port 2. Isolators limit any noise acting back on the system to the thermal noise of resistor R_i and temperature T_i which may be 2K or less. Both signals are amplified by low noise amplifiers before demodulation by means of a double balanced mixer. A carrier suppression stage is included, whereby excess carrier may be attenuated by interference with an out-of-phase local oscillator. The re-entrant cavity, which is magnetically levitated is held within its position bandwidth near, but not touching the end of the antenna, by means of a servo control system. See part VI (3) for further details.

There are five major noise sources in this system:

a) Phase noise in the pump oscillator, which produces a signal indistinguishable from the motion signal from the transducer.

b) FM to AM conversion noise: residual frequency fluctuations in the pump oscillator are converted to AM noise by the high Q(> 10^8) response curve of the stabilisation cavity. This AM signal appears in the final demodulated output, again indistinguishable from signal.

c) Thermal noise from lossy components such as the transmission lines, and noise from each amplifier in the microwave circuit.

d) Noise from residual AM noise in the pump oscillator.

e) Noise from the double balanced mixer.

A detailed analysis of these noise contributions has been made by A.G. Mann[28]. All can be controlled in principle, to close to the quantum limit, using existing techniques and devices. For example, a TE_{011} mode superconducting cavity of Q only ~10^8 is sufficient to achieve phase noise spectral densities 10^{-16} Hz^{-1} at 1 kHz from the carrier[30]. This represents a transducer noise number contribution from phase noise ~10^2. Raising the cavity Q to 10^9 (a commonly achieved value) would bring this noise contribution down to the quantum limit.

Finally all transducers, both active and passive are limited in noise number by the noise number of the amplifier with which they are used. Figure 20 shows the noise number of a variety of amplifiers from audio to microwave frequencies. [50]

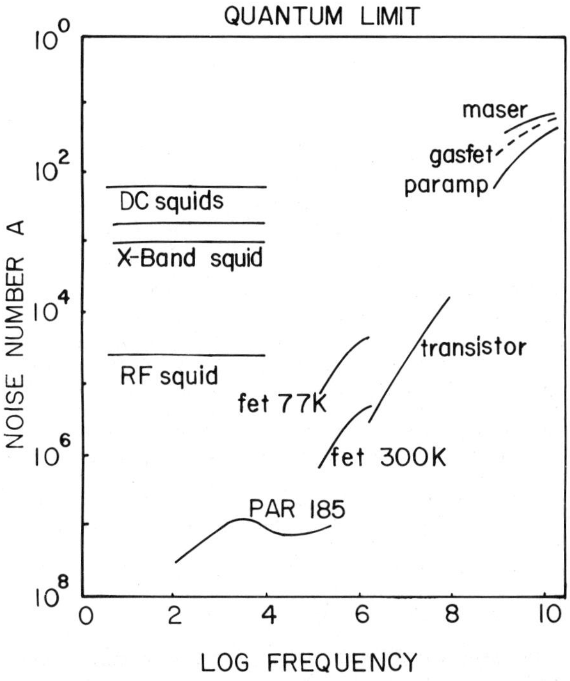

Figure 20. Amplifier noise in the range 1 Hz - 10^{10} Hz.

We note moderate approaches to the quantum limit in the audiofrequency region by SQUIDs, and at microwave frequencies by masers, parametric amplifiers and GaAs FET amplifiers. This data explains the clear choice of SQUID's for passive transducers (which we shall discuss further). They show also the reason that high frequencies, $\sim 10^{10}$ Hz, are chosen for parametric transducers, rather than the range 10^6-10^8 Hz where amplifier performance is rather poor.

Two of the noise sources discussed here contribute a fluctuating force to the antenna. The first is the well known back action force acting via Z_{12} as given in equation (13). The source of this noise is the resistor in the isolator, and for T_i = 4K this is a small effect. The second and much more serious contribution is AM noise in the pump oscillator. The presence of AM noise at the ω_a sideband frequency of the pump directly produces a fluctuating force on the antenna. For small values of $\beta(\sim 10^{-3})$ this effect is also small, but as $\beta \to 1$ (ultimately required for a rapid transducer response time) the AM noise will have to be controlled 2 orders of magnitude below the existing state of the art.

Some of the pump noise contributions can be considerably reduced if the transducer uses not one re-entrant cavity, but a balanced pair of cavities. Such a scheme is used in the LSU transducer (see paper by Hamilton in these proceedings). A pair of cavities may be mounted on either side of a diaphragm such as illustrated in Figure 21.

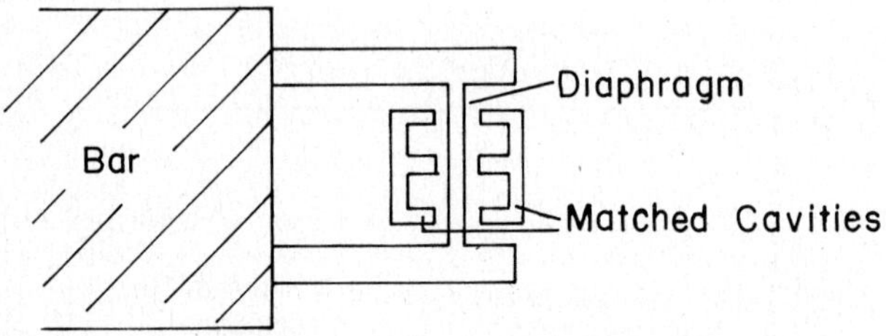

Figure 21. Balanced cavity parametric transducer.

When excited by the same pump source it is easy to arrange that the two signal contributions add while the AM and FM pump noise contributions subtract. The noise reduction will be determined by the accuracy of the tuning and matching of the cavities. The advantages of a balanced system are offset, however, by the problem of Q-degradation of the antenna by the complex mechanical system which must be attached to the end face to enable the cavities to be tuned correctly.

5. Passive Transducers

Three different passive transducer schemes have been used on gravitational wave antennae. The first, using piezoelectric (PZT) crystals, has the disadvantage that the PZT material is mechanically lossy, causing serious Q-degradation of an antenna unless it is very weakly coupled. The output impedance of PZT is easily matched to an FET amplifier, which, as Figure 20 shows, has rather poor noise performance. The second scheme avoids the mechanical losses of the PZT by replacing it with an externally polarised capacitor. Voltage changes are produced by the relative motion of two capacitor plates with constant charge. The capacitor can avoid the losses of the PZT, but still a high impedance amplifier is most easily used. An FET is the best choice and again it is too noisy. Matching to the very low input impedance of a SQUID would be difficult with such a device.

The third and most successful passive transducer scheme uses a superconducting inductive readout coupled to a SQUID as was illustrated in Figure 11(a). The method is conceptually simple. A persistent current flows in a superconducting inductor L, which is in the form of a flat "pancake" coil. The inductance is proportional to the spacing x between the inductor and a superconducting ground plane: $L \sim L_o + ax$. Since flux is conserved in superconducting circuits, LI is a constant independent of the spacing x, and current I must vary inversely as x, so that for small x, $I(x) \approx I_o - bx$.

The variations in the current I(x) are read out by coupling to a SQUID device. Practical inductive readout coils can be impedance matched to the few μH input inductance of most SQUIDs. Thus in principle the noise performance need only be limited by the noise performance of the SQUID. In practice electrical losses in the superconducting circuit can lead to significant degradation of performance, however.

A passive inductive transducer of the type discussed in general here, is discussed in the paper by Michelson in these proceedings. Here we will make some general comments, and briefly discuss the operation of SQUIDs themselves.

There are two types of quantum interference devices commonly used, DC SQUIDs and RF SQUIDs. The DC SQUID contains two Josephson junctions or weak links in a superconducting loop, whereas the RF SQUID contains only one. Superconducting Cooper pairs can tunnel through the weak links. In the case of the DC SQUID the impedance of the loop is modulated by external flux; it is oscillatory with a period of one flux quantum $\phi = h/2e$. This results from interference associated with phase shifts across the Josephson junctions in the presence of shielding currents and external flux. By using modulation and feedback it is possible to servo control the flux seen by the loop to a constant value. The current required to null the flux introduced by, say, a coil coupled to a transducer, is linearly related to the input current. Such a system enables the SQUID to resolve very small fractions of a flux quantum, in the range $10^{-5} - 10^{-7}\ \phi_o$.

RF SQUIDs are modulated by an AC field at frequencies varying from 20 MHz to 10 GHz. Hysteretic transitions in the superconducting loop modulate the RF pump signal which enables small changes in flux to be detected. Servo control is also used to stabilise the external flux seen by the loop. There are some difficulties in coupling external flux to the very small loops of DC SQUIDS and as Figure 20 shows, operating devices are still some way from the quantum limit. However noise measurements on uncoupled DC SQUIDs encourage optimism that coupled DC SQUIDs may approach a noise number $A \sim 1$ in the near future. (See [31] and references therein). The best microwave RF SQUID is comparable to the best existing DC SQUID, and quantum limited sensitivity is probably also possible.

Although SQUID's themselves are complex devices requiring precision thin film photo fabrication technology, once developed, they can provide simple high performance amplifiers easily used in transducers that in principle can have noise number comparable to that of the SQUID. Only the problem of AC losses remains to prevent this. To obtain a reasonably high coupling factor β (defined by equation 8) large electric or magnetic coupling fields are required. For a capacitively coupled transducer β is given by

$$\beta = \tfrac{1}{2}CV^2/m\omega^2x^2 \qquad (37)$$

which is Q_e times smaller than the coupling factor for a parametric transducer with the same values of C and V (equation 34). The quantity CV^2 is replaced by LI^2 for an inductive transducer. Thus the passive transducer must maximise the coupling energy density to obtain sufficient coupling, and in the case of the superconducting inductive transducer this requires the use of high magnetic fields, comparable with the critical field of niobium.

For reasons not properly understood, it has been found difficult to prevent AC losses in the superconducting circuits that carry the high persistent currents necessary to create the desired coupling field. This causes a reduction in the mechanical Q factor of the transducer, thus degrading the overall antenna-transducer system performance. The Stanford group has made progress in reducing these losses by careful surface preparation. See Michelson's paper in these proceedings for more details. As an alternative, it may be possible to use sense inductors without large persistent currents by using a coil in the field of a permanent magnet.[33]

Because of the problem of coupling a passive transducer to a large mass antenna, most passive transducer systems presently being developed use a resonant mass as an impedance matching element between the antenna and the transducer. The Stanford transducer uses a two mode resonant diaphragm, whereas at Maryland, Richard[34] has constructed a 3-mode transducer, in which the energy is coupled successively from the bar, to an intermediate mass resonator and on to a small mass diaphragm. The transducer senses the motion of this small mass. Such a scheme allows large coupling factors β to be attained at lower magnetic fields. Energy transfer occurs more rapidly with a 3-mode transducer; this may allow the measurement bandwidth, (or the sampling time τ_s) to be decreased,* which can both increase the time resolution and allow the Brownian motion contribution to be reduced, according to equation (16).

---

*It is important to be clear about the meaning of the sampling time τ_s. It does not refer to the rate of data acquisition by the computer, which can obviously be increased to any desired value. The sampling time, defined in section III, is a measure of the total instrumental bandwidth of the measurement, which may be determined by analog or digital filtering of the signal from the transducer.

V. ANTENNA MATERIALS: INTRINSIC PROPERTIES AND ACOUSTIC LOSSES

1. Antenna Materials

As discussed in the introduction, we really need some nuclear matter with $v_s \to c$ for construction of gravitational wave antennae. Since this is not available we must find a form of molecular matter which, to maximise coupling to gravitational waves, combines high velocity of sound v_s, high density ρ, and low acoustic loss Q^{-1}.

At a particular frequency the best antenna material will have the largest value of $Q\rho v_s^3$. This quantity is proportional to the ratio of energy absorbed ($\sim\rho v_s^3$) and the thermal noise in the antenna ($\sim Q^{-1}$). Of the three controlling parameters, only the Q-factor can be modified significantly in a particular material, depending on its preparation and suspension. Table V lists the values of ρ, v_s, and ρv_s^3 for various materials, along with the maximum achieved Q-value to date, and the figure of merit $Q\rho v_s^3$. The table shows that nearly one order of magnitude improvement is obtained (at a given frequency) in ρv_s^3 by going over from aluminium or niobium, to sapphire, and when the Q factor is included, the very low losses is sapphire make it about 500 times better than Nb or Aℓ (at a given operating temperature). Silicon also is more than 100 times better than Nb and Aℓ. Unfortunately, at present silicon and sapphire are not available in sufficiently large masses for these apparent advantages to be useful. Note also that a lower Q-factor can always be compensated for by sufficient cooling, so that fundamentally only the ρv_s^3 term need be considered.

For comparison, Table V also shows lead and tungsten. Lead is very poor, because of its low sound velocity, whereas tungsten is comparable to silicon. If massive high Q tungsten bars could be obtained, they would have the significant advantage that the cryogenic system necessary to house the antenna would be far smaller (and cheaper and simpler) than that needed for lower density materials.

Table V. Comparison between Antenna Materials

Material	ρ (gms/cm^3)	v_s (km/sec)	Q	ρv_s^3 (10^{13}kg sec^{-3})	$Q\rho v_s^3$ (10^{20}kg sec^{-3})
Aluminium 6061	2.7	5.1	5×10^6	36	18
Aluminium 5056	2.7	5.1	7×10^7	36	250
Niobium	8.57	3.4	6×10^7	34	200
Silicon	2.33	8.5	2×10^9	140	2.8×10^4
Sapphire	3.98	9.4	3×10	330	10^5
Lead	11.36	1.1		1.5	
Tungsten	18.8	4.3		150	

2. Q-measurements in niobium

At UWA J. Ferreirinho has made an extensive study of the Q of niobium[35], in the hope of learning how to obtain extremely high Q values. Here I want to report some of the main results of this work.

Disc shaped samples were chosen for this study, excited in flexural modes, and suspended by a thin rod attached to the central node, which itself was suspended by a fine wire. The set up is shown in Figure 22. The discs were approximately 120 mm diameter, and 3 mm thick. By accurately calibrating the temperature dependence of the frequency of each samples it was possible to monitor both the temperature and the Q-factor of samples without the need of attaching a thermometer, which could seriously degrade the Q. The Q-measurements were accurate and reproducible to ~1%, and accurate temperature resolution allowed a sharp jump in Q at the transition temperature to be resolved within 20 mk.

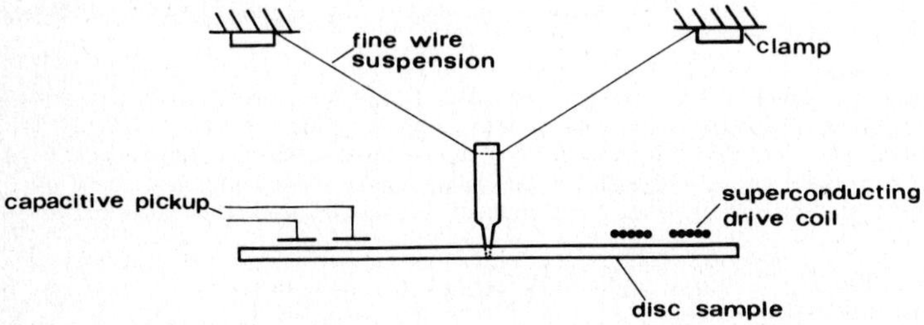

Figure 22. Suspension system for acoustic loss measurements on Nb discs.

Figures 23 and 24 show the results of a succession of measurements starting from cold worked samples, and extending to samples more and more highly annealed. The measurements show several general features. The maximum Q in the temperature range 2 to 10 degrees rises steadily for more annealed samples. A jump in Q at the transition temperature is enhanced, and for the higher anneals a substantial minimum develops in the vicinity of 2K. Q-factors as high as 5×10^7 occur in the disc samples, which is to be compared with 6×10^7 measured at 4.2K in a 30 cm x 5 cm bar. A sample machined from a piece of electron beam melted ingot material, which has a crystal size of several centimetres shows quite different behaviour.

The dramatic jump in Q at the superconducting transition is a manifestation of the thermoelastic effect. Vibration gives rise to compression and rarefaction on opposite sides of the niobium disc. The strain is related to temperature through the coefficient of thermal expansion. Vibration of the sample causes a time dependent temperature difference across it: under compression it is heated, under rarefaction it is cooled. Thus heat flow acts to restore thermal equilibrium. For thick samples the temperature gradient is small enough that the thermoelastic losses are usually negligible, but for thin discs or diaphragms it can be more significant.

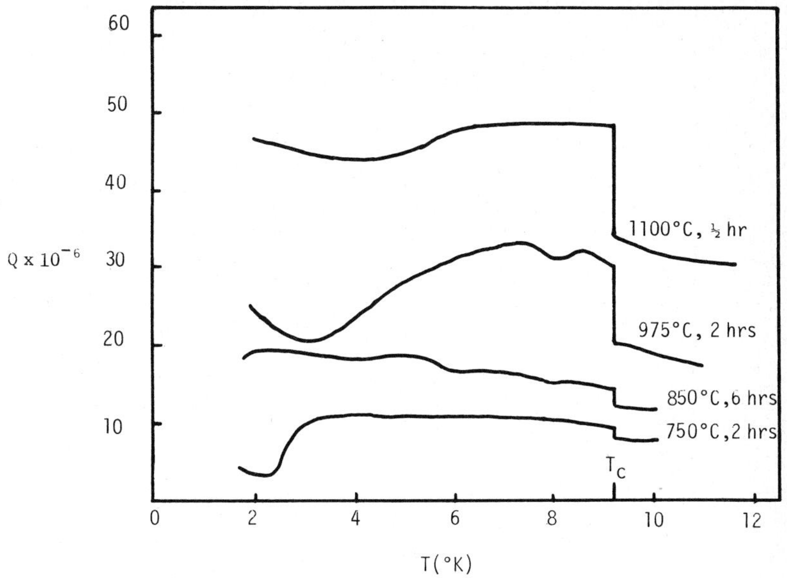

Figure 23. Temperature dependence of the Q-factor of niobium samples annealed in a vacuum of 10^{-4} torr, for temperatures and times shown.

The magnitude of the thermoelectric effect is determined by the coefficient of thermal expansion α and the specific heat c. Furthermore the effect depends most strongly on the ratio between the period of oscillator of the sample, and the thermal relaxation time τ_{th}. This in turn is determined by the sample thickness d, it's specific heat, and thermal conductivity K. Explicitly, for plane bending the thermoelastic limited Q value, Q_{th} is given by

$$Q_{th} = \left(\frac{1-\sigma}{1+\sigma}\right) \frac{c}{E\alpha^2 T} \left(\frac{1+\omega^2\tau_{th}{}^2}{\omega\tau_{th}}\right) \tag{38}$$

where $$\tau_{th} = \frac{d^2 c}{\pi^2 K} .$$

Here σ, E, and T are the Poissons ratio, Young's modulus and temperature of the sample. At T_c there is a sudden jump is specific heat. This causes a sudden reduction of the thermoelastic loss, causing the Q to rise suddenly. Full details of this effect are published in ref [36]. Note that even if $c/E\alpha^2 T$ is small, the thermoelastic effect will not be serious unless τ_{th} is in the range of say 10^{-2}-10^{-4} seconds for a typical gravitational wave antenna. This will generally only occur with thin samples, such as the discs used here, or diaphragms used in transducers.

The thermoelastic loss will generally be smaller with high Debye temperature materials, such as sapphire, where α becomes very small at low temperatures. Also in superconductors the reduction of thermal conductivity at low temperatures

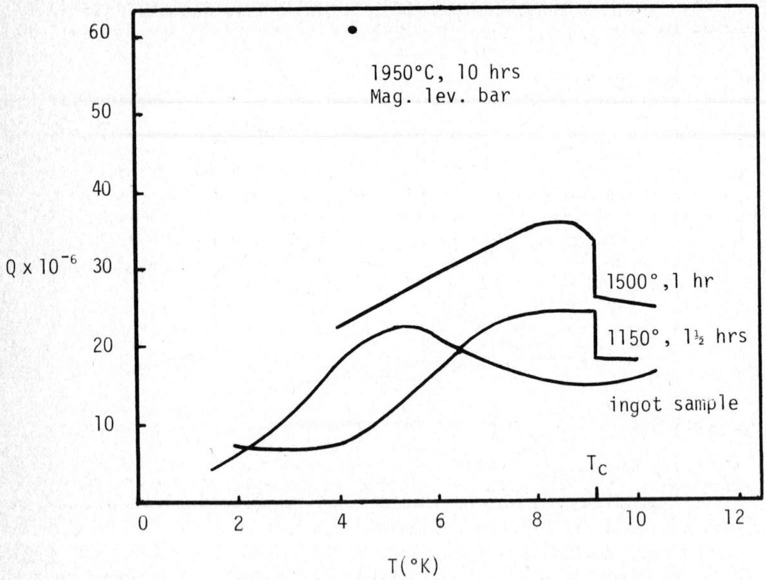

Figure 24. Temperature dependence of the Q-factor of two highly annealed disc samples, a disc sample cut from an ingot of electron beam melted material, and a highly annealed bar sample. Both the bar and the ingot had a crystal size of several cm.

limits the effect to thin diaphragms. Variations in specific heat at low temperatures can, however, cause Q_{th} to have unexpected temperature dependence. Since the thermoelastic loss is an exactly calculable thermodynamic effect, it is always possible to determine in advance the thermoelastic contribution to any structure.

The second main feature of the data of Figures 23 and 24 is the minimum in Q which occurs at a temperature ~2K. For higher anneals the minimum generally becomes more enhanced. For an "optimum anneal" of 1100°C for ½ hour, the minimum is very weak, and a high Q, roughly temperature independent, is obtained. For the ingot sample the Q falls with rather a different temperature dependence. There is evidence that the Q rises below 1.4K, and it is possible that at sufficiently low temperatures the acoustic losses will become very small. However a broad spectrum of relaxation losses associated with dislocations could give rise to a low Q-factor over a broad temperature range, and there is no reason why this should not extend to very low temperatures.

These results may mean that it is advantageous to operate niobium bars at temperatures $\gtrsim$ 4K, or else below 1K. However there are some discrepancies. The ingot sample itself shows an anomalous Q-dependence on temperature compared with the annealed disc samples. A high annealed bar, tested at 4.2K, showed a Q-factor of 6×10^7, well above the values seen in the high annealed disc samples at this temperature. It has also been found that surface damage and contamination increases the acoustic loss in discs. It is possible that the high surface to mass ratio of the disc samples introduces additional surface losses which would be greatly reduced in bars.

VI. SUSPENSION AND ISOLATION

1. Introduction

Any mechanical resonator that is required to have a high quality factor should be suspended from a node of the mode of interest, to minimise both acoustic loss and external acoustic excitation through the suspension point. This rather obvious point has never, to my knowledge, been applied to a resonant bar. The reason is that the node of the fundamental mode of a bar is at the centre of mass, which is not conveniently accessible for suspension. Even such nodal suspension has limitations however due to the finite area required for the support. Moreover material anisotropy can cause the nodal point to differ from the centre of mass (this is a significant effect in niobium) which can make the predetermination of the node very difficult.

2. Cable Suspension

The first method of suspension, cable suspension, was pioneered by Weber. The bar is balanced on a high strength cable stretched around the longitudinal centre of the bar. Braginsky has achieved Q-factors 3×10^9 in sapphire bars supported in this way by a fine polished tungsten wire[37]. The part of the cable in contact with the bar presumably is forced to participate in the "breathing mode" of the bar. In general the motion of the bar will exert a time varying longitudinal force on the cable, which can lead to energy loss through longitudinal acoustic excitation. The energy may be lost in the cable itself, or into the cable suspension point. If the cable hangs exactly vertical, however, the breathing mode has no vertical component at the tangent point, and longitudinal excitation does not occur. Furthermore, if a cable is attached tangentially to a bar, (not necessarily vertical) the longitudinal excitation of the cable is second order in the amplitude of the breathing mode, and may well be negligible (I thank M.J. Buckingham for pointing this out). The breathing mode always causes a transverse motion at the tangent point of the cable. Thus a transverse acoustic wave always propagates into the cable. To obtain maximum Q-values the Moscow group carefully tuned the length of the suspension wire for their sapphire bar, to one quarter wavelength for the transverse wave at the fundamental longitudinal mode frequency of the bar.[38]

At the lower Q-values associated with room-temperature $A\ell$ bars cable suspension appears to be reliable. It is easy to show, however, that a cable suspension can cause low frequency seismic noise to be upconverted via non-linear frictional coupling.[39] The process is analogous to the excitation of a violin string by low frequency bowing. In this case seismic noise at the natural pendulum or rocking frequency of the bar excites static/sliding frictional transitions near the cable tangent point. This gives rise to small strain changes in the bar, which can excite the fundamental mode to temperatures greatly exceeding the thermodynamic temperature. Moreover, occasional large seismic events can cause rare excitations which can easily mimic gravitational wave signals.

A simple analysis gives the following result for the mean acoustic power entering the low frequency longitudinal modes of the antenna as a result of a low frequency amplitude of oscillation of the bar-cable system:

$$P_a = \frac{16\, t^{5/2} \sigma^{\frac{1}{2}} a_r^2 b\omega_r}{\omega_a m^2 \ell^3} \left(\tfrac{1}{2}\mu_s - \mu_d\right) \qquad (39)$$

Here t is the tension in the cable σ is the cable mass per unit length, a_r and ω_r are the amplitude and frequency of the rocking motion measured at the end of the bar, b is effective offset of the cable from the centre of suspension, m and ℓ are the antenna mass and length, μ_s and μ_d are the static and dynamic coefficients of friction between the bar and the cable. Note that P_a increases quadratically with a_r; for typical antenna parameters one finds that vibration amplitudes ~1 - 10 μm are sufficient to cause excitation of antennae to mode temperatures ~$10 - 10^3$ °K. At the low rocking frequencies of antennae it is very difficult to prevent such motion.

Frictional transitions can be overcome by welding or other forms of rigid contact. The Stanford antenna is supported by four titanium cables attached to welded lugs on the bar. The low levels of excess noise observed suggest that this is a good solution. The cables are not attached at nodal points, but again, they are tuned to λ/4 to prevent acoustic energy loss.

3. Magnetic Levitation

Our experience at UWA has shown that magnetic levitation is a reliable means of obtaining a high Q suspension with good vibration isolation. However it is restricted to bars made from, or coated with, superconductors having a reasonably high critical field Hc_1. The 100 Gauss critical field of aluminium restricts magnetic levitation to bars less than 1 cm in diameter. Niobium, with a 1.9 kG critical field, is restricted to about 20 cm diameter.

In the early 1970's attempts were made at Stanford to plasma spray NbTi alloy (a high field type II superconductors) onto aluminium bars. Eventually the work was abandoned since high critical fields could not be reproducibly obtained. It is important that the superconducting material have good stability to flux penetration. In niobium irreversible flux penetration occurs just above Hc_1. In type II superconductors flux penetration can occur far below the upper critical field Hc_2, thus high field superconductors cannot necessarily be used to coat non-superconducting bars.

A magnetically levitated antenna requires a large amount of instrumentation both to levitate it, and to enable its position in space to be accurately known. Superconducting "pancake coils" do not automatically lead to a stable levitation configuration; thus the superconducting coil assembly generally needs additional trim coils to make adjustments to the position of the bar. Coils are also necessary to control the longitudinal position of the bar.

At UWA we have developed precision radiofrequency position monitors[40] and flux pumps[41] to enable accurate levitation control. The superconducting circuit diagram for our 67 Kg antenna is shown in figure 25. Flux can be pumped into seven different superconducting coils, and transformer-coupled into several others. Small heaters (heat switches) are used to open and close superconducting circuits. A non-contacting trasducer is levitated on a bifilar coil which produces a very soft linear bearing with a stiff transverse spring constant. A bifilar coil is also used to provide a stiff magnetic spring between the bar and the transducer, which helps reduce the low frequency motion of the transducer due to seismic noise. (The bar-transducer frequency can be raised to about 40 Hz) A superconducting magnetic drive assembly at the rear of the transducer allow it is servo controlled and locked to the resonance of the re-entrant cavity.

Figure 26 shows the levitated antenna-transducer system for our 1 metre, 67 Kg antenna. Microwave power is coupled to the re-entrant cavity transducer through a high electrical Q superconducting cavity stabilised oscillator (SCSO) cavity.

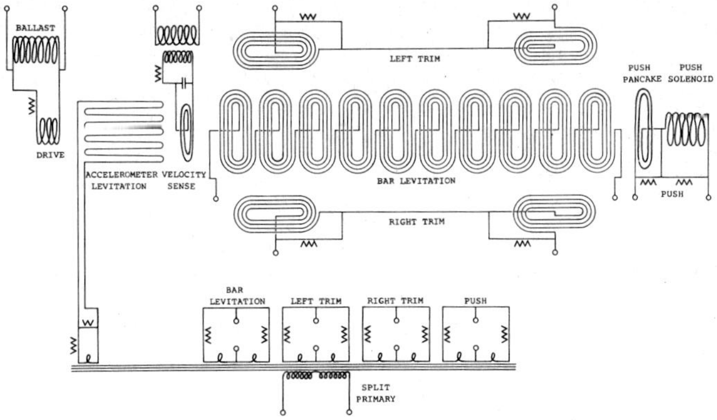

Figure 25. Superconducting circuit for magnetically levitated antenna with non-contacting transducer.

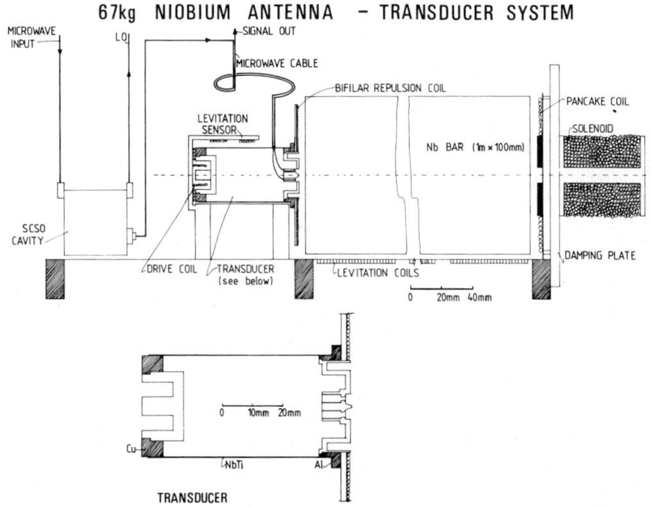

Figure 26. Cross-sectional diagram of magnetically levitated antenna system.

Thin microwave cables (0.5 mm diameter) are used to reduce vibrational coupling. The drive assembly uses a high field SmCo magnet. The levitation coils are mounted underneath the aluminium levitation cradle, so that in event of failure of a superconducting coil the flux collapses slowly due to eddy currents, thus preventing localised heating and damage to the superconducting wire. A damping plate at the end of the bar, made from pure copper, is used to damp the seismically excited low frequency longitudinal motion of the bar in its cradle. The system shown here is still under test. However in a small 30 cm, 5.6 kHz prototype antenna-transducer system we found that there was no detectable acoustic excitation above the thermodynamic Brownian amplitude at 4.2K, even though the levitation cradle was itself not vibration isolated from the cryostat. The antenna noise temperature was 40 mK[42]. It is essential to take great care that noise in the servo control system does not cause excess noise motion in the transducer. We use low pass filters, and notch filters in the output stage of the servo system to minimise this effect.

Magnetic levitation can cause a degradation of the Q-factor of a levitated bar, since the vibration of the bar modulates the levitation field, giving rise to eddy current losses in the copper cladding of the NbTi superconductor, and in the Aℓ cradle. In practice this effect will limit the Q-value of Nb bars to 10^8-10^9, depending on bar geometry and the height of levitation. At the present achieved Q-values magnetic levitation losses are therefore negligible.

4. Four point suspensions

Several groups have developed four point suspensions, otherwise known as "dead bugs", which were first developed by Richard at the University of Maryland. The suspension consists of a massive base which supports four flexible legs on which the bar sits. The legs participate in both the longitudinal and the breathing motion of the bar, so it is important that the legs have low acoustic loss, low stiffness in the longitudinal and vertical directions (relative to the bar), and small size and mass.

At UWA we have experimented with 4-point suspensions and found considerable problems. We have obtained excellent results with small scale systems: A bar of aluminium alloy 5083, 1 metre long by 10 cm diameter had a Q-factor $\sim 3 \times 10^7$ at 20K, comparable to the results obtained by Suzuki[43] for Aℓ 5056 alloy. (It is very difficult to determine whether the observed Q-value is intrinsic, or limited by the suspension.) Unfortunately the properties of 4-point suspensions do not scale linearly with increasing antenna size. A four point suspension tested for our 1.5 tonne Nb bar clearly exhibits loss at a Q-level $\sim 10^6$, although the free vibration frequency of the legs, and the vertical suspension frequency under load were comparable to the small scale system.

Other groups have also had difficulties, low Q and poor reproducibility, with 4-point suspensions. They are difficult to analyse completely. Acoustic transmission line losses may occur, so they cannot simply be described by lumped equivalent circuits. However, our results with the 1 metre Aℓ bar show that high Q-factors can be obtained, and given a satisfactory design the 4-point suspension system is very simple and convenient.

5. Vibration Isolation

Every suspension system described above gives a certain amount of vibration isolation, since a system which minimises the degradation of the Q-factor of an antenna will also isolate against incoming noise at the same frequency. Further isolation is still essential however, and traditionally, following Weber, bars have been isolated by stacks of steel and rubber that form a multipole low pass filter. The steel (or lead or concrete) itself is small enough (say 20 cm diameter x 4 cm thick) that its internal modes are well above the antenna frequency. Sheets of commercially available vibration isolation rubber are placed between the steel masses. Figure 27 shows a cross section of such a stack at UWA. Three stacks using 10 kg lead discs support a 50 cm diameter steel disc from which hangs the experimental chamber which contains the 1.5 tonne Nb antenna.

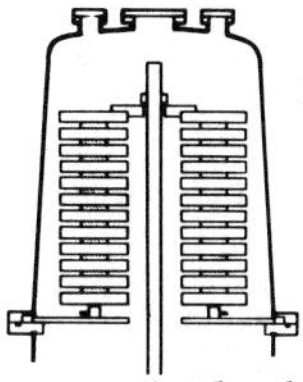

Figure 27: Lead and rubber antivibration stack used to isolate the 1.5 tonne antenna at UWA.

In a cryogenic system it is essential to isolate the antenna from the vibration caused by boiling cryogenic fluids. In most cryostats the bar suspension system is carefully isolated from the cryogenics. However electrical leads must be thermally grounded to prevent excess heat from entering the antenna or transducer. Thus some noise in the leads is inevitable. At Stanford and Maryland vibration isolation filters consisting of chains of masses hanging from each other on fine wires are used to attenuate noise in the wires. The incoming cables are bonded successively to each mass. (See Michelson's paper for detail.)

Possibly the most serious vibration source is *low frequency* seismic or environmental noise. Most antivibration stacks have a roll off frequency of 20 - 100 Hz. Below this frequency seismic noise can be enhanced. The low frequency noise can excite non-linear processes which, as we saw earlier, can lead to strong excitation at the signal frequency. Stress-induced stress relaxation in the antenna itself is one such process which could cause excitations correlated with low frequency accelerations of the antenna. The Chinese groups have used massive concrete platforms supported by air-springs to obtain roll-off frequencies as low as 0.5 Hz.[44] Even lower frequency isolation may be necessary to obtained sufficient environmental immunity.

VII PROSPECTS FOR IMPROVED SENSITIVITY

1. The Ten Resonant Mass Gravitational Wave Groups

In the following section we begin with a summary of the specific techniques and distinctive features of the ten active experimental groups using resonant mass antennae. All projects are still in the active development phase and only one group has achieved long term high sensitivity operation (Stanford, $h \sim 10^{-18}$). Most groups aim to reach or surpass the quantum limit in the long term, but necessarily progress will be in small steps, as various new technologies are developed.

Information on the groups is given in Table VI. The main features of each project are given, including the currently planned antenna frequencies. Further details should be obtained from the groups themselves.

Table VI. Resonant Mass Gravitational Radiation Experiments

Group	Distinctive Features	Frequency
University of Maryland J. Weber, J-P. Richard, H.J. Paik et al.	Room temperature $A\ell$ bars, massive cryogenic $A\ell$ bars with 3 mode SQUID transducers. Ultra low temperatures planned.	1.6 kHz 800 Hz
Stanford University W. Fairbank, P. Michelson, M. McAshan et al.	Large mass cryogenic $A\ell$ bars 2-mode transducer with SQUID readout. Ultra low temperatures planned.	840 Hz
Louisiana State University W.O. Hamilton, W.C. Oelfke et al.	Large mass cryogenic $A\ell$ bars. Balanced parametric upconverter transducer. Ultra low temperatures planned.	840 Hz
Moscow State University V. Braginsky et al.	Sapphire bars 10-100 kg, $Q \sim 3 \times 10^9$. "Horned" antenna with parametric upconverter transducer.	20-40 kHz
University of Rome E. Amaldi, G. Pizzella G. Pallotino et al.	Various massive cryogenic $A\ell$ bars. Ultra low temperatures planned. Transducer using DC SQUID.	1.8 kHz 840 Hz
University of Rochester D. Douglass, W. Johnson et al	Cryogenic $A\ell$ bars (also silicon) SQUID passive transducer and SQUID parametric upconverter transducer.	2.3 kHz
University of Western Australia M.J. Buckingham, C. Edwards, D.G. Blair	Cryogenic Niobium bars, 67 kg and 1.5 tonne. Non-contacting parametric upconverter transducer.	1.7 kHz 700 Hz
Zhongshan University Guangzhou Hu Enke et al.	Massive $A\ell$ bar, tuned and low frequency antenna 300K. Cryogenic operation planned.	1. kHz 20-50 Hz
Institute of Physics, Academia Sinica, Beijing Qin Rong Xian et al.	Massive $A\ell$ bar, and low frequency tuning fork antenna 300K. Cryogenic operation planned.	1.7 kHz 20-50 Hz
University of Tokyo H. Hirakawa et al.	Tuned antenna for crab pulsar, 300K. Cryogenic operation planned. Parametric and passive capacitive transducers.	60 Hz

2. Prospects for Improvements: Linear Systems

The best sensitivity achieved by a gravitational wave antenna is still far from the quantum limit. Improvements can be obtained by cooling to lower temperatures, raising the Q-factor of the antennae, and improving the transducer. All antennae have been limtied by transducer properties up to now. Room temperature antenna are limited by the losses in the PZT, and the Stanford antenna is limited by losses in the superconducting circuit. The UWA prototype antenna was limited by series noise due to phase noise in the pump oscillator. However without the use of higher Q-factors or ultra low temperatures thermal noise will eventually dominate as transducers are improved. The situation is well illustrated by some noise accounting on the UWA 67 kg antenna.

To estimate the dominant noise contributions we divide the noise into three components and express them in terms of noise number:

Thermal noise number: $$A_T = \frac{kT_a\tau_m}{\hbar Q} \tag{40}$$

Back action noise number: $$A_B = \frac{k}{\hbar\omega_a M}\,\frac{|Z_{12}|^2}{R}\,(T_i+T_R)\tau_m \tag{41}$$

where T_i and T_R are the temperatures of the isolator and the re-entrant cavity (see Figure 19).

Series noise number: A_s

$$A_s = \frac{M}{\hbar\omega_a\tau_m}\left\{\frac{k(T_{amp}+T_R)R}{|Z_{21}|^2} + 4\omega_a^2x_o^2\left(\frac{\omega_a}{\omega_p}\right)^2 S_\phi + (\Delta x_o^2+x_s^2)S_{AM}\omega^2\right\} \tag{42}$$

The three contributions to the series noise given here are the amplifier and re-entrant cavity noise, the pump phase noise, and AM to FM conversion noise due to a residual seismic noise amplitudes x_s and servo control offset error Δx_o, in the presence of an AM noise spectral density S_{AM}.

We will now look at the values of A_T, A_B and A_S for typical or realistically achievable system parameters given below.

$$A_T \approx 6000 \text{ for } T_a = 4.2\text{K},\ Q = 4\times10^7,\ \tau_m = 0.1$$

$$A_B \approx 15 \text{ for } T_i = T_R = 4.2\text{K},\ Z_{12} = 30\ \text{NA}^{-1},\ R = 10^7\ \Omega,\ M = 67\ \text{kg}.$$

$$A_s \approx \underset{(T_{amp})}{1000} + \underset{(S_\phi)}{6700} + \underset{(S_{AM})}{700} = 8400 \text{ for } Z_{21} = 3\times10^8\ \text{V/ms}^{-1},$$

$$T_{amp} = 10^3\text{K},\ \Delta x_o = x_s = 10^{-11}\text{m},\ s_\phi = 10^{-14}\ \text{Hz}^{-1},\ S_{AM} = 10^{-16}\ \text{Hz}^{-1}.$$

The contributions to A_S are indicated in brackets. The phase noise contribution is the dominant noise source in this case. If S_ϕ is reduced to 10^{-15} Hz^{-1} A_S reduces to 1470.

For the cases considered here the low value of A_B compared with A_S reflects a poorly impedance matched transducer. However, given the low β value implied by the figures used here the best optimisation is the one for which $A_T + A_B = A_S$. The 0.1 second sampling time τ_S assumed here is not far from the optimum for $S_\phi = 10^{-14}$ Hz^{-1}. In the case of $S_\phi = 10^{-15}$ a shorter sampling time would give reduced total noise. An impedance matching element (such as a resonant diaphragm) or improved coupling by raising the electric field strength across the capacitance gap of the transducer, would increase both Z_{12} and Z_{21}, causing increased back action noise and reduced series noise. Again optimisation would require reduced τ_S, leading again to overall noise reduction.

Summing $A_T + A_B + A_S$, with a conservative 40% margin included, one can expect a 67 Kg antenna with today's technology to have a noise number $\sim 2 \times 10^4$. The amplitude sensitivity Δx is given by

$$\Delta x = \left(\frac{A\hbar}{2M\omega_a}\right)^{1/2} .$$

For the assumed parameters our 67 kg niobium antenna will then have strain sensitivity $h \sim 2 \times 10^{-18}$ at 1750 Hz. Applying the same noise number to a 1500 kg antenna system one can obtains $h \sim 2 \times 10^{-19}$ at 700 Hz. To assume the same noise number at the lower frequency does assume some system improvement however, since many of the noise sources such as S_ϕ and S_{AM} scale as ω_a^{-2}.

It is easy to see how antennae can be improved significantly beyond the sensitivities quoted above. We have tested a cooled 10 GHz GaAs FET amplifier with a noise temperature of 23K at 12K operating temperature.[45] It is expected to have a noise temperature of 15K at 4.2K — a noise number of 20. Degenerate parametric amplifiers can be expected to have noise temperatures of a few degrees Kelvin. By using superconducting cavities with Q-factors between 10^9 and 10^{10} it is possible to reduce S_ϕ to less than 10^{-17} Hz^{-1} and S_{AM} should be reduced to less than 10^{-18} Hz^{-1}. These improvements allow the series noise A_S to be reduced to about 50 for $\tau_S \sim 0.1$ seconds and for an increased bandwidth, obtained by reducing τ_S to 10^{-2} seconds, A_S rises to $\sim$ 500. The reduced value of τ_S reduces A_T to $\sim$ 600 while A_B is reduced to 1.5. The improved system would have a noise number $\sim$ 1200 corresponding to strain sensitivity $h \sim 4 \times 10^{-19}$ for the 67 kg antenna, and $h \sim 5 \times 10^{-20}$ for the 1500 kg antenna. Again improved impedance matching could reduce the noise further.

Further improvements will be difficult without either raising the Q-factor of the bar, or lowering the temperature. If ultra low temperature cooling is to be avoided it may be necessary to use massive bars of a higher Q material such as sapphire. Due to its optimum properties it is worth asking what may be the maximum sensitivity of a sapphire bar. The high velocity of sound would allow the construction of a sapphire bar say 10 metres long, with a frequency of 500 Hz. With $T_a \sim 1K$, $\tau_m \sim 10^{-2}$ sec and $Q \sim 10^9$ the thermal noise number $A_T \sim 1$. Suppose the total noise number can be reduced to 10. Then the strain sensitivity is improved two order of magnitude compared with the immediately forseeable sensitivity of a 1500 Kg Nb antenna - $h \sim 2 \times 10^{-22}$. At this sensitivity even low efficiency events in the Virgo cluster should be observable.

3. Prospects for improvements using BAE Techniques

In this section I will briefly discuss applications of back-action evading measurement techniques to gravitational wave antennae. I assume familiarity with the paper by C. Caves in these proceedings.

Caves has shown[46] that a lossless transducer which has phase sensitive gain (obtained by modulating the electric field that couples the transducer to the antenna) can have sensitivity to one quadrature of the signal only, while being insensitive to the other. Back action noise is only fed into the quadrature to which the transducer is not sensitive. The device is therefore described as back action evading (BAE). The quadratures X_1 and X_2 are quantum mechanically conjugate, hence in principle one can obtain arbitrarily high sensitivity to X_1 at the expense of X_2.

For antennae with thermal noise number $A_T > 1$ (all existing antennae except Braginsky's small sapphire bars) there is very little advantage to such schemes since all one achieves is more sensitivity to the limiting thermal noise. It is possible that future high Q low temperature antennae will benefit from BAE techniques, however. Meanwhile experimentalists are offered the opportunity to exercise their minds in devising practical designs for the proposed devices. This could at least lead to improved designs for conventional transducers.

Caves' equivalent circuit (see Caves' paper in these proceedings) can be realised most easily by assuming the use of a balanced and lossless transformer to couple the pump signal to the transducer. The device is basically the double pumped upconverter described by Figure 14. The two pump sidebands are obtained by modulating the carrier ω_p at frequency ω_a, and removing the carrier to obtain a signal $A \sin \omega_p \cos \omega_a$ consisting of sidebands $\omega_p \pm \omega_a$. The pump signal is coupled across a split capacitor, which is part of a high Q resonator. The transformer which couples in the pump must not allow losses from the resonator or its Q will be degraded. The importance of this resonator is that it acts as a filter to allow power flow at the frequency ω_p which now contains signal information X_1, but to prevent power flow at frequencies $\omega_p \pm 2\omega_a$ which contain unwanted X_2 information. Johnson and Bocko[32] have proposed a scheme which uses a transformer although transformer losses are not analysed.

The simplest approach to BAE transducers consists of using an existing re-entrant cavity transducer, and modulating the pump signal. For this to work the cavity Q must be high enough to significantly reject unwanted power flow at $\omega_p \pm 2\omega_a$. This in turn means that phase and amplitude noise in the pump signal will be significantly degraded, since the cavity is modulated off-resonance. The Lorentzian response of the cavity enhances pump noise at the signal frequency ω_p, while attenuating the pump power at frequency $\omega_p \pm \omega_a$. (Reference [47] analyses this problem in more detail as applied to a proposed configuration for a BAE transducer.) It follows that pump noise sets severe limits on the maximum achievable sensitivity in single cavity BAE transducers. There is an optimum Q-factor above which sensitivity is degraded due to the pump noise. As a result the single cavity approach is unlikely enable to large increases in sensitivity. Hamilton[48] has demonstrated that the single cavity BAE scheme does indeed work in a high noise classical limit. However much work, and new ideas are still needed before low noise devices surpass the standard quantum limits.

4. Conclusion

To conclude I would like to make a few speculative comments on the nature of the observed coincidences that have been seen so far. As I stated in Section I, there is no clearly understood explanation for Weber's original results, nor the few additional examples of coincidences which have been reported subsequently by other workers. Firstly, it seems quite unlikely that the coincidences observed to date represent gravitational wave pulses. At the observed signal strengths many solar masses would have to be converting to gravitational waves with efficiency greater than 10% every day, at distances closer than the galactic centre. It is rather inconceivable that such events would go unnoticed by conventional astronomy.

The second possibility is that the observed coincidences have been simply statistical fluctuations. As Weber has shown, this is extremely unlikely. It is true, however, that observer bias, through selection of threshold levels, or through *a posteriori* selection of data can easily occur, thereby reducing the statistical significance of the observations. The threshold levels (for distinguishing possible signal events) should therefore be chosen in advance on the basis of individual antenna performance. Similarly the criterion for satisfactory operation of the antenna should be determined in advance of the data analysis, and thereafter *all* data should be analysed. If predetermined threshold levels are not used the data should be analysed "blind": an unknown time delay should be inserted in one data set. There is no evidence that the reported coincidences have been due to these sorts of selection effects, but experimentalists should still take the greatest precautions to avoid such bias.

The third possibility is that electromagnetic interference has occurred. Great care has obviously been taken to shield all antennae. However very little is known about very low frequency electromagnetic pulses that may be produced in the upper atmosphere and even by meteorites. Electromagnetic pulses could interact directly with the antenna, amplifier, or transducer, or even through magnetic interaction with steel and rubber vibration isolation filters. Some attempts have been made to try to correlate low frequency electromagnetic signals with the signals from bars[49]. More work may be necessary to conclusively rule out this cause, however.

Finally, is it possible that seismic disturbances themselves could be correlated over long baselines? Could local seismic disturbances be triggered by electromagnetic fluctuations so as to cause coincident excitations of widely spaced antennae? Experiments should be done comparing widely spaced seismometers to check for such effects, however unlikely they may seem.

The Stanford group has already used a "second harmonic veto" to eliminate excitations of possible seismic origin from their data. This could be greatly extended if seismometers and other transducers were routinely used in conjunction with resonant bars. Also the excitation amplitudes of the 3rd and higher harmonics could be compared. Only signals showing zero excitation of all even modes, and excitation falling roughly as $1/n^2$ for the odd modes (depending on the pulse signal spectrum) can be possible gravitational wave candidates.

Today it is most important that coincidence experiments at the 10^{-18} sensitivity achieved at Stanford be undertaken, with two or more groups observing, to look for possible signals from our galaxy. The cryogenic antennae at Rome, Maryland, Louisiana and Perth are close to operation and sensitivity comparable to the Stanford result should be achieved. One significant coincidence could herald the beginning of gravitational wave astronomy.

ACKNOWLEDGEMENTS

I wish to thank all the gravitational wave experimenters who through discussions and hospitality over the years have contributed to these lectures. I apologise to those who through lack of space I have failed to reference. I thank Peter Michelson and Joe Weber for some useful comments, and the organisers of this school for inviting me. Thanks to Tony Mann, Laurie Mann, Peter Veitch, and John Ferreirinho for data and diagrams used in the paper. This work was supported by the ARGS.

REFERENCES

[1] Weber, J., Phys. Rev. 117, 306 (1960).

[2] Sakharov, A.D., Sov. Phys. Doklady. 12, 1040 (1968).

[3] Weber, J., Phys. Rev. Lett. 22, 1320 (1969).

[3b] Ferrari, V., et al., Phys. Rev. D 25, 2471 (1982). See also J. Weber in Gen. Rel. and Grav. Vol 2, E. A. Held, Plenum (1980) p. 435.

[4] Fairbank, W.M., et al. in Proc. Varenna Conf. on Gen. Rel., Ed. B. Bertotti (1972).

[5] Blair, D.G. and Candy, B.N. To be published.

[6] Tamman, G.A., Ann. N.Y. Acad. Sci. 302, 61 (1978).

[7] Manchester, R.N. in Grav. Rad., Collapsed Objects and Exact Solutions, Ed. C. Edwards, Springer-Verlag, Berlin (1980).

[8] Jones, P.B., Astrophys. J. 204, 602 (1976).

[9] Gunn, J.E. and Ostriker, J.P., Astrophys. J. 160, 979 (1970).

[10] Roberts, D.H. and Sturrock, P.A., Astrophys. J. 173, L33 (1972).

[11] Ruderman, M.A. and Sutherland, P.G., Astrophys. J. 196, 51 (1975).

[12] Phinney, E.S. and Blandford, R.D., M.N.R.A.S. 194, 137 (1981).

[13] Amnuel, P.R. and Guseinov, O.H., Astrophys. J. (Supp) 41, 327 (1979).

[14] Amnuel, P.R. and Guseinov, O.H., Astrophys. and Space Sci. 82, 3 (1982).

[15] Savonije, G.D., Astron. and Astrophys. 71, 352 (1979).

[16] Shklovski, I.S., Nature 279, 703 (1979).

[17] Li Qi Bim, Acta Astron. Sinica 19, 211 (1979).

[18] Van den Heuvel in IAU Symposium #93, Ed. D. Sugimoto et al., Reidel, Dordrecht (1980) p. 155.

[19] Talbot, R.J., Astrophys. J. 205, 535 (1976).

[20] Gibbons, G.W. and Hawking, S.W., Phys. Rev. D 4, 2191 (1971).

[21] Braginsky, V.B., Lecture given at Louisiana State University (1975).

[22] Braginsky, V.B., Phys. Experiments with Test Bodies, NASA Tech. Trans. F672 NTIS Springfield (1970).

[23] Giffard, R.P., Phys. Rev. D 14, 2478 (1976).

[24] Heffner, H., Proc. I.R.E. 50, 1604 (1962).

[25] Caves, C.M. et al: Rev. Mod. Phys 52, 341 (1980).

[25] contd.

Braginsky, V.B. in Grav. Rad. and Grav. Collapse Proc. IAU Symp No. 64 Ed. C. deWitt, Reidel, Dordrecht, p. 29.

Unruh, W.G., Phys. Rev. D 18, 1764 (1978).

[26] Manley, J.M. and Rowe, H.E., Proc. IRE 44, 904 (1956).

[27] Giffard, R.P. (private communication).

Blair, D.G. in Grav. Rad. Collapsed Objects and Exact Solutions, Ed. C. Edwards, Springer Verlag, Berlin (1980) p. 299 and p. 314.

Paik, H.J. in Proceedings of Second Marcel Grossmann Conference, Ed. R. Ruffini, North Holland (1982).

[28] Mann, A.G., Ph.D. Thesis, Univ. of Western Australia.

[29] James, R.N., Ph.D. Thesis (pending), University of Western Australia.

[30] Mann, A.G. and D.G. Blair. To be published in J. Phys. E.

[31] Johnson, W.W. and Bocko, M., Phys. Rev. Lett. 47, 1184 (1981).

[32] Bocko, M. and Johnson, W.W., Phys. Rev. Lett. 48, 1371 (1982).

[33] Hoffman, A.W., et al., Rev. Sci. Inst. 47, 1441 (1976).

[34] Richard, J-P., in Grav. Rad., Collapsed Objects and Exact Solutions, Ed. C. Edwards, Springer-Verlag, Berlin (1980) p. 370.

[35] Ferreirinho, J., Ph.D. Thesis (pending), University of Western Australia.

[36] Blair, D.G. and Ferreirinho, J., Phys. Rev. Lett. 49, 375 (1982).

[37] Bagdasarov, H., et al. Quoted in Ref 25, V.B. Braginsky.

[38] Braginsky, V.B. Private Communication.

[39] Blair, D.G. in Proc. 2nd Marcel Grossmann Meeting on Gen. Rel., Ed. R. Ruffini, N. Holland (1982) p. 1125.

[40] Mann, A.G. and Blair, D.G., Cryogenics 20, 645 (1980).

[41] Bernat, T.P. et al., Rev. Sci. Inst. 46, 582 (1975).

[42] Blair, D.G. and Mann, A.G., Il Nuovo Cimento 61, 73 (1981).

[43] Suzuki, T., et al., Phys. Lett. 67A, 2 (1978).

[44] Chen Jia Yan, preprint, Zhongshan Univ. 10 July (1981).

[45] Tomassetti, G., et al., NRAO Electronics Division Internal Report No. 222 (1981).

[46] Caves, C. in Quantum Optics, Experimental Gravitation and Measurement Theory Ed. P. Meystre and M.O. Scully, Plenum. To be published.

[47] Blair, D.B., Phys. Lett. To be published (1982).

[48] Hamilton, W.O. Lecture presented at Les Houches Summer School (1982).

[49] Weber, J. Private Communication.

The choice of a microwave pump frequency $\sim 10^{10}$ Hz for parametric transducers is clear. At this frequency ruby masers, GaAs FET amplifiers and parametric amplifiers all moderately approach the quantum limit. However at the low frequency end of the spectrum superconducting quantum interference devices (SQUID's) also show good noise performance. Rapid advances in SQUID technology offer hope for improvements towards the quantum limit. SQUID's are most easily used with passive inductive transducers, as we will discuss below.

Since SQUID devices can be operated at frequencies ~1 MHz, it is feasible to design a parametric transducer pumped at low radio frequencies. Such a transducer can use either inductive or capacitive sensing elements in a resonant LC circuit. Johnson and Bocko[31] have recently shown that such a transducer pumped at less than 1 MHz, and amplified by a DC SQUID can in principle approach the quantum limit, and exceed it if quantum non-demolition techniques are used.[32]

GRAVITATIONAL ANTENNAE WEBER TYPE: THE PROBLEM OF HIGH SENSITIVITY

V. B. Braginsky

Department of Physics
Moscow State University
Moscow, U.S.S.R.

INTRODUCTION

The creation of terrestrial gravitational antennae, which began due to pioneer efforts of professor J. Weber [1], involved the necessity to solve many very different both theoretical and experimental physical problems. Partial or complete solution of each of these problems allows to advance toward the main goal: to create a gravitational antenna, whose sensitivity is high enough to detect gravitational radiation from nonterrestrial sources predicted by astrophysicists. At present on our planet there are two groups of laboratories in which experimentalists are creating antennae to detect short bursts of gravitational radiation from astrophysical catastrophies (which take place far from the Earth). In the first group modernized Weber-type antennae are created. In the second group the so called laser antennae on free masses are created. Several hundred articles and reports on different parts and features of these antennae are published, even the number of review articles written in different time exceeds ten. The author of this lecture thinks that comparative analysis of advantages and disadvantages of different methods and tricks used in laboratories will not be a fruitful one because the successful use of any experimental method or trick does not depend only on its potential capacity but does also depend on the "culture" and experience in a definite field in a laboratory. Thus, the author decided to describe the main problems, which are to be solved to realize very sensitive gravitational antenna of Webber type, to estimate the level of sensitivity, which may be obtained within a few years, basing on the program developed in the Department of Physics at Moscow State University. The list of problems which are not thoroughly examined and which deserve attention of both experimentalists and theoreticians is also included in this lecture.

As it is known [1,2] (see also review articles [3,4,5]) a classical quadrupole oscillator, which consists of two masses m separated at distance ℓ and coupled by a spring with rigidity $K = m\omega_M^2$ may be excited by an a.c. component of Rieman tensor R^j_{oko} :

$$m \frac{d^2x^i}{dt^2} + H \frac{dx^j}{dt} + Kx^j = F_{FL} - mc^2 R^j_{oko} x^k , \qquad (1)$$

where H - the coefficient of friction, c - the speed of light, F_{FL} - the sum of fluctuational forces. One may conclude from the equation (1) that in classical approximation a force is a signal, and the signal-to-noise ratio S/N is

$$\frac{S}{N} = \frac{mc^2 \ell R}{F_{FL}} \qquad (2)$$

and the "response" of the oscillator (the left part of the equation is responsible for the "response") may be measured with as high accuracy as necessary.

In the last years astrophysicists-theoreticians prefer to use dimentionless variation of the metric h for the description of the gravitational radiation. The term h is connected with the Rieman tensor in the following way (see e.g. [2,5]):

$$R_{joko} = -\frac{1}{2}\ddot{h}^{TT}_{jk} \quad . \tag{3}$$

Many authors have published articles about the value of h near our Earth due to different astrophysical catastrophies. The reader may find the review of the latest research in this area in the review article [5] and many details on this problem in the book [6].

According to the modern picture of the astrophysical catastrophies an experimentalist in optimistic mood may expect approximately once per month a short burst with an amplitude $h \simeq 2x10^{-19}$. This burst has a form close to one period of a sine wave and duration $\tau_{gr} \simeq 10^{-3} \div 10^{-4}$ sec. If $\omega_M \simeq 2\pi/\tau_{gr}$ (the relative difference between ω_M and $2\pi/\tau_{gr}$ may be $\simeq$ 50%) then the gravitational antenna will respond to such a burst with a change of amplitude of oscillation Δx_{gr}:

$$\Delta x_{gr} \simeq \frac{1}{2} h\ell \quad . \tag{4}$$

It is known that in the Weber type antennae instead of localized masses and spring low quadrupole modes of cylinders are used. For the lowest quadrupole mode of a cylinder whose length is ℓ_{CYL} and mass is m_{CYL} the equivalent effective parameters of a quadrupole antenna are:

$$\ell_{EFF} \simeq \frac{2}{3}\ell_{CYL} \quad , \quad m_{EFF} \simeq \frac{1}{3} m_{CYL} \quad .$$

It is evident, that the condition $\omega_M \simeq 2\pi/\tau_{gr}$ for the lowest quadrupole mode may be rewritten in the following form: $\tau_{gr} v \simeq 2\ell_{CYL}$, where v - is the speed of sound. Using the estimates $\tau_{gr} \simeq 10^{-3} \div 10^{-4}$ sec one has to choose $\ell_{CYL} \simeq 5x10^{1} \div 10^{3}$ cm if the cylinders are made from materials with $v \cong 5x10^{+5} \div 10^{+6}$ cm/sec. It is more appropriate to rewrite the response of the antenna in the following form:

$$\Delta X_{gr} \simeq \frac{1}{4}\tau_{gr}\, v\, h \tag{5}$$

This simple formula may be regarded as initial for the analysis of the Weber type antennae. An experimentalist should make such conditions in which Δx_{gr} is greater than Δx_{FL} - change of the amplitude of oscillations due to the forces F_{FL} , and the experimentalist has to create such a sensitive readout device which permits to register very small Δx_{gr}.

CLASSICAL LIMITATIONS FOR THE SENSITIVITY

a) General relations

In classical approach experimentalist has good reason to suppose that his readout system (in our case - a device which registers the coordinate: the difference between the positions of two local masses $\simeq$ difference between two points in the cylinder) does not act back on the oscillator. The real back action of the readout system (both classical and quantum) will be discussed in the next paragraph. Fluctuational force F_{FL} is the sum of the Nyquist force (which creates the thermal oscillations) and random acoustical and seismical actions. The last two components formally must not be regarded as noise: it is possible to measure these components independently by additional devices and thus their actions on the antenna may be substracted. It is appropriate to emphasize here, that even in the first series of professor Weber's experiments and in similar experiments of other laboratories at the beginning of the 70-ies simple methods of acoustical and seismical isolation (high vacuum and antiseismical filters) were sufficient to reach the sensitivity of the antennae at the level $h \simeq 1x10^{-20}$. Thus, in classical approximation only the Nyquist force is a source of unavoidable noise. This force gives birth to random variations of the amplitude of oscillations Δx_T, which during averaging time τ are equal to:

$$\Delta x_T = \sqrt{\frac{2kT_M\tau}{m_{EFF}\,\omega_M Q_M}} \,, \tag{6}$$

where k - is the Boltzman constant, T_M - the temperature of the mechanical heat bath, $Q_M = m_{EFF}\omega_M/H$ - the mechanical quality factor of the oscillator (oscillation mode of the cylinder). The averaging time τ may be longer than $\tau_{gr} \simeq 2\pi/\omega_M$ because the oscillator with $Q_M >> 1$ "remembers" short (knock-type) action of the gravitational wave burst.

The condition $\Delta x_{gr} \gtrsim \Delta x_T$ gives simple formula which permits estimates of the smallest classical value $(h_{CLASS})_{min}$ based on the assumption that the only source of noise is the mechanical heat bath:

$$(h_{CLASS})_{min} \gtrsim \frac{4}{\tau_{gr}v}\sqrt{\frac{2kT_M\tau}{m_{EFF}\,\omega_M Q_M}} \simeq 4\sqrt{\frac{k}{\pi v^2}}\sqrt{\frac{T_M}{m_{EFF}Q_M}}\sqrt{\frac{\tau}{\tau_{gr}}} \,. \tag{7}$$

The ratio τ/τ_{gr} may be either equal to unity, or greater. In the second case the problem of registering small oscillations is less difficult to solve (smaller bandwidth of registration decreases the role of additional noise in the readout system), but at the same time the value $(h_{CLASS})_{min}$ increases.

The formula (7) shows that an experimentalist who wants to create a high sensitive Weber-type antenna, in fact has in his disposal only one factor: $T_M/(m_{EFF}Q_M)$ This experimentalist has to choose such a material as to achieve a large mass m_{CYL} on the one hand and the highest possible value Q_M on the other hand. In the laboratories which create the second generation of Weber-type antennae there are now two ways in the selection of the material for the cylinders: polycrystallic metallic antennae from aluminium, alloy N5056 and niobium with total mass near one ton or heavier and relatively light antennae from monocrystalls - dielectrics sapphire and silicon.

The values m_{EFF} and Q_M for antennae in different laboratories are given in Table 1.

Table 1

Material	T_M	m_{EFF}	Q_M	$m_{EFF}Q_M$
Al	4°	$2x10^6$ gram	$5x10^6$	10^{13} gram
N5056: Nb	4°	$5x10^5$ gram	$(6\div8)x10^7$	$(3\div4)x10^{13}$ gram
Al_2O_3: Si	4°	$5x10^3$ gram	$(2\div5)x10^9$	$(2,5\div1)x10^{13}$ gram

The factors $m_{EFF}Q_M$ from Table 1 for different antennae show that at present these factors are practically the same and thus the potential classical sensitivities of these antennae are equal.

Substituting in the formula (7) $m_{EFF}Q_M \simeq 3x10^{13}$, $v = 10^6$ cm/sec (for sapphire), $T_M = 0.3°K$ we obtain the estimates $(h_{CLASS})_{min} \simeq 4x10^{-21}$ if $\tau \simeq \tau_{gr}$. This estimate is two order smaller than optimistic astrophysical prediction $h \simeq 2x10^{-19}$, which was mentioned above.

b) Fundamental limitations for Q_M.

It is reasonable to inquire what the factors are which define Q_M and how high Q_M may be. Partial answer to this question may be obtained for relatively "simple" antennae which are made of monocrystal-dielectric.

In the dielectric materials there is a fundamental mechanism of losses: due to the phonon-phonon interaction. Due to this effect the value Q_M is limited:

$$(Q_M)^{-1}_{ph-ph} \simeq \frac{C_p T_M \gamma^2}{Y} \frac{\omega_M \tau_{ph}}{1+(\omega_M \tau_{ph})^2} \quad ; \quad \tau_{ph} \simeq \frac{3\kappa}{C_p v_D^2} , \tag{8}$$

where C_p is the heat capacity, Y is the Young modulus, γ is the Gruneisen constant, τ_{ph} is the relaxation time of phonons, κ is the heat conductivity coefficient, v_D is the Debye speed of sound. Substituting in formula (8) $\omega_M = 4x10^4$ rad/sec and other values for sapphire we obtain $(Q_M)^{-1}_{ph-ph} \simeq 1x10^{-13}$ if $T_M = 2°K$, $(Q_M)^{-1}_{ph-ph} \simeq 1x10^{-16}$ if $T_M = 0.3°K$. These estimates show that experimentally observed Q_M for sapphire (as well as for silicon) are not limited by fundamental losses.

Fundamental losses in metals due to phonon-electron interaction are much greater. For example, in pure aluminium at $T_M = 4°K$ due to this mechanism the product $Q_M\omega_M$ is $\simeq 300$ times less than for sapphire.

c) The losses in the surface and suspension

The difference between the estimates for Q_M which are determined by fundamental losses and experimentally observed Q_M for mechanical resonators from monocrystal-dielectrics may be explained in part on the basis of existing pictures of losses in the surface of cylinders and in the suspension. The surface of the resonator is shaped and polished. Due to these processes the surface consists of small crystallites separated by microslots. Mechanical oscillations of the resonator give birth to a.c. nonhomogeneous deformations in the crystallites of random shapes. The nonhomogeneous deformations produce nonhomogeneous heat of the crystallites and thus produce losses. The following formula permits to estimate approximately these losses:

$$(Q_M)^{-1}_{SURF} \simeq \frac{4b\gamma T_M \alpha}{D} \frac{\omega_M \tau_T^*}{1+(\omega_M \tau_T^*)^2} \quad ; \quad \tau_T^* \simeq \frac{a^2 C_p}{\kappa} , \tag{9}$$

where b is the depth of the layer, which is damaged by shaping and polishing, a - is the average size of one crystallite (usually $b \simeq (10 \div 10^2)$ a), α - is the factor of thermal volume expansion, D - is the diameter of the cylinder. Other values in formula (9) are the same as in formula (8). Supposing that $a \simeq 10^{-3}$ cm, $b = 10^2 a$, $D = 10$ cm, $T_M = 2°K$, $\omega_M = 4x10^4$ rad/sec, we obtain $(Q_M)^{-1}_{SURF} \simeq 1x10^{-19}$. But at room temperature this effect is much greater and $(Q_M)^{-1}_{SURF} \simeq 1x10^{-9}$.

The dissipation in the suspension is probably the most serious source of losses and it limits Q_M.

The most simple method (which does permit to reach $Q_M \simeq 5x10^9$ for a cylinder of sapphire) is the suspension of the cylinder on a thin cable. The cable is located in a nodal plane of the lowest longitudinal quadrupole mode. This method has been used in the first experiments by J. Weber. Due to the finite value of the Poisson coefficient σ and finite quality factor of the cable there are losses of mechanical energy of the oscillation and thus there is a decrease of Q_M. Simple engineer's type calculations give an approximate expression for this kind of losses:

$$(Q_M)^{-1}_{SUSP} \simeq \frac{\rho_{CAB}\, S_{CAB}\, \ell_{CAB} \sigma^2\, D^2}{2\, m_{EFF}\, Q_{CAB}\, \ell^2_{CYL}} \, , \qquad (10)$$

where ρ_{CAB} - is the density of the material of the cable, S_{CAB} - is its geometrical cross-section, ℓ_{CAB} - is the length of the cable, Q_{CAB} - is the quality factor of longitudinal oscillation of the cable, D - is the diameter of the cylinder. Formula (10) does not take into account the possible antiresonance effect, which may reduce the value $(Q_M)^{-1}_{SUSP}$.

Substituting in formula (10) $\rho_{CAB} \simeq 20$ gram/cm^3, $\sigma = 0.25$, $D = 10$ cm, $\ell_{CYL} = 10^2$ cm, $S_{CAB} = 2\ 10^{-3}$ cm^2, $\ell_{CAB} = 5$ cm, $m_{EFF} = 5\text{x}10^3$ gram, $Q_{CAB} = 10^3$, we obtain $(Q_M)^{-1}_{SUSP} \simeq$ $\simeq 1\text{x}10^{-10}$. This estimate is close to the observed one for the cylinders of sapphire and silicon. It is appropriate to mention here that the quality factor at the level $Q_M \simeq 5\text{x}10^9$ may be achieved only if some additional technological operations are made. These operations are not described in this lecture, the reader may find them in the book [7]. It is necessary to emphasize that at present the experimentalists have no suspension systems which permit to approach quality factor determined by fundamental losses if $T_M \lesssim 4°$K; nor there is any satisfactory theory of the losses in the system of suspension.

THE SYSTEM FOR REGISTRATION OF SMALL OSCILLATIONS

a) Historical remarks, classical limit

In the first generation of the Weber-type antennae at the beginning of the 70-ies the piezoelectric transducers were used to register small oscillations of massive aluminium cylinders. These transducers were sensitive enough to detect oscillations which correspond to $h \simeq 10^{-16} \div 10^{-17}$ but were not sensitive enough for smaller values of h. In the second generation of antennae they were replaced by parametric transducers, in which small mechanical oscillation modulates the flux of a.c. microwave power or the flux of d.c. electrical power. At present in the laboratories different modifications of such parametric transducers are used: in the Stanford University, the Rochester University, University of Maryland [8,9,10] single-contact SQUID's with microwave pumping are used and two-contacts SQUID's with d.c. pumping are planned to be used, in the Moscow State University and in the University of Western Australia [7,11] - capacity pickoff systems with microwave pumping are applied, in the Louisiana State University - the use is made of inductive parametric transducer [12]. The "Theory" of these transducers was developed practically immediately after they were proposed for gravitational antannae. The results of this analysis may be formulated in the following manner:

1. Parametric transducer produces dynamical action on an antenna: it changes ω_M and Q_M, but these effects may compensated (see e.g. [13]).

2. Parametric transducer, which has a finite temperature T_e, in classical approximation is a source of random mechanical force which excites the antenna. In the case of optimal pumping the random force excites fluctuational changes of antenna's oscillations which produce the detectable microwave power flux modulation in the presence of electrical fluctuations. To this optimal pumping corresponds the smallest change of the antenna's oscillation amplitude $\Delta x_{CLASS,READOUT}$:

$$\Delta x_{C,R} \simeq \sqrt{\frac{k\,T_e}{2\,\omega_p m_{EFF}\omega_M}}\,, \tag{11}$$

where ω_p - frequency of the microwave pumping. Formula (11) is valid if the ratio T_M/Q_M is small enough for $\Delta x_{C,R,} \gg \Delta x_T$ (see formula (6)), and if the value T_e is approximately equal to the noise temperature of the amplifier T_{AMPL} which is connected with the parametric transducer to amplify the modulation components. If $T_{AMPL} \ll T_e$, then the classical limit (11) may be substantially decreased [14].

Formula (11) (if ω_p is replaced by a characteristic frequency [15]) is also valid for transducers on SQUID with two contacts. It should be emphasized once more that formula (11) is valid only in classical approximation and $kT_e/\omega_p > \hbar$

Subsequent analysis completed in 1978 [16,17] has shown that irrespective of the type of the transducer, only due to the Heisenberg's uncertainty relation for the coordinate and the momentum when the coordinate $x(t)$ is registered permanently in the bandwidth $\Delta\omega \lesssim \omega_M$ and with averaging time $\tau \gtrsim 2\pi/\omega_M$ the smallest error for the coordinate is equal to

$$\Delta x_{SQL} \simeq \sqrt{\frac{\hbar}{2m_{EFF}\,\omega_M}}\,. \tag{12}$$

This value Δx_{SQL} (usually called special quantum limit) coincides with the uncertainty of the oscillator coordinate in quantum coherent state. The result for Δx_{SQL} cannot be regarded as surprising if one takes into account that the operator of the coordinate does not commute with itself in time. Thus formula (12) is the limit for the classical formula (11) if the readout system registers permanently the coordinate of the antenna. A detailed analysis [16,17] (see also review articles [18,19]) has shown that there are methods, which permit to register the mechanical oscillator response Δx which is less than Δx_{SQL}. These methods got the name "quantum-non-demolition methods". The second part of this section contains a detailed description of one of such methods.

Combining formula (5) and (12), it is possible to obtain simple analytical expression for h_{SQL} - the smallest detectable amplitude of the gravitational radiation burst when the coordinate of the antennae is registered permanently:

$$h_{SQL} \simeq \sqrt{\frac{4\hbar}{\pi v^2 \tau_{gr} m_{EFF}}} \tag{13}$$

For a light dielectrical antenna made of sapphire or silicon with $m_{EFF} \simeq 5\text{x}10^3$ gram the value $h_{SQL} \simeq 5\text{x}10^{-20}$, for a heavy metallic antenna (see Table 1) $h_{SQL} \simeq 5\text{x}10^{-21}$. Comparing these estimates with $(h_{CLASS})_{min} \simeq 4\text{x}10^{-21}$ (see section II), which is based on the assumptions: a) the antenna is pure "classical" (the only noise source is the heat bath, b) the parameter $Q_M\, m_{EFF}$ corresponds to the existing, one may conclude that the sensitivity of the antennae now (for the achieved Q_M) depends mainly on the system of registration.

It is appropriate to mention here that the first run of the antenna with total mass of aluminium cylinder near five tons at the Stanford University gave the estimate for the sensitivity $h \simeq 4\text{x}10^{-18}$ [8].

b) The sensitivity of Weber-type antenna with QND-coordinate readout system

To detect the response of the antenna which is less than Δx_{SQL} it is necessary to use one of the quantum-consistent QND procedures of measurements: it is possible to measure permanently the energy of the oscillator, it is possible to measure stroboscopically the coordinate during a short period of time comparing with $2\pi/\omega_M$, and repeating the measurement exactly after the period, it is possible to measure permanently one of the two quadrature components of the coordinate (see original articles [16,17] and the review articles [18,19]. The latter procedure is the most attractive one from the engineer's point of view. The Hermitian operators $\hat{X}_1$ and $\hat{X}_2$ of the antenna, which is regarded as a quantum oscillator, are connected with the operators of the coordinate $\hat{x}$ and the momentum $\hat{x}$ as follows:

$$\hat{X}_1 = \hat{x}\cos\omega_M t - \frac{\hat{p}}{m_{EFF}\omega_M}\sin\omega_M t,$$
$$\hat{X}_2 = \hat{x}\sin\omega_M t + \frac{\hat{p}}{m_{EFF}\omega_M}\cos\omega_M t. \qquad (14)$$

The value $[\hat{x}, \hat{p}] = i\hbar$, thus $[\hat{X}_1 , \hat{X}_2] = \frac{i\hbar}{m_{EFF}\omega_M}$ and

$$\Delta X_1 \, \Delta X_2 > \frac{\hbar}{2m_{EFF}\omega_M} .$$

If the measurement of the coordinate is permanent, then $\Delta X_1 = \Delta X_2 = h_{SQL}$. But it is possible to make the measurement in such a way, that the readout system will give the information only about X_1. Then it is possible to make the readout system so sensitive that $\Delta X_1 < \Delta x_{SQL}$ and the antenna will be able to register pulses of gravitational radiation arriving in "convenient" phase which are less than h_{SQL} (see formula (13)). In this procedure the ratio $\Delta X_2/\Delta x_{SQL}$ will be equal to the ratio $\Delta x_{SQL}/\Delta X_1$ and the uncertainty relation will remain fulfilled.

The analysis of such a scheme was briefly outlined in [20]. A more detailed description is presented here.

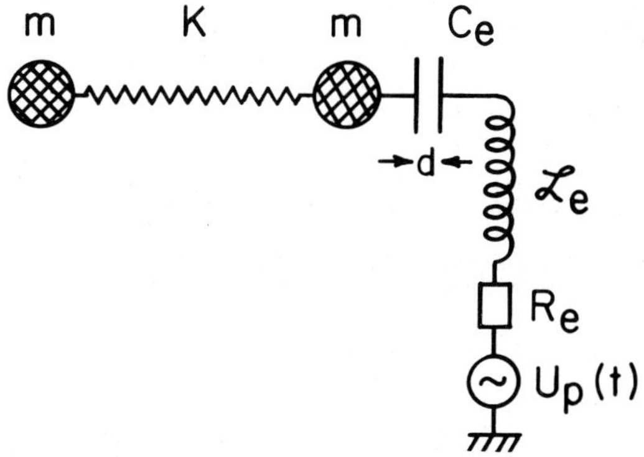

Figure 1:

Suppose that in a usual scheme of capacity parametric pickoff system coupled with gravitational antenna (see Fig. 1) the following changes are made: a) the value Q_e is high enough and $\omega_e/Q_e \ll \omega_M$; b) the pumping generator has a modulated amplitude: $U_p = U_o \cos\omega_e t \cos\omega_M t$. Suppose also that the only source of noise is the thermal noise of the e.m. resonator whose temperature is T_e and $kT_e > \hbar\omega_e$. For such pumping the readout system will respond mainly to the change ΔX_1 and the thermal noise will give rise mainly to a random change ΔX_2. Let us assume that the selected averaging time $\tau \simeq \tau_e^* = \tau_e^* = 2Q_e/\omega_e$, then clasical calculations give the following result:

if the amplitude of the pumping U_o in the resonator satisfies to the quality

$$\left(\frac{U_o}{d}\right)^2_{optim} = E_o^2 = \frac{8m_{EFF}\omega_M^2}{C_e\, Q_e} , \tag{16}$$

then during $\tau \simeq \tau_e^*$ due to thermal electrical oscillations and electrical pumping in the antenna random mechanical oscillations will be excited. Their uncertainties will be equal to

$$(\Delta X_1)_{T_e} \simeq \sqrt{\frac{kT_e}{2m_{EFF}\omega_p\omega_M}}\ \frac{1}{\sqrt{\omega_M\tau_e^*}} , \tag{17}$$

$$(\Delta X_2)_{T_e} \simeq \sqrt{\frac{kT_e}{2m_{EFF}\omega_p\omega_M}}\ \sqrt{\omega_M\tau_e^*} , \tag{18}$$

$$(\Delta X_1)_{T_e}\,(\Delta X_2)_{T_e} \simeq \frac{kT_e}{2m_{EFF}\omega_p\omega_M} > \frac{\hbar}{2m_{EFF}\omega_M} \tag{19}$$

because according to the condition $kT_e/\omega_e > \hbar$.

If during the averaging time τ due to an external force (for example due to the burst of gravitational radiation) the component X_1 in the antenna changes and $\Delta X_1 \gtrsim (\Delta X_1)_{T_e}$ then in the e.m. resonator at the presence of the pumping (16) will appear electrical oscillations additional to thermal and with energy $\gtrsim kT_e$. This additional portion of the energy can be registered if the noise temperature of the amplifier connected to the e.m. resonator is less than T_e. These classical calculations are on the one hand quantum consistent because the Heisenberg uncertainty relations are fulfilled automatically, on the other hand the conditions in the scheme of measurement ($kT_e/\omega_e > \hbar$ and $T_{AMPL} \lesssim T_e$) in fact solve the problem of classical element in the quantum measurement.

In addition to formula (16) on the optimal pumping it is necessary to meet some conditions which are not very severe from an engineer's point of view:

$$\frac{\Delta\omega_p}{\omega_p} < \frac{1}{\omega_M\tau_e^*}\,\frac{1}{Q_e} \ ; \ \frac{\Delta\omega_M}{\omega_M} < \frac{1}{(\omega_M\tau_e^*)^2} \ ; \ \frac{\Delta U_p}{U_p} < \frac{1}{4\omega_M\tau_e^*} , \tag{20}$$

where ΔU_p is the difference between the amplitude of two components of pumping if $U_p(t)$ is not exactly equal to $U_o \cos\omega_e t \cos\omega_M t$.

If now we suppose $(\Delta X_1)_{T_e} \simeq \Delta x_{gr}$ (see formula (5)) then the smallest detectable value $(h_{QND})_{min}$ for the discussed procedure of measurement is equal to:

$$(h_{QND})_{min} \simeq \frac{4}{\tau_{gr} v} \sqrt{\frac{k\,T_e}{2m_{EFF}\omega_p\omega_M}} \frac{1}{\sqrt{\omega_M \tau_e^*}} \simeq \sqrt{\frac{4K}{\pi^2 v^2}} \sqrt{\frac{T_e}{m_{EFF} Q_e}} \quad . \tag{21}$$

It is appropriate to remind that formula (21) is based on the conditions $\tau \simeq \tau_e^*$ and $T_{AMPL} \lesssim T_e$. Comparing now $(h_{QND})_{min}$ with h_{SQL} (formula (13)) one can note that the key element in this transducer is the quality factor Q_e of the e.m. resonator. The higher Q_e the smaller is the factor $(\omega_M \tau_e^*)^{-\frac{1}{2}} = (\omega_M Q_e / 2\omega_e)^{-\frac{1}{2}}$.

On the other hand the comparison of formulae (21) and (7) shows that the condition $(h_{QND})_{min} < (h_{CLASS})_{min}$ may be written in the following form:

$$\frac{T_e \; \tau_{gr} \; \omega_e}{Q_e^{\,2}} < \frac{T_M}{Q_M} \quad . \tag{22}$$

Thus, the possibility to gain substantially in sensitivity taking into account the classical in form, but quantum in essence, noise of the readout system depends mainly on the quality factor of the e.m. resonator Q_e. The highest values of Q_e were obtained in microwave superconductive resonators. The detailed analysis of the problem is presented in Ref. [7]. We give here the summary of this analysis. According to the experience gained by experimentalists the value Q_e may be presented in the following form:

$$Q_e = \frac{\Gamma}{\Sigma R_s} \;, \quad \Sigma R_s = A(R_s)_{THEOR} + R_o \;, \tag{23}$$

where Γ is the so called geometrical factor which depends on geometrical form of the resonator and which has the dimension of resistance, ΣR_s is the surface resistance of the superconductor really measured in the experiment, $(R_s)_{THEOR}$ is the surface resistance in the Bardeen-Cooper-Schriffer theory, A is the dimentionless factor of the order of unity, R_o is the residual surface resistance. For a microwave resonator with located capacity $\Gamma \simeq (\omega_e C_e)^{-1}$. The value $(R_s)_{THEOR}$ exponentially vanishes with the decrease of the temperature and practically when $T \simeq 0.1\,T_e$ (T_e is the temperature of the transition) $\Sigma R_s \simeq R_o$. The residual surface resistance R_o does not depend on the temperature, it depends on the manufacturing techniques, on the level of impurities, etc. The best known methods of the "preparation" of superconductors give $R_o \simeq 1\text{x}10^{-9}$ ohm in the microwave region. If we use this estimate and suppose that $\omega_e = 2\text{x}10^{10}$ rad/sec, $C_e = 1$ pF, then we may expect to reach $Q_e \simeq 5\text{x}10^{10}$. Factor $(\omega_M \tau_e^*)^{-\frac{1}{2}} \simeq 3\text{x}10^{-3}$ corresponds to this quality factor, if $\omega_M = 4\ 10^4$ rad/sec, and $(h_{QND})_{min} \simeq$ $\simeq 6\text{x}10^{-22}$ for $T_e = 2°K$, $m = 5\text{x}10^3$ gram, $v = 1\ 10^6$ cm/sec and $(h_{QND})_{min} \simeq$ $\simeq 6\text{x}10^{-23}$ for the heavy antennae. Comparing the obtained estimates for $(h_{QND})_{min}$ with the estimates $(h_{CLASS})_{min} \simeq 4\text{x}10^{-21}$ in paragraph 2, it is possible to make the following conclusions: a) the experimentalists may reach the sensitivity $h \simeq 4\text{x}10^{-21}$ even using a light antenna, b) there is every reason to seek for new ways to enhance the factor Q_M. At the same time the calculations given above are in fact only calculations, so far nobody measuring the response of an oscillator "cross" the threshold which corresponds to ΔX_{SQL}. Recently the program of an experiment aimed at "crossing" this threshold was announced [21].

Let us briefly discuss another additional quantum problem connected with the analyzed procedure of measurement. As it was mentioned above, to reach the sensitivity of the antenna which corresponds to $(h_{QND})_{min}$, it is necessary to have optimal pumping with amplitude E_o (see formula (16)). It is evident that the value E_o does not exceed the value of electrical breakdown (this is also a quantum effect). For the estimates used above: $\omega_M = 4\text{x}10^4$ rad/sec, $C_e = 1$ pF, $Q_e = 5\text{x}10^{10}$, $m_{EFF} = 5\text{x}10^3$ gram, the value $(E_o)_{optim} \simeq 1$ CGS and for the heavy antenna $(E_o)_{optim} \simeq 10$ CGS. These two estimates are far from the value of the electrical breakdown. At the same time it is evident that if in an experiment it is not possible to reach sufficiently high Q_e, then the sensitivity for heavier antennae will not be defined by formula (21) for $(h_{QND})_{min}$ but by the permitted (nonoptimal) amplitude of the pumping.

The reader may find details of the capacity pickoff system which permits to register $\Delta x \simeq 2x10^{-17}$ cm in [22]. The methods of "coupling" of light antennae with capacity pickoff systems are described in [23].

THE COMPARISON OF SENSITIVITIES OF DIFFERENT TYPES OF ANTENNAE

The antennae on free masses with laser system of small displacements registration are competing with the second generation Weber antennae. It is easy to obtain the ultimate sensitivity of the antenna on free masses if one takes into account that the uncertainty of the coordinate of a free mass m during the averaging time τ cannot be less than $\Delta x_{FR.M} = \sqrt{\hbar\tau/m}$ [24,13]. If we suppose $\tau = \tau_{gr}$ and $\Delta x_{FR.M} \simeq \Delta x_{gr} \simeq \frac{1}{2} h\ell$, then

$$(h_{FR.M})_{min} \simeq \frac{2}{\ell}\sqrt{\frac{\hbar\tau}{m}} \qquad (24)$$

Substituting in formula (23) $\tau_{gr} = 1x10^{-4}$ sec, m = 10^4 gram, $\ell = 10^5$ cm,[1/] we obtain $(h_{FR.M.})_{min} \simeq 1x10^{-22}$. This estimate is less than $(h_{CLASS})_{min} \simeq 4x10^{-21}$ for the already obtained level of the parameter $m_{EFF}\, Q_M$ (see par. II) and greater than $(h_{QND})_{min}$ for the heavy antennae for the expected parameter T_e/Q_e. This comparison shows that the potential sensitivities for both types of antennae are approximately equal and that in principle these sensitivities are sufficient to have two order reserve from an optimistic estimate $h \simeq 2x10^{-19}$. The antennae on free masses have several evident advantages: a) there is no necessity to use cryogenic technique for them, b) these antennae have wider bandwidth than Weber-type antennae. Together with advantages the antennae on free masses have some disadvantages: a) it is much more difficult to isolate these antennae from seismical and acoustical perturbances: b) these antennae have no "memory" on a knock force action as Weber-type antennae and thus in the system of registration it is necessary that the time of measurement should be equal to or less than τ_{gr} ; c) to approach the level of sensitivity close to the one determined in formula (24) a very powerful optical pumping is necessary[2/]. Formally the antenna on free masses with the base ℓ , aimed at detecting a gravitation pulse with duration τ_{gr}, has a nonzero level of quantum sensitivity (see formula (24)), but the Weber-type antenna has the level of sensitivity which depends only on values Q_M and Q_e (some theoreticians probably will regard this limitation as a pure technological one). It is likely that only real "competition" between the antennae of these two types will show which type is more sensitive.

UNSOLVED PROBLEMS

In this short concluding paragraph the author decided that it is appropriate to list some unsolved problems which deserve attention of both experimentalists and theoreticians.

1. First of all it is necessary to emphasize that enhancement of the values Q_M and Q_e will give the higher sensitivity. It is also evident that there is no reason to search for the ways to increase only one of these values unless an alternative procedure of measurements is not proposed.

2. It is necessary to mention that the described QND measurements procedure (which includes a classical element) requires that the averaging time is equal to τ_e^*. The sensitivity of the antenna goes up with the increase of τ_e^* but in the

discussed method simultaneously the resolution in time becomes worse. Till now there is no procedure of measurements (including classical element in the measuring device) which permits to have "QND-sensitivity" and resolution time of the order of τ_{gr}. The potential sensitivity to register the bursts of gravitational radiation during the time τ_{gr} would allow to detect the delay, the direction to the sources and the velocity of the propagation of the bursts using several antennae in different locations on our planet.

3. Probably it is reasonable to estimate once more the possibility to detect the response of the antenna using the method based on QND-measurements of energy.

The newly discovered properties of dielectric materials with high nonlinearity and low level of dissipation are likely to permit to realize the method of counting of microwave quanta without their absorbtion [28].

---

[1] These values are expected in the final versions of the antennae at Caltech, University of Glasgow and M. Planck Institute ([25,26]),(see also review articles [3,4]).

[2] The possible solution of this problem is described in [27].

REFERENCES:

[1] Weber, J., Phys. Rev. 117, 307, 1960.

[2] Misner, C.W., Thorne, K.S., and Wheeler, J.A., Gravitation, (Freeman and Co., 1973).

[3] Douglass, D.H., Braginsky, V.B.,"Gravitational-Radiation Experiments," in General Relativity An Einstein Centenary Survey, (ed) S.W. Hawking, W. Israel, Cambridge University Press, 1979.

[4] Braginsky, V.B., Rudenko, Phys. Rev. 46, 165, 1978.

[5] Thorne, K.S., Rev. Mod. Phys., 52, 285, 1980.

[6] Smarr, L., (ed), "Sources of Gravitational Radiation," Cambridge University Press, 1978.

[7] Braginsky, V.B., Mitrofanov, V.P., Panov, V.I., "Systems with Small Dissipation," Nauka, 1981, in Russian.

[8] Giffard, R.P., Michelson, P.F., Taber, R.C., "Noise in Resonant Gravitational Wave Detectors," Stanford, Preprint, 1981.

[9] Douglass, D.H., et al. In Proc. of the Second Marcel Grossman Meeting, Ed. R. Ruffini, North Holland, 1980.

[10] Ho Junk Paik, "Unified Theory of Gravitational Radiation Detectors For Pulses and Monochromatic Signals," University of Maryland, preprint, 1981.

[11] Blair, D., Rev. Sci. Instr., 50, 286, 1979, GR 9 Abstracts, 2, 411, 1980.

[12] Kadlec, J., Hamilton, W.O., In Proc. of the Second Intern. Conf. on Superconducint Devices, Berlin, 1980.

[13] Braginsky, Manukin, A. B., "Measurements of Weak Forces in Physics Experiments," Ed. Douglass, D., The University of Chicago Press, 1977.

[14] Gusev, A.V., Rudenko, V.N., Radiotechnika i Electronica, 21, 865, 1976.

[15] Gusev, A.V., Rudenko, V.N., JETP, 74, 819, 1978.

[16] Braginsky, V.B., Vorontsov, Y.I., Khalili, F. Ya., Pisma JETP, 27, 296, 1978.

[17] Thorne, K.S., et al. Phys. Rev. Lett., 40, 667, 1978.

[18] Caves, C.M., et al., Rev. Mod. Phys., 52, 341, 1980.

[19] Braginsky, V.B., Vorontsov, Y.I., Thorne, K.S., Science, 209, 547, 1980.

[20] Panov, V.I., Khalili, F. Ya., GR 9 Conf. Abstracts, v. 2, 397, 1980.

[21] Johnson, W.W., Bocko, M., Phys. Rev. Lett., 47, 1184, 1981.

[22] Braginsky, V.B., Panov, V.I., Popeliniuk, V.D., Pisma JETP, 33, 423, 1981.

[23] Mitrofanov, V.P., Lemann, H., GR-9 Abstract, v. 2, 418, 1980.

[24] Braginsky, V.B., Vorontsov, Y.I., Sov. Phys. Uspechi, 114, 41, 1974.

[25] Drever, R., et al., In Proc. of Second Marcel Grossman Meeting, Ed. R. Ruffini, 1980, North Holland.

[26] Schilling, R., Schwupp, L. Winkler, W.,Billing, H., Maischberger, K., Rüdiger, A., Preprint, MPI - PAE/ASTRO, 231, M. Planck Inst. Munich, 1980.

[27] Caves, C.M., Phys. Rev. Lett. 45, 75, 1980.

[28] Braginsky, V.B., Viatchanin, S.P., Sov. Physics, Dokladi, 263, 1982.

TWO POINTS OF VIEW ON GRAVITATIONAL ENERGY

Yvonne Choquet-Bruhat

I.M.T.A. Université Paris VI
4, Place Jussieu, 75005 Paris
FRANCE

1 - INTRODUCTION

Radiation is conventionally energy transport without material support. It is a well known phenomena in electromagnetism, experimentally as well as theoretically. The gravitational field has several aspects similar to those of the electromagnetic one, but also essential differences, one of them being the impossibility of defining at one given point of space time the energy of the gravitational field with respect to an observer defined by the unit vector tangent to its timelike trajectory. This "non local" character of gravitational energy is in fact obvious from a formulation of the equivalence principle which says that the gravitational field appears as non existent to one observer in free fall. It is, mathematically, a consequence of the fact that the pseudo riemannian connexion which represents the gravitational field can always be made to vanish along a given curve by a change of coordinates.

The existence of a gravitational field manifests itself to a plurality of observers by their relative acceleration through the equation of geodesic deviation :

$$\frac{d^2 n^\mu}{ds^2} = R_{\alpha\ \beta\gamma}^{\ \mu} U^\alpha n^\beta U^\gamma$$

where $R_{\alpha\beta,\lambda\mu}$ is the Riemann curvature tensor of space time. This double 2-forms plays in many ways, for the gravitational field, the role of the 2-form $F_{\alpha\beta}$ of the electromagnetic field. Mathematically they are both curvatures of connexions associated with the gage group of the theory. However there is a fundamental difference in the physical interpretation since in the electromagnetic case the connexion represents the potential, while in gravitation it represents the field itself, as required by the equivalence principle - a physical fact. Also as a consequence of this principle the gravitational field has, as its source, not only the stress energy of matter and all other fields, but is also its own source, fact which appears mathematically in the non linearity of Einstein equations. One could also say that, in the case of gravitation, charge and energy, which are well defined and distinct concepts for all other fields, become one notion, still difficult to grasp in its full generality : even with respect to a family of observers there is no unambiguous definition of gravitational energy, in the general case of an arbitrary space time.

I shall in the following give two examples of a rigorous mathematical study which leads to the appearance of a positive conserved quantity which it is legitimate to consider, in the context where it appears, as the energy of the gravitational field. The first example will be a high frequency perturbation of a given background, whose energy density can be defined locally, the second the global energy of an asymptotically flat space : I shall in treating this example, give a new 3+1 formulation of Einstein equations (obtained in collaboration with T. Ruggeri), which splits them into the constraints and a hyperbolic evolution system, without use of harmonic coordinates.

2. HIGH FREQUENCY WAVES

A high frequency wave, considered as "ripples" of a given background, is a perturbation of the type $h_{\alpha\beta}(x, \omega\varphi(x))$, with x a point of the space time, and φ a smooth function on it called the phase function; ω is a dimensionless parameter which will be large in applications. Its introduction makes easy to keep track of the different order of magnitudes. The full space time metric is,

$$(2\text{-}1) \qquad g_{\alpha\beta}(x, \omega\varphi(x)) = \bar{g}_{\alpha\beta}(x) + \varepsilon\, h_{\alpha\beta}(x, \omega\varphi(x))$$

where $\bar{g}_{\alpha\beta}$ is the "background metric", ε is a dimension less parameter. The final results depend on the order of magnitude of ε with respect to ω^{-1}.

Plugging (2-1) into the Einstein equations $R_{\alpha\beta} = 0$ gives by straightforward computations, the conditions to be satisfied by $h_{\alpha\beta}$ in order to verify Einstein equations at various orders of magnitude. Two cases have been mainly studied in the litterature : $\varepsilon = \omega^{-2}$ (Choquet-Bruhat, C.R.A.S. 258, 3809-3812 (1964), et 1th Congrès Marcel Grossmann, Ruffini ed. 1977, Ribeiro Gomes, thèse Université de Coimbra (1966)) et $\varepsilon = \omega^{-1}$ (first considered by Isaacson, Phys. Rev. 166, 1263-1272 (1968), under the special form $h_{\alpha\beta} = a_{\alpha\beta}\, e^{i\omega\varphi}$, generalized in Choquet-Bruhat, Comm. Math. Phys. 12, 16-35 (1969), whose treatment we follow here).

In both cases it is found that for $h_{\alpha\beta}$ to be a significant perturbation, that is not of the type $h_{\alpha\beta} = \ell_\alpha t_\beta + \ell_\beta t_\alpha$ with $\ell_\alpha = \partial_\alpha\varphi$ which can be made to vanish by a high frequency change of coordiantes preserving the background, we must have

$$(2\text{-}2) \qquad \bar{\ell}^\lambda \ell_\lambda = 0 \qquad , \qquad \ell_\lambda = \partial_\lambda\varphi$$

that is the constant phase submanifolds must be null, and $h_{\alpha\beta}$ must satisfy the four algebraic relations

(2-3) $$2\,\bar{\ell}^{\lambda} h_{\alpha\lambda} - \ell_{\alpha} h = 0 \quad , \quad h = \bar{g}^{\lambda\mu} h_{\lambda\mu}$$

The significant part of a high frequency wave has two polarization modes, like other types of gravitational waves.

In both cases the significant part of the perturbation obey propagation equations along the rays (trajectories of the vector field ℓ^{λ}), they are the "geometrical optics" approximation of the gravitational wave. They read if the coordinate x^{o} is taken to be the "retarded time", that is $x^{o} = \varphi(x)$

(2-4) $$-\ell^{\lambda}\bar{\nabla}_{\lambda} h'_{ij} - \frac{1}{2} h'_{ij} \bar{\nabla}_{\lambda} \bar{\ell}^{\lambda} = 0 \quad , \quad h'_{ij} = \frac{\partial h_{ij}}{\partial(\omega\varphi)} \quad .$$

Note that in a non flat background the propagation induces a mixing of the polarization modes. From (2-4) one deduces the conservation law

(2-5) $$\bar{\nabla}_{\lambda}(e\,\bar{\ell}^{\lambda}) = 0 \quad , \quad e = \frac{1}{4} h'_{ij} \bar{h}'^{ij} \geqslant 0$$

The scalar e reads in arbitrary coordinates :

(2-6) $$e = \frac{1}{4}(\bar{h}'^{\lambda\mu} h'_{\lambda\mu} - \frac{1}{2}(h')^{2})$$

is conserved along the rays. It is positive, and zero only for non significant perturbations. Moreover if we treat in the same spirit the Maxwell - Einstein system (Choquet-Bruhat in "Gravitation" papers in honor of N. Rosen, Kuper and Peres, ed. Gordon and Breach, 1971) we find a conservation law analogous to (2-5), but with the addition to e of the energy of the high frequency electromagnetic wave. It is therefore legitimate to consider e as the (local) energy density of the gravitational high frequency perturbation [(1)].

There is a difference in the cases $\varepsilon = 0(\omega^{-2})$ and $\varepsilon = 0(\omega^{-1})$ on the conditions which must link the background to the perturbation.

1. If $\varepsilon = 0(\omega^{-2})$ the background metric must itself be a solution of Einstein empty space equations.

2. If $\varepsilon = 0(\omega^{-1})$ a rigorous, simple, mathematical argument shows that the background Einstein tensor and the high frequency perturbation must be linked by the relation :

(2-7) $$\bar{S}_{\lambda\mu} = E \ell_\lambda \ell_\mu$$

where E is the average energy of the wave over wave fronts :

(2-8) $$E(x) = \lim_{T=\infty} \frac{1}{T} \int_0^T e(x,\xi)\, d\xi$$

E is conserved along the rays

(2-9) $$\nabla_\lambda (E \bar{\ell}^\lambda) = 0$$

$E \ell_\lambda \ell_\mu$ is the effective stress energy tensor of the radiation.
The high frequency formalism is easy to apply to the Einstein-Maxwell system, and shows that, in the generic case, an electromagnetic wave generates a gravitational wave and vice-versa. If $\varepsilon = \omega^{-1}$ the relation (2-7) is to be replaced by

(2-10) $$\bar{S}_{\lambda\mu} - \bar{\tau}_{\lambda\mu} = E \ell_\lambda \ell_\mu$$

where $\bar{\tau}_{\lambda\mu}$ is the Maxwell background tensor and E the sum of the averaged energies of the gravitational and electromagnetic waves, with radial rays.

The simplest choice of background giving non trivial results (Choquet-Bruhat, Coll. C.N.R.S n° 220, 1973) in the case $\varepsilon = \omega^{-1}$ is the Reissner-Nordström-Vaidya spherically symmetric metric

$$ds^2 = (1 - \frac{2m(u)}{r} + \frac{q^2}{2r^2}) + 2\, du\, dr - r^2(d\theta^2 + \sin^2\theta\, d\varphi^2)$$

with a background electrostatic, spherically symmetric field with charge q.
If we denote $x^o = u$, $x^1 = r$, $x^A = (\theta,\psi)$ for A =(2,3), the electromagnetic and gravitational high frequency waves has for non vanishing components

$$F_{OA} = b_A(u,\theta,\psi,\omega\varphi)$$

$$h_{22} = r\,\alpha(u,\theta,\psi,\omega\varphi) \quad , \quad h_{33} = - h_{22} \sin^2\theta$$

$$h_{23} = r\,\beta(u,\theta,\psi,\omega\varphi)$$

their local energy density is :

(2-11) $$e(x, \omega\varphi) = \frac{1}{r^2} (\frac{\alpha'^2}{2} + \frac{\beta'^2}{2\sin^2\theta} + b_2^2 + \frac{b_3^2}{\sin^2\theta})$$

The functions α, β, b_A must be such that

(2-12) $$E = \lim_{T = \infty} \frac{1}{T} \int_0^T e(x,\xi)\, d\xi = - \frac{2}{r^2} \frac{dm}{du}$$

relation which gives the mass loss by radiation

Three supplementary conditions to be satisfied can be fullfilled, either by a non significant perturbation, either by introducing a third lower order term in the expansion (2-1). One or the other of the method shows the non existence of axially symmetric such h.f. perturbations (for details see the references).

3 - GLOBAL ENERGY

For a quantum physicist energy is the "generator of time translation", an operator which is well defined when the corresponding classical dynamical system has a time independant hamiltonian. The classical energy corresponding to a trajectory of this dynamical system is the numerical value of the hamiltonian.

It is known that General Relativity can be put in Hamiltonian form. Let γ_{ij} be the (time dependant) metric of a slice S_t of a space time $V = S \times \mathbb{R}$, and K^{ij} its extrinsic curvature. Set

(3-1) $$P^{ij} = K^{ij} - \gamma^{ij} K^{\ell}_{\ell}$$

then Einstein equations in empty space split into the constraints (D space covariant derivative, $R(\gamma)$ scalar curvature of γ)

(3-2a) $$\mathcal{H} \equiv 2\alpha^2 S^{oo} \equiv R(\gamma) - P_{ij} P^{ij} + \frac{1}{2} (P^{\ell}_{\ell})^2 = 0$$

(3-2b) $$\mathcal{H} \equiv \alpha S^{io} \equiv D_i P^{ij} = 0$$

and an hamiltonian system

(3-3a) $$\frac{d\gamma_{ij}}{dt} = \frac{\delta H}{\delta P^{ij}}$$

(equivalent to the definition of P^{ij})

and

(3-3b) $$\frac{dP^{ij}}{dt} = - \frac{\delta H}{\delta \gamma_{ij}}$$

(equivalent to Einstein equations $S^{ij} = 0$)

the derivatives are functional derivatives in the L^2 sense on S_t, meaning that if δH is a derivation of H induced by variations $\delta\gamma_{ij}$ and δP^{ij} we have

$$\delta H \equiv \int_{S_t} \left(\frac{\delta H}{\delta\gamma_{ij}} \delta\gamma_{ij} + \frac{\delta H}{\delta P^{ij}} \delta P^{ij}\right) d\mu(\gamma)$$

H is the Regge-Teitelboim hamiltonian :

$$H = \int_{S_t} (\alpha\mathcal{H} + \beta_i \mathcal{J}^i)\, d\mu(\gamma) + 16\,\Pi\, m \tag{3-4}$$

where m is an integral on the boundary of S_t which comes in when performing integration by parts in the variation of the A.D.M hamiltonian.

For an empty space solution of the constraints m is the numerical value of the hamiltonian, therefore the "energy" of the solution at time t. For a closed space (S_t compact without boundary) m = 0, for an asymptotically flat space

$$m = \int (\partial_i\, g_{ij} - \partial_j\, g_{ij})\, n^j\, ds$$

where the integral is on the sphere at infinity. It has been proved (most recent proof : E. Witten, Comm. maths. Phys. 1981) to be positive, and zero only for flat space. This energy is independant of t because precisely a solution of Einstein equations satisfies the hamilton equation (3-3).

4 - HYPERBOLIC 3+1 DECOMPOSITION (Choquet-Bruhat and Ruggeri C.R.A.S. 1982)

The equations (3-3a) and (3-3b) look like an ordinary differential system, but are not, since the right hand side involves derivations of the unknown in the space variables. In fact it has not been possible to prove an existence theorem for this system, with unknown γ_{ij} and P^{ij} with given lapse and shift (except for analytic data, but since the solution does not depend continuously on the data, the usefulness for practical purposes is doubtful).

I shall show that by choosing a zero shift, and an appropriate lapse, one can deduce from the system, and the constraints, an hyperbolic system for γ_{ij} and P^{ij}. One can then prove existence theorems (and continuous dependance on the data) without any further hypothesis or choice of coordinates.

Let the space time metric, with zero shift, be

$$ds^2 = -\alpha^2\, dt^2 + g_{ij}\, dx^i\, dx^j \tag{4-1}$$

The relation between P^{ij} and $\dot{g}^{ij}$ is simply

$$\text{(4-2)} \qquad \dot{g}^{ij} = 2\,\alpha\, P^{ij} - \alpha\, g^{ij}\, P \quad , \quad \dot{g}^{ij} = \partial g^{ij}/\partial x^o$$

While the evolution system is read from the explicit identity, with R^{ij} the Ricci tensor of S_t :

$$\text{(4-3)} \qquad \begin{aligned} S^{ij} \equiv & - P^{ij} + \alpha(R^{ij} - \tfrac{1}{2} g^{ij} R) + \alpha(2\, P^{ik} P_k{}^j - \tfrac{3}{2} P\, P^{ij} \\ & - \tfrac{1}{2} g^{ij} P^{hk} P_{hk} + \tfrac{1}{4} g^{ij} P^2) - D^i D^j \alpha + g^{ij} D^h D_h \alpha \end{aligned}$$

A straight-forward computation gives an identity of the form :

$$\text{(4-4)} \qquad \begin{aligned} \alpha^{-1} \dot{S}^{ij} + \alpha(D^i S^{jo} + D^j S^{io} - g^{ij} D_h S^{ho}) \equiv & - \frac{1}{\alpha^2} \ddot{P}^{ij} + D^k D_k P^{ij} \\ & + (g^{ij} D^h D_h - D^i D^j)(\alpha^{-2} \dot{\alpha} - \tfrac{1}{2} P) + Q^{ij} \end{aligned}$$

where Q^{ij} contains only derivatives of P^{hk} of order $\leqslant 1$ and of g_{hk} and α of order $\leqslant 2$. We make the choice of lapse

$$\text{(4-5)} \qquad 2\,\alpha^{-2}\,\dot{\alpha} = P$$

that is (since $\beta = 0$)

$$\text{(4-6)} \qquad \alpha = e^{-1/2} (\det g_{ij})^{1/2}$$

where e is a given tensor density, independant of time . The system (4-2) and (4-3) with $S^{\alpha\beta} = 0$ (or $S^{\alpha\beta} = T^{\alpha\beta}$, with an appropriate model for the sources) is then an hyperbolic system, whose propagation law is determined by the light cone $- \alpha^2\, \xi_o^2 + g_{ij}\, \xi^i\, \xi^j = 0$. It is a third order system but there is no difficulty in proving for this system an existence theorem, with data in the usual Sobolev spaces ($\gamma_{ij} \in M_s$, $P_{ij} \in H_{s-1}$, $s \geqslant 3$, notations of Choquet-Bruhat, Christodoulou et Francaviglia, Ann. I.H.P. (1978)).

The machinery of Bianchi identities shows that a solution of the system (4-3),(4-4), satisfying initially the constraints (3-2) (and the non derivated equations at the initial time) will satisfy the full Einstein system in all its existence domain.

An explicit expression for Q^{ij} is simpler when instead of P^{ij} one works with K_i^j, or K_{ij}. The formulas are then respectively, if one sets $k_{ij} = \alpha K_{ij}$, $a_i = \alpha^{-1}\, \partial_i \alpha$,

$f_{(ij)} = f_{ij} + f_{ji}$

$$\dot{g}_{ij} = -2\,k_{ij}$$

$$\Box k_{ij} + 3\,k_{k(i}\,R_{j)}{}^{h} - 2\,R_{i\ j}^{\ h\ m}\,k_{hm} + 2k\,R_{ij} - 2\,a_{(i}\,D_{j)}k - 4\,k\,D_{i}\,a_{j} - k_{h(i}\,D_{j)}a^{h}$$

$$+ 2\,a^{h}\,D_{(i}\,k_{j)}\,k_{j,h} - a^{h}D_{h}\,k_{ij} - 2\,a^{h}\,a_{(i}\,k_{j)h} - 3\,k\,a_{i}\,a_{j} - 4\,\alpha^{-2}\,k_{ij}\,k_{jm}\,k^{hm}$$

$$= 2\,k_{h(i}\;{}^{(4)}R^{h}{}_{j)} + 2\,k^{(4)}\,R_{ij} - {}^{(4)}\dot{R}_{ij} - D_{(i}(\alpha^{2}\,S^{o}_{j)})$$

and also

$$\Box k^{i}_{j} + k^{h}_{j}\,R^{i}_{h} - k^{i}_{h}\,R^{h}_{j} + 2\,k\,R^{i}_{j} - 2\,R^{ih}{}_{j\ell}\,k^{\ell}_{h} + 2\,a_{\ell}(D^{i}\,k^{\ell}_{j} + D_{j}\,k^{i}_{\ell})$$

$$- a_{\ell}\,D^{\ell}\,k^{i}_{j} - 2(a^{i}\,D_{j}\,k + a_{j}\,D^{i}\,k) + k^{\ell}_{j}\,D^{i}\,a_{\ell} + 3\,k^{i\ell}\,D_{j}\,a_{\ell} - 4\,k\,D^{i}\,a_{j}$$

$$- 2\,k\,a^{i}\,a_{j} + 2\,k^{i\ell}\,a_{j}\,a_{\ell} \equiv - D^{i}(\alpha^{2}\,S^{o}_{j}) - D_{j}(\alpha^{2}\,S^{io}) - \alpha^{-2}\,\frac{\partial}{\partial x^{o}}\,(\alpha^{2\,(4)}R^{i}_{j})$$

FOOTNOTES :

(1) The vector ℓ being here well defined e is also well defined. There is a problem of scale factor in the case of discontinuity or shock waves (I thank A. Ashtekar for calling my attention to this point).

ON THE EXISTENCE OF ASYMPTOTICALLY FLAT AND EMPTY SPACES

Helmut Friedrich

Hochschule der Bundeswehr Hamburg
- Fachbereich Maschinenbau -
Holstenhofweg 85
2000 Hamburg 70
Federal Republic of Germany

It is shown that Penrose's geometrical concept of "asymptotical flatness" not only allows to investigate null infinity in terms of local differential geometry but also to discuss the existence of solutions of Einstein's vacuum field equations which have a smooth structure at null infinity by solving local initial value problems. For this purpose a regular representation of the conformal vacuum field equations is derived and a technique to reduce initial value problems for these equations is proposed.

INTRODUCTION

To be able to make meaningful statements about the behaviour of "far fields" of bounded gravitating systems, Penrose introduced the notion of an "asymptotically empty and flat space" [1, 2]. This is by definition a space and time orientable space-time $(\hat{M},\hat{g})$ such that: (i) $\hat{M}$ can be considered as an open submanifold of a manifold M with boundary I^+ and I^-, and one has $M = \hat{M} \cup I^+ \cup I^-$, (ii) on M exists a Lorentz metric g and a function (the "conformal factor") Ω such that:

$$\Omega > 0 \text{ on } \hat{M},\ \Omega \equiv 0 \text{ on } I^{\pm},\ d\Omega \neq 0 \text{ on } I^{\pm},\ g_{\mu\nu} = \Omega^2 \hat{g}_{\mu\nu} \text{ on } \hat{M}, \tag{1.1}$$

(iii) every null geodesic in $\hat{M}$ has a past endpoint on I^- and a future endpoint on I^+, (iv) the metric $\hat{g}$ satisfies the vacuum field equations $\hat{R}_{\mu\nu}[\hat{g}_{\lambda\rho}] = 0$ in a connected neighbourhood of $I^{\pm}$.

Here and in the following all fields, manifolds, etc. will be considered as "sufficiently smooth". Among various versions of the definition of asymptotically flat and empty spaces I have chosen this one because it allows to derive various properties of the space time which I want to retain while giving up others later. To understand what the conditions mean I will report some results. By inspecting (1.1) one finds that one has the

$$\text{freedom to replace } (\Omega,g) \text{ by } (\Theta\Omega,\Theta^2 g) \text{ with } \Theta > 0 \text{ on } M \tag{1.2}$$

without changing anything. Replacing on $\hat{M}$ the "physical" metric $\hat{g}$ by the "unphysical" metric g one gives up a particular scaling and is left only with the "conformal structure" on $\hat{M}$, that is: the metric up to arbitrary positive factors or, equivalently, the field of null cones on $\hat{M}$. Since null hypersurfaces are by definition surfaces which are tangent to the light cones, they are the same for $(\hat{M},\hat{g})$ and $(\hat{M},g)$. So are the null directions at which the null cones touch the null hypersurfaces and hence the null geodesics as integral curves of these direction fields. In view of the fundamental importance of the light cone structure for radiative phenomena one may expect still to be able to make useful statements in (M,g) about processes involving radiation. In fact, the equations for zero restmass and spin s fields and for gauge fields and their potentials are even invariant under conformal rescalings. Though the null geodesics as point sets are defined by the conformal structure, affine parameters depend on the choice of scaling. However, from (1.1) one can deduce a statement which is true for any choice of Ω: a null geodesic in $\hat{M}$, which ends on I^- or I^+ has finite affine parameter length with respect to g but infinite parameter length with respect to $\hat{g}$. So the condition (1.1) means that by a suitable scaling factor all measures can be scaled down in $(\hat{M},\hat{g})$ in such a way, that "infinity becomes finite" as far as null geodesics are concerned. Moreover, this can be done in such a way that:

the endpoints of null geodesics generate smooth hypersurfaces $I^{\pm}$. (1.3)

The surface I^- (resp. I^+) is called "past (resp. future) null infinity". The assumptions imply that both surfaces are diffeomorphic to $R \times S^2$, that they are null hypersurfaces with respect to g and that the conformal Weyl tensor for g vanishes there. Since the Weyl tensor is invariant under conformal rescalings, one has $\hat{C}^{\mu}{}_{\nu\lambda\rho} = C^{\mu}{}_{\nu\lambda\rho}$ on $\hat{M}$. By condition (iv) it represents the curvature of $\hat{g}$ near $I^{\pm}$, which consequently falls off to zero if one approaches null infinity. The concept of null infinity not only implies a fall-off at infinity as expected of far fields of bounded sources but it allows to discuss in detail how this happens since one has all the methods of local differential geometry available to investigate the fields at $I^{\pm}$. Among all the mathematical results and their convincing physical interpretation (see M. Walker's lecture) which justify to take the concept of an asymptotically empty and flat space as a basis for the discussion of far fields, the fact that it provides the only exact definition of gravitational radiation in general relativity makes it particularly interesting. However, one can still ask difficult questions about the appropriateness of this concept. These are mainly concerned with the interplay of the geometrical conditions (i, ii) and the requirement (iv) that $(\hat{M},\hat{g})$ be a solution of a differential equation. What is the structure of the sources which are compatible with these conditions (or possibly weakened versions)? If one has a field configuration with a smooth past null infinity, under which conditions will it evolve such as to develop a smooth structure in the future? How are the surfaces I^+, I^- related? The answers to these questions require a knowledge about the global behaviour of solutions of Einstein's field equations which is not at our disposal, yet. The question I want to discuss here is: Are the fall-off requirements implicit in (1.1) natural conditions for Einstein's vacuum field equations? I want to point out that this question is not a new one. On the contrary, the definition above was given after the asymptotic behaviour of solutions of Einstein's vacuum field equation, which approach the flat metric at null infinity in a certain sense, had been carefully studied[3,4].These studies gave all the basic physical interpretations and insights which determined the present idea which we have about the behaviour of far fields and the concept of null infinity proved to be completely consistent with this idea. However, nothing was known about the convergence of the formal "Bondi-type" expansions which provided the main tool for these investigations. Till now, only a few exact solutions are known to satisfy the conditions (i, ii, iv) [5, 6].

To make the question raised above more precise, I want to investigate an initial value problem for Einstein's vacuum field equations, where data are given on a hypersurface, which is to represent I^-. One can only expect to obtain a unique solution which takes these data, if one can control what comes in from the infinite timelike past. This can be done by giving in addition data on a spacelike surface S, which intersects I^- in a spacelike two-surface Z. The problem then splits into two parts: (i) The standard initial value problem with data on S. The Cauchy horizon of the possible solution represents near Z a smooth null hypersurface N of topology $R^+ \times S^2$. (ii) The initial value problem with the data on N which are implied by (i) and the data given on I, the future of Z in I^-. While N is a characteristic for the vacuum filed equations, I is only asymptotically a characteristic for these equations, therefore (ii) will be called the "asymptotic characteristic initial value problem". The basic difficulty will be to set up "decent" initial value problems. I will try to explain what this means and where the particular difficulties come from. The solution I want to discuss requires a lengthy analysis of the formal properties of Einstein's field equations. Since this will not leave much space to give all the physical interpretations of the quantities and equations encountered on the way, I suggest to look these up in the beautiful lecture which was given almost 20 years ago at this summer school by Sachs [7] on related topics.

REDUCTION OF INITIAL VALUE PROBLEMS

Since Einstein's field equations are invariant under coordinate transformations, they have some strange features (shared by the equations of other gauge theories) which do not allow to apply in a simple way known results about partial differential equations to some initial value problem for these equations. I want to illustrate these difficulties by discussing the essential steps required for "reducing" a standard initial value problem where data are given on a spacelike hypersurface S.

Let x^μ some coordinates in a neighbourhood of S such that $S = \{x^1 = 0\}$. The field equation being of second order, one will give $g_{\mu\nu}$ and $g_{\mu\nu,1}$ as Cauchy data on S (a comma denoting partial derivatives).

Since the functional dependence of the metric depends on the choice of coordinates, the field equations alone cannot fix the metric uniquely, once data are given on S. One has to specify the coordinate system. However, in any coordinate system as above one finds that the equations $G^1{}_\mu = 0$, where $G_{\mu\nu} = R_{\mu\nu} - \frac{1}{2} g_{\mu\nu}R$ is the Einstein tensor, do only contain derivatives with respect to x^1 up to first order and therefore imply "constraint equations" on the Cauchy data. As a first step one has to solve the constraint equations. Without going into this difficult problem (see J. York's lecture) I want to mention that this leads to the problem of solving elliptic partial differential equations on S.

In any coordinate system the vacuum field equations can be written:

$$0 = R_{\mu\nu} = R^{(h)}_{\mu\nu} + \frac{1}{2}(g_{\mu\alpha}\Gamma^\alpha{}_{,\nu} + g_{\nu\alpha}\Gamma^\alpha{}_{,\mu}) \tag{2.1}$$

where

$$R^{(h)}_{\mu\nu} = -\frac{1}{2} g^{\alpha\beta} g_{\mu\nu,\alpha\beta} + L_{\mu\nu}, \quad \Gamma^\alpha = g^{\mu\nu}\Gamma^\alpha{}_{\mu\nu} \tag{2.2}$$

and $L_{\mu\nu}$ depends only on the metric and its first derivatives. Since the connection coefficients $\Gamma_\alpha{}^\beta{}_\delta$ contain first order derivatives of the metric the right member of (2.1) contains a complicated system of second order derivatives. This defies all attempts to apply any of the known theorems about partial differential equations to solve an initial value problem for (2.1). One will try to overcome this difficulty by fixing a coordinate system. The search for suitable coordinates will be guided by the type of differential operator which one expects to come out. Linearized theory and the experience with other field theories suggest that the propagation of the field will be governed by wave equations. This would also be mathematically very convenient since for this type of equations one disposes of methods to prove existence and uniqueness theorems for initial value problems. Equations (2.1) and (2.2) suggest the gauge condition $\Gamma^\mu = 0$. In fact, one can always find coordinates in a neighbourhood of S by solving with suitable data on S the wave equation

$$\nabla_{\mu'}\nabla^{\mu'}x^\mu = 0 \tag{2.3}$$

in any coordinate system $x^{\mu'}$. If one expresses (2.3) with respect to the coordinates x^μ then it reads just $\Gamma^\mu = 0$. Coordinates satisfying these conditions are called "harmonic". In these coordinates (2.1) simplifies to the "reduced vaccum field equation"

$$R^{(h)}_{\mu\nu} = 0. \tag{2.4}$$

Since equation (2.4) is again of wave equation type we can try to obtain a solution by solving the "reduced problem". For given Cauchy data which satisfy $G^1{}_\mu = 0$, $\Gamma^\mu = 0$ on S, there exists a unique solution of (2.4) which takes these values on S. However, we do not know whether the solution so obtained satisfies the harmonic gauge. Since the metric is not explicitly given to check that, the only way to make sure that it is in fact a solution of (2.1) consists in showing that the gauge $\Gamma^\mu = 0$ propagates. Some algebra shows that from $G^1{}_\mu = 0$, $\Gamma^\mu = 0$ on S and (2.4) it follows that $\Gamma^\mu{}_{,1} = 0$ on S. The fact that $g_{\mu\nu}$ solves (2.4) entails that the Bianchi identities $\nabla_\mu G^{\mu\nu} = 0$, which hold for any metric, take the form

$$g^{\alpha\beta}\,\Gamma^\mu{}_{,\alpha\beta} + L^{\mu\rho}_{\ \ \nu}\,\Gamma^\nu{}_{,\rho} = 0 \tag{2.5}$$

of a linear homogeneous "subsidiary equation" for Γ^μ. The quantities $L^{\mu\rho}_{\ \ \nu}$ are determined by $g_{\mu\nu}$. This is again a wave equation, for which we have a uniqueness theorem. Since the Cauchy data vanish on S, the gauge must be satisfied everywhere. Hence any solution of the reduced problem solves (2.1).

This method of reducing the initial value problem was discovered by Choquet-Bruhat thirty years ago and was for a long time the basis of all existence proofs for initial value problems for Einstein's field equations. It works equally in the case of a characteristic initial value problem where data are given on two null-hypersurfaces (thought of being embedded in space-time) which intersect in a spacelike two-surface [8, 9, 10]. The existence proofs usually ensure the existence of a solution in a certain restricted neighbourhood of the initial surface. Since (2.4) is a complicated quasilinear system, of which one knows that it allows for solutions which become singular after a finite time, it is very difficult to make global statements about solutions. Only recently it has been shown that for suitable data there exist solutions which include complete spacelike surfaces boosted relative to the initial surface [11].

With the reduced equations available one would like to solve the asymptotic characteristic initial value problem for the equation $\hat{R}_{\mu\nu}[\hat{g}_{\lambda\rho}] = 0$. In terms of the physical metric $\hat{g}$ this means that one has to show the existence of global solutions which contain the past of some nullgeodesics up to infinite values of their affine parameters. That already goes far beyond what can be achieved with the techniques available now. Furthermore, one would have to make sure that the solution is such that one has (1.3) and that it approaches in an appropriate sense the data given on I. Since this cannot be done with the present methods, one has to abandon this approach.

The definition of asymptotical flatness suggests to pose a local initial value problem for the non-physical metric g. If $\hat{g}_{\mu\nu} = \Omega^{-2}\, g_{\mu\nu}$ is put into the vacuum field equations and everything is expressed in terms of the Ricci tensor and the covariant derivative with respect to g, the following partial differential equation for $g_{\mu\nu}$ is obtained:

$$R_{\mu\nu}[g_{\lambda\rho}] = 3\,\Omega^{-2} g_{\mu\nu}\,\nabla_\sigma\Omega\nabla^\sigma\Omega - \Omega^{-1}(2\nabla_\mu\nabla_\nu\Omega + g_{\mu\nu}\,\nabla_\sigma\nabla^\sigma\Omega). \tag{2.6}$$

Writing this in harmonic coordinates, now with respect to g, again the wave operator appears on the left hand side. However, the attempt to make the problem a local one, must be paid for with the occurrence of singular terms on the right hand side. The global requirements for $\hat{g}$ have been converted into the conditions that these expressions (and possibly their derivatives up to a given order) have smooth limits on I. This is harmless if one calculates a formal expansion of the field. If one wants to give a general existence proof, however, one has to work with estimates and these can hardly take care of the singular terms, let alone respect their specific algebraic structure, which is so decisive in singular problems. There seems to be no (possibly singular) transformation which makes (2.6) regular and preserves the nice form of the differential operator in (2.2).

The way out is to look for a representation of equation (2.6), in which no singular terms occur. One may expect that such a representation must look quite different from (2.6) and that the method to reduce the equations by introducing harmonic coordinates to obtain a "nice" differential operator fails. One must also envisage the possibility that one cannot get a wave operator. There exists another type of equations which in fact covers most of the equations in mathematical physics, which describe propagation phenomena. These are the "symmetric hyperbolic systems" of first order [12], which are of the form:

$$A^{\mu} t_{,\mu} + B \cdot t = 0 \tag{2.7}$$

with square matrices A^{μ}, B which satisfy

$$\begin{aligned} &\text{a) } {}^{t}\bar{A}^{\mu} = A^{\mu}, \text{ i.e. } A^{\mu} \text{ is hermitian,} \\ &\text{b) there exists } \tau_{\mu}, \text{ such that } A^{\mu}\tau_{\mu} \text{ is positive definite.} \end{aligned} \tag{2.8}$$

The matrices may depend on the unknown t, then the equation (2.7) is called "quasilinear", otherwise linear. The conditions (2.8) are sufficient to derive the so-called "energy estimates" which provide the basic tool for proving existence and uniqueness theorems for initial value problems for systems of this type. Such theorems for quasilinear symmetric hyperbolic equations are available in the literature [9,13]. We are faced now with two problems which have to be solved simultaneously: to find a regular representation of equation (2.6) which allows a reduction to one of the types of equations discussed above.

The solution I want to propose is based on the consideration of a rather extensive system of differential equations, the (regular) "conformal vacuum field equations". A very detailed discussion of these equations is required to reduce the asymptotic characteristic initial value problem to a characteristic initial value problem for a symmetric hyperbolic system. Since this cannot be done here, I want to illustrate the reduction technique by applying it to a characteristic initial value problem for a system of gauge field equations. This will give the opportunity to discuss for a simpler situation various features of the problems posed by the conformal vacuum field equations.

The equations to be solved are

$$\nabla_{\mu} A_{\nu} - \nabla_{\nu} A_{\mu} + [A_{\mu}, A_{\nu}] - F_{\mu\nu} = 0 \tag{2.9}$$

$$\nabla_{\mu} F^{\mu}{}_{\nu} + [A_{\mu}, F^{\mu}{}_{\nu}] = 0 \tag{2.10}$$

where A_{μ} denotes the potential, $F_{\mu\nu}$ the gauge field, which both take their values in the Lie algebra of some gauge group G, and the square brackets denote the Lie product. From (2.9) follows the Bianchi identity

$$(\nabla_{\mu} F_{\nu\lambda} + [A_{\mu}, F_{\nu\lambda}] + \text{cyclic}) = 0 \,. \tag{2.11}$$

Let us assume that the non-physical spacetime (M,g) is given and that data are prescribed on the nullsurfaces N and I which intersect in Z. Since the spinframe formalism is so well adapted to the null geometry and makes it particularly easy to keep track of the symmetries of the equations and the unknowns, I will employ it here, however, without discussing it at length (see [14, 15]). Let $e_{aa'} = \bar{e}_{aa'}$ be a pseudo orthonormal frame such that

$g(e_{aa'}, e_{bb'}) = \varepsilon_{ab}\varepsilon_{a'b'}$; $e_{00'}$ (resp. $e_{11'}$) is tangent to the nullgeodesics on N (resp. I); $e_{10'}, e_{01'}$ are tangent to N, I and Z; $e_{11'}$ is parallely propagated on I and all fields are parallely propagated on M in the direction of $e_{00'}$. (2.12)

By this choice of frame we have for the connection coefficients: $\Gamma_{00'ab} = 0$ on M and $\Gamma_{11'}{}^{0}{}_{1} = 0$ on I. The gauge field is represented by a symmetric spinor φ_{ab} such that with the usual correspondance between spinor indeces and space-time indeces one has:

$$F_{\mu\nu} = \varphi_{ab}\varepsilon_{a'b'} + \bar{\varphi}_{a'b'}\varepsilon_{ab}\ , \quad A_{\mu} = A_{aa'}\ .$$

By defining the quantities

$$h_{c'c} = \nabla^{a}{}_{c'}\varphi_{ac} - [A_{ac'},\varphi^{a}{}_{c}]$$
$$l_{aa'bb'} = \nabla_{aa'}A_{bb'} - \nabla_{bb'}A_{aa'} + [A_{aa'},A_{bb'}] - (\varphi_{ab}\varepsilon_{a'b'}+\bar{\varphi}_{a'b'}\varepsilon_{ab})$$

equations (2.9), (2.10), (2.11) can be written

$$h_{c'c} = 0,\quad l_{aa'bb'} = 0\ . \tag{2.13}$$

These equations can be simplified by using the gauge freedom to obtain

$$A_{00'} = 0 \text{ on M},\quad A_{11'} = 0 \text{ on I}\ . \tag{2.14}$$

Writing (2.13) somewhat more explicitly to see which directional derivatives are involved, gives

$$\begin{aligned}
-h_{0'0} &= e_{00'}(\varphi_{10}) - e_{10'}(\varphi_{00}) + 2\Gamma_{10'}{}^{d}{}_{0}\varphi_{d0} - [A_{10'},\varphi_{00}]\\
-h_{0'1} &= e_{00'}(\varphi_{11}) - e_{10'}(\varphi_{10}) + \Gamma_{10'}{}^{d}{}_{0}\varphi_{d1} + \Gamma_{10'}{}^{d}{}_{1}\varphi_{0d} - [A_{10'},\varphi_{01}]\\
h_{1'1} &= e_{11'}(\varphi_{01}) - e_{01'}(\varphi_{11}) + H_{1'1}\\
h_{1'0} &= e_{11'}(\varphi_{00}) - e_{01'}(\varphi_{10}) + H_{1'0}\\
l_{00'bb'} &= e_{00'}(A_{bb'}) - (\varphi_{0b}\varepsilon_{0'b'}+\bar{\varphi}_{0'b'}\varepsilon_{0b})\\
l_{01'10'} &= e_{01'}(A_{10'}) - e_{10'}(A_{01'}) + K + \varphi_{01} - \bar{\varphi}_{0'1'}\\
l_{11'bb'} &= e_{11'}(A_{bb'}) - e_{bb'}(A_{11'}) + L
\end{aligned}$$

with suitable quantities $H_{a'a}$, K, L which do not contain any derivatives.

The equations (2.13) being of first order, the Cauchy data are given by $A_{aa'},\varphi_{ab}$ on N and I. Inspecting the equations on N one finds that 8k interior equations are implied on these data, where k = dim(G) and real equations have been counted. There are two reasons for this number. Since system (2.13) is overdetermined in the sense that there are more equations than unknowns, it implies 5k interior equations on any hypersurface. That there are more interior relations implied on N shows (and is the defining property) that N is a "characteristic" of equations (2.13). These two facts work together in a very nice way. While in the case of a standard initial value problem the constraints often lead to elliptic equations, here one finds the

Lemma: Given the "reduced data" φ_{00} on N, φ_{11} on I, $\varphi_{01} + \bar{\varphi}_{0'1'}$ and $A_{01'}$ on Z, fields $A_{aa'} = A^{*}_{aa'},\varphi_{ab} = \varphi^{*}_{ab}$ on N and I which imply these data and satisfy the interior equations implied by (2.13) are fixed uniquely by the latter. They can be obtained by integration of ordinary differential equations on the nullgeodesics which generate the initial surfaces.

In fact, if φ_{00} is given on N, $l_{00'10'} = 0$, $-h_{0'0} = 0$ reduces to a system of ordinary differential equations on N and can be integrated to obtain φ_{01} and $A_{01'}$. The initial value φ_{01} on Z can be found by solving $l_{01'10'} = 0$ on Z for $\varphi_{01} - \bar{\varphi}_{0'1'}$. Similarly now $-h_{0'1} = 0$, $l_{00'11'} = 0$ give φ_{11}, $A_{11'}$ on N. By the same procedure one calculates the data on I. Note, that at this stage it is open, whether the data satisfy $l_{01'10'} = 0$ which defines an interior equation on N and I. This will follow later.

It is a remarkable feature of the characteristic initial value problem that the constraint equations can be solved by integration of a sequence of systems of ordinary differential equations. This fact will be observed again in the case of Einstein's field equations. It allows to specify the reduced data freely. After having found Cauchy data which satisfy the constraints, one would like to solve (2.13). This system is over-determined and it cannot be seen immediately, whether it belongs to one of the types of equations discussed before. One can try to derive a second order system for the potential as one does for Maxwell's equation. This would result in a procedure very similar to the reduction of Einstein's equation by choosing harmonic coordinates. For the reasons discussed above I do not want to do that. Instead I want to solve a first order system. Any solution of (2.13) must solve the following systems of "reduced equations"

$$l_{00'bb'} = 0, \quad -h_{0'1} = 0, \quad -h_{0'0} + h_{1'1} = 0, \quad h_{1'0} = 0 . \tag{2.15}$$

This system is of the type (2.7), (2.8) hence represents a quasilinear symmetric hyperbolic system. One can assume that there exists a unique solution $\overset{*}{A}_{aa'}$, $\overset{*}{\varphi}_{ab}$ of these equations which coincides on N and I with the Cauchy data which have been determined in the Lemma. Since (2.15) contains linear combinations of (2.13) and some equations of the system (2.13) have even been "forgotten", it has to be shown that $\overset{*}{A}_{aa'}$, $\overset{*}{\varphi}_{ab}$ in fact solve (2.13). By a straightforward calculation one can show that the identities

$$\nabla^{aa'} h_{a'a} = -[A^{aa'}, h_{a'a}] - [\varphi_{ab}, l^{a}{}_{a'}{}^{ba'}] \tag{2.16}$$

$$(\nabla_{aa'} l_{bb'cc'} + [A_{aa'}, l_{bb'cc'}] + \text{cyclic}) = \varepsilon_{ab}\varepsilon_{a'c'} h_{b'c} \tag{2.17}$$

must hold for any fields $A_{aa'}$, φ_{ab}. If one takes, however, the solution of (2.15) equation (2.16) and equation (2.17) for aa' = 00' can be written (observing (2.14))

$$(e_{00'} + e_{11'})(h_{1'1}) = \Gamma h_{1'1} + [\overset{*}{A}_{01'}, h_{1'1}] - [\overset{*}{\varphi}_{ab}, l^{a}{}_{a'}{}^{ba'}] \tag{2.18}$$

$$e_{00'}(l_{bb'cc'}) = \Gamma^{dd'ee'}_{bb'cc'}\, l_{dd'ee'} + \varepsilon_{0b}\varepsilon_{0'c'} h_{b'c} \tag{2.19}$$

where the Γ's are functions of the connection coefficients. By calculating the Cauchy data from the reduced data the equations

$$l_{01'10'} = 0 \text{ on } Z; \quad h_{0'b} = 0, \; l_{00'bb'} = 0 \text{ on } N; \quad h_{1'b} = 0, \; l_{11'bb'} = 0 \text{ on } I \tag{2.20}$$

have been solved. Comparison of these with (2.15) yields that $\overset{*}{A}_{aa'}$, $\overset{*}{\varphi}_{ab}$ satisfy $h_{b'b} = 0$ on N and I. From (2.19), (2.20) then follows $l_{bb'cc'} = 0$ on N. Evaluation of (2.17) for aa' = 11' on I gives also $l_{bb'cc'} = 0$ on I. The "subsidiary equations" (2.18), (2.19) form again a symmetric hyperbolic system which has the uniqueness property. We have seen that the unknowns $h_{1'1}$, $l_{aa'bb'}$ vanish on N and I, hence they must vanish everywhere and $\overset{*}{A}_{aa'}$, $\overset{*}{\varphi}_{ab}$ solve (2.13). We have the result: Given arbitrary reduced data on N and I, then there exists a unique solution of (2.13) which induces these data on the initial surfaces.

The gauge field equations (2.9), (2.10) are conformally invariant. This means that the restriction to $\hat{M}$ of the local solution of these equations on (M,g) is a global solution on $(\hat{M},\hat{g})$, in the sense that it is defined up to past null infinity. Though general relativity is a gauge theory it is not conformally invariant. The conformal Weyl tensor is conformally invariant and the contracted vacuum Bianchi identities, considered as gauge field equations for the Weyl tensor, are conformally invariant in a sense (see (3.4)). However, if one writes the field equations similar to (2.9), (2.10), (2.11) one has to add equations for, let say, the frame field (this determines the soldering of the frame bundle, the origin of the difference between relativity and other gauge theories). Rescaling the metric amounts to rescaling the frame field and since the frame field equations couple to the equations for the connection and the curvature the rescaling produces Ricci curvature, as (2.6) shows. Nevertheless, there seems to be "just enough conformal invariance" as to set up a regular system.

REDUCTION OF THE ASYMPTOTIC CHARACTERISTIC INITIAL VALUE PROBLEM

As a first step to set up a treatable initial value problem, a regular system of equations, the "conformal vacuum field equations" will be derived. The unknowns will be $g_{ik} = g(e_i, e_k)$ and

$$t = (e^{\mu}{}_{k}, \gamma^{i}{}_{jk}, d^{i}{}_{jkl}, s_{ij}, \Omega, \Sigma_i, s)$$

where $e^{\mu}{}_{k}$ is a frame field, given with respect to some coordinate system x^{μ}, $\gamma_{j}{}^{i}{}_{k}$ are the connection coefficients with respect to that frame, defined by $\nabla_j e_k = \nabla_{e_j} e_k = \gamma_j{}^i{}_k\, e_i$, Ω is the conformal factor, Σ_i its differential, $s = \frac{1}{4}\nabla_k \nabla^k \Omega$, $d^i{}_{jkl} = \Omega^{-1} c^i{}_{jkl}$ is the Weyl tensor $c^i{}_{jkl}$, rescaled by Ω^{-1}, $s_{ij} = R_{ij} - \frac{1}{4} R g_{ij}$ is the traceless part of the Ricci tensor R_{ij} and all tensors are expressed with respect to the frame e_k. The following equations must hold if (2.6) is satisfied [16]:

The conditions that the connection is metric and torsion free

$$e_k(g_{ij}) = \gamma_k{}^l{}_i\, g_{lj} + \gamma_k{}^l{}_j\, g_{li} \tag{3.1}$$

$$e^{\mu}{}_{j,\nu}\, e^{\nu}{}_{k} - e^{\mu}{}_{k,\nu}\, e^{\nu}{}_{j} = (\gamma_k{}^i{}_j - \gamma_j{}^i{}_k) e_i{}^{\mu}. \tag{3.2}$$

The representation of the curvature by its irreducible parts

$$e_k(\gamma_l{}^i{}_j) - e_l(\gamma_k{}^i{}_j) + Q(\gamma,\gamma) = \Omega d^i{}_{jkl} + g^i{}_{[k} s_{l]j} + g_{j[l} s_{k]}{}^i + \frac{1}{6} R\, g^i{}_{[k} g_{l]j} \tag{3.3}$$

where Q is a quadratic function of the connection coefficients. For any metrik h_{ik} the Bianchi identity holds, which can be written

$$(*) \quad \nabla_i c^i{}_{jkl} = \nabla_{[k} s_{l]j} + \frac{1}{12} h_{j[l} \nabla_{k]} R$$

where the quantities are defined here with respect to h_{ij} similarly as those above with respect to g_{ij}. If $h = \hat{g}$, the Ricci tensor vanishes and (*) reads

$$\hat{\nabla}_i \hat{c}^i{}_{jkl} = 0.$$

The invariance of the Weyl tensor and the transformation property of the connection under conformal rescalings imply that this equation transforms into

$$\nabla_i\, d^i{}_{jkl} = 0. \tag{3.4}$$

Considering equation (*) now for h = g and combining it with (3.4) gives

$$\nabla_{[k}\, s_{l]j} = d^i{}_{jkl}\, \Sigma_i - \frac{1}{12} g_{j[l}\, \nabla_{k]} R \tag{3.5}$$

with

$$\nabla_i\, \Omega = \Sigma_i\,. \tag{3.6}$$

The tracefree part of (2.6) can be written

$$\nabla_i \Sigma_j = -\frac{1}{2}\, \Omega\, s_{ij} + s\, g_{ij}\,. \tag{3.7}$$

By taking a covariant derivative of this equation, commuting derivatives and contracting, one obtains the equation

$$\nabla_i s = -\frac{1}{2} s_i{}^k \Sigma_k - \frac{1}{24} \Omega \nabla_i R - \frac{1}{12} R \Sigma_i . \tag{3.8}$$

Finally, the trace of (2.6) gives

$$\Omega \nabla_k \nabla^k \Omega = 2 \nabla_k \Omega \nabla^k \Omega - \frac{1}{6} R \Omega^2. \tag{3.9}$$

It is not possible to solve for R without getting singularities or to deduce a differential equation for R without getting higher order derivatives of other quantities. However, for any metric h and any positive function Θ, the Ricci scalars with respect to h and with respect to $\Theta^2 h$ are related by

$$\Theta R[h] - \Theta^3 R[\Theta^2 h] = 6 \nabla_k \nabla^k \Theta.$$

For an arbitrary "initial value" of Θ on N and I there exists a unique solution of the linear wave equation $6 \nabla_k \nabla^k \Theta = \Theta R[h]$ in a neighbourhood of $N \cup I$, which takes this value. With this function one has $R[\Theta^2 h] = 0$. If we exploit now (1.2) we can assume that Ω has been chosen such that

$$R = 0 \tag{3.10}$$

in a neighbourhood of $N \cup I$.

Equation (3.9) is still singular since the principal part is multiplied by the factor Ω which vanishes on I. The main reason for the introduction of equation (3.8) is the surprising fact that with its help we get rid of (3.9). If equations (3.1)-(3.8) and (3.10) hold, one has

$$\nabla_i (\Omega \nabla_j \nabla^j \Omega - 2 \nabla_j \Omega \nabla^j \Omega) = -4 \nabla^j \Omega (\nabla_i \nabla_j \Omega + \frac{1}{2} \Omega s_{ij} - \frac{1}{4} g_{ij} \nabla_k \nabla^k \Omega) = 0.$$

Consequently (3.9) must be satisfied everywhere if it holds at one point. On the other hand $I = \{\Omega = 0\}$ is by assumption a null hypersurface (in fact, it follows from (3.9) the $I^{\pm}$ must be null hypersurfaces). Therefore Σ_k must be given as initial value on I such that $\Sigma_k \Sigma^k = 0$. Hence any solution of (3.1) - (3.8) and (3.10) which takes this initial value on I satisfies (3.9). Consequently it is sufficient to solve (3.1) - (3.8) with the gauge (3.10). These equations represent the regular system of "conformal vacuum field equations" we have been looking for. Note that (2.6) partly turns up in (3.7) with quite a different interpretation as before, and that it is partly hidden in (3.8).

So far, the choice of coordinates and frame fields has been left completely open. As in the discussion of the characteristic initial value problem for the gauge field equations, we will again choose a pseudo-orthonormal frame. Equation (3.1) reduces in that case to an algebraic condition for the connection coefficients. Writing the other equations in the spin frame notation, the conformal vacuum field equations take the form

$$e^\mu{}_{cc',\nu}\, e^\nu{}_{bb'} - e^\mu{}_{bb',\nu}\, e^\nu{}_{cc'} = \varepsilon^{ae}(\Gamma_{bb'ec}\, e^\mu{}_{ac'} - \Gamma_{cc'eb}\, e^\mu{}_{ab'}) + \varepsilon^{a'e'}(\bar{\Gamma}_{bb'e'c'}\, e^\mu{}_{ca'} - \bar{\Gamma}_{cc'e'b'}\, e^\mu{}_{ba'}) \tag{3.11}$$

$$\Gamma_{cc'ad,\nu}\, e^\nu{}_{bb'} - \Gamma_{bb'ad,\nu}\, e^\nu{}_{cc'} = Q^*(\Gamma,\Gamma) - \Omega\, \varphi_{abcd}\, \varepsilon_{c'b'} - \Phi_{adc'b'}\, \varepsilon_{cb} \tag{3.12}$$

$$\nabla^f{}_{b'}\, \varphi_{abcf} = 0 \tag{3.13}$$

$$\nabla_a{}^{f'}\, \Phi_{bcd'f'} = \varphi_{abcf}\, \Sigma^f{}_{d'} \tag{3.14}$$

$$\nabla_{bb'}\,\Omega = \Sigma_{bb'} \tag{3.15}$$

$$\nabla_{bb'}\,\Sigma_{aa'} = -\,\Omega\,\Phi_{aba'b'} + s\,\varepsilon_{ab}\,\varepsilon_{a'b'} \tag{3.16}$$

$$\nabla_{bb'}\,s = -\,\Phi_{bdb'd'}\,\Sigma^{dd'} \tag{3.17}$$

The unknown will again be denoted by

$$t = (e^{\mu}{}_{aa'},\ \Gamma_{aa'bc},\ \varphi_{abcd},\ \Phi_{aba'b'},\ \Omega,\ \Sigma_{aa'},\ s).$$

Here $\varphi_{abcd} = \varphi_{(abcd)}$ is the rescaled Weyl spinor and $\Phi_{aba'b'} = \bar{\Phi}_{aba'b'} = \Phi_{(ab)(a'b')}$ represents the traceless part of the Ricci tensor. $Q^*(\Gamma,\Gamma)$ in (3.12) is a quadratic function of the connection coefficients.

While equations (3.13) - (3.17) are equations for tensor quantities, equations (3.11), (3.12) are equations for gauge dependant quantities. Before fixing a gauge for the coordinates and the frame one has to determine by some conditions on N and I the initial value for the function Θ by which we have obtained (3.10). I do not want to discuss all the details of the gauge, but mention only those conditions which are most important for the following considerations. The frame $e_{aa'}$ will be assumed to satisfy the conditions (2.12). The coordinate x^1 be a null coordinate which on I induces that affine parameter on the null geodesics with tangent vector $e_{11'}$, which vanishes on Z. The coordinate x^2 is chosen to be that affine parameter on the null geodesics generating the surface $\{x^1 = \text{const}\}$ which vanishes on Z. The vectors $e_{01'}, e_{10'}$ are chosen to be tangent to $\{x' = \text{const}\}$ on I. Then $e_{00'}$ is the gradient of x^1. By this choice of gauge one has in particular:

$$\Gamma_{00'ab} = 0, \quad e^{\mu}{}_{00'} = \delta^{\mu}{}_{2}\,. \tag{3.18}$$

The system (3.11) - (3.17) can be split now into three subsets: a subsystem which only contains the operators $e_{00'}$, $e_{01'}$, $e_{10'}$ and which consequently implies interior equations on N, a subsystem which only contains the operators $e_{11'}$, $e_{01'}$, $e_{10'}$, hence induces interior equations on I, and a subsystem which only contains $e_{01'}$, $e_{10'}$ and therefore implies interior equations on N, I and Z. Inspecting the equations of the first subset on N more carefully one finds that with the exception of φ_{0000} for any unknown contained in t, which is not known by the choice of gauge, there is exactly one equation, where the operator $e_{00'}$ acts on that quantity. The structure is in fact very similar to that found in the case of the gauge field equations and one can prove the

Lemma: Given arbitrary "reduced initial data"

$$\Gamma_{01'00},\ \varphi_{0001},\ \varphi_{0011} + \bar{\varphi}_{0'0'1'1'},\ \Phi_{001'1'} \text{ on Z}$$

$$\varphi_{0000} \text{ on N},\ \varphi_{1111} \text{ on I},$$

> the unknown $t = t^*$ is fixed uniquely on $N \cup I$, if it implies these data and if it satisfies the interior equations implied by the conformal vacuum field equations on N and I. It can be obtained by integration of ordinary differential equations on the null geodesics which generate N and I.

By taking formally directional derivatives of (3.11) - (3.17) one can deduce interior equations on N and I for all derivatives of t up to arbitrary order. They allow to calculate all derivatives of t on N and I by integration of ordinary differential equations. Therefore the reduced data determine uniquely a "Bondi-type-expansion" of the fields, which can be shown to be a formal solution of all equations (3.11) - (3.17).

Again we have the remarkable fact that the reduced data can be specified freely. Their physical and geometrical meaning has been discussed in the literature [7, 17]. In particular φ_{1111} measures the incoming radiation field on I. It depends only on the scaling of $e_{11'}$ and the phase of $e_{01'}$ and may thus be considered as an object defined on I endowed with its inner geometry. If one starts from a situation where the free data on N and I vanish, the future development of space time is completely determined by φ_{1111}.

Proceeding in analogy with the initial value problem for the gauge field discussed before, one can define the following system of "reduced conformal vacuum field equations" which must be satisfied by any solution of equations (3.11) - (3.17) with the gauge discussed above:

$$
\begin{aligned}
\Omega_{,\mu} e^{\mu}{}_{00'} &= \Sigma_{00'} \\
\Omega_{,\mu} e^{\mu}{}_{00'} &= - \Phi_{0b0'b'}\,\Sigma^{bb'} \\
\nabla_{00'}\Sigma_{bb'} &= - \Omega\, \Phi_{0b0'b} + s\, \varepsilon_{0b}\varepsilon_{0'b'} \\
\Gamma_{cc'ab,\mu} e^{\mu}{}_{00'} &= - \varepsilon^{ts}\Gamma_{t0'ab}\Gamma_{cc's0} - \varepsilon^{t's'}\Gamma_{0t'ab}\,\bar{\Gamma}_{cc's'0'} \\
&\quad - \Omega\, \varphi_{abc0}\varepsilon_{c'o'} - \Phi_{abc'0'}\varepsilon_{c0} \\
- \nabla_{0}{}^{f'}\Phi_{bc1'f'} &= - \varphi_{0bc}{}^{f}\Sigma_{f1'} \\
- \nabla_{0}{}^{f'}\Phi_{bc0'f} + \nabla_{1}{}^{f'}\Phi_{bc1'f'} &= - \varphi_{obcf}\Sigma^{f}{}_{0'} + \varphi_{1bcf}\Sigma^{f}{}_{1'} \\
\nabla_{1}{}^{f'}\Phi_{bc0'f'} &= \varphi_{1bcf}\Sigma^{f}{}_{0'} \\
- \nabla^{f}{}_{0'}\varphi_{111f} &= 0 \\
- \nabla^{f}{}_{0'}\varphi_{ab0f} + \nabla^{f}{}_{1'}\varphi_{ab1f} &= 0 \\
\nabla^{f}{}_{1'}\varphi_{0C0f} &= 0
\end{aligned}
\qquad (3.19)
$$

This again is a quasilinear symmetric hyperbolic system. One can prove the following

Theorem [16]

> A solution $t = (e_{aa'}{}^{\mu}, \Gamma_{aa'bc}, \varphi_{abcd}, \Phi_{aba'b'}, \Omega, \Sigma_{aa'}, s)$ of the reduced conformal vacuum field equations (3.19) which takes on N and I the initial value t* calculated in the preceding lemma, is a solution of the conformal vacuum field equations (3.11) - (3.17). Furthermore, the equation $\Omega\, \nabla_k \nabla^k \Omega = 2\nabla_k \Omega\, \nabla^k \Omega$ is satisfied, the metric g defined by $g^{\mu\nu} = \varepsilon^{ab}\, \varepsilon^{a'b'}\, e^{\mu}{}_{aa'}\, e^{\nu}{}_{bb'}$ is a solution of (2.6) and the metric $\hat{g}_{\mu\nu} = \Omega^{-2}\, g_{\mu\nu}$ is a solution of the asymptotic characteristic initial value problem.

The structure of the proof of this theorem is similar to the analogous proof in case of the gauge field equations discussed above, however, somewhat more involved. Among other fields the solution of (3.19) defines a metric, a metric connection and a tensor which possesses all the symmetry properties of a curvature tensor the Ricci scalar of which vanishes. But only from (3.19) it is not known, whether this tensor is the curvature tensor of this connection, or whether the connection is torsion free. But by exploiting the Bianchi identities for this connection and the symmetries of various tensor fields involved, one can derive again a subsidiary equation for an unknown z which is essentially given by the differences of the left and right members of the equations (3.11) - (3.17) evaluated for the solution of the reduced equations. The subsidiary equations turn out to be again a linear homogeneous symmetric hyperbolic system. Similarly as above, one can show that z vanishes on I and N and consequently everywhere.

Because of the last result and the techniques available to deal with symmetric hyperbolic systems and characteristic initial value problems, the reduced conformal vacuum field equations provide a basis for a general existence and uniqueness proof for the asymptotic characteristic initial value problem with data of low differentiability. If analytic reduced initial data are given, one can show with a suitably modified Cauchy-Kowalevskaja technique that a formal Bondi-type expansion for a solution of (3.19) converges. From this follows the result [18]:

> Given analytic reduced data on N, I and Z, there exists a unique analytic solution of the asymptotic characteristic initial value problem in a neighbourhood of Z, which takes these data.

Thus there exist "many" solutions of Einstein's vacuum field equations which have a smooth "piece of past (or future) null infinity".

The technique discussed above to reduce characteristic initial value problems can with only slight modifications be employed to reduce standard initial value problems. By using the conformal vacuum field equations, the standard Cauchy problem mentioned in the beginning, where data are given on a spacelike hypersurface S which intersects past null infinity at Z, is reduced to a standard Cauchy problem for a symmetric hyperbolic system. If data are given on S which satisfy the constraints implied on S by (3.11) - (3.17), the results by Kato [13] ensure the existence of a unique development of these data containing some neighbourhood of S. The past development of S has a Cauchy horizon, which near Z represents a smooth null hypersurface on which $\Omega \equiv 0$ and $d\Omega \neq 0$ hold. Thus it provides a piece of past null infinity of that development.

The fact that Einstein's vacuum field equations are such that they allow to discuss the existence of solutions which satisfy the condition (i, ii) (with only one surface I required to exist) in terms of local initial value problems show that Penrose's conditons are in perfect agreement with the requirements of the field equations. Whether the methods which have been proposed here will be of any help to obtain statements about the much more difficult and still global problems involving past and future null infinity remains to be seen.

Apart from these considerations the techniques discussed here may be expected to be of some practical use. The fact that global solutions can be determined by solving local initial value problems should be of assistance for example in computer work. The problem of the "outer boundary" (see T. Piran's lecture) which arises because of the necessity to have a finite number of grid points may in some problems be avoided by using the conformal vacuum field equations and giving data on past null infinity. Another reason why it may be of advantage to work with the conformal vacuum field equations is the fact that a solution t tells immediately much about the structure of the space time given by it, because all unknowns and even some coordinates have a geometrical or physical interpretation. For example, if one specifies initial data on a null hypersurface, one is faced with the difficulty that in a general situation this surface will develop caustics and selfintersections. However, it turned out that the quantity t carries all the information necessary to analyse this type of singularity [19].

REFERENCES

[1] Penrose, R., Conformal Treatment of Infinity, in: De Witt and De Witt (eds.), Relativity, Groups and Topology (Gordon and Breach, New York, 1974).

[2] Penrose, R., Zero rest-mass fields including gravitation: asymptotic behaviour, Proc. Roy. Soc. (Lond.) A 284 (1965), 159-203.

[3] Bondi, H. et. al., Gravitational waves in general relativity VII. Waves from axi-symmetric isolated systems, Proc. Roy. Soc. (Lond.) A 269 (1962) 21-52.

[4] Sachs, R.K., Gravitational waves in general relativity VII. Waves in asymptotically flat space time, Proc. Roy. Soc. (Lond.) A 270 (1962) 103-126.

[5] Ashtekar, A. and Dray, T., On the Existence of Solutions to Einstein's Equation With Non-Zero Bondi News, Commun. Math. Phys. 79 (1981) 581-589.

[6] Schmidt, B.G., The Decay of the Gravitational Field, Commun. Math. Phys. 78 (1981) 447-454.

[7] Sachs, R. Gravitational Radiation, in: De Witt and De Witt (eds.), Relativity, Groups and Topology (Gordon and Breach, New York, 1974).

[8] Choquet-Bruhat, Y. and York, J.W., The Cauchy Problem, in: Held, A. (ed.), General Relativity and Gravitation, Vol. 1 (Plenum, New York, 1980).

[9] Fischer, A.E. and Marsden, J.E., The initial value problem and the dynamical formulation of general relativity, in: Hawking, S.W. and Israel, W. (eds.), General Relativity (Cambridge, University Press, 1979).

[10] Müller zum Hagen, H. and Seifert, H.-J., On Characteristic Initial Value and Mixed Problems, GRG 8 (1977) 259-30.

[11] Christodoulou, D. and O'Murchadha, N.O., The Boost Problem in General Relativity, Commun. Math. Phys. 80, (1981), 271-300.

[12] Courant, R. and Hilbert, D., Methods of Mathematical Physics (Interscience, New York, 1962).

[13] Kato, T., The Cauchy Problem for Quasi-Linear Symmetric Hyperbolic Systems, Arch. Ration. Mech. Anal. 58 (1975), 181-205.

[14] Penrose, R., Structure of Space-Time, in: De Witt, C.M. and Wheeler, J.A. (eds.), Battelle Rencontres (Benjamin, New York, 1968).

[15] Newman, E. and Penrose, R., An Approach to Gravitational Radiation by a Method of Spin Coefficients, J. Math. Phys., 3 (1962), 566-578.

[16] Friedrich, H., The asymptotic characteristic initial value Problem for Einstein's vacuum field equations as an initial value problem for a first order quasilinear symmetric hyperbolic system, Proc. Roy. Soc. (Lond.) A 378, (1981) 401-421.

[17] Penrose, R., Relativistic Symmetry Groups, in: Barut, A.O. (ed.), Group Theory in Non-linear Problems (Reidel, New York, 1974).

[18] Friedrich, H., On the existence of analytic null asymptotically flat solutions of Einstein's vacuum field equations. Proc. Roy. Soc. (Lond.) A 381 (1982) 361-371.

[19] Friedrich, H. and Stewart, J.M., Characteristic initial data and wave front singularities in general relativity, Max-Planck-Institute Green Report MPA 17 (1982).

EQUATIONS OF MOTION: THE STATE OF THE ART
A ROUND TABLE DISCUSSION

Reported by Abhay Ashtekar
Physics Department,Syracuse University,Syracuse,N.Y.13210,U.S.A.;and,
Département de Physique,Université de Clermont-Fd.,63170Aubière, France

The session was recorded and the report follows the transcript very closely.In order to make the report as faithful to the original discussion as possible, only a minimal amount of editing was done. However, since the participants did not have the opportunity to see this report before publication, only the reporter is responsible for possible inaccuracies.
Panel: Thibaut Damour,Ron Kates,Bernd Schmidt,Bernard Schutz, Kip Thorne and Martin Walker.
Organizer and Moderator: Abhay Ashtekar.

Opening remarks:

I think that it is fair to say that among the various branches of classical relativity, it is difficult to find any which is as controversial as Equations of Motion. If you choose a paper at random in this field, you would almost invariably find that it begins by listing the mistakes of all previous authors! And, it is generally true that the mistakes have occurred. However, it is not always so clear that all the criticisms are relevent. This is because two types of things can happen. First, one may have an approximation scheme and make a mistake *within* the scheme. An example of this is computational errors. Everyone agrees that these are genuine mistakes. However, something more subtle can also happen.This has to do with the *relation* between two schemes: An author may feel that the approximation scheme used by another author is not "good enough", or, a technique is not "sufficiently rigorous". And now of-course the distinctions become more subtle and what is "right" and what is "wrong" is not so crystal clear. The overall state of the field is perhaps best illustrated by the fact that I was asked to arrange this session largely because I have not worked in this field and can be therefore reasonably unbiased.

One might wonder why this field has evolved in this way, just this one field in mathematical relativity. There is not just one reason, but a whole bunch of them. The first and the foremost reason is that the field is very difficult. It requires that one do both, develop a conceptual framework and solve difficult technical problems. Secondly, one has to develop an approximation scheme and test it against observations such as those related to the binary pulsar. This is much more difficult than, for example, proving an exact result which does not face a direct experimental confrontation; techniques needed are substantially more diverse. And the third reason, I think, is a psychological one. The calculations are difficult and long and often need a year or two to complete. And when one has invested so much effort, it is difficult to accept that one made a mistake, perhaps right in the first few steps.

All these things point towards just one thing: The field is difficult and important and one has to be very critical in examining the various methods. Now is a good time to do this examination because the Paris group has made what seems to be a very significant progress; one now has at least a precise framework in terms of which one can formulate one's questions. I hope the discussion will shed light on the state of the art. The immediate question is not that of superiority of one method over another. Rather, we would like to get a good picture of the assumptions, the drawbacks and the advantages of various methods. That is, irrespective of future plans, one would like to know where exactly one stands today. I have asked the speakers to say what their goals are --a lot of the controversy that I referred to in the begining arises because different people have different goals-- what their assumptions are and what the merits and the drawbacks of their approaches are.

The way this session will work is the following. There will be three short talks. The two main approaches to the problem are the post-Newtonian approach and the post-Minkowskian approach. Bernie Schutz will give his version of the first and Thibaut Damour will summerize the highlights of the work of the Paris group on the second. But first, Kip Thorne will put us all in the right mood by making some introductory remarks on what was for a long time considered to be the "standard" derivation of the radiation reaction formula.

Kip Thorne: The "standard" derivation via the Landau-Lifshitz pseudo-tensor.

Being a very naive physicist, I am going to take the role of the devil's advocate (except I really believe what I am going to say, more or less !) I want to present the standard argument --which gives the standard answer in agreement with the radiation reaction observed in the binary pulsar-- as I have believed it since I was a graduate student. It predates the matched asymptotic expansions, pre-dates the Chandrasekhar-Esposito work on fluids, the recent Paris work, and so forth. My personal feeling is that this particular approach --which is nothing but the application of the conservation law to the pseudo-tensor-- has a high probability of being secure and had a high probability of being so right from the begining. The first step in this approach is to take any slow motion source and write down its metric in the local wave zone as a power series in 1/r :

$$dS^2 = -(1-\frac{2M}{r})\,dt^2 + \frac{4\,\varepsilon_{jkm}\,S_k\,n_m\,dt\,dx^j}{r^2} + (1+\frac{2M}{r})\,\delta_{jk}\,dx^j\,dx^k$$
$$+(\text{gravitational wave terms} \sim 1/r)$$

This is the standard form of the metric with the mass term, the angular momentum term, the mass term in the spatial metric due to harmonic gauge and the gravitational wave terms. The wave terms can be expanded in terms of spherical harmonics and the key point is that they have the angular dependence with $l \geqq 2$. The dominant piece is the quadrupole contribution. The other key point is that, up to the order $1/r^2$, everything else is in the monopole and the dipole terms. The next step is to use the standard equations involving the L-L pseudo-tensor that you will find in the section 101 of the Classical Theory of Fields. Recall that there is a super-potential $H^{\alpha\beta\mu\nu}$ with symmetries of the Riemann tensor, constructed from the contravariant metric density: $H^{\alpha\beta\mu\nu} = g^{\alpha\beta}\, g^{\mu\nu} - g^{\alpha\nu}\, g^{\beta\mu}$. Let me now do a 2-dimensional integral

$$P^\mu := (1/16\pi) \int H^{\mu\alpha 0 j}{}_{,\alpha}\; d^2 S_j$$

of the divergence of H in the local wave zone. I will take the surface to be of constant time. This integral is so designed that the P^0 part picks out precisely the M which appears in the metric. That is, P^0 picks out the 1/r-part of the $l = 0$ piece of the metric. Similarly, P^k picks up the 1/r-part of the $l = 1$ piece of the metric. Thus, P^k is the 3-momentum, which now turns out to be zero. The next step is to take these equations and do some straightforward mathematics, not generally covariant mathematics but the one done as though "these coordinates were flat". You take the time derivative inside the integral. After a little simplification, you obtain the standard result:

$$\frac{dP^\mu}{dt} = (1/16\pi) \int H^{\mu\alpha 0 j}{}_{,\alpha 0}\; d^2 S_j \;=\; -\int (-g)\, t^{\mu j}_{LL}\; d^2 S_j \;.$$

I will now do time-average over the characteristic time-scale of the emission of waves --I have learnt from Rich Isaacson that this is a good thing to do-- and then do some standard manipulation of the L-L pseudo-tensor for this metric. The result is:

$$< \frac{dM}{dt} > = \int < (-g)\; t^{0j}_{LL} > d^2 S_j \;=\; (-1/5) < \dddot{Q}_{jk}\, \dddot{Q}_{jk} >$$

So, this argument says that if you accept the form of the metric in the local wave zone, then a series of mathematical identities lead you to the result that the secular change of the M which appears in the metric is governed by the third time-derivative of the quadrupole moment of the source.

The next thing you do is to apply this to a binary system such as the binary pulsar. (For this, the standard reference is P.Peters, Phys.Rev.136B,1224(1964).) What you have to do is to determine M in terms of the properties of the source. One can do this to various degrees of sophistication. The net result is:

$$M = m_1 + m_2 - \frac{m_1 m_2}{2\,a} + M_{PN} + M_{P^2N}$$

where a is the semi-major axis of the Newtonian orbit. Thus, the M which governs the distant Kepler orbits is the sum of the individual gravitating masses m_1 and m_2, the Newtonian binding energy and a post-Newtonian and a second post-Newtonian contribution. I do not know the last two terms exactly but I do know their orders of magnitude. Now, using the standard analysis of the rate of change of the quadrupole moment of a binary system, one has the rate of change of M :

$$< \frac{dM}{dt} > = (-32/5)\ (m_1^2\ m_2^2)(m_1+m_2)(1+\frac{73}{24}\,e^2+\frac{37}{96}\,e^4)a^{-5}(1-e^2)^{-7/2}$$

Thus, aside from the unknown post-Newtonian corrections, the rate of change depend only on m_1,m_2,a and the eccentricity e of the orbit.

Now suppose we want to know the long term evolution of the binary system: $\Delta t >> M_{PN}\ (<dM/dt>)^{-1}$.(For the binary pulsar, this gives $\Delta t >> 1000$ years.)We are guaranteed that the changes in M can not come out of the post-Newtonian contributions to M because these contributions are too small. And, I would say that it is "*physically obvious*" that m_1 and m_2 will not change due to wave emission. Here is where you can argue with me. But I think I am very safe because of simple astrophysical arguments. (m_1 and m_2 could change if the orbital motion would resonate with the pulsations of the star. But the frequencies are so far apart that there is no way that this could happen.) Thus, the only thing that could contribute to the change in M is the standard Newtonian binding energy. And this gives the standard radiation reaction result. Of-course, this discussion is not applicable to the binary pulsar for which we have only a few years' data. So, we must consider the *short-term evolution*. For the binary pulsar, this means that we consider $P = 7.75$ hours $<< \Delta t <<$ 1000 years. Now I must do something slightly more dangerous. Again, I would say that it is "*physically obvious*" that m_1 and m_2 will not change. But now, since Δt is small, the change in M is also small, being about 1% of the unknown post-Newtonian terms. So, it is possible that these terms could be the major contributors. If they are, one would get a theoretical result which is different from what is observed.Now the only way that the post-Newtonian terms could be significant contributors is if they are very sharply varying functions of the orbital parameters. And, as a physicist, I would say that "*this is highly unlikely*".I simply can not believe that you can do a calculation and find such a functional dependence. And so, until someone actually does the calculation and shows that I am either right or wrong, I feel that I am quite secure of the standard result even for the short-term evolution.

This is the way that the old fashioned argument goes.

Discussion:

Schmidt: I will make a short comment. I do think that,basically, physics has to proceed in this way. But I also think that this is just the starting point. If one wants physics to be a rational enterprise --and this means if one wants physics to really go on-- one must realize that phrases like "I believe" or "it is physically obvious" are in fact indications that there is still some lack of understanding. Therefore,I think that, if we first analyse things this way, and if it works, then it does not mean that one has to stop there. It still remains an interesting task to make this framework compatible with the mathematical structure of the theory. And this is not a purely mathematical question because it is not like asking: solve this equation. Rather, in this game, there is still to exist a framework which would enable one to ask precise questions.And I think that the construction of such a framework is really part of understanding physics.

Schutz: I think I agree a little bit with what Bernd said. But you have to realize that if one wants to clean up *all* the things that are physically obvious, then you are getting in to things that are not just within general relativity but also astrophysics and in to difficult questions connected with the fact that the stars are not point masses. So, I think one has to be careful as to what the problem we want to solve is. We have to focus on one problem at a time because I dont think we can solve all problems at once.

Schmidt: But no one was demanding this.

Gary Horowitz: I have a question about your derivation.You restricted yourself to the near radiation zone. But it seems to me that almost all observations that we make take place in the far radiation zone. Is there a standard argument which says that this does not make any difference ?

Thorne: This, I discussed in detail in my own lectures.But basically, I restricted myself to the near zone because I did not want to deal with the difference between the Schwarzschild radius, the luminosity distance and so forth. Thus, it is the mathematical convenience. Also, in the real universe, there are a lot of lumps and I did not want to propagate through them. For the binary pulsar, it is quite adequate to pick the local wave zone which is 1% of the distance to the nearest star. Doing integrals in that region is quite adequate for radiation reaction.

Bill Unruh: Just one thing. On the last point about the functional behavior of M and S, I have some vague ideas as to how they might actually become sharply varying functions of the orbital parameters.

Thorne: I must say that this is a sufficiently serious weak point in the analysis that is is absolutely essential that somebody should go in and straighten it out.

Unruh: The analogy is to the charged particle orbiting around the black hole. One can look at the radiation reaction and compute the field that is sitting just at the location of the particle. And I can vaguely see waves traveling down, scattering off the black hole to the particle such that the phase is right so that you dont get a retardation but actually get the result that the back-reaction vector is in fact constant. So the particle may go around that orbit a long time and may then suddenly drop down to a new orbit so that the phase relation has flipped sign and the radiation reaction is much larger than what one might have expected.So, you may have orbits which are fairly stable over reasonable time periods and fairly unstable over reasonable time periods. And the particle may jump from one orbit to another. Ofcourse, this does not mean that this sort of behavior does occur. But it possibly casts doubt on the assumption that things are not sharply varying functions.

Thorne: A key thing about the short-term evolution is the following. The analysis itself, without anything else, tells us that there are two conserved quantities up through P^2N order. They are the M and the S that appear in the metric in the local wave zone. And we know that up to the Newtonian order, there are two more conserved quantities, a and e ,which are more intimately related to the orbit, in terms of which we chose to express M and S . In the question, "Are these things sharply varying functions of orbital parameters?", I meant orbital parameters which *are conserved quantities at some lower order.* I can well believe that if you use parameters which are not conserved at some lower order, you can quickly build terms in the calculation that look dangerous. But, it seems to me that the real mathematical issue here is that, if you express this in terms of quantities that are conserved at a lower order, such as a and e , then do you get sharply varying functions ? So, if I were to go about making this rigorous, that is the question to ask.

Schutz: But the phrase 'sharply varying' can be interpreted in two different senses. The first is in the limit in which all densities go to zero and everything becomes very very slow motion. The second is in the case of a *particular system* such as the binary pulsar where one worries about strong internal gravity. And such a system could put us sufficiently far from the limit that the functions for that system are degenerate. For such a system, one just takes the result as an act of faith.

Thibaut Damour: Highlights of the work of the Paris group.

I will use the convention that Kip asked the experimentalists to follow in their Round Table Discussion the other day and write the things that have already been accomplished with a red chalk and the incomplete parts as well as the drawbacks with a white chalk.

We embarked on this project because the binary pulsar is really one of the most impressive tests of general relativity and of finiteness of the velocity of propagation of the gravitational interaction. There has been a lot of thorough and beautiful experimental work and we wanted a theoretical framework which could match the standard set by the experimentalists. Kip told us about the conseved quantities, M and S. But at the lowest order, one is observing much more than that: one is also seeing the local dynamics of the orbit. So, we wanted the following:

- complete equations of motion; they simply did not exist in the literature before.
- the gravitational field both in the near and the far zone; other methods are applicable only in the near zone. We wanted the far-field as well because we wanted to show asymptotic flatness.(Acually, I should not use the term 'asymptotically flat'.But I will.)
- the no-incoming-radiation condition; this is different from the outgoing wave conditions used in the literature.
- an analysis which is applicable to compact objects, i.e., objects whose radius is so small that you have to take in to account strong gravitational fields.

These four points are written in red because this part of the program is completed.

Protests from the audiance

Well, I wrote this in red on purpose; we can have some discussion this way.Let me now go to drawbacks. I am aware of them,you know! These, I will write in white.

- errors are not estimated. This is the main drawback of all approaches. This approach looks better than others in many ways. But still, I cannot be more precise about errors.
- we do not have a complete matching of the sources to the field (although we have a good matching of the field to the sources.) What I showed in the lecture was that *if you assume* that everything is correct near the compact objects and then go far in the external field, you get boundary conditions for matching to a compact object that are sufficient for solving the problem. But the internal problem is not solved.
- $I^{\pm}$ have not been studied. From our explicit solution to the field equation, we would like to compute the equations of motion and see if one really gets well-defined $I^{\pm}$ as you go along the null geodesics of our metric (rather than those of the Minkowskian background) and if the no-incoming-radiation condition is satisfied on I^{-} .

This is all that I have to say.

Ashtekar: I think we are going to have a lot of discussion. But judging from the protests that were made during the "red part" of Thibaut's report, I feel that, if we had used a different convention and used the red chalk for statements that all the experts here agree on and white for statements on which there is still disagreement, then the colours on the summary table should have been reversed!

Discussion:

Kates: As I remember, in your first lecture you said that for the Schwarzschild perturbations, you could gauge away all the $l= 1$ solutions.This would mean that there are no solutions, not equivalent to gauge, of the Regge-Wheeler equations or for any other equations for the invariant Schwarzschild field. Now consider a term in the external meiric which goes like $rY_{1m}\, dT^2$. This is essentially an acceleration. I dont see how you can possibly rule out a perturbation which looks like this.

Damour: In the external field, you have a Fermi-Walker coordinate system.

Kates: Exactly. The point is that you would like to show that the black hole or the neutron star moves along some sort of a world-line which takes away this term. You can make it zero by putting the object on a world line. But you can perturb the *internal* schwarzschild solution by adding a term which goes like $\varepsilon z\, dT^2$ essentially.

Damour: Yes. That means you did not choose your internal coordinate system such that is is adapted to the object or to its external field.

Kates: That is right. You choose a coordinate system which is accelerated. But that is a choice of gauge. So, I dont see how your proof that the black hole follows a world line can be independent of gauge.

Damour: It is. You can change the gauge afterwards; not at this point. It would be nice to have a complete metric for the internal field and that can be done from our explicit expressions now. But that is part of the "internal-metric problem". And I did say that the work is incomplete in this respect.

Thorne: Basically, in the EIH method, the use of the surface integral guarantees that you wont have this problem. Damour does not use the surface integrals but his method is equivalent.

Kates : It guarantees that you dont have acceleration in the external field, or in the Schwarzschild part ?

Thorne: The EIH analysis guarantees that the particle moves along a geodesic of the external field which guatantees that, in the gauge where the acceleration is zero, the Fermi normal frame will correspond to the asymptotic rest-frame of the particle.

Unruh: But the particle doesn't move along the geodesic of the external field! For example, in this room, the particle reacts to the field right at that particle.And this includes contributions from the internal field as well.

Damour: Here, the external field is essentially the effective field.

Thorne: The radiation reaction pieces of the metric are also a part of the external field,if you think about the type of matching that goes on in this calculation.

Schutz: I would like to ask, not a technical question, but something more of a principle. The thing that most fascinated me about your lectures is the use of the analytical continuation method. You would agree with me that, in this method, once you have the solution, you have to check that the boundary conditions and the regularity conditions are satisfied before you are through. So I am not completely clear as to what checks have been performed or will be performed to verify that a)you have a solution to Einstein's equation; and, b) it satisfies sensible conditions.

Ashtekar: Let me amplify this comment. Normally, when one has differential equations in physics, one feeds in the appropriate boundary conditions in the process of obtaining the solution. Here, the situation is different. Thibaut and co-workers first take a fictitious source, solve the equation and then take a certain limit. At the end of the day, you do have a solution to the equations you are interested in. But since the boundary conditions were not fed-in, you have to verify that the solution you get is the physically sensible one. In Thibaut's lectures, there were remarks that the solution is unique in a certain sense. If so, one could presumably justify it. But I am not sure if the uniqueness statement is a conjecture or a claim. Also, what are the boundary conditions that the solution satisfies? Why are they physically reasonable ?

Damour: I will say what has been achieved. You have a metric which is a functional of two world-lines in Minkowski space and it satisfies the harmonic Einstein's equation and the harmonic gauge condition. So, it is a solution of Einstein's equation, which is a functional of two world lines.

Schmidt: Are the lines specified at this stage or not ?

Damour: Now they have to satisfy the equation of motion. What are the boundary conditions that the solution satisfies for some reasonable sources? The final solution is obtained by using retarded integrals along the past Minkowski cones. So, although it is not checked, it is very probable that Sommerfeld's no-incoming-radiation condition is satisfied. Near the world-lines, you can explicitly check that the field behaves like the Schwarzschild metric up to third order. In addition, there are terms of a very particular structure which depend on the companion mass. These terms disappear if the masses are infinitely separated and are less divergent at $r = 0$. The Uniqueness result would be established if one could show that if you have a solution like this, it matches to a compact object. That is, one has to construct explicitly a source which matches our solution.

Ashtekar: So the uniqueness result belongs to the "white part" ?

Damour: There was an in-between uniqueness result *in the perturbative sense*.

Ashtekar: Is that something established or it is something you would like to do?

Damour: It is established. But you make strong perturbative assumptions.

Schutz: I think of the problem as follows. There are two compact objects, say neutron stars, and the space-time is regular everywhere. And these lines, if they exist, are only vaguely defined, may be inside the objects. But you are talking about a view in which there is an exterior metric and your statements are valid in some asymptotic sense which, again, you haven't made clear to me. These lines are not the positions of the bodies since the bodies are extended. So, what do you mean by the lines satisfying the equation of motion ?

Damour: Operationally, the lines are defined by the metric itself. They are not defined as the centers of masses. If you want to know what material point corresponds to the line, you have to solve the source solution completely. Intuitively, near the object, the field is very nearly Schwarzschild. So, there is spherical symmetry. And you define the world-line to be the center of symmetry in the harmonic chart that you are using outside.

Walker: Let me say why I protested earlier against your second and third point in red. Paint any two worldlines in flat space. Then the first of your equations (the harmonic Einstein's equation) is identically satisfied by your metric. Then you have to adjust the world-lines such that the second equation (the harmonic condition) is satisfied. And now, the point is that to check asymptotic flatness, and also that there is no incoming radiation, you have to put in the information that is in those world lines. And that you dont have.

Damour: In the P^2N approximation, we have it. But if you ask me if we have an analytic solution all over Minkowski space, we dont.

Thorne: I am not understanding what it is that you dont have.

Damour: The metric is given as a function of the points in Minkowski space *and* as a functional of two world-lines. You have the metric only when you have fixed the world-lines. So, the behavior of $g_{ab}(x)$ as x goes to $I^{\pm}$ will depend upon the behavior of the world-lines in the infinite future and infinite past. So you want a good control on this behavior. You can not just assume that they are straight lines in the past; this has to follow from the equations of motion.

Walker: It is certainly possible to paint a couple of world-lines on Minkowski space which may not satisfy the second equation such that the metric which is determined by them has incoming radiation. Therefore, you have to look at the motion before you can make the second and the third claim in red.

Schutz: You use a flat-space retarded picture and it is not clear to me what that implies for the real space-time. But to be fair to you,I would like to say that the entire problem that we are discussing now is not a deficiancy of just your approach; it is shared by all methods which use no-incoming-radiation condition.

Damour: Yes. And this is the first time that there is enough information to address these questions.

Unruh: In solving the field equations, one sets up gauge conditions right in the begining. I wonder if it might not be possible to go the other way around and solve the general field equations without reference to any gauge condition and *then* find a suitable gauge that will simplify the subsequent calculations. For example, one can write the Schwarzschild solution in such a way that the linear term is infact the exact solution. What that suggests is that one should look for a gauge in which all the second and higher order terms drop away. I am fairly sure that you can not do this in general. But one may be able to get very very simple higher order equations by choosing the gauge *post-facto* rather than choosing it beforehand.

Damour: The problem is that, since the original equation is not hyperbolic, the solution may not exist if you dont impose gauge conditions in the begining.

Unruh: The solution of the usual equation, $\Box h$ = something, is simply the retarded integral.

Damour: No. If the equation is not hyperbolic, you have to satisfy integrability conditions. And this gives a strong restriction on the right hand side. But I agree that if you can solve the equation at each level, the post-facto gauge condition will simplify the calculations at the next level.

Jim Bardeen: I have a comment about $I^{\pm}$. The pulsar has been orbiting around only for a finite time and the existence of I^{-} really refers to the infinite past. So, I think these questions may be for mathematicians. I dont think they are questions of Physics.

Ashtekar: It is certainly an idealization to consider $I^{\pm}$. But you would have to replace these boundary conditions by some other plausible ones which refer only to finite time and show that they are satisfied, if you want to be more realistic. I agree that one should not get hung up on these particular conditions if better ones can be found. But the problem is to find them.

Doug Eardley: I have a question, I guess for everybody. Thibaut has shown that there is a conserved angular momentum at the P^2N order with some corrections to that due to gravitational radiation. On the other hand, we heard that at I there are intrinsic ambiguities in the definition of angular momentum due to supertranslations. Is it clear to anybody how these two facts are related ?

Schmidt: But Thibaut starts on a fixed Minkowski space. He is not investigating the issue of *changing* this Minkowski space. And once you have a fixed Minkowski space, you have the Poincaré group and you can do the usual things.

Eardley: But you would lose this Poincaré group at some stage in the perturbation expansion. And the question is if Thibaut has reached this stage yet.

Thorne: It seems to me that you do not need a fixed Minkowski background to get the angular momentum up to this order. There is really an experimental prescription to determine what it is; one can put in a gyroscope. The place where difficulties occur in the slow motion approximation --and I hope that the analysis at I will confirm this-- is where the asymptotic center of mass frame changes in response to the loss of linear momentum due to the gravitational radiation.These changes cause difficulties about the point about which you want to define angular momentum.These difficulties will occur at some higher order than what Thibaut is working at.

Kates: We found logarithmic terms in $1/c$ in the equations of motion at the P^2N order. Can you check your second, i.e. G^2, iteration to see if those terms arise ? If they do, do you get infinities ?

Damour: They dont appear at the order we looked at. But they could appear at higher orders. It is a part of what I want to check in the estimation of errors. But you wont get infinities. At most, you would get logarithm of something that depends on how long the system stays bound.

Bernard Schutz: A statistical approach to radiation reaction.

I am glad that Jim Bardeen made the remark that questions about I do not necessarily belong to the domain of physics. Because of this, I dont have to begin as everyone else does, that is, by criticizing others. Toshi Futamasse sketched, in his talk, how one gets the quadrupole formula using our approach to the equations of motion. I will therefore restrict myself to points of principle.

The first thing is motivation. Really, all I wanted was the quadrupole formula! I did *not* want to look at the gravitational waves coming from the pulsars. I only wanted the radiation reaction and the formula for $\dot{P}$.

Two things about the "standard" approach bothered me. The first is that, in some derivations, infinite integrals occur even at orders that one might have thought to be important. I wanted to understand why a nice theory like general relativity led to such strange things. The second thing is that I never really understood radiation reaction. We are told that the binary system reacts to the radiation that it gives off. But you can not really say how much gravitational radiation is given off until you are way out in the wave zone. And, by that time, the stars have done whatever they do in reaction to the emission. This picture seems strange to me. The two bodies are creating some *local* field and are responding to that field. So, I thought that there should be an essentially local way of doing this problem. If it turns out that the reaction is accompanied by radiation going out to infinity, it would be nice; it would mean that Einstein's theory is conservative. But I did not want to *use* this conservative nature of the theory or a global approach because all I wanted was to know what was going on near the bodies.

In electrodynamics, one uses retarded integrals. It is pretty much considered a law of Nature. And, in Minkowski space, it is possible to consider it as a law (although even here it is not a verifiable law.) But when relativists tried to apply this thinking to general relativity, they ran in to trouble because they could not have all the properties of retarded radiation. First of all, the condition could be formulated only in the asymptotically flat space-times where one can hopefully get I . Even in this case, the requirement that there be no incoming radiation at I^- does not imply that there is only outgoing radiation at I^+ ; there is back-scattering. So, the nice symmetry of the retarded fields in Minkowski space can not be brought over to general relativity. Moreover, we only have one space-time and it does not have a I^-; it has a cosmological singularity instead. So, it can not be maintained that retarded potentials or their generalizations *must* be used in general relativity in radiation reaction problems. I am not saying that it is wrong to do that. But it is an idealization. And it has a lot of drawbacks because of global problems. Some of the criticisms of Thibaut's work are deeply rooted in the difficulty in solving global problems in general relativity. They are interesting problems and I would not say that he should stop working on them. But these problems are not particularly related to the formula for $\dot{P}$. That formula is a *local* formula. What should replace this idealization then ? Well, the binary pulsar is sitting in a bath of gravitational radiation. We all have the feeling that this radiation is random and is hitting the pulsar from all directions. (In fact, it is this feeling that justifies the application of no-incoming-radiation condition to the binary pulsar.) So, it seemed to me that one can get rid of all global problems by using the idea of averaging right from the start. Thus, the basic idea is to allow the radiation to come in all possible ways and obtain, not an exact evolution of the binary pulsar, but *an expected evolution of an ensemble of binary pulsars*. More precisely, the idea is the following. From observations, we can deduce the positions and velocities of the two bodies at an instant of time. But we do not know anything about the free part of the gravitational field at the initial instant. One way to face this problem is to say that there should be no incoming radiation. My way is to allow radiation but average over the free part of the gravitational field (i.e. free-data.) Of course, I am not trying to cover any physics by just saying that one should average; I can get any answer I want by averaging appropriately. But the point is that a very simple prescription of averaging gives the experimental result: one just requires that the ensemble-mean of the free-data should vanish at the initial instant of time.

Another important point is that if you want an approximation which is valid in the Newtonian limit, the approximation can not be uniform over all of space-time. For, if we let the binary pulsar go, ultimately the stars would spiral together and collide so that the situation would be very far from that predicted by Newtonian theory in which the stars can just go around forever. So, any approximation to such a system is not uniform in time. Consequently, for a particular system, I want to make predictions only for a finite time. Thus, I have only to consider a finite region to specify the initial data. This is where I do the averaging. But, as I make the system weaker and weaker and go towards the Newtonian limit, the time for which I can predict becomes longer and longer. This is the basis of what Toshi described. Let me recall that we can show that the Newtonian theory is an asymptotic approximation to general relativity. It seems that no one has bothered to show the sense in which it is an asymptotic approximation before. Finally we can get a formula for $\dot{P}$ and show that it is an asymptotic approximation to the period change of the binary pulsar.

Now, to the negative side. There are some philosophical objections against the averaging idea. Secondly, the averaging that we do is rather naive. Finally, as in other methods, the errors are not estimated. There are two kinds of errors. Asymptotic approximation means that I can always choose a system weak enough so that my Newtonian approximations are good to whatever accuracy you want to choose. But I should be permitted to make the system weakly relativistic in that sense. But the binary pulsar is just one system and you can not apply a limiting procedure to a single system. This is the first source of errors. The other is that the ensemble variance does matter. The size of the radiation that I take here is important. So, we have to check this using the observed stochastic backgrounds and things like that. But I should say that no one has come as close to estimating errors so far. We *can* write down the error terms. The estimates are, however, too complicated at the moment.

Discussion:

Unruh: Your averaging is done at a particular time. Doesn't this imply that the situation is time-symmetric? If so, does it mean that the pulsar evolves from some compact system in the past?

Schutz: Yes and no. We are familiar with the same paradox in statistical mechanics. In a naive picture, if you observe a thermodynamic system which is not in equilibrium and has an absurdly low entropy, then the most probable thing is that you observed a fluctuation; the entropy is increasing both forward and backward in time. That is a statistical result. And the same thing will be true here. To be more philosophical, one is asking only for future predictions. That is, one is asking: If you have this amount of information now, what is the sensible prediction for future? One is not asking for past-evolution. If you dont like the physical underpinning of this, then you can use any of the other approaches with their drawbacks.What averaging gets you,is a local problem.

Kates: You didn't mention in your list of drawbacks the issue of compact objects.It seems to me that for a compact object such as the binary pulsar, the post-Newtonian expansion is not really valid.Thibaut's work as well as the three zone matching have an advantage in this respect. But I also think that compact objects could be incorporated in your scheme with some more work.

Schutz: I completely agree. It is entirely possible that our error terms are bigger than those in other approaches.

Several participants: Eventually, someone is going to have to look at what is happening to the fluid motion, the pressure etc. In the post-Newtonian discussions, where pressure and fluid velocities are small, people have looked at these things for perfect fluids. But for compact objects, no one has really discussed this problem. Numerical relativity may be the only way to do it.

Schutz: That's right. As Jim said, there is physics and there is mathematics. I am convinced from all the work that has been done so far that, for radiation reaction, the physics is okay. So, the important issues are not the mathematical issues in the relativity theory, but issues like the ones you raised.

William Shaw: I think there have been at least three unfair attacks on I and mathematics ! The I -structure is guaranteed to exist only in those situations which *are* physically interesting. If the system was radiating intensely for infinite time, the properties of I would be destroyed and you wont be able to use even the mathematics of I . So, I is giving sensible boundary conditions.

Schutz: I agree.

Bardeen: The point is that, for our universe, I does not exist.

Ashtekar:That point is not significant. By the same argument you can throw away the entire scattering theory in quantum mechanics and high energy physics. We also dont have a Minkowski space in our universe! I is certainly an idealization. The notion of isolated systems is an idealization. And it is not peculiar to general relativity. It is made in other branches of physics too.

Thorne: I dont understand the point that errors are not estimated. Again, I am just a poor physicist. But I would have said that the errors are of the order of 10^{-6}, i.e., going up one more order in that expansion. And, I would have thought that I could even calculate the post-Newtonian corrections to this, if you permit me that certain things at higher order are not sharply varying functions.

Schutz: Wait. There is more to it. In a different theory of gravity, that estimate would be all wrong. It is only the equivalence principle that allows us to say that we can forget about the 10^{-1} factor inside the neutron star.

Thorne: I saying that, I meant to assume the equivalence principle. I think one *could* calculate the next order corrections to this somewhat easily if you permit the leaps of faith that I made at the end of my talk.So, why do you say that the errors are not estimated ?

Walker: You can not write inequalities.

Damour: Yes. The errors would be of the order of magnitude Kip said. It is a matter of rogour only.

Horowitz: In the light of this question of error estimates, I might just mention that there is now work going on with colleagues in which one gets an *exact*formula for the energy that is radiated,in terms of sources. It is an exact formula for solutions to Einstein's equation with sources. One would be able to use it to derive an approximate formula using any approximation technique you choose. Since one would start from a formula valid in the exact theory, it is,at least in principle, easy to estimate the errors. The exact formula is derived using the Witten spinors and the arguments that went in to the positive energy theorems.

Concluding remarks:

I hope that the session served its purpose.As an outsider, I can say for myself that now I have a much better feeling for the subtleties involved in the two approaches. The two approaches are indeed very complimentary. The Paris group emphasizes the post-Minkowski approximation and uses what may be called global methods. In particular, they wish to impose the no-incoming-radiation condition. The Cardiff group, on the other hand, follows the post-Newtonian scheme and uses local methods. In particular, they wish to average out the free-data for gravitational waves at an initial instant of time and then let the system go. The Paris group is interested in the exact evolution of an isolated binary system, while the Cardiff group analyses the expected evolution of an ensemble of binary systems. It is indeed very interesting to see that such diverse methods address the same physical problem.

Both approaches have some puzzling aspects, primarily, I suppose, because both methods are somewhat unconventional. In the Paris work, the use of analytical continuation and Riesz functions makes the analysis somewhat mysterious. Why should this mathematical technique of replacing the physical sources by complex tensor fields, solving the problem for these fields and then taking analytic continuation,yield a physically sensible answer to such a complicated problem? How does this method "know" about the physical boundary conditions? The final solution has an unique asymptotic expansion near the world-lines. For non-rotating sources, the expected approximate spherical symmetry near the world-lines implies that the solution should resemble the Schwarzschild metric up to some order, say in the expansion in r . And the analytic continuation method fulfils this expectation in a precise sense. But for rotating sources, one would expect the uniqueness to fail; apriori, even in low orders in expansion, the differences between various rotating sources should show up. Yet, analytical continuation apparently leads to an unique answer! What is the distinguished axi-symmetric metric approached asymptotically by this solution? Is it the Kerr metric? That would be very interesting. But it may also mean that the method is geared to black holes and not to general neutron stars.In the Cardiff approach, a special status is given to the "initial" time at which the ensemble is so to say "prepared". For example, it is only at this initial instant that the average value of the free-data vanishes. This special status also seems a bit mysterious. One can of course say that the same problem arises also in other applications of statistical mechanics. But that hardly removes the mystery. Secondly, although the initial goal in this approach was somewhat limited, one would like to know if it can now be made more complete, perhaps even as complete as the Paris work.

These questions, I feel, are interesting in their own right. I agree that their analysis can hardly change the status of the formula for $\dot{P}$. But, having put in so much effort to construct a conceptual framework, it seems to me that one should not be satisfied just with a formula, however significant it may be. As is often the case, the insights that one may gain by answering such questions may well be of crucial help elsewhere, not just in general relativity but also in other branches of mathematical physics.

Finally, let me say that there are of course other groups which are working, or have worked, extensively on equations of motion. Not everything that is interesting could be included in the program today partly because of time limitation and partly because not all groups are represented at this School. So, the discussion is far from being exhaustive.

GAUGE AND RADIATION CONDITIONS IN NUMERICAL RELATIVITY

James M. Bardeen

Physics Department FM-15
University of Washington
Seattle, Washington 98195
U.S.A.

Gauge conditions suitable for numerical calculations of emission of gravitational radiation by compact sources are explored, with particular emphasis on algebraic conditions which simplify the structure of the Einstein equations. The expansion of the radiation field in powers of r^{-1} is compared in different gauges, and formulas for outgoing wave boundary conditions and asymptotic energy flux in the waves are obtained in the radial gauge which are accurate through order r^{-2}.

INTRODUCTION

The numerical calculation of the emission of gravitational radiation from collapsing stars or other highly dynamical strong field configurations in general relativity is a difficult task. For the asymptotically flat systems I will be considering here, the existence of gravitational radiation requires at least two spatial degrees of freedom, so there are severe practical constraints on the number of grid points in any one spatial direction. The assumption of axisymmetry, which seems necessary to make the problem manageable numerically at the current state of the art, means that the gravitational radiation will carry off only a rather small fraction of the mass of the system and that in the near zone and particularly in the interior of the star the longitudinal dynamics of the collapse will dominate what eventually turns into gravitational waves in the wave zone. Particular care, by means of gauge conditions and choice of variables, must be taken to try to separate as much as possible the radiative from the longitudinal degrees of freedom, and to do so in a way which is numerically feasible. Furthermore, the numerical grid will not extend far into the wave zone, so how the wave amplitude and energy flux is estimated at the edge of the grid and how the outgoing radiation condition is imposed are rather delicate questions.

A noteworthy previous attempt at assessing various approaches to gauge and radiation conditions is that of L. Smarr at the 1978 Battelle Symposium.[1] Since then there have been some new ideas on how to formulate the equations (e.g., by Nakamura et al[2] and by Bardeen and Piran[3]). I will briefly discuss the advantages and disadvantages of some of the new and old gauge conditions as I see them, using as a foil the pure quadrupole wave solution of the linearized Einstein equations recently published by Teukolsky[4]. Teukolsky's solution is in the transverse-traceless gauge, but can easily be transformed into the linearized versions of the various numerically useful gauges.

The radial gauge advocated by Bardeen and Piran[3] lends itself to analytic exploration of the asymptotic behavior of radiation, since it is easy to expand systematically in spherical harmonics. Expressions are derived in this gauge for the energy flux and amplitude of the radiation as a function of polar angle for an axisymmetric system on the basis of information about the metric functions at a finite radius, accurate through terms of order r^{-2} in a wave zone expansion.

Combining these expressions gives an outgoing wave boundary condition which can be applied at a finite radius.

The framework in which I will discuss gauge conditions is the 3 + 1 approach to the Einstein equations. The spacetime gauge is determined by a combination of a hypersurface condition and a spatial gauge condition. The hypersurface condition, which determines the lapse function α, usually consists of a condition on the extrinsic geometry of the constant-time hypersurface, i.e., on the extrinsic curvature tensor K_{ij}. The maximal hypersurface condition, $\mathrm{Tr}K \equiv K^i{}_i = 0$, is widely known for simplifying the initial value problem and for its singularity-avoidance properties.[6] The other hypersurface condition considered here is the polar hypersurface condition, $K^\theta{}_\theta + K^\phi{}_\phi = 0$, which may have certain advantages in the exterior of a collapsing star.[3]

The three spatial gauge conditions are some combination of conditions on the shift vector β^i and on the spatial metric γ_{ij}. The spatial coordinates will be topologically spherical polar coordinates r, θ, ϕ, since it is these coordinates which are suitable for discussing approach to asympotic flatness at large distances from a compact source (collapsing star or whatever).

When three-covariant equations are written, it is with the understanding that indices are raised and lowered with the spatial metric γ_{ij} and that D_i is the covariant derivative with respect to γ_{ij} in the constant-time hypersurface.

SPECIFIC SPATIAL GAUGE CONDITIONS

The Eulerian gauge, $\beta^i = 0$, has been used in the Eppley-Smarr[7] colliding black hole calculation and in the Nakamura, et al[8] calculation of the collapse of rotating stars. As long as the hypersurfaces have a regular intrinsic and extrinsic geometry no spatial coordinate singularity will develop. However, there is no simplification of the spatial metric, except by a high degree of symmetry, and a large coordinate shear may arise, particularly if there are strong vortical motions in the matter.

The minimal distortion gauge condition $D_j\, \partial_t(\tilde{\gamma}^{ij}) = 0$, where $\tilde{\gamma}_{ij} \equiv \gamma_{ij}/(\det \gamma)^{1/3}$, has been proposed as a radiation gauge by Smarr and York[9]. The gauge is implemented by a vector elliptic equation for the shift vector,

$$\Delta\beta^i + \frac{1}{3} D^i(D_\ell\beta^\ell) + R^i{}_\ell\beta^\ell = -2\alpha j^i - 2(K^{i\ell} - \frac{1}{3}\gamma^{i\ell}K)\, D_\ell\alpha \,. \qquad (1)$$

Here j^i is the momentum density of the matter in the hypersurface. In a sense this gauge eliminates "gauge waves" as much as possible, and allows little coordinate shear. It reduces to the transverse-traceless gauge in the linearized theory. Unfortunately, in the absence of a high degree of symmetry the practical difficulties of working with an unconstrained γ_{ij} and the vector elliptic equation seem prohibitive.

Both of the above gauges have the problem that the spatial coordinates at any one time depend on an initial choice of spatial coordinates and on the past history of the solution. This may make interpretation of solutions and comparison of different solutions difficult.

Spatial gauge conditions which consist of algebraic conditions on the form of the spatial metric tensor can lead to considerable simplification of the spatial Ricci tensor R_{ij} and thus to important practical advantages in numerical calculations. In view of the focus on gravitational waves which for the most part will propagate radially, begin by setting

$$\gamma_{r\theta} = \gamma_{r\phi} = 0. \qquad (2)$$

Represent the spatial line element as

$$d\ell^2 = \psi^4[A^2dr^2 + r^2B^{-2}d\theta^2 + r^2B^2(\sin\theta d\phi + \xi d\theta)^2]. \tag{3}$$

I will assume axisymmetry, so the four remaining metric functions ψ, A, B, ξ, are functions of time t, r, and $x \equiv \cos\theta$. This form explicitly separates out what are the asymptotic wave amplitudes, $\eta \equiv B^2 - 1$ and ξ.

The third algebraic gauge condition is constrained by the need to preserve regularity of the spatial coordinates. Consider conditions of the form

$$A = \psi^p B^q. \tag{4}$$

Local flatness on the polar axis implies $B = 1$ at $x = \pm 1$ for all r. Local and asymptotic flatness imply $A = 1$ and $r = 0$ and $A \to 1$ as $r \to \infty$. In general $\psi(r = 0)$ is not equal to $\psi(r \to \infty)$, so in Eq. (4) p must equal zero.

Bardeen and Piran[3] show that the shift vector is regular at $r = 0$, so initially regular spatial coordinates remain regular, only if $q = -1$. This leads to the <u>isothermal gauge</u>, which has been used by Smarr and Wilson[10] for axisymmetric non-rotating collapse. In this gauge the equations for the shift vector and for ψ (from the Hamiltonian constraint) are elliptic and relatively time consuming in numerical calculations.

The other possibility is to set $\psi = 1$ everywhere. Then A and B are independent metric functions. This is the <u>radial gauge</u>. The proper area in a constant-r two-surface is just $r^2\sin\theta d\theta d\phi$. Now, as is discussed in detail in Ref. 3, the shift vector and "non-dynamical" metric function (here A) are found from parabolic equations, which are amenable to efficient numerical solution. Both are outward-parabolic, with initial conditions at $r = 0$ determined by regularity. The radial gauge is free of coordinate singularity only as long as the area of constant-r two-spheres increases monotonically outward, and requires Euclidean or $S^2 \times R$ topology for the hypersurfaces. In collapsing star calculations both conditions will be satisfied initially. While the radial gauge may in principle become singular at a finite coordinate time on maximal hypersurfaces, it requires very special conditions, and it seems plausible that polar hypersurfaces will never get into trouble. The radial gauge cannot handle colliding black holes, since the initial data violate the topology restriction.

GAUGE TRANSFORMATIONS FROM THE TEUKOLSKY QUADRUPOLE WAVE SOLUTION

To see how radially propagating gravitational waves look in the above gauges, consider the exact solution of the linearized Einstein equations for a radially propagating pure quadrupole wave obtained by Teukolsky.[4] Teukolsky's solution is in the transverse-traceless gauge, but the gauge transformations to the four gauges mentioned above are easy to find. The transverse-traceless gauge has $\alpha = \beta^i = 0$. Let

$$\gamma_{ij} = f_{ij} + h_{ij}, \tag{5}$$

where f_{ij} is the flat-space metric in spherical polar coordinates. The even-parity axisymmetric version of Teukolsky's solution has

$$h_{rr} = 2UP_2(x), \tag{6a}$$

$$r^{-1}h_{r\theta} = -V\sin\theta\, dP_2/dx, \tag{6b}$$

$$r^{-2}h_{\theta\theta} = W(1 - x^2)\, d^2P_2/dx^2 - U, \tag{6c}$$

$$(r\sin\theta)^{-2}h_{\phi\phi} = -W(1 - x^2)d^2P_2/dx^2 + U(1 - 2P_2(x)), \tag{6d}$$

where

$$W = \frac{1}{4}[r^{-1}F^{(4)} + 2r^{-2}F^{(3)} + 9r^{-3}F^{(2)} + 21r^{-4}F^{(1)} + 21r^{-5}F], \tag{7a}$$

$$V = -[r^{-2}F^{(3)} + 3r^{-3}F^{(2)} + 6r^{-4}F^{(1)} + 6r^{-5}F], \tag{7b}$$

$$U = 3[r^{-3}F^{(2)} + 3r^{-4}F^{(1)} + 3r^{-5}F], \tag{7c}$$

and

$$F = F(u) \equiv F(t-r) \quad , \tag{8a}$$

$$F^{(n)} = d^n F/du^n \quad , \tag{8b}$$

for an arbitrary $F(u)$. The even-parity "wave amplitude" corresponding to the metric function η in Eq. (3) is

$$\eta = \frac{1}{2}(h^{\phi}{}_{\phi} - h^{\theta}{}_{\theta})$$
$$= -\frac{1}{4}[r^{-1}F^{(4)}+2r^{-2}F^{(3)}-9r^{-3}F^{(2)}+3r^{-4}F^{(1)}+3r^{-5}F](1-x^2)d^2P_2/dx^2 \ . \tag{9}$$

A general gauge transformation is generated by a time displacement ε^t and a spatial displacement ε^i. The induced changes in the metric, to first order, are

$$\delta h_{ij} = D_i\varepsilon_j + D_j\varepsilon_i \tag{10a}$$

$$\delta\beta_i = \varepsilon^t{}_{,i} - \varepsilon_{i,t} \tag{10b}$$

$$\delta\alpha = \varepsilon^t{}_{,t} \ . \tag{10c}$$

The hypersurface condition provides an equation for ε^t. The maximal hypersurface condition, Tr $K = 0$, gives

$$\Delta\alpha = \Delta\,\varepsilon^t{}_{,t} = 0 \ . \tag{11}$$

The most general solution for ε^t which satisfies $\varepsilon^t \to 0$ as $r \to \infty$ is

$$\varepsilon^t = r^{-1}\dot{a}_0 + r^{-3}\dot{a}_2P_2(x) \ , \tag{12}$$

where a_0 and a_2 are unknown functions of time and, e.g., $\dot{a} \equiv da_0/dt$. In a complete solution a_0 and a_2 would be determined by regularity conditions at $r = 0$, but the Teukolsky solution only applies outside the source of the gravitational waves and in itself gives no information about $a_0(t)$ and $a_2(t)$.

The equation for the lapse function implied by the polar hypersurface condition is discussed in Ref. 3. Here I just give the linearized equation for ε^t,

$$2r\varepsilon^t{}_{,r} + [(1-x^2)\varepsilon^t{}_{,x}]_{,x} = r^2[UP_2(x)]_{,t} \ . \tag{13}$$

The solution with $\varepsilon^t \to 0$ as $r \to \infty$ is <u>unique</u>,

$$\varepsilon^t = [-\frac{3}{2}r^{-2}F^{(2)}+3r^{-3}F^{(1)}+o(r^{-4})]P_2(x), \tag{14}$$

without any knowledge of the source distribution at small r.

Given ε^t, the lapse function follows from Eq. (10c). Before going any further, it should be noted that the non-radiative quadrupole contributions to α and the spatial metric are of order r^{-3}. A physically static exterior solution will in general have $F^{(2)} \neq 0$, and therefore $F^{(1)}$ and F will necessarily depend on time. This is a reflection of the well-known fact in the context of plane gravitational waves that the transverse-traceless gauge condition can only be implemented for non-zero frequencies.

The solution for the ε^i associated with a given spatial gauge condition will depend on the hypersurface condition, since they are coupled through Eq. (10b). I will just quote the results for ε^i and the <u>change</u> in the "wave amplitude" η for each of the four spatial gauge conditions and two hypersurface conditions considered here.

A) Eulerian Gauge.

a) Maximal Hypersurfaces.

$$\varepsilon^r = -r^{-2}a_0 - 3r^{-4}a_2P_2(x) \quad , \tag{13a}$$

$$\varepsilon^\theta/\sin\theta = -r^{-5}a_2dP_2/dx \quad , \tag{13b}$$

$$\delta\eta \;=\; -\,r^{-5}a_2(1-x^2)d^2P_2/dx^2 \;. \tag{13c}$$

b) Polar Hypersurfaces.

$$\varepsilon^r = [\tfrac{3}{2}\,r^{-2}F^{(2)}+O(r^{-4})]P_2(x) \;, \tag{14a}$$

$$\varepsilon^\theta/\sin\theta = [\tfrac{3}{2}\,r^{-4}F^{(1)}-3r^{-5}F+O(r^{-6})]dP_2/dx \;, \tag{14b}$$

$$\delta\eta = [\tfrac{3}{2}\,r^{-4}F^{(1)}-3r^{-5}F+O(r^{-6})](1-x^2)d^2P_2/dx \;. \tag{14c}$$

B) Minimal Distortion Gauge. Solve Eq. (1) for β^i; the solution contains unknown functions of time $b_0(t)$ and $b_2(t)$ because one cannot apply the boundary condition at $r=0$:

$$\beta^r = r^{-2}\dot{b}_0 + 3r^{-4}\dot{b}_2P_2(x) \;, \tag{15a}$$

$$\beta^\theta/\sin\theta = r^{-5}\dot{b}_2\; dP_2/dx \;. \tag{15b}$$

The solutions for ε^r, $\varepsilon^\theta/\sin\theta$, and $\delta\eta$ on maximal hypersurfaces are the same as Eqs. (13) if a_0 and a_2 are replaced by (a_0+b_0) and (a_2+b_2), respectively. On polar hypersurfaces the leading terms are the same as Eqs. (14).

C) Isothermal Gauge. Require $h_{r\theta}=0$, $h_{\theta\theta}=r^2h_{rr}$. For both hypersurface conditions

$$\begin{aligned}\varepsilon^r/r = {} & [b_0+\tfrac{1}{2}r^{-2}b_2-\tfrac{1}{4}\,r^{-2}F^{(3)}+O(r^{-4})]P_0\\ & +[-2r^{-2}b_2+\tfrac{1}{4}\,r^{-2}F^{(3)}+O(r^{-4})]P_2(x) \;,\end{aligned} \tag{16a}$$

$$\varepsilon^\theta/\sin\theta = [r^{-2}b_2+\tfrac{3}{4}\,r^{-3}F^{(2)}+\tfrac{3}{4}\,r^{-4}F^{(1)}+O(r^{-5})]dP_2/dx \tag{16b}$$

$$\delta\eta = [r^{-2}b_2+\tfrac{3}{4}\,r^{-3}F^{(2)}+\tfrac{3}{4}\,r^{-4}F^{(1)}+O(r^{-5})](1-x^2)d^2P_2/dx^2 \;. \tag{16c}$$

The unknown functions $b_0(t)$ and $b_2(t)$ (not the same as b_0 and b_2 in Eqs. 15) are again present because the Teukolsky solution does not extend to $r=0$.

D) Radial Gauge. Require $h_{r\theta}=0$, $h_{\phi\phi}+\sin^2\theta h_{\theta\theta}=0$. The parabolic equation for $\varepsilon^\theta/\sin\theta$ is integrated outward, so there is an unknown function $b_2(t)$ which carries information about the boundary condition at $r=0$. For both hypersurface conditions.

$$\varepsilon^r/r = [-3r^{-3}b_2-\tfrac{3}{2}\,r^{-3}F^{(2)}+O(r^{-5})]P_2(x) \;, \tag{17a}$$

$$\varepsilon^\theta/\sin\theta = [r^{-3}b_2 + r^{-3}F^{(2)}+\tfrac{3}{2}\,r^{-4}F^{(1)}+O(r^{-5})]dP_2/dx \;, \tag{17b}$$

$$\delta\eta = [r^{-3}b_2+r^{-3}F^{(2)}+\tfrac{3}{2}\,r^{-4}F^{(1)}+O(r^{-5})](1-x^2)d^2P_2/dx^2 \;. \tag{17c}$$

The leading term in η, of order r^{-1} (see Eq. 9), is gauge-invariant, and is the asymptotic wave amplitude as $r\to\infty$. However, in a numerical calculation one is unable to calculate η very far into the wave zone, so terms higher order in r^{-1} are likely to confuse attempts to make the extrapolation to future null infinity. The terms present in Eq. (9) all involve the same function of retarded time, so in principle one could try to disentangle $F(u)$ from data at finite r to rather high accuracy. The Eulerian and minimal distortion gauges modify η in almost the same way, and on either maximal or polar hypersurfaces are quite close to the transverse-traceless gauge. Of the two, the Eulerian gauge is more practical in numerical calculations. Still, there are good reasons to consider one of the two algebraic gauge conditions. In both there are non-radiative terms in η with globally determined coefficients which cannot be directly related to the asymptotic wave amplitude, a term of order r^{-2} for the isothermal gauge and of order r^{-3} for the radial gauge. The radial gauge has the advantage that the r^{-2}

term in η is guaranteed to be the same as in the transverse-traceless gauge and is available to help find the asymptotic wave amplitude.

So far I have ignored the odd-parity gravitational waves, which given axisymmetry show up in the metric function ξ in Eq. (3). In the linearized theory the odd-parity axisymmetric waves are unaffected by gauge transformations, and one can just look up in the form of these waves in Teukolsky's paper.[4]

ASYMPTOTIC WAVE FORMS AND ENERGY FLUXES

The physical information about the gravitational radiation one would like to extract from a numerical calculation are the asymptotic waveforms as functions of retarded time and direction of emission. For the two independent polarizations, and assuming axisymmetry, these are

$$(r\eta)_\infty \equiv \lim_{r\to\infty} (r\eta)\Big|_{\text{fixed } u,x} \tag{18a}$$

and

$$(r\xi)_\infty \equiv \lim_{r\to\infty} (r\xi)\Big|_{\text{fixed } u,x} \quad . \tag{18b}$$

If these are known, the asymptotic energy flux in gravitation waves is given, as a function of direction, by

$$P^r = T^{or} = (16\pi r^2)^{-1} < [\frac{\partial}{\partial\mu} (r\eta)_\infty]^2 + [\frac{\partial}{\partial\mu} (r\xi)_\infty]^2 > \quad , \tag{19}$$

where the angle brackets denote a time average.

Smarr[1] discusses various formulas which in some sense attempt to measure a "local" energy flux at the edge of the numerical grid. These formulas can be covariant "curvature" formulas which are gauge-invariant but do not directly give an energy flux, or "connection" formulas which do give an energy flux but are only asymptotically gauge-invariant. However, all of these formulas are really physically meaningful only if the edge of the grid is at a large enough radius that the asymptotic terms are dominant. the very notion of a local energy flux is physically ambiguous in general relativity.

The approach I favor is to use the known asymptotic behavior of the metric functions in the gauge one is working in to make the best possible estimate of the asymptotic wave amplitudes defined by Eqs. (18) from the data one has available at a finite radius. The procedure may be gauge-dependent, but the final result is not (except for errors in the extrapolation). The extrapolation can be made more easily in some gauges than others. In the last section the radial gauge was shown to have an advantage over the isothermal gauge in this regard.

As an example, consider in the radial gauge linearized perturbations about a spherically symmetric vacuum background on maximal or polar hypersurfaces. The perturbations will be allowed to have an arbitrary dependence on polar angle, but will be still taken as axisymmetric.

The background has

$$A = (1 - 2M/r + c^2 r^{-4})^{-\frac{1}{2}} \quad , \tag{20a}$$

$$\alpha = A^{-1} [1 + \dot{c} \int_\infty^r A(y)^3 \, y^{-2} dy] \quad , \tag{20b}$$

$$\beta^r = r^{-2} c \, \alpha \; ,$$

$$K^r{}_r = -2K^\theta{}_\theta = -2K^\phi{}_\phi = 2c/r^3 \quad . \tag{20c}$$

The unknown function c(t) reflects the lack of knowledge about how regularity at $r = 0$ fixes the maximal slicing. On polar hypersurfaces $c = 0$, and the background is the Schwarzschild metric. The background retarded time is

$$u = t - \int^{r}(1 - 2M/y)^{-1}dy + c\int_{\infty}^{r} A(y)(1 - 2M/y)^{-1}y^{-2}dy \, . \tag{21}$$

When the Einstein equations in the radial gauge[3] are linearized in axisymmetric, but not spherically symmetric, perturbations away from this background a significant advantage of the radial gauge becomes manifest. The various metric functions and other variables have straightforward expansions in Legendre polynomials, the axisymmetric spherical harmonics. For instance, η, ξ, $K_+ = \frac{1}{2}(K^{\phi}{}_{\phi} - K^{\theta}{}_{\theta})$, $K_- = (r^2\sin\theta)^{-1}K_{\theta\phi}$ all go as $(1 - x^2)d^2P_\ell/dx^2$, while δA goes as $P_\ell(x)$, and $G = \beta^{\theta}/\sin\theta$ goes as dP_ℓ/dx. The general retarded solution through order r^{-2} in an asymptotic expansion in powers of r^{-1} is fairly straightforward to find. All I will give here is the result for the metric functions most directly representing the gravitational waves. The "even-parity" wave amplitude is

$$\eta \cong (1 - x^2) \sum_{\ell=2}^{\infty} d^2P_\ell/dx^2 \left[r^{-1}dH_\ell^+/du + \tfrac{1}{2}(\ell - 1)(\ell + 2)r^{-2}H_\ell^+(u) + O(\ln r/r^3)\right]. \tag{22}$$

The solution for ξ has exactly the same form, but with independent functions of retarded time $H_\ell^-(u)$ in place of the $H_\ell^+(u)$. If the system is symmetric about the equatorial plane only even ℓ appear in the expression for η and only odd ℓ in the expression for ξ.

To find the asymptotic energy flux as given by Eq. (19), we need

$$\frac{\partial}{\partial u}(r\eta)_\infty = (1 - x^2) \sum_{\ell=2}^{\infty} (d^2P_\ell/dx^2)(d^2H_\ell^+/du^2) \tag{23}$$

and similarly for ξ. If η is only known on a numerical grid, it may be awkward to evaluate Eq. (23) directly from Eq. (22). The identity

$$(\ell - 1)(\ell + 2)d^2P_\ell/dx^2 = -\left[(1 - x^2)\frac{\partial^2}{\partial x^2} - 6x\frac{\partial}{\partial x} - 4\right] d^2P_\ell/dx^2 \tag{24}$$

and expressions for $\partial\eta/\partial t$ and $\partial\eta/\partial r$ obtained from Eq. (22) can be used to write

$$\frac{\partial}{\partial u}(r\eta)_\infty \cong (\alpha A)^{-1}r\,\partial\eta/\partial t - 2\eta + \tfrac{1}{2}(1 - x^2)\left[(1 - x^2)\frac{\partial^2}{\partial x^2} - 6x\frac{\partial}{\partial x}\right]\left[\eta/(1 - x^2)\right] + O(r^{-2}) \tag{25a}$$

and

$$\frac{\partial}{\partial u}(r\eta)_\infty = -A^{-2}r\,\partial\eta/\partial r - 3\eta + \tfrac{1}{2}(1 - x^2)\left[(1 - x^2)\frac{\partial^2}{\partial x^2} - 6x\frac{\partial}{\partial x}\right]\left[\eta/(1-x^2)\right] + O(r^{-2}) \, . \tag{25b}$$

Exactly similar expressions relate $\partial(r\xi)_\infty/\partial\mu$ to ξ and its derivatives at a finite radius.

The difference of Eqs. (25a) and (25b) gives the outgoing wave boundary condition for η,

$$\alpha^{-1}\, r\,\partial\eta/\partial t + A^{-1}r\,\partial\eta/\partial r + \eta \cong 0 \, , \tag{26}$$

and similarly for ξ.

Except for the geometrical factors of α and A, Eqs. (25) and (26) have the same form as for gravitational waves in fully linear theory about flat space. Both expressions for $\partial(r\eta)_\infty/\partial u$ are well posed numerically, in that they have a single dominant term with relatively small corrections. Their form does suggest that in integrating the Einstein equations numerically, one should use $\eta/(1-x^2)$, which is regular and non-zero at $x=\pm 1$, rather than η, as the fundamental variable, and similarly $\xi/(1-x^2)$ instead of ξ. This can be done without introducing any singular terms into the equations.

Whether Eq. (25a) or Eq. (25b) gives the best estimate for $\partial(r\eta)_\infty/\partial u$ is not obvious and may well depend on the nature of the particular system. Eq. (25b) does have the advantage that the non-radiative quadrupole term which may be present with a relatively large coefficient in order r^{-3} in η (see Eq. 17c) is exactly canceled. However, whether the numerical scheme being used calculates time derivatives or radial derivatives more accurately may turn out to be more important.

Any attempt to extend the above analysis to higher order in r^{-1} would require taking higher order derivatives of η and ξ and is probably not justified numerically.

A similar prescription in, say, the isothermal gauge would at least be more complicated to derive, since η no longer has such a simple expansion in Legendre functions. Also, the non-radiative r^{-2} term in η in this gauge causes trouble.

CONCLUSIONS

The radial gauge, in comparison with the isothermal gauge, gives a particularly clean description of the asymptotic radiation field. The method for estimating the energy flux at future null infinity given numerical values of the metric functions out to some finite radius described here (Eqs. 19 and 25) should be more reliable in practical numerical calculations than any of the methods earlier proposed,[1] but this remains to be demonstrated in actual examples. If the topological nature of the spacelike hypersurfaces does not allow the radial gauge to be used, then a more careful look at the asymptotic radiation field in the isothermal gauge may be desirable to see just what $\mathcal{O}(r^{-2})$ information is available.

The Euclidean gauge isolates the radiation field just as well as the "radiation gauge" of Smarr and York[9], and saves having to solve a complicated vector elliptic equation for the shift vector. If there is enough symmetry to make the Ricci tensor tractable and if the nature of the problem is such that coordinate shear is not too severe, the Euclidean gauge can certainly be a viable alternative to the radial gauge, as was demonstrated in the Eppley-Smarr colliding black hole calculation[7]. What is still important is the use of metric functions which are asymptotically the wave amplitudes. For instance, it will be very hard to see the radiation if $g_{\theta\theta}$ and $g_{\phi\phi}$ are basic variables in the calculation, so η is found as a small difference between two numbers of order unity. If spherical coordinates are used, metric functions equivalent to η and ξ in the radial gauge can be defined, and Eqs. (25) and (26) should still be applicable, except perhaps for somewhat different coefficients from the background metric.

REFERENCES

[1] Smarr, L., Gauge conditions, radiation formulae and the two black hole collision, in: Smarr, L. (ed.), Sources of Gravitational Radiation (Cambridge University Press, Cambridge, 1979).

[2] Maeda, K., Sasaki, M., Nakamura, T. and Miyama, S., Prog. Theor. Phys. 63 (1980) 719.

[3] Bardeen, J. M. and Piran, T., in preparation; see also the lectures of T. Piran in this volume.

[4] Teukolsky, S., Phys. Rev. D 26 (1982) 745.

[5] York, J. W., Kinematics and dynamics of general relativity, in: Smarr, L. (ed.), Sources of Gravitational Radiation (Cambridge University Press, Cambridge, 1979).

[6] Eardley, D. and Smarr, L., Phys. Rev. D 17 (1978) 2529.

[7] Eppley, K. R. and Smarr, L., preprint 1978; also see Ref. 1.

[8] Nakamura, T., Prog. Theor. Phys. 65 (1981) 1876.

[9] Smarr, L. and York, J. W., Phys. Rev. D 17 (1978) 1945.

[10] Wilson, J. R., A numerical method for relativistic hydrodynamics, in: Smarr, L. (ed.), Sources of Gravitational Radiation (Cambridge University Press, Cambridge, 1979); Smarr, L. and Wilson, J. R., preprint 1978.

GENERAL RELATIVISTIC COLLAPSE OF ROTATING STARS

Takashi Nakamura

Department of Physics, Kyoto University, Kyoto 606, Japan

Combining Geroch's and the ADM formalisms, we give a new formalism, (called [(2+1)+1]-formalism) to treat the dynamical problems of space-time having a rotational Killing vector. By using this formalism, numerical calculations have been made for the collapse of rotating supermassive stars ($\sim 10^8\ M_\odot$) and rotating stars of $10M_\odot$. The number of calculated models is 22. It is suggested that Kerr black holes may be formed for wide ranges of initial conditions if q(=total angular momentum/M(GM/C)) is smaller than unity. For $q > 1$, an expanding disk, ring or jets appears. The present numerical results approve the cosmic censorship hypothesis.

§1. INTRODUCTION

Fig. 1 shows a standard viewpoint of gravitational collapse of a rotating star to a black hole [1]. One of the purpose of numerical relativity is to simulate the collapse of a rotating star (such as Fig. 1) under realistic initial conditions. However, to know both the dynamics of matter and the propagation of gravitational radiation seems to be very difficult (See Piran's lecture) [2].

Therefore in Kyoto group [3], we divide the problem into some steps.

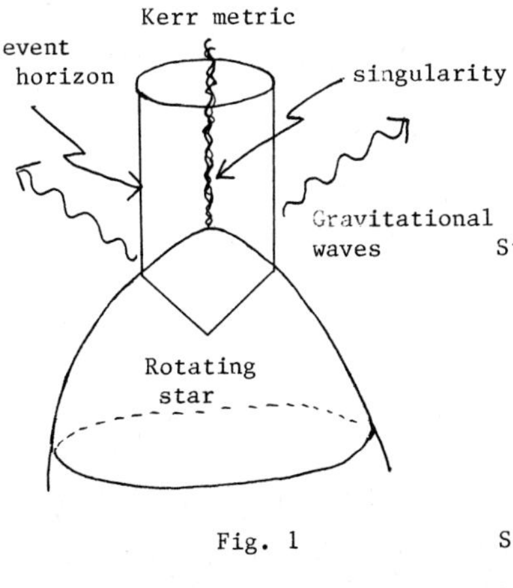

Fig. 1

Step 1 We calculate the time evolution of pure gravitational waves in 2-dimensional (2D) code (2-dimension means the dimension of spatial coordinates is two.). In this step the question is: "Is it possible to simulate the propagation of gravitational wave by a computer?" The answer is "Yes". Smarr [4], Eppley [5], and Miyama [6] calculated this problem.

Step 2: We try to know the dynamics of a collapsing, rotating star in 2D code. In this step, we don't try to estimate the amount of the gravitational waves. The relevant question is: "Is it possible to simulate the collapse of a rotating star (or matter) up to the formation of an apparent horizon?" The answer to this question will be given in the present article.

Step 3: Combining the techniques in step 1 and step 2, we simulate Fig. 1 in 2D, that is, we try to know both the dynamics of matter and the propagation of gravitational waves generated by the non-spherical motion of matter.

Step 4: We simulate Fig. 1 in 3D.

However, I expect, we need about ten years for step 3. The reason is as follows: In Newtonian collapse of a rotating star, there is a standard problem, that is, the collapse of isothermal gas under the condition that the initial density distribution is uniform and the initial angular velocity is constant. Since 1972, many authors (more than ten groups) have calculated this problem. But their results are different. Some say that a ring is formed. Others say that a ring is not formed. The reason for this difference is the artificial transfer of angular momentum in an Eulerian method. In Kamiya's calculation [7] no ring is formed. As he used a Lagrangian method, angular momentum is locally conserved. Norman, Wilson and Barton [8] carefully treated the angular momentum transfer in an Eulerian method. They found that if there is little artificial transfer of angular momentum no ring is formed and the collapse is a runaway yielding central disk-like regions of increasing mass density and flatness.

Comparing with the Newtonian case, we can say in our general relativistic case;

(1) Basic equations are more complicated.
(2) There is no standard problem like Newtonian case.
(3) Different authors will use different numerical methods.
(4) Moreover different authors will adopt different coordinate conditions.

To know the truth, the experience in Newtonian 2D collapse tells us that different groups with different methods should solve the same problem and compare their results. In our general relativistic case also, we should calculate the time evolution of the same initial data by using different codes and coordinate conditions. For this process we need about ten years, I expect.

In this article, I would like to show the first numerical results of the general relativistic collapse of rotating stars (above mentioned step 2). Questions related to the present article is as follows: Let us define $q \equiv J/MGM/C$ where J and M are the total angular momentum and the gravitational mass of the star, respectively. A Kerr black hole means $q \leq 1$. Then,

1 If the collapsing star has $q > 1$, what happens?
2 If $q \leq 1$, a Kerr black hole is really formed? No naked singularity like in Tomimatsu-Sato metrics appears?

§ 2. [(2+1)+1]-FORMALISM [10]

In the axially symmetric space-time, there is a rotational Killing vector (ξ_μ). This implies we can divide out the Killing direction by using Geroch's three dimensional formalism for space-time with one Killing vector [9]. Let us define λ, $h_{\mu\nu}$, ω_μ and $\varepsilon_{\mu\nu\rho}$ as

$$\lambda^2 = \xi_\mu \xi^\mu, \quad h_{\mu\nu} = g_{\mu\nu} - \lambda^{-2}\xi_\mu \xi_\nu, \quad \omega_\mu = \varepsilon_{\mu\nu\rho\sigma}\xi^\mu \nabla^\rho \xi^\sigma \text{ and } \varepsilon_{\mu\nu\rho} = \lambda^{-1}\xi^\sigma \varepsilon_{\mu\nu\rho\sigma}.$$

Then, the four-dimensional Einstein equations become the set of equations for $h_{\mu\nu}$, λ and ω_μ;

$$^{(3)}R_{\mu\nu} = (2\lambda^4)^{-1}[\omega_\mu \omega_\nu - h_{\mu\nu}\omega^\rho \omega_\rho] + \lambda^{-1} D_\mu D_\nu \lambda + 8\pi (J_{\mu\nu} - h_{\mu\nu}(J_\rho^\rho + \lambda^{-2}J)/2), \tag{1}$$

$$\lambda^{-1} D^\rho D_\rho \lambda = -(2\lambda^4)^{-1}\omega^\rho \omega_\rho - 4\pi(\lambda^{-2}J - J_\rho^\rho), \tag{2}$$

$$D_{[\mu}\omega_{\nu]} = 8\pi \lambda \varepsilon_{\mu\nu\rho} J^\rho \tag{3}$$

and

$$D^\rho[\lambda^{-3}\omega_\rho] = 0, \tag{4}$$

where D^μ and $^{(3)}R_{\mu\nu}$ are covariant derivative and 3-dimensional Ricci tensor with respect to $h_{\mu\nu}$. J, J_ρ and $J_{\rho\sigma}$ are defined by

$$J = T_{\mu\nu}\xi^{\mu}\xi^{\nu}\ ,\quad J_{\rho} = h_{\mu\rho}\xi_{\nu}T^{\mu\nu}$$

and

$$J_{\rho\sigma} = h_{\rho\mu}h_{\sigma\nu}T^{\mu\nu}\ ,$$

where $T_{\mu\nu}$ is energy-momentum tensor of matter. Next we define a projection tensor as

$$H_{ab} = h_{ab} + n_a n_b$$

where n_a is a unit normal of t=const hypersurface. We define α (lapse function) and η^A (shift vector) as

$$ds^2 = h_{ab}dx^a dx^b = -\alpha^2 dt^2 + H_{AB}(dx^A + \eta^A dt)(dx^B + \eta^B dt).$$

Let the extrinsic curvature be expressed by χ_{AB} (Samll Latin indices refer to the ranges 0, 1, 2 and capital Latin ones, 1, 2.). Moreover, we define various quantities as

$$H = \det(H_{AB}),\ \chi = \chi^A_A\ ,\ \lambda K^{\varphi}_{\varphi} = -n^{\mu}\partial_{\mu}\lambda\ ,\ E^A = \varepsilon^{AB}H^b_B w_b \lambda^{-2}\ ,$$

$$B_{\varphi} = n_a w^a \lambda^{-2}\ ,\ \varepsilon_{AB} = n^c\varepsilon_{cAB}\ ,\ \rho_H = n_a n_b J^{ab}\ ,\ J_{\varphi} = -n_a J^a\ ,$$

$$J^A = -n_a H^A_b J^{ab}\ ,\ S^A = H^A_b J^b \text{ and } S_{AB} = H_{Aa}H_{Bb}J^{ab}.$$

If we carry out projection of all the tensors appeared in Eqs.(1) to (4) like the (3+1)-split, we obtaine the [(2+1)+1]-representation of the Einstein equations [10] as

$$\partial_0 H_{AB} = -2\alpha\chi_{AB} + \eta_{A\|B} + \eta_{B\|A}\ , \tag{5}$$

$$\begin{aligned}\partial_0 \chi_{AB} = {} & \eta^C\chi_{AB\|C} + \alpha[{}^{(2)}R_{AB} + \chi\chi_{AB}] - 2\alpha\chi^C_A\chi_{CB} - \alpha_{\|A\|B} + (\chi_{AC}\eta^C_{\|B} + \\ & \chi_{BC}\eta^C_{\|A}) - \alpha\lambda^{-1}\lambda_{\|A\|B} + \alpha K^{\varphi}_{\varphi}\chi_{AB} - \alpha[\varepsilon_{CA}\varepsilon_{DB}E^C E^D - H_{AB}(E^C E_C - B^2_{\varphi})]/2 \\ & - 8\pi\alpha[S_{AB} + \tfrac{1}{2}H_{AB}(\rho_H - S^C_C - \lambda^{-2}J)]\ ,\end{aligned} \tag{6}$$

$$\partial_0\lambda = \eta^A\partial_A\lambda - \alpha\lambda K^{\varphi}_{\varphi}\ , \tag{7}$$

$$\begin{aligned}\partial_0 K^{\varphi}_{\varphi} = {} & \eta^A\partial_A K^{\varphi}_{\varphi} + \alpha K^{\varphi}_{\varphi}(K^{\varphi}_{\varphi} + \chi) - H^{AD}(\partial_A\alpha)(\partial_B\lambda)\lambda^{-1} - \alpha({}^{(2)}\Delta\lambda)\lambda^{-1} \\ & - \alpha(E_A E^A - B^2_{\varphi})/2 - 4\pi\alpha[\rho_H - S^A_A + \lambda^{-2}J]\ ,\end{aligned} \tag{8}$$

$$\chi^2 - \chi^{AB}\chi_{AB} + {}^{(2)}R = 2\lambda^{-1}\,{}^{(2)}\Delta\lambda - 2\chi K^{\varphi}_{\varphi} + (E_A E^A + B^2_{\varphi})/2 + 16\pi\rho_H\ , \tag{9}$$

$$\lambda^{-1}(\lambda\chi^B_A)_{\|B} - \lambda^{-1}(\partial_A\lambda)K^{\varphi}_{\varphi} - \partial_A(\chi + K^{\varphi}_{\varphi}) = 8\pi J_A - B_{\varphi}\varepsilon_{CA}E^C/2\ , \tag{10}$$

$$\begin{aligned}\partial_0(\lambda^2\sqrt{H}E^A) = {} & (\eta^B(\lambda^2 E^A)_{\|B} + \varepsilon^{AB}\eta^C_{\|B}\,\varepsilon_{DC}\lambda^2 E^D)\sqrt{H} \\ & + \sqrt{H}\,\varepsilon^{AB}\partial_B(\alpha\lambda^2 B_{\varphi}) - 16\pi\alpha\lambda S^A\sqrt{H}\ ,\end{aligned} \tag{11}$$

$$\partial_0(\lambda^{-1}\sqrt{H}B_{\varphi}) = \partial_A(\eta^A\sqrt{H}B_{\varphi}\lambda^{-1}) + \partial_A(\alpha E_B\varepsilon^{BA}\sqrt{H}\lambda^{-1})\ , \tag{12}$$

and

$$(\lambda^2 E^A)_{\|A} = 16\pi\lambda J_{\varphi}\ . \tag{13}$$

In Eqs.(5) to (13), ${}^{(2)}\Delta$, $\|$, ${}^{(2)}R$ and ${}^{(2)}R_{AB}$ are Laplacian, covariant differentiation, scalar curvature and Ricci tensor with respect to H_{AB} , respectively.

We assume the perfect fluid for $T_{\mu\nu}$,

$$T_{\mu\nu} = \rho(1+\varepsilon+P/\rho)u_\mu u_\nu + P g_{\mu\nu},$$

where ρ , ε and p are proper mass density, internal energy per gram and pressure, respectively. The hydrodynamics equations can be written by using J_A , J_φ , ρ and ρ_H as;

i) Energy equation

$$\partial_0(\alpha u^0\sqrt{H}\lambda\rho\varepsilon) + \partial_A(\alpha u^0\sqrt{H}\lambda U^A\rho\varepsilon) = -P\{\partial_0(\alpha u^0\sqrt{H}\lambda) + \partial_A(\alpha u^0\sqrt{H}\lambda U^A)\}, \quad (14)$$

ii) Euler equations

$$\begin{aligned}\partial_0(\lambda\sqrt{H}J_A) + \partial_B(U^B\lambda\sqrt{H}J_A) &= -\alpha\lambda\sqrt{H}(\partial_A P + (P+\rho_H)\alpha^{-1}\partial_A\alpha) \\ &+ \alpha\lambda\sqrt{H}(P+\rho_H)[(\partial_A H_{BC})V^B V^C/2 + \alpha^{-1}V_C\,\partial_A\eta^C] \\ &+ \alpha\lambda\sqrt{H}\,\lambda^{-1}J_\varphi[E_A + \varepsilon_{AC}(2B_\varphi V^C - \lambda^{-2}\varepsilon^{C,B}(\partial_B\lambda)V^\varphi)], \quad (15)\end{aligned}$$

iii) Conservation of angular momentum

$$\partial_0(\lambda\sqrt{H}J_\varphi) + \partial_A(U^A\lambda\sqrt{H}J_\varphi) = 0, \quad (16)$$

iv) Conservation of baryon number

$$\partial_0(\alpha u^0\sqrt{H}\lambda\rho) + \partial_A(U^A\alpha u^0\sqrt{H}\lambda\rho) = 0, \quad (17)$$

v) Equation of state

$$P = P(\rho, \varepsilon) \quad (18)$$

vi) Normalization of four-velocity

$$\alpha u^0 = 1/\sqrt{1 - V^B V_B - V^\varphi V_\varphi}, \quad (19)$$

where

$$V^B = (P+\rho_H)^{-1}J^B, \qquad J^\varphi = (P+\rho_H)V^\varphi$$

and

$$U^A = \alpha V^A - \eta^A. \quad (20)$$

One can see that the basic equations in the [(2+1)+1]-formalism strongly resemble those of a non-rotating system with toroidal magnetic field B_φ and poloidal electric fields E^A . Angular momentum density J_φ behaves like electric charge density. Conservation of angular momentum corresponds to conservation of electric charge. Moreover, there are "Lorentz force" like terms in the Euler equations (Eq.(15)).

Our method for evolving the basic quantities is so-called the free evolution [11]. We solve the constraint equations (Eqs.(9), (10) and (13)) only at t=0 to determine the initial data. For $t>0$ we solve Eqs.(5) to (8), (11) and (12) as well as the hydrodynamics equations (Eqs.(14) to (20)). We use the constraint equations for $t>0$ to see the accuracy of the numerical calculations.

We adopt the cylindrical coordinates R, Z and φ. We assume that the system has reflection symmetry about z=0 plane. In this case, the regularity conditions at R=0 and the reflection symmetry enable us to use the following basic variabl es instead of the original variables appeared in Eqs.(5) to (20),

$$B \equiv \lambda/R, \quad a \equiv (\sqrt{H_{RR}} - B)/R^2, \quad C \equiv H_{Rz}/R/z, \quad F \equiv \sqrt{H_{zz}},$$

$$k^R_R \equiv (\chi^R_R - K^\varphi_\varphi)/R^2, \quad k^z_R \equiv \chi^z_R/R/z, \quad K^z_z \equiv \chi^z_z, \quad e^R \equiv E^R/R^2, \quad e^z \equiv E^z/R/z$$

$$b_\varphi \equiv B_\varphi/R^2/Z,\ \tilde{\eta}^R \equiv \eta^R/R,\ \tilde{\eta}^Z \equiv \eta^Z/Z,\ Q_b \equiv \alpha u^0 B\sqrt{H}\rho,\ h \equiv 1+\varepsilon+P/\rho,$$
$$Q_R \equiv B\sqrt{H}J_R/Q_b/R,\ Q_Z \equiv B\sqrt{H}J_Z/Q_b/Z,\ \Omega \equiv B\sqrt{H}J_\varphi/Q_b/R^2,\ \alpha u^0 = B\sqrt{H}$$
$$(\rho_H+P)/h/Q_b,\ \tilde{V}^R \equiv V^R/R,\ \tilde{V}^Z \equiv V^Z/Z,\ \check{U}^R \equiv \alpha\tilde{V}^R - \tilde{\eta}^R,\ \check{U}^Z \equiv \alpha\tilde{V}^Z - \tilde{\eta}_Z.$$

By this choice of the basic variables, the regularity at R=0 is automatically satisfied. In general, any quantity Q is a function of $x(\equiv R^2)$ and $y(\equiv Z^2)$.

§ 3. INITIAL VALUE EQUATIONS

The method for solving the initial value equations is beautifully reviewed in York's article [12]. Following York's method, we assume at t=0,

$$\gamma_{ij} = \phi^4(\delta_{ij})_{flat} \quad \text{and} \quad K_{ij}^{TT} = 0.$$

We solve the Hamiltonian constraint equations and momentum constraint equations using Robin's and vector Robin's condition. The initial value equations become

a) the Hamiltonian constraint equation,

$$4(\partial_x\phi + x\partial_{xx}\phi) + 2\partial_y\phi + 4y\partial_{yy}\phi$$
$$= -2\pi(\rho_H\phi^6)/\phi - \phi^5 x\{x(\partial_x W^\varphi)^2 + y(\partial_y W^\varphi)^2\}$$
$$-\phi^5\{(K_R^R)^2 + (K_Z^Z)^2 + (K_\varphi^\varphi)^2 + 2xy(k_R^Z)^2\}/8,$$

b) the angular momemtum constraint equation

$$(8+24x\phi^{-1}\partial_x\phi)\partial_x W^\varphi + 4x\partial_{xx}W^\varphi$$
$$+(2+24y\phi^{-1}\partial_y\phi)\partial_y W^\varphi + 4y\partial_{yy}W^\varphi = 8\pi J_\varphi x^{-1},$$

c) the momentum constraint equation

$$(16x/3)\partial_{xx}w^R + 4y\partial_{yy}w^R + (32/3 + 32x\phi^{-1}\partial_x\phi)\partial_x w^R$$
$$+(2+24y\phi^{-1}\partial_y\phi)\partial_y w^R + 8\phi^{-1}\partial_x\phi\, w^R + 4/3\, y\,\partial_{xy}w^Z$$
$$+(2/3+24y\phi^{-1}\partial_y\phi)\partial_x w^Z - 8y\phi^{-1}\partial_x\phi\,\partial_y w^Z - 8\phi^{-1}\partial_x\phi\, w^Z = 8\pi J_R/R,$$

$$4x\partial_{xx}w^Z + 16/3\, y\,\partial_{yy}w^Z + (4+24x\phi^{-1}\partial_x\phi)\partial_x w^Z$$
$$+(8+32y\phi^{-1}\partial_y\phi)\partial_y w^Z + 16\phi^{-1}\partial_y\phi\, w^Z + 4/3\, x\,\partial_{xy}w^R$$
$$-16x\phi^{-1}\partial_y\phi\,\partial_x w^R + (4/3+24x\phi^{-1}\partial_x\phi)\partial_y w^R - 16\phi^{-1}\partial_y\phi\, w^R = 8\pi J_Z/Z,$$

where (Rw^R, Zw^Z, W^φ) is the longitudinal part of K_{ij}. The asymptotic behavior of ϕ, w^R, w^Z and W^φ for $r\to\infty$ are given by

$$\phi \to 1 + \text{const}/r, \quad W^\varphi \to \text{const}/r^3$$
$$w^R \to C_1/r^3 - C_2\, 3R^2/r^5/2 \quad \text{and} \quad w^Z \to C_1/r^3 + C_2(2Z^2+R^2)/2/r^5.$$

§ 4. COORDINATE CONDITIONS AND METHOD FOR FINITE DIFFERENCE

a) Coordinate conditons

We use zero shift vector, i.e., the coordinate lines agree with the normal lines. For the lapse function we use two kinds of slices;

1) Maximal slicing i.e., $\quad \chi_R^R + \chi_Z^Z + K_\varphi^\varphi = 0$

2) Hyper geometric slicing [13]

In this slice α is determined by

$$r^{-2}\frac{d}{dr} r^2 \frac{d}{dr}\alpha = V_0 \,\mathrm{sech}^2(dr)\,\alpha \,, \tag{21}$$

where V_0 and d are two constants which are determined at each time step appropriately. The solution of Eq.(21) is expressed by the hypergeometric function.

b) Method for finite difference [13]

1) Grids

A grid point is determined by

$$\left.\begin{aligned} x_{i+1} - x_i &= 1.4\,(x_i - x_{i-1}) \\ y_{i+1} - y_i &= 1.4\,(y_i - y_{i-1}) \end{aligned}\right\} \; i = 2, 3, \cdots\cdots .$$

The number of grids is typically 28 × 28. Some of the models are calculatedy by using finer grids (42 × 42). The outer most grid point has a coordinate (25 M, 25 M). This is far enough for the gravitational potential. For example $\phi \sim 1.04$. But it is not far enough to estimate the gravitational wave whose wave length is expected to be 16 M .

2) Finite difference method

For the hydrodynamics equations, donor cell type method is used unless R=0 or Z=0. For example, for R=0 and Z=0, the hydrodynamics equations become

$$\partial_0 Q + 2\,\tilde{U}^R Q + \tilde{U}^z Q = S_Q$$

where S_Q is the source term. For the evolution equations of space-time geometry, Friedrich-Lax type viscosity terms are added to make the numerical systems stable.

§5. GENERAL RELATIVISTIC COLLAPSE OF ROTATING STARS [14]

We use the units of mass, length and time as $M=M_b$, $L=GM_b/c^2$ and $T=GM_b/c^3$ where M_b is the total rest mass of baryon. Let $\rho_3(r)$ and r_0 be the density distribution of N=3 polytrope and an initial radius of a star, respectively. We use the following initial conditions:

$$\rho_H \phi^6 = \begin{cases} \rho_3(r) & \text{for } r \le \rho_3^{-1}(10^{-6}\rho_3(0)) \equiv r^* \\ 10^{-6}\rho_3(0) & \text{for } r > r^* \end{cases}$$

and

$$J_R/R = J_z/z = \begin{cases} \rho_H C_V & \text{for } r \le r_0 \\ \rho_H C_V \exp(1-(r/r_0)^2) & \text{for } r > r_0 \end{cases}$$

$$J_\varphi = x\,\rho_H\,\Omega_0 \exp(-C_\varphi x/r_0^2)\,,$$

where C_V , Ω_0 and C_φ are the constants which determine the initial velocity, the initial central angular velocity and the rotation law, respectively.

As an equation of state, we use

$$P = \rho\varepsilon/3\,.$$

Initial distribution of ε is taken as

$$\varepsilon = K\,\rho^{1/3}.$$

Now r_0 , C_V , Ω_0 , C_φ and K determine the initial conditions uniquely. In all the calculated models, r_0 is 14.5 and C_V is chosen so that the infall velocity at $r=r_0$ becomes the free fall velocity. Instead of Ω_0 and K, we use J and U defined by $J=E_{rot}/|E_{grav}|$ and $U=E_{int}/|E_{grav}|$ where E_{rot} , E_{int} and E_{grav} are the rotational energy, the internal energy and the gravitational energy of a star, resepctively.

As the rotation laws, we use two C_φ's as

a) Rotation law A; C_φ =2 (almost rigidly rotating case)

b) Rotation law B; C_φ=10 (strongly differential rotation case)

In Table 1, the initial parameters of each model are shown. Since the models are characterized mainly by q and the rotation law we use them as a name of each model. For example A146 means the collapse of the rotating supermassive star with q=1.46 and the rotation law A. Case C corresponds to the collapse of a star of $10M_\odot$ [13], with

$$J_R = J_z = 0\ , \quad \rho = 3\times10^{13}\exp(-(x+y)/4.5)\ g/cm^3,$$

$$\Omega = \Omega_0 \exp(-x/4.5)$$

and

$$P = \begin{cases} \rho\varepsilon/3 & \text{for} \quad \rho \le \rho^* = 3\times10^{14}\ g/cm^3 \\ (\rho-\rho^*)\varepsilon + \rho^*\varepsilon/3 & \text{for} \quad \rho > \rho^*, \end{cases}$$

where Ω is the initial angular frequency.

Table 1. Initial parameters and main results of the calculated models. In the sixth column, max and hyper mean the maximal slicing and the hypergeometric slicing, respectively. In the eighth column, the important characteristic of each model is written.

Model	Case	q	U	J	Time Slice	Horizon?[a)]	Remarks
A146	A	1.46	0.94	0.77	max	no	jet
A122	A	1.22	0.86	0.51	max	no	jet
A105	A	1.05	0.84	0.37	max	yes	
A93	A	0.93	0.82	0.29	max	yes	
A75	A	0.75	0.82	0.19	max	yes	
A50	A	0.50	0.81	0.08	max	yes	
B143	B	1.43	1.01	1.20	max	no	expanding disk
B121	B	1.21	0.88	0.76	max	no	expanding disk
B104	B	1.04	0.84	0.54	max	no	expanding disk
B92	B	0.92	0.82	0.42	max/hyper	yes	
B74	B	0.74	0.81	0.27	max/hyper	yes	
B51	B	0.51	0.81	0.12	max	yes	
C137	C	1.37	0.25	1.56	hyper	no	expanding ring
C109	C	1.09	0.23	0.79	hyper	no	expanding ring
C95	C	0.95	0.22	0.55	hyper	no	expanding ring
C86	C	0.86	0.21	0.45	hyper	yes	ring singularity
C80	C	0.80	0.21	0.36	hyper	yes	ring singularity
C64	C	0.64	0.20	0.22	hyper	yes	ring singularity
C56	C	0.56	0.20	0.17	hyper	yes	ring singularity
C48	C	0.48	0.20	0.12	hyper/max	yes	ring singularity
C32	C	0.32	0.20	0.05	hyper	yes	

a) A method for identifying an apparent horizon is shown in Ref. [15].

1) Rotation law A

In this rotation law, the centrifugal force has a maximum value at $R \cong 0.35 r_0$ where $\rho_3(R)$ is less than $0.1\ \rho_3(0)$. This means if the mass shedding occurs, it will occur from the outer part of the star. In the following, we show the details of the numerical results of the three typical models.

a) Model A50

In this model, the rotation is very slow. At t=0.287, the matter distribution is almost spherical and the velocity pattern shows the spherical collapse. (Fig. 2(a)) This feature is kept through the entire time up to when the apparent horizon (dashed line) is formed. (Fig. 2(b)) Although the matter distribution becomes slightly oblate by the effect of rotation, all the matter will be swallowed into the slowly rotating black hole.

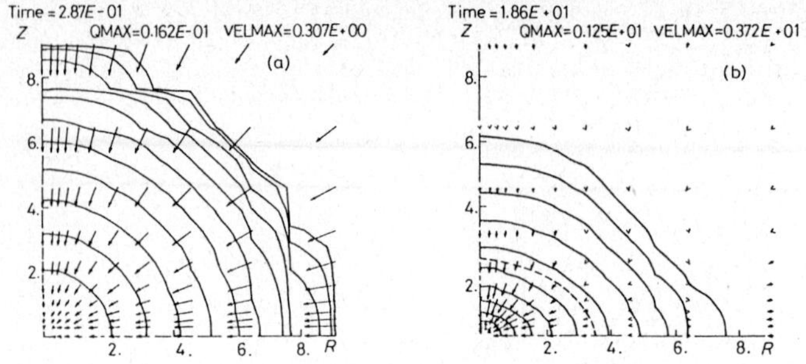

Fig. 2

b) Model A105

In this model, the star is rather rapidly rotating. At t=11.5 (Fig. 3(a)), the matter falls vertically for $R \lesssim 2$. The collapse in the equatorial plane is considerably suppressed by the effect of rotation. For $2.4 \lesssim R \lesssim 7.7$, the outflow velocity reaches up to 0.3c. Finally, the oblate shape core is formed in the central region and an apparent horizon is formed outside this core. (Fig. 3(b)) The outer envelope expands along the lateral direction with relativistic velocity. We can expect that some part of this envelope will return to the central black hole and the other part will expand to infinity. Thus the ultimate fate of the collapsing supermassive star in this model is completely different from that in Model A50.

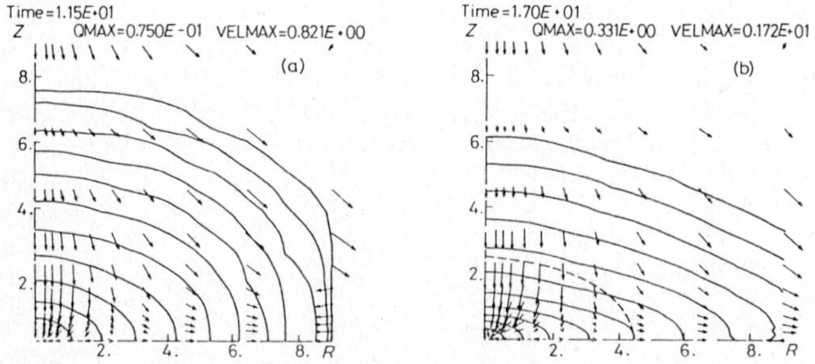

Fig. 3

c) Model A146

At t=5.76, the matter in the central part falls almost vertically. For $2 \lesssim R \lesssim 6.5$, we can see a strong outflow with the velocity up to 0.5. (Fig. 4(a)) At t=18.8, the central core bounces and a shock wave is formed. Near the equatorial plane the outflow extends up to R=9. The outer thin envelope falls vertically to this outflow and the shock front is formed. (Fig. 4(b)) At t=23.2, we can see the strong jet along the rotational axis. The central core has almost stopped moving and the rather dense envelope expands both in the lateral direction and in the Z-direction. (Fig. 4(c)) Finally the strong jet reaches Z=9. (Fig. 4(d)) The kinetic and the internal energy of this jet are 2×10^{-3} and 1.5×10^{-3} in our units, respectively. The total mass of the jet is 5×10^{-3}. Thus the mean kinetic energy per gram of this jet becomes 0.4 (3.6×10^{20} ergs/g). The total mass and the angular momentum of the relaxed core are 0.21 and 4×10^{-2}, respectively. As the core has a rather small value of $q(\approx 1.0)$, it may recollapse eventually and a black hole may be formed after all.

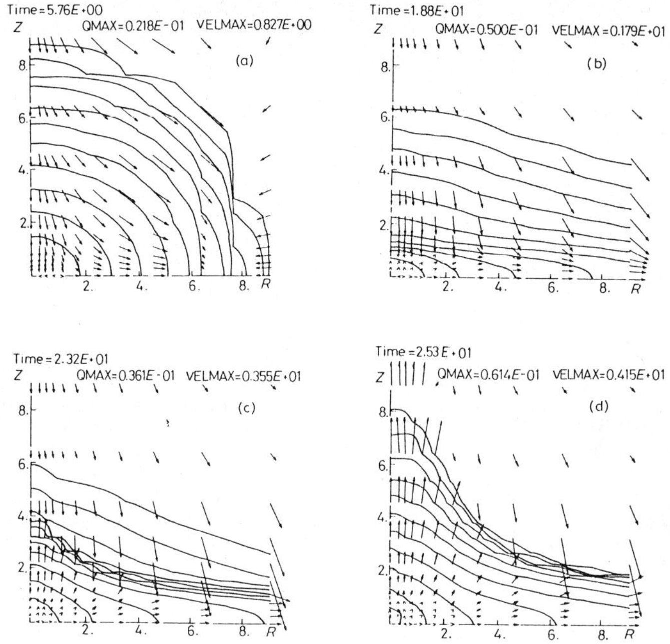

Fig. 4

2) Rotation law B

In this rotation law, the centrifugal force is more effective for small R. This means that, if the mass shedding occurs, it will occur from the central region. In the following, we show the details of the numerical results of the three typical models.

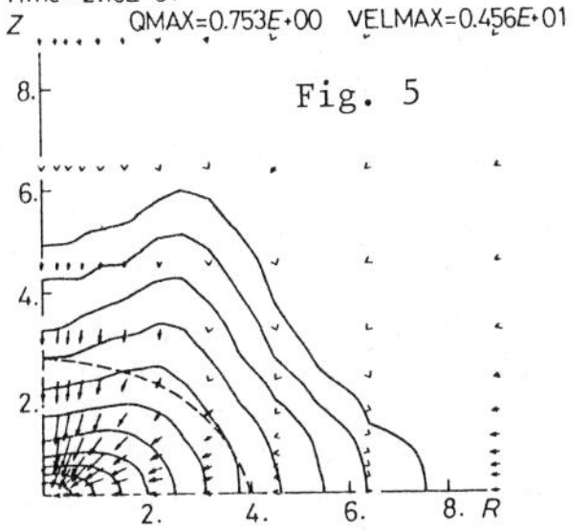

Fig. 5

a) Model B51

In Fig. 5, we show the density contours and the flow pattern at t=21.6. Although A50 and B51 have almost the same angular momentum, we can see that the central core is deformed rather strongly in B51. Of course, this is due to a rapidly rotating core because of the differential rotation of the rotation law B.

b) Model B92

In this model, the centrifugal force near the center is greater than the gravitational force at t=0. This fact causes the outflow of the matter from a small R region. As the rotation is very slow for large R, the matter in the outer part falls almost spherically. (Fig. 6(a)) At t=11.5, the inflow in the Z-direction and the outflow in the lateral direction form a disk in the central region. (Fig. 6(b)) At t=17.3, the outgoing velocity of the disk is considerably decelerated. The outer envelope falls into this disk vertically and forms the almost steady shock. For large R, a very thin envelope expands in the lateral direction. (Fig. 6(c)) In this model, we have tried to identify an apparent horizon, but in vain. We have recalculated this model using the hypergeometric slicing. In this slicing, an apparent horizon is identified. This is due to the fact that, if one uses

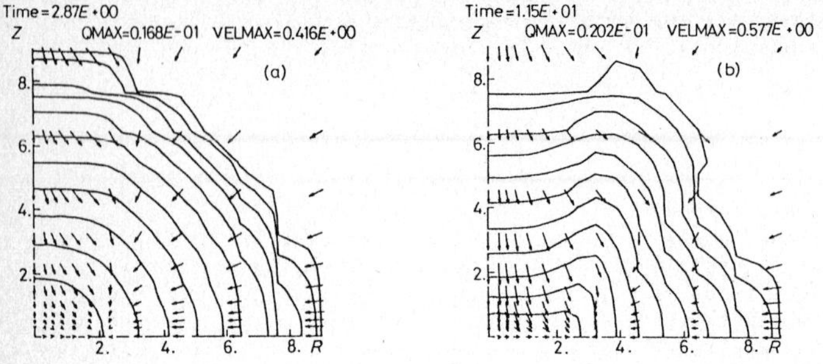

Fig. 6

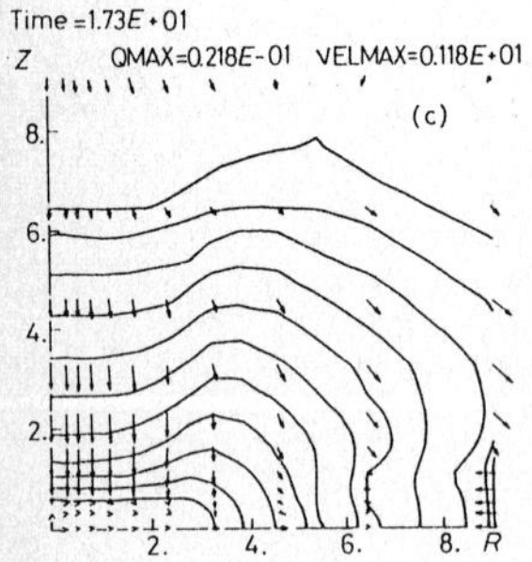

the maximal slicing as a time slice, the proper time of the co-moving observer, whose four velocity is that of the matter, stops increasing too soon after the density distribution becomes disk-like.

c) Model B143

In this model, we can see the outflow for small R even at rather early time. (Fig. 7(a)) At t=11.6, an expanding disk is clearly formed. (Fig. 7(b)) At t=17.5, the expansion velocity of the disk is decelerated in the central part and it is the fastest at the edge of the disk. (Fig. 7(c)) At t=20.8, the central part of the disk is almost stopped. The outer thin envelope falls into the disk continuously and forms the almost steady shock front. As the expansion velocity is

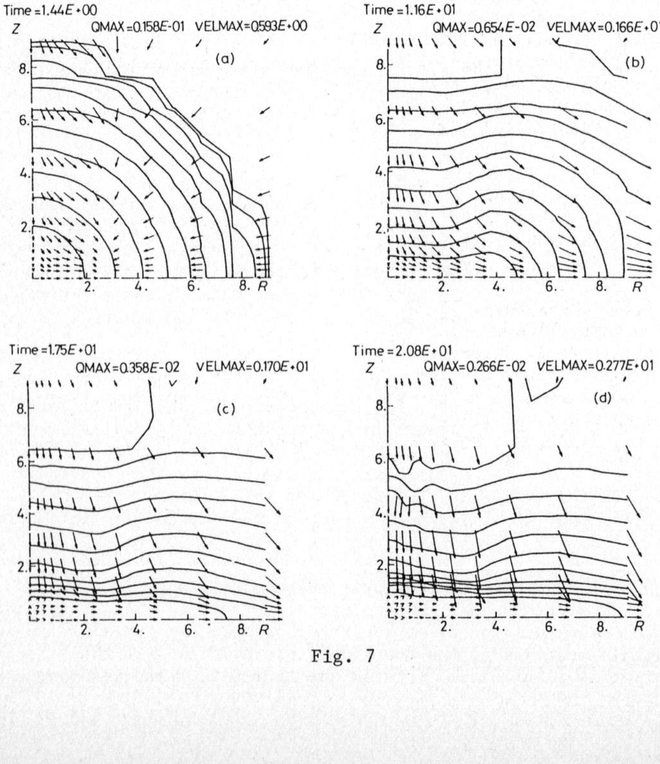

Fig. 7

very large in this model, all the matter except the central part will go away from the system. In this model, no jet is formed contrary to the model A146. (Fig. 7(d))

§ 6. CONCLUSIONS

The apparent horizons are formed for $q \lesssim 1.05$ in case A, $q \lesssim 0.92$ in case B and $q \lesssim 0.86$ in case C. These models are different from each other in their equation of state, initial density distribution and rotation law. However, they have almost the same critical value of q for the formation of the apparent horizon. In all the models in which the apparent horizon is formed, nothing peculiar has been foound outside the apparent horizon. If we remember that the singularity of the Kerr black hole is hidden by the event horizon for $q < 1$, our numerical results suggest that the Kerr black holes may be formed for wide ranges of the initial conditions provided that the initial density and the angular velocity decreases with the radius. For $q > 1$, the dynamics of matter strongly depends on the initial conditions and the equation state. Jets (case A), an expanding disk (case B) or an expanding ring (case C) appears.

As I mentioned before the question in Step 2 is; "Is it possible to simulate the collpase of a rotating star up to the formation of an apparent horizon?" The answer to this question seems to me "Yes". Now, we can enter into Step 3 and in near future, we will be able to give the amount and the spectrum of the gravitational waves generated in the course of the collapse of a rotating star to the experimenters of gravitational waves.

REFERENCES

1 Penrose, R., IAU Symposium No.64, p.82.
2 Piran, T., this volume.
3 Nakamura, T., Maeda, K., Miyama, S. and Sasaki, M., Prog. Theor. Phys. 63 (1980), 1229; "Proceedings of the 2nd Marcell Grossmann Meeting" Ed. Ruffini, R., North Holand, 1982; IAU Symposium No.93, p.326.
4 Smarr, L., Ann. N.Y. Acad. Sci. 302 (1977), 569.
5 Eppley, K., "Sources of Gravitational Radiation", ed. L. Smarr (Cambridge University Press, 1979), p.275.
6 Miyama, S., Prog. Theor. Phys. 65 (1981), 894.
7 Kamiya, Y., Prog. Theor. Phys. 58 (1977), 802.
8 Norman, M.L., Wilson, J.R. and Barton, R.T., Astrophys. J. 239 (1980), 968.
9 Geroch, R., J. Math. Phys. 12 (1971), 98.
10 Maeda, K., Sasaki, M., Nakamura, T. and Miyama, S., Prog. Theor. Phys. 63 (1980), 719.
11 Piran, T.,J. Comp. Phys. 35 (1980), 254.
12 York, J., this volume.
13 Nakamura, T., Prog. Theor. Phys. 65 (1981), 1876.
14 For details see Ref. 13 and Nakamura, T., Prog. Theor. Phys. Supple. 70 (1981), 202; Nakamura, T. and Sato, H., Phys. Letters 86A (1981), 318; Prog. Theor. Phys. 66 (1981), 2038; Prog. Theor. Phys. 67 (1982), 1396.
15 Sasaki, M., Maeda, K., Miyama, S. and Nakamura, T., Prog. Theor. Phys. 63 (1980), 1051.

INTERACTION OF GRAVITATIONAL WAVES WITH AN ELASTIC SOLID MEDIUM

B. Carter

Groupe d'Astrophysique Relativiste
Observatoire de Paris
92 Meudon, France

Contents

1 INTRODUCTION

Although the presently most promising approach to the direct detection of gravitational radiation would seem to be provided by use of appropriate electromagnetic field configurations (e.g. that of an optical interferometer) the original and until now most highly developed method has been based on the use of an elastic solid configuration, traditionally a cylindrical bar of the kind originally introduced by Weber. A highly simplified but essentially adequate description of the interaction of gravitational radiation with such an apparatus was given by Weber himself in his seminal 1960 paper [1]. For a more detailed analysis, and for the treatment of more general configurations such as that of the earth as a whole, a system of wave equations governing the interaction of weak gravitational radiation with an elastic solid medium was derived soon after by Dyson [2], Papapetrou [3] and others, subject to the limitation that non-linearities due to self-gravitation of the solid medium are neglected, as is entirely justifiable in a terrestrial context.

While the final outcome of the present article will be a derivation of the weak field wave equations to which we have just referred, we shall nevertheless use a quite different approach from that of Dyson and Papapetrou. Instead of working throughout in an only approximately self-consistent linearised scheme, as they did, we shall first set up the exactly consistent fully non-linear theory of the interaction of a gravitational field with an elastic solid in accordance with Einstein's theory. The general, non-linear theory is in any case needed for application to the more exotic context of neutron star deformations, as discussed e.g. by Carter and Quintana [4]. Starting from this mathematically sound basis, we shall then proceed to the derivation of the weak field limit in two successive stages of approximation: we shall first impose the restriction that the gravitational radiation be weak, even though the unperturbed background field may still be strong (as in the case of a neutron star); finally we shall impose the condition that the background field also be weak (as in the case of the earth) so as to obtain the Dyson-Papapetrou equations.

Unlike the treatments used by othe authors such as those of the schools of Eringen (see e.g. Maugin [5]) or of Souriau (who was the first to set up the fully non-linear elasticity theory used here [6]) our present treatment will be based on the use of the concept of convected differentials, a powerful technique for the analysis of elastic media (elastic or otherwise) that generalises the more restricted convected differentiation procedure first introduced by Oldroyd [7] . In providing a self-contained introduction to the general concept of convected differentials and differentiation, and to their application to the theory of an elastic solid and its interaction with gravitational radiation, the present article condenses several previous publications describing work carried out in collaboration with H. Quintana [8], [9], [10], [11], [12]. This article thus serves to update an earlier introductory survey by Ehlers [13].

2 KINEMATICS OF A MATERIAL MEDIUM: MATERIAL REPRESENTATION

In Newtonian theory a material medium is usually visualized as a three-dimensional manifold whose configuration at a given instant is specified by a non-singular mapping into three-dimensional Euclidean space, the motion of the medium being given by the time variation of the mapping. However in General Relativity theory, where there is in general no canonically preferred set of three-dimensional sections (Euclidean or otherwise) of the fundamental four-dimensional spacetime manifold, $\mathcal{M}$ say, it is more convenient and natural to proceed the other way about. The medium itself is still to be conceived in the abstract as a three-dimensional manifold, $\mathcal{X}$ say, (whose points represent idealised particles of the material) but its motion can be specified by a necessarily degenerate (four to three dimensional) mapping, $\mathcal{P}$ say, of the world-tube traversed by the matter in $\mathcal{M}$ onto the manifold $\mathcal{X}$, the world-line of each idealised particle of the medium being projected under $\mathcal{P}$ onto the corresponding point in $\mathcal{X}$.

We shall use Greek indices $\mu,\nu,\ldots$ to specify ordinary spacetime tensors on $\mathcal{M}$, and capital Roman indices $A,B,\ldots$ to specify tensors on the manifold $\mathcal{X}$ representing the medium. The spacetime indices $\mu,\nu,\ldots$ may be thought of in the traditional manner as specifying tensor components defined in terms of a local system of coordinates x^μ ($\mu = 1,2,3,4$) on $\mathcal{M}$ while similarly the material indices $A,B,\ldots$ may be thought of as defined in terms of local coordinates X^A ($A = 1,2,3$) on $\mathcal{X}$. However, following Penrose [14], it will also be convenient to interpret the index symbols in the abstract manner as merely an indication of the tensorial (or more general) character of the quantities concerned (rank, co/contravariant quality, and in the present case association with $\mathcal{M}$ or $\mathcal{X}$) rather than as integers specifying concrete components. Thus with the indices interpreted in this loose sense, the statement that a point with coordinates X^A in $\mathcal{X}$ is the image under $\mathcal{P}$ of a point with coordinates x^μ in $\mathcal{M}$ may legitimately be epressed in a simple and natural manner by

$$X^A = \mathcal{P}(x^\mu) \tag{2.1}$$

whereas with a strict traditional interpretation of A and μ such an equation would be nonsense.

The operation $\mathcal{P}$ of projection from $\mathcal{M}$ onto $\mathcal{X}$ evidently induces a corresponding projection, which we shall also denote by $\mathcal{P}$, from tangent vectors at any given point x^μ in $\mathcal{M}$ onto tangent vectors at the corresponding point $\mathcal{P}(x^\mu)$ in $\mathcal{X}$. In an obviously natural notation we shall denote the projected image of a tangent vector by the same basic symbol, distinguishing the image from the original vector only by the appropriate change from Roman to Greek of the index symbol, i.e. for any spacetime tangent vector ξ^μ we shall set

$$\xi^A = \mathcal{P}(\xi^\mu) \tag{2.2}$$

Due to the degeneracy of $\mathcal{P}$ there is in general no correpondingly induced projection operation for covectors except in the particular case of a covector α_μ that is orthogonal to the congruence of world-lines in the sense that

$$u^\mu \alpha_\mu = 0 \tag{2.3}$$

where the vector u^μ is tangent to the world line at the spacetime point in question. In this particular case the projection will induce a correponding covector on $\mathcal{X}$, for which as before we shall use the same basic symbol, i.e. we shall write

$$\alpha_A = \mathcal{P}(\alpha_\mu) \quad , \tag{2.4}$$

and in this case the operation is reversible, i.e. we shall have a bijection

$$\alpha_\mu \leftrightarrow \alpha_A \tag{2.5}$$

between orthogonal covectors at x^μ in $\mathcal{M}$ and covectors at $\mathcal{P}(x^\mu)$ in $\mathcal{X}$. We can use the (pseudo-)metric tensor $g_{\mu\nu}$ on the spacetime manifold $\mathcal{M}$ (with signature −+++ and units such that c=1) to define a corresponding bijection for tangent vectors by restricting our attention to tangent vectors on $\mathcal{M}$ that are orthogonal to the world lines in the metric sense, i.e.

$$u_\mu \xi^\mu = 0 \qquad , \qquad u_\mu = g_{\mu\nu} u^\nu \tag{2.6}$$

Subject to this restriction the projection (2.1) will have the same reversibility property as (2.4) i.e.

$$\xi^\mu \leftrightarrow \xi^A \tag{2.7}$$

in the same sense as (2.5).

The natural 1-1 correspondence that has just been defined between vectors or covectors orthogonal to the world lines in spacetime and vectors or covectors in the material medium can evidently be extended directly to general orthogonal tensors as defined in terms of tensor products of orthogonal vectors and covectors. This correspondence is of vital importance for setting up any physical theory of the mechanical behaviour of the medium, since its spacetime evolution must be described in terms of geometrical quantities (tensors etc.) defined in spacetime, whereas its intrinsic properties can only be described in terms of quantities defined directly in terms of the manifold $\mathcal{X}$ representing the material medium. (a requirement commonly dignified as the "principle of material objectivity")

Since there is no guarantee that all physically relevant spacetime tensors will turn out to be automatically orthogonal to the world lines, it is important to remark that they can always be canonically decomposed into a set of orthogonal tensors of equal or lower order by using the orthogonal projection tensor γ^μ_ν. In terms of the normalised unit tangent vector u^μ and the corresponding covector u_μ defined by

$$u^\mu u_\mu = -1 \tag{2.8}$$

this orthogonal projection operator is defined in terms of the unit tensor g^μ_ν by

$$\gamma^\mu_\nu = g^\mu_\nu + u^\mu u_\nu \tag{2.9}$$

In the particular case of an ordinary tangent vector v^μ the natural decomposition into a set consisting of an orthogonal part $_\perp v^\mu$ and a scalar $v^\parallel$ is given by

$$v^\mu = {}_\perp v^\mu + v^\parallel u^\mu \tag{2.10}$$

where

$$_\perp v^\mu = \gamma^\mu_\nu v^\nu \qquad , \qquad v^\parallel = -u_\mu v^\mu \tag{2.11}$$

while for a general covector ω_μ we similarly have

$$\omega_\mu = {}_\perp\omega_\mu + \omega_\parallel u_\mu \tag{2.12}$$

where

$$_\perp\omega_\mu = \gamma^\nu_\mu \omega_\nu \qquad , \qquad \omega_\parallel = -u^\mu \omega_\mu \tag{2.13}$$

This allows us to represent them in terms of sets of corresponding geometrical quantities defined at the corresponding point in the material medium in the form

$$v^\mu \longleftrightarrow \{ {}_\perp v^A , v^\parallel \} \tag{2.14}$$

and

$$\omega_\mu \longleftrightarrow \{ {}_\perp\omega_A , \omega_\parallel \} \quad , \tag{2.15}$$

the extension to general tensors of higher order being straightforeward albeit cumbersome.

3 KINEMATICS OF A MATERIAL MEDIUM: CONVECTED DIFFERENTIALS

The concept of material representation of spacetime tensors in terms of sets of tensors defined on the medium space (as exemplified by (2.14) and (2.15)) gives rise naturally to the concept of <u>material variation</u> defined as the difference between the material representations in any Lagrangian (i.e. world line preserving) variation between different configurations, which may either arise from a mapping between different physically conceivable evolutions of the medium or else merely from a time displacement in a single evolution. The spacetime tensor corresponding to the infinitesimal material variation between nearby states of evolution of the medium will be referred to as the convected differential [12]. We shall use the symbol Δ to denote an ordinary Lagrangian differential and we shall use the notation $d[\ ]$ for the corresponding convected differential. Thus in the case of a vector and a covector respectively (2.14) and (2.15) give rise to the correspondences

$$d[v^\mu] \leftrightarrow \{\Delta_\perp v^A, \Delta v^{\|}\} \tag{3.1}$$

and

$$d[\omega_\mu] \leftrightarrow \{\Delta_\perp \omega_A, \Delta \omega_{\|}\} \tag{3.2}$$

To evaluate these expressions we use the fact that a world line preserving variation can only change the magnitude but not the direction of the unit tangent vector u^μ: explicitly

$$\Delta u^\mu = \tfrac{1}{2} u^\mu u^\nu u^\rho \Delta_{\rho\sigma} \tag{3.3}$$

where we use the abbreviation

$$\Delta_{\rho\sigma} = \Delta g_{\rho\sigma} \tag{3.4}$$

for the Lagrangian variation of the metric. In the case of a vector we obtain

$$\Delta v^{\|} = -u_\nu \Delta v^\nu - v^\nu \Delta u_\nu \tag{3.5}$$

$$\Delta_\perp v^\mu = \gamma^\mu_\nu \Delta v^\nu + v^\nu (u^\mu \Delta u_\nu + u_\nu \Delta u^\mu) \tag{3.6}$$

Since the bracketed quantity in the last expression is automatically parallel to u^μ it does not contribute to the material projection, so that we obtain

$$\Delta_\perp v^A = \mathcal{P}(\Delta_\perp v^\mu) = \mathcal{P}(\gamma^\mu_\nu \Delta v^\nu) \tag{3.7}$$

and hence

$$\begin{aligned} d[v^\mu] &= \gamma^\mu_\nu \Delta v^\nu + u^\mu \Delta v^{\|} \\ &= \Delta v^\mu - u^\mu v^\nu \Delta u_\nu \end{aligned} \tag{3.8}$$

In the case of a covector we obtain

$$\Delta \omega_{\|} = -u^\nu \Delta \omega_\nu - \omega_\nu \Delta u^\nu \tag{3.9}$$

$$\Delta_\perp \omega_\mu = \gamma^\nu_\mu \Delta \omega_\nu + \omega_\nu (u^\nu \Delta u_\mu + u_\mu \Delta u^\nu) \tag{3.10}$$

both terms in the last expression being automatically orthogonal to u^μ. Thus using

$$\Delta_\perp \omega_A = \mathcal{P}(\Delta_\perp \omega_\mu) \tag{3.11}$$

we immediately obtain

$$\begin{aligned} d[\omega_\mu] &= \Delta_\perp \omega_\mu + u_\mu \Delta \omega_{\|} \\ &= \Delta \omega_\mu + \omega_\nu u^\nu \Delta u_\mu \end{aligned} \tag{3.12}$$

The extension to a general tensor is now automatic: it suffices to add an appropriately analogous term for each extra index. Thus for a general mixed tensor $T^{\mu\cdots}{}_{\nu\cdots}$ one obtains the relation [12] between convected and Lagrangian differentials in the form

$$\begin{aligned} d[T^{\mu\cdots}{}_{\nu\cdots}] = \Delta T^{\mu\cdots}{}_{\nu\cdots} &+ T^{\mu\cdots}{}_{\rho\cdots} u^\rho \Delta u_\nu + \cdots \\ &- T^{\rho\cdots}{}_{\nu\cdots} u^\mu \Delta u_\rho - \cdots \end{aligned} \tag{3.13}$$

where the Lagrangian differential of the covector u_μ is obtainable by substituting the formula (3.3) in the expression

$$\Delta u_\mu = g_{\mu\nu} \Delta u^\nu + u^\nu \Delta_{\mu\nu} \tag{3.14}$$

An important particular case [8] covered by the general formula (3.13) is that in which instead of making a comparison between nearby but different states of material motion (as one needs to do in perturbation theory) one wishes to study <u>time</u> variations in a single given state of motion. This correpcnds to the case in which the Lagrangian variation is simply given by <u>Lie differentiation</u> with respect to a time displacement vector field, ζ^μ say, which we shall denote by $\zeta\pounds$, i.e. we set

$$\Delta = \zeta\pounds \tag{3.15}$$

where the vector ζ^μ is an arbitrarily normalised tangent to the flow, which can therefore be expressed in the form

$$\zeta^\mu = u^\mu \Delta\tau \tag{3.16}$$

where $\Delta\tau$ is an arbitrary scalar field interpretable as representing the local value of the corresponding infinitesimal proper time displacement allong the world lines. Although the various separate terms in (3.13) will involve derivatives of ξ^μ, the intrinsic nature of the material variation will ensure that the convected differential will only depend on the scalar value of the displacement $d\tau$ at the point under consideration, so that it will take the form

$$d\,[T^{\mu\cdots}{}_{\nu\cdots}] = [T^{\mu\cdots}{}_{\nu\cdots}]^{\bullet}\, d\tau \tag{3.17}$$

where the tensor $[T^{\mu\cdots}{}_{\nu\cdots}]^{\bullet}$ so defined is what we refer to as the convected derivative. By direct substitution of (3.15) and (3.16) in (3.13) one can check that the terms involving gradients of $d\tau$ do indeed cancell out, so that one recovers the original formula [8] forthe convected derivative, namely

$$[T^{\mu\cdots}{}_{\nu\cdots}]^{\bullet} = \dot{T}^{\mu\cdots}{}_{\nu\cdots} + T^{\mu\cdots}{}_{\rho\cdots}(\dot{u}_\nu + \nabla_\nu)u^\rho + \cdots - T^{\rho\cdots}{}_{\nu\cdots}(\dot{u}_\rho + \nabla_\rho)u^\mu - \cdots \tag{3.18}$$

where ∇_μ is the usual metric covariant differentiation operator and where we use a simple dot without square brackets to denote covariant differation with respect to proper time, i.e. $^{\bullet} = u^\rho\nabla_\rho$. In the particular case of the unit tangent vector itself, the dot operation gives the acceleration vector, whose covariant form is also expressible as a Lie derivative:

$$\dot{u}_\mu = u\,\pounds\, u_\mu \tag{3.19}$$

Just as (3.13) is a generalisation of the earlier formula (3.18), so also (3.18) is itself a generalisation of a previous formula given by Oldroyd [7] for the particular case of tensors entirely orthogonal to the world lines, for which, as pointed out by Ehlers [13], the convected derivative reduces to the orthogonal projection of the Lie derivative. An important example is the divergence tensor $\theta_{\mu\nu}$ of the material flow, as defined by the decomposition

$$\nabla_\mu u_\nu = \theta_{\mu\nu} + \omega_{\mu\nu} - u_\mu \dot{u}_\nu \tag{3.20}$$

where the vorticity tensor $\omega_{\mu\nu}$ is antisymmetric and $\theta_{\mu\nu}$ is symmetric. It is related to the strain tensor $\gamma_{\mu\nu}$ (i.e. the covariant version of the orthogonal projection tensor (2.9)) by

$$\theta_{\mu\nu} = \tfrac{1}{2}[\gamma_{\mu\nu}]^{\bullet} \tag{3.21}$$

4 MECHANICS OF A PERFECT ELASTIC MEDIUM

The convercted differential and derivative that were described in the previous section are potentially useful for the kinematic analysis of any kind of material medium. One of the simplest applications is to the theory of a medium whose mechanical behaviour satisfies the following (by now standard) criterion of perfect elasticity. A perfect elastic medium can be characterised succinctly by the condition that its energy-momentum tensor is a material function of the metric tensor with respect to the flow field specified by its timelike eigenvector. This means that the energy momentum tensor takes the form

$$T^{\mu\nu} = \rho u^\mu u^\nu + p^{\mu\nu} \tag{4.1}$$

where the pressure tensor satisfies the orthogonality condition

$$p^{\mu\nu} u_\nu = 0 \tag{4.2}$$

so that the material representation of $T^{\mu\nu}$ is expressible as

$$T^{\mu\nu} \longleftrightarrow \{p^{AB}, 0, \rho\} \quad , \tag{4.3}$$

and this representation must be a function of the corresponding representation of the metric tensor, namely

$$g_{\mu\nu} \longleftrightarrow \{\gamma_{AB}, 0, -1\} \tag{4.4}$$

Thus at each point in the three-dimensional manifold $\mathcal{X}$ representing the medium there are well defined functions determining the pressure components p^{AB} and also the density ρ in terms of the strain components γ_{AB} . There is however a restriction that prevents these functions from all being chosen arbitrarily, namely the local energy-momentum conservation law

$$\nabla_\mu T^{\mu\nu} = 0 \tag{4.5}$$

which has four independent components, whereas the acceleration of the flow has only three independent degrees of freedom. In order to avoid having an overdetermined system of equations of motion, one must require that the component of (4.5) allong the flow (i.e. the conservation of rest frame energy as distinct from momentum) should be satisfied as an identity. The remaining independent equations are given by

$$\gamma^\mu_\nu \nabla_\rho T^{\rho\nu} = 0 \tag{4.6}$$

which is equivalent to the equations of motion

$$\rho \dot{u}^\mu = - \gamma^\mu_\nu \nabla_\rho p^{\rho\nu} \quad . \tag{4.7}$$

The equation that must be satisfied identically is

$$u_\nu \nabla_\mu T^{\mu\nu} = 0 \tag{4.8}$$

which is equivalent to

$$\dot{\rho} = -(\rho \gamma^{\mu\nu} + p^{\mu\nu}) \theta_{\mu\nu} \tag{4.9}$$

Now it follows from (3.21) that this last can be expressed in terms of convected derivatives as

$$[\rho]^{\cdot} = -\tfrac{1}{2}(\rho\gamma^{\mu\nu} + p^{\mu\nu}) [\gamma_{\mu\nu}]^{\cdot} \tag{4.10}$$

which means that convected variations allong the world lines must satisfy

$$d[\rho] = -\tfrac{1}{2}(\rho\gamma^{\mu\nu} + p^{\mu\nu}) \, d[\gamma_{\mu\nu}] \tag{4.11}$$

and hence that the corresponding variations of the material projections in $\mathcal{X}$ must satisfy

$$d\rho = -\tfrac{1}{2}(\rho\gamma^{AB} + p^{AB}) \, d\gamma_{AB} \tag{4.12}$$

This will be satisfied automatically for an arbitrary equation of state $\rho = \rho(\gamma_{AB})$ if and only if the corresponding equations for the six algebraically independant pressure components are specified by

$$p^{AB} = -2 \frac{\partial \rho}{\partial \gamma_{AB}} - \rho \gamma^{AB} \tag{4.13}$$

By carrying out a second partial differentiation of the single equation of state function for ρ with respect to the strain γ_{AB} we deduce that the material variation of the pressure tensor will be given by

$$dp^{AB} = -\tfrac{1}{2}(E^{ABCD} + p^{AB}\gamma^{CD}) \, d\gamma_{CD} \tag{4.14}$$

where the <u>elasticity tensor</u>, whose material projection is defined by

$$E^{ABCD} = -2 \frac{\partial p^{AB}}{\partial \gamma_{CD}} - p^{AB}\gamma^{CD} \tag{4.15}$$

will obey the symmetry conditions

$$E^{\mu\nu\rho\sigma} = E^{(\mu\nu)(\rho\sigma)} = E^{\rho\sigma\mu\nu} \tag{4.16}$$

as well as the orthogonality requirement

$$E^{\mu\nu\rho\sigma} u_\sigma = 0 \tag{4.17}$$

A familiar special case of a perfect elastic medium is that of an ordinary perfect fluid, which can be defined within the present context by the condition that its density ρ be a function only of the determinant $|\gamma|$ of the material projection of the strain tensor, i.e.

$$\rho = \rho(|\gamma|) \tag{4.18}$$

It follows from (4.13) that the pressure tensor will then take the purely isotropic form

$$p^{\mu\nu} = p\gamma^{\mu\nu} \tag{4.19}$$

with the pressure scalar given by

$$p = -2|\gamma|\frac{d\rho}{d|\gamma|} \tag{4.20}$$

while the elasticity tensor will be given in terms of the bulk modulus

$$\beta = -2|\gamma|\frac{dp}{d|\gamma|} \tag{4.21}$$

by the formula

$$E^{\mu\nu\rho\sigma} = (\beta - p)\gamma^{\mu\nu}\gamma^{\rho\sigma} + 2p\,\gamma^{\mu(\rho}\gamma^{\sigma)\nu} \tag{4.22}$$

5 SMALL GRAVITATIONAL PERTURBATIONS OF AN ELASTIC MEDIUM

Having seen how to set up a system of exactly self-consistent but non-linear equations governing a perfect elastic medium in the framework of General Relativity, we are now ready to derive the linearised wave equation governing small perturbations relative to a known background, such as might be induced by weak incoming gravitational radiation.

It is usually convenient to think of the perturbations as being determined in terms of a vector field ξ^μ that specifies the infinitesimal displacement of the world lines relative to their positions in the known background space. Of course such a displacement is entirely guage dependent and can always be reduced to zero by the use of an appropriate Lagrangian (world line dragging) mapping of the perturbed space onto the background, but it is often convenient to fix the gauge by a more purely geometric requirement such as the preservation of a harmonic coordinate system, which is a generalisation of the usual Newtonian procedure of defining the displacements relative to the fixed Euclidean structure of space. We shall use the symbol δ to denote the Eulerian variations of any quantity as specified by any such geometric prescription for the mapping of the perturbed spacetime onto the unperturbed background. The difference between the Lagrangian variations denoted by Δ and the Eulerian variations denoted by δ is given by Lie differentiation with respect to the corresponding infinitesimal displacement field ξ^μ, i.e.

$$\Delta = \delta + \xi\pounds \tag{5.1}$$

Thus in particular the Lagrangian variation of the metric tensor is given by

$$\Delta_{\mu\nu} = h_{\mu\nu} + 2\nabla_{(\mu}\xi_{\nu)} \tag{5.2}$$

where we use the usual notion

$$h_{\mu\nu} = \delta g_{\mu\nu} \tag{5.3}$$

for the Eulerian variation of the metric arising from the gravitational waves under consideration.

As far as quantities characterising the material medium are concerned, it is easier to work with Lagrangian than Eulerian variations since the former are related directly (via (3.13)) to convected variations and hence to the material variations that are governed directly by the equations of state. In the case of orthogonal covariant tensors, including the special case of scalars, we see from (3.13) that the Lagrangian variation is given directly by the convected variation, and hence from (4.12) we find that the Lagrangian variation of the density is given in terms of that of the metric by

$$\Delta\rho = -\tfrac{1}{2}\rho\,y^{\rho\sigma}\Delta_{\rho\sigma} \tag{5.4}$$

where for future convenience we introduce the abbreviation

$$y^{\rho\sigma} = \gamma^{\rho\sigma} + \rho^{-1}p^{\rho\sigma} \tag{5.5}$$

For a contravariant tensor, however, (3.13) introduces extra terms, so that for the dependence of the Eulerian variation of the pressure tensor in terms of the metric (4.14) gives rise to the formula

$$\Delta p^{\mu\nu} = -\tfrac{1}{2}\left\{E^{\mu\nu\rho\sigma} + p^{\mu\nu}\gamma^{\rho\sigma} - 4\,p^{\rho(\mu}u^{\nu)}u^{\sigma}\right\}\Delta_{\rho\sigma} \tag{5.6}$$

Using these results together with the expression (3.3) for the Lagrangian variation of the flow vector field u^{μ} itself, we are now in a position to work out the perturbed equations of motion by taking the variation of the exact equations of motion (4.7). It is evidently most convenient to start from the Lagrangian variation, i.e.

$$\Delta(\rho\dot{u}^{\mu} + \gamma^{\mu}_{\nu}\nabla_{\rho}p^{\nu\rho}) = 0 \tag{5.7}$$

which works out explicitly as

$$(A^{\mu\nu}{}_{\rho}{}^{\sigma} - \rho\gamma^{\mu}_{\rho}u^{\nu}u^{\sigma})\Delta\Gamma^{\rho}{}_{\nu\sigma} + \gamma^{\mu}_{\rho}\epsilon_{\nu\sigma}\nabla_{\tau}E^{\rho\tau\nu\sigma}$$
$$= \left\{p^{\mu\nu}\dot{u}^{\sigma} - \tfrac{1}{2}\dot{u}^{\mu}p^{\nu\sigma} - 2A^{\mu(\nu}{}_{\rho}{}^{\tau)}(\theta^{\rho}{}_{\tau} + \omega^{\rho}{}_{\tau})u^{\sigma} + \rho\gamma^{\mu}_{\rho}\dot{u}^{\rho}u^{\nu}u^{\sigma}\right\}\Delta_{\nu\sigma} \tag{5.8}$$

using the abbreviation

$$\epsilon_{\mu\nu} = -\tfrac{1}{2}\Delta\gamma_{\mu\nu} = \tfrac{1}{2}\gamma^{\rho}_{\mu}\gamma^{\sigma}_{\nu}\Delta_{\rho\sigma} \tag{5.9}$$

for the relative strain tensor, and

$$A^{\mu\nu}{}_{\rho}{}^{\sigma} = E^{\mu\nu}{}_{\rho}{}^{\sigma} - \gamma^{\mu}_{\rho}p^{\nu\sigma} \tag{5.10}$$

for the modified elasticity tensor first introduced in a classical context by Hadamard. When the Lagrangian metric perturbation $\Delta_{\mu\nu}$ is evaluated by use of (5.2), and the corresponding perturbation of the affine connection components $\Gamma^{\mu}{}_{\nu\sigma}$ is evaluated using the corresponding substitution

$$\Delta\Gamma^{\mu}{}_{\nu\sigma} = \nabla_{(\sigma}\Delta^{\mu}{}_{\nu)} - \tfrac{1}{2}\nabla^{\mu}\Delta_{\nu\sigma}$$
$$= \nabla_{(\nu}\nabla_{\sigma)}\xi^{\mu} + \nabla_{(\nu}h^{\mu}{}_{\sigma)} + \tfrac{1}{2}\nabla^{\mu}h_{\nu\sigma} - \xi^{\rho}R^{\mu}{}_{(\nu\sigma)\rho} \tag{5.11}$$

where the Riemann tensor is defined by

$$(\nabla_{\mu}\nabla_{\nu} - \nabla_{\nu}\nabla_{\mu})\xi_{\rho} = R_{\mu\nu\rho\sigma}\xi^{\sigma}\quad, \tag{5.12}$$

then we see that the basic perturbation equation (5.8) takes the form of a hyperbolic wave equation for the displacement vector ξ^{μ} when $h_{\mu\nu}$ is given. The characteristic cones and the corresponding sound speeds can be worked out directly from (4.7) by considering discontinuities [10] without any need of the full set of perturbation equations given here.

In order to have a complete system of equations governing the interaction of weak gravitational radiation with an elastic medium we need an additional wave equation governing the gravitational perturbation $h_{\mu\nu}$. This is obtainable by taking the appropriate perturbation of the Einstein gravitational equations, which are expressible (in units with G=1) by

$$\hat{R}^{\mu\nu} = 8\pi T^{\mu\nu} \tag{5.13}$$

where the Ricci tensor is defined by

$$R_{\mu\nu} = R_{\mu\rho\nu}{}^{\rho} \tag{5.14}$$

and where we use the notation $\hat{\ }$ for the partial trace subtraction operation defined by

$$\hat{R}^{\mu\nu} = R^{\mu\nu} - \tfrac{1}{2}g^{\mu\nu}R_{\rho}{}^{\rho} \tag{5.15}$$

In our work up to this stage we have been concentrating on material aspects, so that Lagrangian variations have given the simplest formulae. However the advantages of being able to use more general Eulerian variations become apparent now that we come to the properly gravitational aspect, since it is well known that the perturbed Einstein equations in the Eulerian form

$$\delta(\hat{R}^{\mu\nu} - 8\pi T^{\mu\nu}) = 0 \tag{5.16}$$

can be greatly simplified by the imposition of the harmonic gauge condition

$$\nabla_{\mu}\hat{h}^{\mu\nu} = 0 \tag{5.17}$$

Under these conditions most of the terms drop out and one is left with an equation of the form

$$\Box \hat{h}^{\mu\nu} = -16\pi\, \delta T^{\mu\nu} \tag{5.18}$$

where the relevant wave operator is defined by

$$\Box \hat{h}^{\mu\nu} = \nabla_\rho \nabla^\rho \hat{h}^{\mu\nu} - \hat{R}^{\mu\nu} \hat{h}_\rho{}^\rho + 2 C^\mu{}_\rho{}^\nu{}_\sigma \hat{h}^{\sigma\rho} - \tfrac{2}{3} R_\rho{}^\rho \left(\hat{h}^{\mu\nu} - \tfrac{1}{4} g^{\mu\nu} \hat{h}_\rho{}^\rho \right) \tag{5.19}$$

using the standard notation

$$C^{\mu\nu}{}_{\rho\sigma} = R^{\mu\nu}{}_{\rho\sigma} - 2 g^{[\mu}_{[\rho} \left(R^{\nu]}_{\sigma]} - \tfrac{1}{6} g^{\nu]}_{\sigma]} R_\tau{}^\tau \right) \tag{5.20}$$

(with square brackets denoting antisymmetrisation) for Weyl's trace-free conformal tensor. The Eulerian variation of the energy-momentum tensor is obtainable using (5.1) in terms of a Lie derivative and a more easily evaluable Lagrangian variation. Thus starting from (4.1) and again using (3.1), (5.4), and (5.6), we obtain finally

$$\delta T^{\mu\nu} = -\tfrac{1}{2} \left(\mathcal{E}^{\mu\nu\rho\sigma} + T^{\mu\nu} g^{\rho\sigma} \right) \Delta_{\rho\sigma} + 2 T^{\rho(\mu} \nabla_\rho \xi^{\nu)} - \xi^\rho \nabla_\rho T^{\mu\nu} \tag{5.21}$$

where, following Friedman and Schutz [14] we have constructed a generalised (non-orthogonal) elasticity tensor with the same symmetry properties as those of the ordinary elasticity tensor (4.16) according to the prescription

$$\mathcal{E}^{\mu\nu\rho\sigma} = E^{\mu\nu\rho\sigma} + 6 u^{(\mu} u^{\nu} p^{\rho\sigma)} - 8 u^{(\mu} p^{\nu)(\rho} u^{\sigma)} - \rho u^\mu u^\nu u^\rho u^\sigma \tag{5.22}$$

The coupled system of equations (5.8) and (5.18) simplifies considerably when not only the perturbations but also the background gravitational field is weak, as is the case in terrestrial (as opposed to neutron star) applications. In such cases we may suppose that there is a small dimensionless parameter, ϵ, loosely interpretable as an upper bound not only on the order of magnitude of the gravitational wave perturbations $h_{\mu\nu}$, $\epsilon_{\mu\nu}$ etc., but also of the deviations of the background metric from the flat Minkowski form. It then follows from the Einstein equations that the density ρ must also be of linear order in ϵ as the latter tends to zero, while (by the virial theorem) the pressure in the self gravitating system is of even higher order, tending to zero even when divided by ϵ, i.e. in standard notation

$$p^{\mu\nu} = o(\epsilon) \tag{5.23}$$

(in our original derivation [11] a printer's error substituted 0 in place of o throughout.) Since the unperturbed energy-momentum tensor will be at most of linear order in ϵ its perturbation will be of higher order, i.e.

$$\delta T^{\mu\nu} = o(\epsilon) \tag{5.24}$$

so that the gravitational wave equation (5.18) will to lowest order be of simple Dalembertian form, i.e.

$$\nabla_\rho \nabla^\rho h^{\mu\nu} = o(\epsilon) \tag{5.25}$$

It follows that in addition to the harmonic gauge condition we can to this order make the further gauge simplifications

$$h_{\mu\nu} u^\nu = o(\epsilon) \ , \qquad h_\nu{}^\nu = o(\epsilon) \tag{5.26}$$

and to the same order the wave equation for the displacement reduces to the form

$$u^\nu u^\sigma \nabla_\nu \nabla_\sigma \xi^\mu - \rho^{-1} \nabla_\nu \{ E^{\mu\nu\rho\sigma} (\nabla_\rho \xi_\sigma + \tfrac{1}{2} h_{\rho\sigma}) \} = o(\epsilon) \tag{5.27}$$

in agreement with the calculations of Dyson [2] and Papapetrou [3].

As a simple practical application Dyson considered the case of an elastic medium that is isotropic, as it will be in the case of a typical metal when considered on scales large compared with the microscopic crystalline domains. In such a case, (in consequence of (5.23)) the elasticity tensor will take the form

$$E^{\mu\nu\rho\sigma} = \beta\gamma^{\mu\nu}\gamma^{\rho\sigma} + 2\mu(\gamma^{\mu(\rho}\gamma^{\sigma)\nu} - \tfrac{1}{3}\gamma^{\mu\nu}\gamma^{\rho\sigma}) \tag{5.28}$$

where β is the bulk modulus and μ is the rigidity modulus. Now under these conditions, it follows from (5.26) that the only gravitational coupling term in (5.28) reduces to the form

$$\nabla_\nu(E^{\mu\nu\rho\sigma}h_{\rho\sigma}) = 2h^{\mu\nu}\nabla_\nu\mu \tag{5.29}$$

which shows, as pointed out by Dyson, that the gravitational waves couple with the elastic displacement only via non-uniformities of the rigidity. (In the case of a traditional Weber bar detector the relevant non-uniformity is provided by the discontinuity at the surface of the cylinder.)

REFERENCES

[1] Weber, J., Phys. Rev. 117 (1960) 306.

[2] Dyson, F.J., Astroph. J. 156 (1969) 529.

[3] Papapetrou, A., Ann. Inst. H. Poincaré A16 (1972) 63.

[4] Carter, B., and Quintana, H., Astroph. J. 202 (1975) 54.

[5] Maugin, G.A., J. Math. Phys. 19 (1978) 1198.

[6] Souriau, J.M., Géométrie et Relativité (Herman, Paris, 1965)

[7] Oldroyd, J.G., Proc. Roy. Soc. A270 (1970) 103.

[8] Carter, B., and Qintana, H., Proc. Roy. Soc. A331 (1972) 57.

[9] Carter, B. Commun. Math. Phys. 30 (1973) 261.

[10] Carter, B., Phys. Rev. D7 (1973) 1590.

[11] Carter, B., and Qintana, H., Phys. Rev. D16 (1977) 2928.

[12] Carter, B., Proc. Roy. Soc. A372 (1980) 169.

[13] Ehlers, J., in Israel, W., (ed) Relativity, Astrophysics and Cosmology (Reidel, Dordrecht, 1970) 89.

[14] Penrose, R., in DeWitt, C., and Wheeler, J.A., (eds) Battelle Rencontre (Gordon and Breach, New York, 1968)

[15] Friedman, J.L., and Schutz, B.L., Astroph. J. 200 (1975) 204.

THE LOW TEMPERATURE GRAVITATIONAL WAVE DETECTOR AT STANFORD UNIVERSITY

Peter F. Michelson

Physics Department and High Energy Physics Laboratory
Stanford University
Stanford, California 94305

The sensitivity of a 4800 kg cryogenic resonant mass gravitational radiation detector operated at Stanford University is discussed. The rms noise level at the output of the detector corresponds to a dimensionless strain sensitivity of 10^{-18}. The observed noise level has been used to establish a new observational upper limit on the flux of 1 kHz gravity wave bursts.

INTRODUCTION

The sensitivity of resonant-mass gravitational wave detectors is significantly increased by operation at low temperature; the Brownian motion noise of the antenna is reduced and it is possible to use the properties of superconductors to build Josephson-effect parametric amplifiers and low noise electromechanical transducers. Several experimental groups have been working for a number of years on solving the technical problems involved in operating cryogenic detectors and several preliminary results have been published (Boughn, et al. (1977); Amaldi, et al. (1977); Davis and Richard (1980); Blair and Mann (1981)). The detector, which has been operated at Stanford University for more than one year, is between 2 and 3 orders of magnitude more sensitive than any previous detector. The rms output noise level corresponds to a dimensionless strain sensitivity of 10^{-18}. The output has been used to establish a new observational upper limit on the flux of 1 kHz gravity wave bursts. In this lecture I will discuss the Stanford detector, its calibration and the observed output signals.

THE DETECTOR

David Blair (this volume) has discussed the general form of resonant bar detectors shown in Figure 1. The present Stanford detector consists of a $4.8 \cdot 10^6$ g cylindrical aluminum antenna maintained at 4.3 K. The free fundamental longitudinal mode of oscillation has a frequency of 841.66 Hz and a maximum observed Q-value of $5 \cdot 10^6$. The motion of one end of the antenna is converted to an electrical signal by means of a resonant superconducting transducer (Paik (1976)). This signal is amplified by a superconducting Josephson-effect magnetometer or SQUID (Hollenhorst and Giffard (1979)).

The transducer is shown schematically in Figure 2. It consists of a mechanically-resonant diaphragm constructed from niobium which is a superconductor at the detector's operating temperature. A spiral wound, flat superconducting coil faces each side of the diaphragm. This pair of coils is connected in parallel with the input coil of the SQUID. An arrangement of heat switches allows a persistent current to be stored in the superconducting loop formed by the flat coils. Motion of the diaphragm changes the inductance of this loop; because the total magnetic flux through the loop is conserved an output current proportional to the displacement of the diaphragm then flows through the input coil of the SQUID. It is straightforward (Michelson and Taber (1981) to show that this

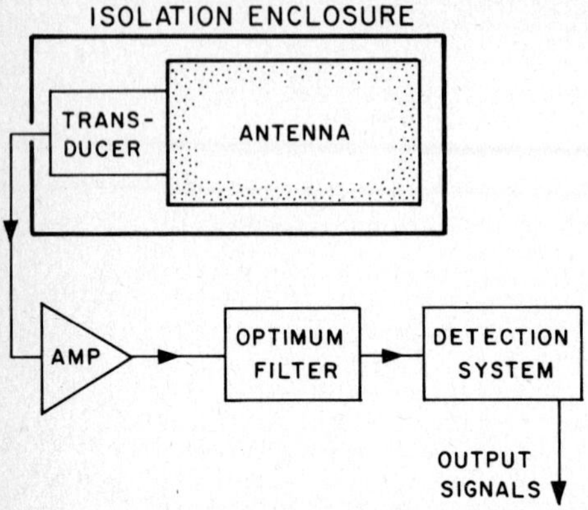

Figure 1
Typical arrangement of a resonant-mass gravitational wave detector. The antenna motion is converted by a transducer into an electrical signal which is amplified by a sensitive amplifier. The output is then suitably filtered and detected.

electromechanical transduction is described by the following equations of motion:

$$\ddot{X}_t + \ddot{X}_a = -\frac{f_t(t)}{m_t} = -\frac{\gamma}{m_t} I_t - \omega_t^2 X_t - \omega_t \dot{X}_t / Q_t + \tilde{F}_t / m_t \tag{1}$$

$$\dot{I}_t = V_t / L_t + \gamma \dot{X}_t / L_t \tag{2}$$

where $-f_t$ is the time-varying restoring force applied to the transducer, m_t is the transducer effective mass and I_t is the signal current flowing into the output terminals. γ is an electromechanical coupling parameter equal to $I_o(dL/dx)$ where I_o is the persistent current stored in the transducer. V_t is the transducer output voltage and X_t is the displacement of the diaphragm relative to the position of the end of the antenna X_a. $\tilde{F}_t$ is a fluctuating Nyquist force associated with mechanical losses in the diaphragm due to the finite quality factor of the diaphragm Q_t. This noise source has a spectral density given by

$$S_F(\omega) = 2k_B T \,\omega_t m_t / Q_t \tag{3}$$

where T is the temperature of the diaphragm and k_B is Boltzmann's constant.

The equation of motion for the fundamental mode of the antenna can be written as

$$\ddot{X}_a + \omega_a^2 X_a + (\omega_a / Q_a)\dot{X}_a = \frac{F_g(t) + \tilde{F}_a(t) + f_t(t)}{m_a} \tag{4}$$

where m_a is the effective mass of the antenna. $F_g(t)$ is the time-dependent driving force that results from projecting the tidal gravitational force onto the lowest eigenmode of the antenna. $\tilde{F}_a$ is the fluctuating Nyquist force due to dissipation in the antenna. It has a spectral density of the same form as eq. (3).

Equations (1) - (4) are a complete description of the detector except for the SQUID amplifier. In the present mode of operation the SQUID can be represented by a linear current amplifier in series with an input inductance L_s (Hollenhorst and Giffard (1980)). Then V_t and I_t are related by

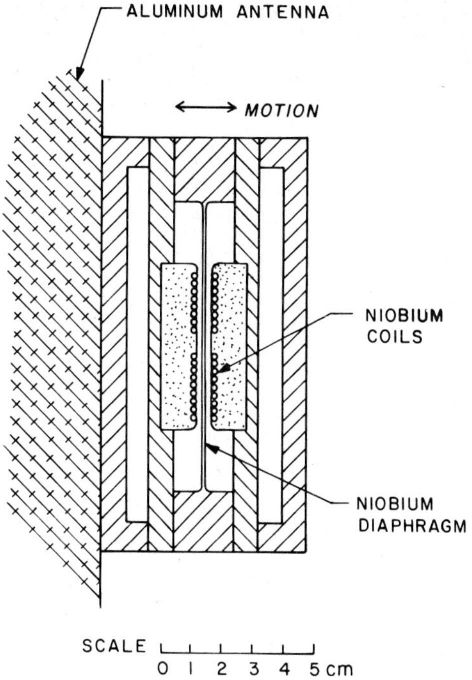

Figure 2
Superconducting electromechanical transducer. A thin circular niobium diaphragm is clamped at its edge to one end of the antenna. By storing a persistent current in the flat coils that face the diaphragm the transducer resonant frequency is tuned to match that of the antenna.

$$V_t(t) = - L_s \dot{I}_t - I_t R_e + \tilde{V}_e + \tilde{V}_a \quad . \tag{5}$$

The resistance R_e represents the ac electrical dissipation present in the transducer and $\tilde{V}_e$ is the associated Nyquist voltage noise. $\tilde{V}_a$ is the back-reaction voltage noise of the SQUID. The current noise of the SQUID I_a only appears as an additive broadband noise source at the output. The spectral densities of the SQUID noise sources can be specified in terms of a noise temperature T_N and a bandwidth τ^{-1} such that

$$S_{I_a}(\omega) = kT_N\tau/L_S$$

$$S_{V_a}(\omega) = kT_N L_S/\tau \quad . \tag{6}$$

Equations (1) - (6) are a nearly complete description of the detector and can be summarized by the electromechanical equivalent circuit shown in Figure 3. In addition to the noise sources described above, the detector is subject to a variety of external non-thermal noise sources. These will be discussed in a later section.

The upper solid curve in Figure 4 shows the measured output noise power spectrum of the complete detector. The spectrum calculated using the model described above is also shown. The relative contributions from various noise sources in the detector can be varied to give an optimum overall signal-to-noise (SNR) by adjusting the parameters of the detector such as transducer mass, SQUID inductance, etc.

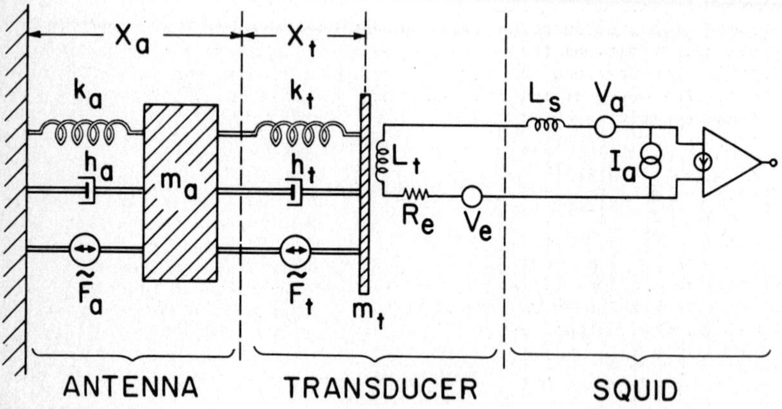

Figure 3

Electromechanical equivalent circuit of a gravitational wave antenna with a resonant transducer. All the important noise sources arising from electrical or mechanical dissipation in the detector are shown and are discussed in the text.

OPTIMUM SIGNAL-TO-NOISE-RATIO AND DETECTOR NOISE TEMPERATURE

In his lecture Blair has discussed the advantages of using high-Q resonant bar antennas for detecting impulsive sources of gravitational radiation. A straightforward method for optimizing the detector parameters and the data filtering algorithm (Tyson (1974); Kafka (1975); Pizzella (1979); Michelson and Taber (1981)) is provided by the theory of optimum linear filtering (Whalen (1971)).

If our objective is to detect a gravitational tidal force $F_g(t)$ applied to the antenna in the presence of Gaussian noise then the optimum SNR that can be achieved is

$$\rho_o = \frac{1}{2\pi}\int_{-\infty}^{\infty} \frac{|M(\omega)|^2 |K_s(\omega)|^2}{S_n(\omega)} d\omega \tag{7}$$

where $M(\omega)$ is the Fourier transform of $F_g(t)$, $K_s(\omega)$ is the transfer function from the input to the output and $S_n(\omega)$ is the spectral density of the output noise. To actually achieve the SNR given by eq. (7) the detector output is filtered before detection by a linear filter with transfer function given by

$$K_f(\omega) = M^*(\omega)|K_s(\omega)|^2/S_n(\omega) \quad . \tag{8}$$

In actual practice, the filtering is implemented by a combination of analog and digital signal processing. Notice that the filter is in general a noncausal filter.

For an impulse signal of duration much less than the detector bandwidth (certainly a reasonable approximation) the quantity $|M(\omega)|^2$ is equal to $2\varepsilon m_a$ where ε is the energy that the gravitational burst would deposit in the antenna if it were initially at rest. The detector noise temperature T_d is defined so that $\varepsilon = k_B T_d$ for $\rho_o = 1$. Thus we can write

$$T_d = \frac{2\pi}{k_B m_a}\left[\int_{-\infty}^{\infty} \frac{|K_s(\omega)|^2}{S_n(\omega)}\, d\omega\right]^{-1} \tag{9}$$

The right-hand side of eq. (9) is multiplied by a factor of 2 because it is conventional to refer the noise temperature to the mean square of the envelope of the filtered detector output. With this definition the limiting detector noise temperature is $2T_N$.

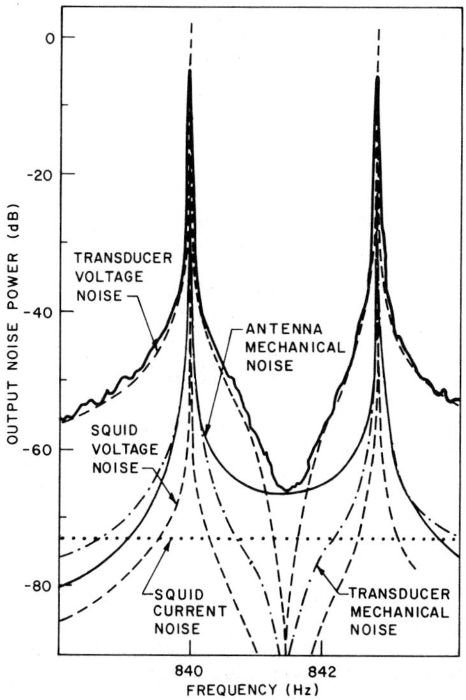

Figure 4
Measure output noise spectrum of the detector (upper solid curve). Also shown are the calculated contributions from various sources described in the text. The antenna thermal noise dominates in a 0.5 Hz bandwidth about the uncoupled antenna frequency. Elsewhere the transducer electrical noise dominates. The optimization of the detector design requires proper attention to all of these noise sources.

Since the detector noise sources discussed in the previous section are expected to be Gaussian distributed, the linearly-filtered detector output in the absence of signals is also expected to be Gaussian distributed. Thus the expected distribution of $\varepsilon_f(t)$, the squared envelope of the filtered output, is an exponential (Whalen (1971)) given by

$$P(\varepsilon_f)d\varepsilon_f = (1/k_BT_d)\exp(-\varepsilon_f/k_BT_d)d\varepsilon_f \ . \tag{10}$$

In the presence of an input signal of known strength ε_c (for example, a calibration pulse), the expected output distribution function is a Rician distribution given by

$$P(\varepsilon_f|\varepsilon_c)d\varepsilon_f = (1/k_BT_d)\exp[-(\varepsilon_f+\varepsilon_c)/k_BT_d]\ I_o(\sqrt{\varepsilon_f\varepsilon_c}/k_BT_d)d\varepsilon_f \tag{11}$$

where I_o is the modified Bessel function of zero order. In the limit $\varepsilon_c >> kT_d$, this distribution is a Gaussian with mean value ε_c.

Figure 5 shows the measured histogram of the filtered output for a typical 24 hour period. The distribution is very close to the expected behavior and the slope corresponds to T_d = 20.6 mK. The solid curve in Figure 6 shows the distribution of ε_f obtained in the presence of a test pulse (see below) of energy $\varepsilon_c = k_B \cdot$ 50 mK for 100 test pulses. The dashed line shows the Rician distribution expected in the presence of noise corresponding to the measured noise temperature of 20.6 mK. This kind of data shows that the effects of noise on the signals is well understood. The typical measured temperatures are also in agreement with detailed calculations given by Michelson and Taber (1981).

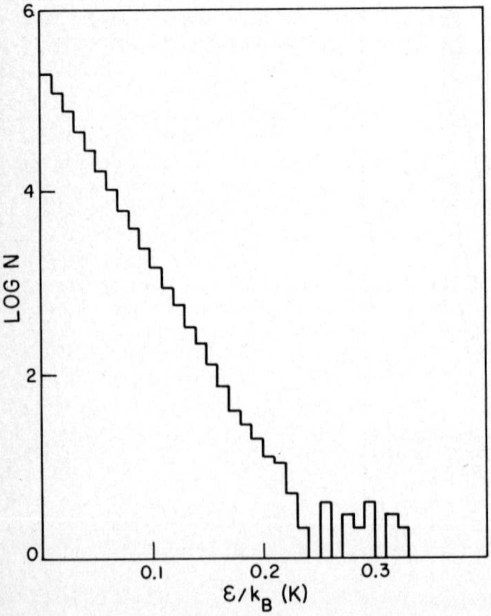

Figure 5

Typical distribution of the squared envelope of the filtered detector output. This is a histogram of data taken for a 24 hour period. The distribution is well expressed by eq. (10) with a slope corresponding to T_d = 20.6 mK.

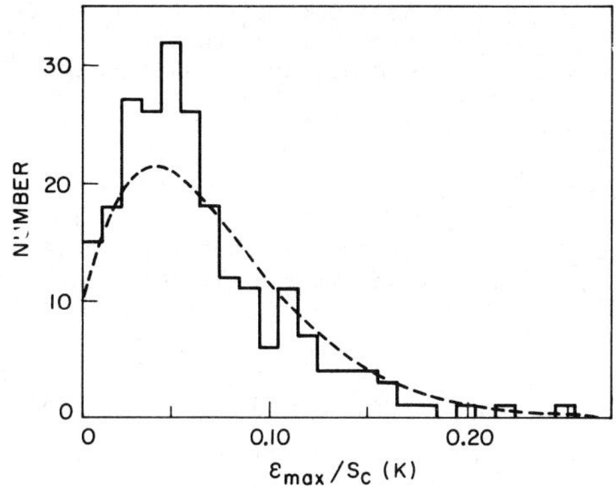

Figure 6
Distribution of the squared envelope of the output in the presence of calibration pulses. The solid line is the distribution obtained by applying 100 test pulses of effective energy $\varepsilon_c = k_B \cdot 50$ mK. The dashed line is the Rician distribution expected in the presence of noise corresponding to the measured noise temperature of 20.6 mK.

DETECTOR CALIBRATION: THE SELF-CALIBRATING CALIBRATOR

The calibration of the detector is done using a simple technique originally suggested by Stephen Boughn. A known force is applied to the antenna by a small weakly-coupled piezoelectric test transducer attached to the end of the antenna away from the main transducer. The output of the detector is examined at the appropriate time and a calibration factor for the detector can be determined. In practice the calibration factor is determined by averaging the response to many calibration pulses with $\varepsilon_c \gg kT_d$.

In order to apply a pulse of known strength the test transducer itself must be calibrated. This is accomplished in a simple manner (Giffard (1980)). Assuming only that the piezoelectric test transducer is nearly lossless and nonresonant and can be described by a 2 x 2 impedance matrix Z (see Blair's lectures), it can be shown that the energy deposited in an antenna initially at rest by applying a voltage pulse of n_c cycles at the antenna resonant frequency is

$$\varepsilon_c = \frac{\pi^2 n_c^2}{\omega_a^2 m_a} V_c^2 \left|\frac{z_{12}}{z_{22}}\right|^2 \qquad (12)$$

where V_c is the RMS amplitude of the applied voltage.

If after applying the voltage pulse to the test transducer we immediately connect the transducer input to a current amplifier with zero input impedance then the RMS amplitude of the current which flows I_c is given by

$$\frac{I_c}{V_c R_c} = \frac{\pi}{\omega_a m_a} \left|\frac{z_{12}}{z_{22}}\right|^2 . \qquad (13)$$

Using sufficiently large voltage pulses in order to obtain a measurable current the unknown impedance ratio $|z_{12}/z_{22}|^2$ is determined. Then much smaller voltage calibration pulses are applied and, using eq. (12), the main transducer is calibrated.

OBSERVATIONS WITH THE DETECTOR

Without coincidence operation with another detector of comparable sensitivity it is not possible to draw positive conclusions concerning gravitational wave signals from any observational data. However, using data recorded from January through May of 1981, we have set a measured upper limit on the distribution of gravitational wave pulses reaching the detector at the time of the experiments. (Boughn et al (1982)). Figure 7 is a summary of these observations. The solid line is a smoothed estimate at the 3σ level based on the observed event rate (dashed line). Using this data we have estimated the accidental coincidence rate we could expect if the Stanford detector were operated in coincidence with another detector of similar sensitivity. The dotted line in Figure 7 shows that substantial improvement could be obtained.

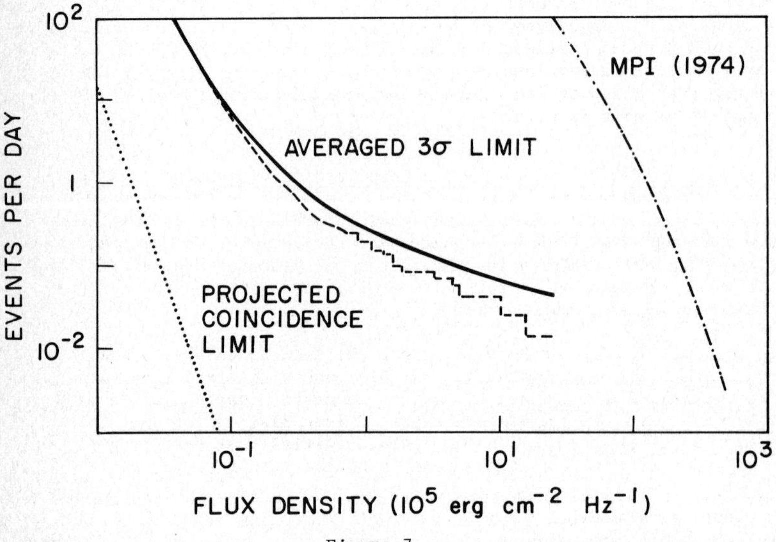

Figure 7
Plot of upper limits on the rate and strength of gravitational wave pulses which were reaching the earth during the observations. The solid line is the smoothed 3σ limit averaged over polarization and direction determined from the observations which are shown as the dashed line. The dot-dashed curve is the upper limit determined by the Munich-Frascati coincidence experiment (Billing et al (1975)). The dotted line is the upper limit that could be achieved by a coincidence experiment involving two $4.8 \cdot 10^6$ g detectors with overall noise temperatures of 20 mK.

DISCUSSION

The solid curve in Figure 7 demonstrates that during the observation period the detector was being excited by pulses with non-Gaussian statistics. Apart from gravitational radiation, the detector is known to be vulnerable to a variety of external disturbances. Some parts of the antenna and its supports are highly stressed and it is probable that occasional acoustic emission takes place. The low signal level electronics can be affected by power line transients. Earthquakes which produce easily perceptible ground motion are known to disturb the antenna. We estimate that the event rate was not significantly affected by acoustic noise, electromagnetic waves in the kHz band or charged particles from cosmic ray showers. If, as the sensitivity of detectors is significantly improved, background events due to acoustic and electromagnetic noise are found, they can be reduced by improving both the mechanical isolation of the antenna and the electromagnetic shielding.

The magnitude of events due to cosmic ray showers can be estimated using a simple heating model orignally suggested by Felix Bloch. This model was motivated by the measurements of Hofstadter and Beron (1969), They found that the acoustic energy deposited in the lowest mode of an aluminum cylinder by a pulse of relativistic electrons is proportional to the square of the number of electrons in the pulse. The heating model accounts for this behavior as follows: A pulse of charged particles loses energy W in the antenna. This local energy loss causes a temperature rise along the path of the particles which, through the thermal expansion coefficient α, induces a strain in the bar. Given this initial strain the wave equation can be solved and the energy in the low frequency eigenmodes calculated. Thus the acoustic energy will depend on the path of the particles as well as the total energy loss. Adopting a one-dimensional model for the bar and averaging over all paths through the bar, we find that the energy deposited in the fundamental mode is given by

$$\varepsilon \simeq \frac{1}{2} M\omega_o^{\,2} \left(\frac{\alpha L W}{c_v M}\right)^2 \tag{14}$$

where c_V is the specific heat and L the length of the bar. Numerically, for the Stanford antenna, this gives

$$T_{eff} = \varepsilon/k_B = (2 \times 10^{-8} K)\left(\frac{W}{100\ \text{MeV}}\right)^2 \tag{15}$$

For single cosmic rays passing through the bar this effect is insignificant. Only an extensive cosmic ray shower which deposits total energy W in the bar within a time $\tau \lesssim 1/\omega_o$ will give an impulsive background signal (with $W = 10^3 \times 100$ MeV, $T_{eff} \simeq 20$ mK). Such bursts are expected to be rare.

Grand Unification Theories have suggested the existence of massive (10^{16}GeV) magnetic monopoles (Preskill (1979); Zel'dovitch and Khlopov (1978)). The energy loss for slow moving monopoles in a metal is significant because of the interaction of the conduction electrons and the time-varying magnetic field of the monopole. Reasonable estimates (Akerlof (1980)) suggest that for aluminum at 4 K the energy loss is about 1 GeV/cm. Using this estimate in eq. (15) gives $T_{eff} = 20$ mK for the passage of a single monopole through the bar. This suggests that it may be very interesting to correlate the output of the present generation of cryogenic gravitational wave detectors with other detectors (Cabrera (1982)) capable of responding to a magnetic monopole. The possibility certainly exists that magnetic monopoles may significantly contribute to the background of events observable with cryogenic gravitational wave detectors.

CONCLUSION

The operation of a 4800 kg cryogenic detector at Stanford University has provided a new observational upper limit on the distribution of wide-band gravitational wave pulses reaching the earth during a typical period. In addition, the successful operation of this detector offers a clear demonstration that long term operation of larger cryogenic detectors is possible. We anticipate that with a few minor modifications of the present detector a noise temperature approaching 200 μK can be reached in the near future. With improvements in SQUID technology and by further cooling of the bar below 1 K, noise temperatures approaching the linear amplifier quantum limit are possible.

ACKNOWLEDGEMENTS

The work I have discussed here is a result of the efforts of the entire Stanford Gravity Wave Group including W. M. Fairbank, M. Bassan, E. Mapoles, M. S. McAshan, K. Ralls, R. C. Taber, M. Taber and B. Moskowitz. We have also benefitted from past collaboration with S. Boughn, R. P. Giffard, J. N. Hollenhorst and continuing collaboration with W. O. Hamilton and his group at L.S.U.

REFERENCES

[1] Akerlof, C., Limits on the Thermoacoustic Detectability of Electric and Magnetic Charges, preprint, Univ. of Michigan (1980).

[2] Amaldi, E., Bordoni, R., Bonifazi, P., Cosmelli, C., Giovanardi, U., Modena, I., Pallotino, G. V., Pizzella, G., and Vannaroni, G., Lett. Nuovo Cimento, 18 (1977) 425.

[3] Beron, B. L. and Hofstadter, R., Phys. Rev. Lett., 23 (1969) 184.

[4] Billing, H., Kafka, P., Maischberger, K., Meyer, F., and Winkler, W., Lett. Nuovo Cimento, 12 (1975) 111.

[5] Blair, D. G. and Mann, A. G., Il Nuovo Cimento, 61B (1981) 73.

[6] Boughn, S. P., Fairbank, W. M., Giffard, R. P., Hollenhorst, J. N., Paik, H. J., and Taber, R. C., Phys. Rev. Lett., 38 (1977) 454.

[7] Cabrera, B., Phys. Rev. Lett., 48 (1982) 1378.

[8] Davis, W. S. and Richard, J. P., Phys. Rev. D, 22 (1980) 2297.

[9] Giffard, R. P., private communication (1980).

[10] Hollenhorst, J. N. and Giffard, R. P., IEEE Trans. Mag., Mag-15 (1979) 474.

[11] Hollenhorst, J. N. and Giffard, R. P., J. Appl. Phys., 51 (1980).

[12] Kafka, P., MPI PAE/Astro. 65, Max Planck Inst., Munich (1975).

[13] Michelson, P. F. and Taber, R. C., J. Appl. Phys., 52 (1981) 4313.

[14] Paik, H. J., J. Appl. Phys., 47 (1976) 1168.

[15] Pizzella, G., Nuovo Cimento, 2 (1979) 209.

[16] Preskill, J. P., Phys. Rev. Lett., 43 (1979) 1365.

[17] Tyson, J. A., in: DeWitt-Morette, C. (ed.), Gravitational Radiation and Collapse, Proceedings of the IAU Symposium, 64 (D. Reidel, Dordrecht, 1974).

[18] Whalen, A. D. , Detection of Signals in Noise (Academic Press, New York, 1971).

[19] Zel'dovitch, Y. D. and Khlopon, M. Y., Phys. Lett., 79B (1978) 239.

DISCUSSION ON OPTICAL DETECTORS OF GRAVITATIONAL RADIATION

A. BRILLET Laboratoire de l'Horloge Atomique
Bât. 221 - Faculté des Sciences - 91405 Orsay

P. TOURRENC Laboratoire "Gravitation et Cosmologie Relativistes"
E.R.A. n° 533 - Institut Henri Poincaré
11, rue P. et M. Curie - 75231 Paris Cedex 05

INTRODUCTION

In the prospect of defining a project for building a gravitational wave antenna in France, we report here on a preliminary study consisting in the comparison between active and passive interferometers and in the evaluation of a "spectroscopic" detection technique. This work results from a collaboration with C.J. Bordé and J. Sharma (L.P.L., Villetaneuse), T. Damour (G.A.R., Meudon), J.Y. Vinet and F. Teissier du Cros (L.O.A., Palaiseau).

Our goal is to design and realize a wideband antenna whose sensitivity would be large enough to detect gravitational bursts resulting from star collapses as far as the Virgo cluster. According to the available theoretical estimates, these events would produce gravitational waves of amplitude $h \simeq 3\,10^{-21}$ to $3\,10^{-24}\,\mathrm{Hz}^{-1/2}$ on earth, with a spectrum extending from 0 to a few KHz. We will take the pessimistic value $h = 3\,10^{-24}\,\mathrm{Hz}^{-1/2}$ as a basis for the following discussion.

In part I we study different displacement sensors. At first sight active devices display less problems in optics and electronics than the passive ones. But, on the other hand, extra noises arise from the medium. An accurate analysis is necessary to know whether these extra noises are negligible or not. In the following we summarize this analysis.

In part II we consider a spectroscopic detector of gravitational radiations. In such an antenna, several difficulties displayed by interferometers do not appear (seismic isolation, laser frequency stability). A proposal was made a few years ago and is still discussed. Unfortunately it was not completely convincing on the theoretical level, moreover no analysis was performed of the signal to noise ratio. Here we study the question and we give a conclusion concerning earth bound experiments.

I. INTERFEROMETRIC DETECTORS : ACTIVE OR PASSIVE ?

We call "interferometric" the detectors which constitute basically in a resonator or an interferometer whose resonant frequency or wavelength is changed by the effect of the gravitational wave. For wideband detection, we want their end mirrors to behave like free masses in the frequency range of interest (100 Hz to 10 KHz).

Since the properties and limitations of passive interferometers (Michelson or Fabry-Perot) are described elsewhere [1], we will mainly consider here the active systems, such as described by Chebotayev [2], and presently implemented in Novosibirsk and Rehovot, and we will compare them with passive devices.

A. Fundamental limitations

Both active and passive devices are limited by fundamental types of fluctuations, that one has to keep in mind when designing an optical displacement sensor for gravitational wave detection :

- quantum limit : the quantum incertitude in the measurement of the position of the free masses yields a minimum uncertainty

$$\text{(I.1)} \qquad \Delta x \geq \sqrt{\frac{\hbar}{M\omega_G}} \simeq 1.6\ 10^{-22}\ m \times Hz^{-1/2}$$

where M is the mass of the mirror (M = 100 kg) and ω_G the frequency of the gravitational wave ($\omega_G = 2\pi \times 10^3$).

In order to reach $h = \frac{\Delta x}{L} = 3\,10^{-24}\ Hz^{-1/2}$, it is thus necessary to increase the length L of the interferometer arms to $L \simeq 50$ m.

- thermal noise : if the mirrors have a resonant mechanical frequency ($\omega_R = 2\pi \times 5000 \gg \omega_G$), and a quality factor Q ($Q \leq 10^5$), their position will fluctuate by an amount :

$$\text{(I.2)} \qquad \Delta x \geq \sqrt{\frac{4kT}{MQ\omega_R^3}} \qquad (\sim 7\,10^{-21}\ Hz^{-1/2}$$

at room temperature). One can see that this limitation is much more restrictive than the quantum noise. It puts a lower limit $L \geq 2$ km on the length of the detector, although it may be possible to reach $Q = 10^6$ at T = 4°K, in which case L needs to be 100 m only.

- photon shot noise : whatever the detection scheme, the shot noise will give a limitation

$$\text{(I.3)} \qquad h_{MIN} \geq \frac{\eta}{Q}\sqrt{\frac{\hbar\omega_L}{P}}\ Hz^{-1/2} ,$$

where P is the laser power and Q is a quality factor associated to the apparatus. Its optimum value is $Q \simeq \frac{\omega_L}{\omega_G}$ (ω_L is the light frequency), since, if Q were larger than this value, the response time of the device would be too long, and the signal would be averaged. The order of magnitude of the constant η is about unity in all the detectors (active or passive) which have been proposed up to now. It results that $h_{MIN} \simeq 10^{-21}\ Hz^{-1/2}$ for 1 Watt Argon laser ($\omega_L = 2\pi \times 6\,10^{14}$ Hz), so that reducing this noise down to $h = 3\,10^{-24}$ asks for an unrealistic power of 100 KWatt.

In passive devices, "recycling" the light [3] would reduce the necessary power down to a few tens of watts, using presently available optical technology. It may be possible also gain nearly one order of magnitude with "squeezing" techniques [4]. Unfortunately, none of these techniques seems to be of practical interest in active devices.

It results from all the above fundamental noise sources that any interferometric device (whether active or passive), aiming at the detection of gravitational waves has to be large (L > 100 m) and to use a high power light source (P > 10 W). For an active detector to be sensitive enough, one would have to imagine some way of "recycling" the light, or to decrease the value of η down to 10^{-2} , which may be possible in nonlinear systems close to bistability.

B. Active interferometric detectors

Let us now describe some possible ways of realizing an active interferometric detector, and try to evaluate their intrinsic noise sources, in excess of the previous fundamental limitations. In all active detectors, the two free masses support the mirrors of a laser resonator inside which is inserted the active medium. The gravitational wave perturbs the length of this resonator, and modifies the optical frequency emitted by the laser. This frequency change can be detected by a frequency discriminant (optical resonance filter) or by observing the beat frequency between this laser detector and a second laser (heterodyne technique).

1) Optical resonance filter [2]

The basic set-up is shown on fig. (1.a) : the light beam from the laser detector (frequency ω_1) is sent through a nonlinear absorption cell (NAC1), whose transmission exhibits a very narrow resonance of halfwidth $\Delta\omega_0 \lesssim \omega_G$ at the frequency ω_0 , characteristic of the atomic or molecular gas contained in the cell. A second laser is frequency stabilized at $\omega_2 \approx \omega_0$ with a second cell (NAC2) and the beat frequency between the two lasers is used to maintain $\omega_1 = \omega_0 + \Delta\omega_0$ by correcting ω_1 with a slow servo loop, so that the transmission of the first cell is very sensitive to any small variation of ω_1 fig. (1.b)

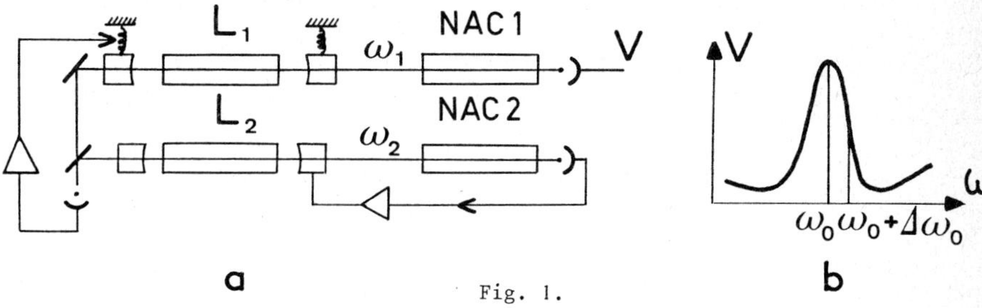

Fig. 1.

It may be interesting, for the non specialist in high resolution spectroscopy, to describe here the techniques which allow the production of very narrow molecular resonances, well below the Doppler broadening ($\Delta\omega_D \sim \omega_0 \frac{\bar{v}}{c} \sim 10^{10} s^{-1}$).

a) Saturated absorption

The saturated absorption technique is a nonlinear technique using two counterpropagating light beams. Let us first consider a first beam, at frequency ω_+, propagating in the z direction inside the gas cell. It interacts resonantly with those molecules whose velocity along the z axis is given by

$$\text{(I.4)} \qquad \omega_+ = \omega_0 \left(1 + \frac{v_z}{c}\right)$$

If the light intensity is strong enough, the velocity distribution of the molecules in the ground and excited states (a and b) will be modified according to fig. (2.a). This will now change the absorption of the second, counterpropagating, beam (ω_-) provided (I.5) $\omega_- = \omega_0 \left(1 - \frac{v_z}{c}\right)$. If $\omega_+ = \omega_-$, then (1) and (2) are verified simultaneously if $v_z = 0$ and $\omega_+ = \omega_0$. The absorption spectrum of ω_- is given by fig. (2.b)

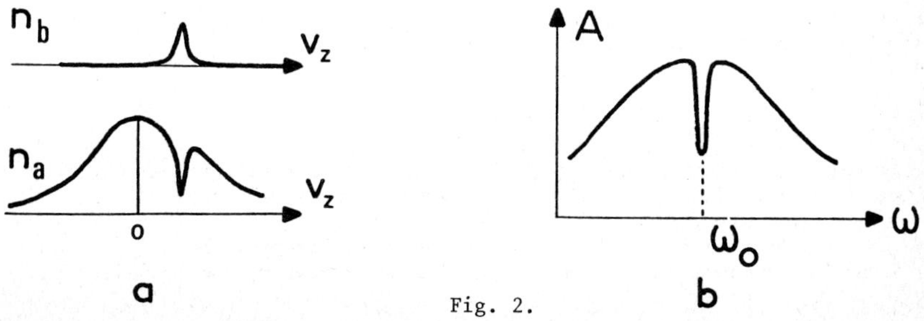

Fig. 2.

The width $\Delta\omega_c$ of the saturated absorption peak is the sum of different contributions :

(I.6) $$\Delta\omega_c = \frac{1}{\tau_n} + \frac{1}{\tau_c} + \frac{1}{\tau_T} + \Delta\omega_s$$, where τ_n is

the natural (spontaneous emission) lifetime, τ_c is the time between 2 collisions in the gas cell, τ_T is the transit time of the molecules through the laser beam ($\tau_T \simeq D/\bar{v}$, D being the beam diameter and $\bar{v}$ the average thermal velocity) and $\Delta\omega_s$ is the Rabi frequency, proportional to the light amplitude. In high resolution experiments, $\Delta\omega_c$ is usually dominated by the transit time ($\bar{v} = 1000\ m s^{-1}$ D = 1 m give $\Delta\omega_T = 1000\ s^{-1}$). This technique is widely used [5] for the realization of optical frequency standards, but the signal to noise ratio is limited by the facts that one has to use very low gas pressures in order to avoid the large pressure broadening due to long range, velocity changing, collisions, and that this technique makes a very inefficient use of the molecules because the only active ones are those belonging to the small velocity class $\Delta v_z < \frac{c}{\omega_0} \Delta\omega_c \sim 10^{-3}\ m\ s^{-1}$.

b) Two-photon Doppler free spectroscopy

A promising way to overcome these problems is to use a two-photon Doppler free technique [6]. In that case, the molecules are asked to absorb simultaneously 2 photons, since the light frequency is about half the transition frequency If the 2 photons are counterpropagating, the resonance condition is

(I.7) $$\omega\left(1+\frac{v_z}{c}\right) + \omega\left(1-\frac{v_z}{c}\right) = \omega_0$$

which is verified whatever v_z if $2\omega = \omega_0$. All the molecules are then involved in the process. Furthermore, pressure and power broadening are smaller than in saturated absorption.

The photon shot noise in the optical resonance filter technique is

(I.8) $$h_{min} \geq \frac{1}{k} \frac{\Delta\omega_0}{\omega_0} \sqrt{\frac{\hbar\omega_L}{\mathcal{E}}} \quad Hz^{-1/2}$$

where k is the contrast of the resonance.

2) Heterodyne technique [2]

The principle of the heterodyne technique is given on fig. (3). The frequency emitted by the laser detector is beated against the frequency of a second laser, which may be a stabilized laser or a second free-mass resonator laser, at right angle from the first one.

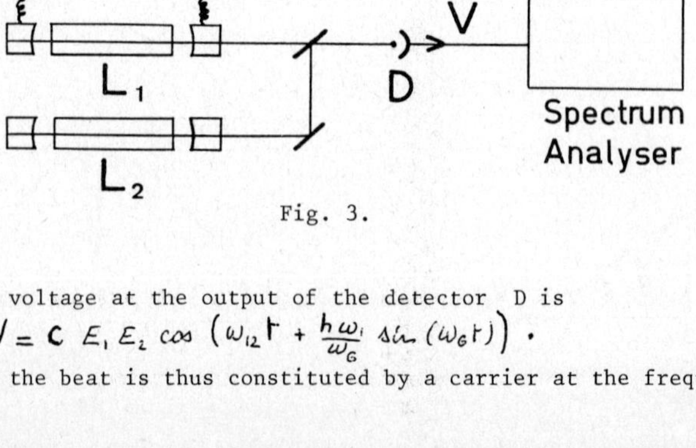

Fig. 3.

The beat signal voltage at the output of the detector D is

$$V = C\, E_1 E_2 \cos\left(\omega_{12} t + \frac{h\omega_1}{\omega_G} \sin(\omega_G t)\right).$$

The spectrum of the beat is thus constituted by a carrier at the frequency

$\omega_{12} = \omega_1 - \omega_2$, plus sidebands of relative amplitude $\frac{h\omega_1}{\omega_G}$ at frequencies $\omega_{12} \pm \omega_G$, and the photon noise in the detection of these sidebands gives

$$h_{min} \geq \frac{2\omega_G}{\omega_1} \sqrt{\hbar\omega_1 \frac{P_1 + P_2}{2 P_1 P_2}} \quad Hz^{-1/2} \qquad \text{(I.9)}$$

if the laser's linewidth is much smaller than ω_G.

C. Noise in active devices

Due to the presence of the amplifying medium inside the detector, active devices show some excess noise. The main noise sources are spontaneous emission noise and index fluctuations of the amplifying medium.

1) Spontaneous emission noise

Spontaneous emission produces phase fluctuations [6] which result in a minimum uncertainty

$$h_s \geq \frac{1}{2Q_L} \sqrt{\frac{\hbar\omega_L}{P_L}} \quad Hz^{-1/2} \qquad \text{(I.10)}$$

where P_L is the total power loss of the cavity, including diffraction losses, and $Q_L \simeq \frac{L\omega_L}{c\beta}$, where c is the velocity of light, L the cavity length and β is the total loss per pass in the cavity.

In order to avoid the laser oscillation in transverse modes, the diffraction losses of the resonator have to be important, and $\beta \geq 5\%$, even in low gain lasers, so the cavity length has to be long (L $>$ 1 km) if one wants to make this noise small enough.

2) Index fluctuations

If we consider a low pressure gas laser (mean free path $>$ beam diameter) the index fluctuations of the medium coming the fluctuations of the number of molecules produce a minimum uncertainty in the optical length of the cavity :

$$h_I \geq \alpha \sqrt{\frac{P}{kT\,\ell w^2} \cdot \frac{2\pi w}{v}} \cdot \frac{\ell}{L} \quad Hz^{-1/2} \qquad \text{(I.11)}$$

where α is the polarisability of the medium, P is the gas pressure, ℓ the length of the active medium and w the average beam diameter inside the amplifying medium. The typical value of h_I for an argon laser will be $h_I \simeq 10^{-18}\,\ell/L\ Hz^{-1/2}$. Even if $\ell/L \simeq 10^{-4}$, the resulting noise is much larger than what is needed for gravitational wave detection. One has to find a medium with much lower fluctuations, or to artificially decrease ℓ/L with the use of a complex resonator.

D. Comparison with passive devices

It is clear that an active device may only be noisier than a passive one. The spontaneous emission noise can take the same value as the photon shot noise if the resonator is long enough, but the index fluctuations, then, will likely become the main limitation. Even if there is some way of reducing them, it seems much better to use a passive system than an active one, for two reasons :

- although a passive device is in principle more complicated, it is also more versatile and gives us the possibility of "recycling" and "squeezing" the light, so that the necessary sensitivity can be reached with reasonable laser powers.

- the technical noises associated with the amplifying medium (discharge fluctuations and oscillations, vibrations from the cooling system) can be served out in passive systems, but in an active device, any servo loop which would take care of them would also supress the device sensitivity to gravitational waves, so these technical noises would have to be reduced by many orders of magnitude relative to the present best technology.

II. SPECTROSCOPIC DETECTORS

Another kind of optical detectors could be provided by spectroscopic means. Such devices have been suggested a few years ago [7]. They show interesting features which are worth to be studied.

a) The experimental scheme

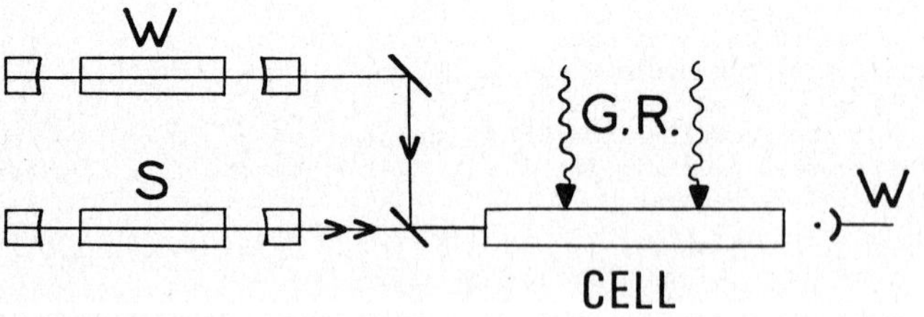

Fig. 4.

Laser S throws light on a cell where atoms are free-falling. Laser W is used as a probe, the frequency of which is tunable. The lasers are assumed to be free-falling. But as they are stabilized on a molecular transition of a gas and as the molecules of the gas are free-falling, isolation from the earth might not be necessary. The gravitational radiation (G.R) falls on the cell. The absorption of the weak light field (w) depends on the gravitational field (G.R) and on the strong light field (S). The power, P_W, of the weak light field is measured when out-going from the cell. We consider, here, P_W as the sum of a zeroth order term and a gravitational correction P_G . P_G depends on the pulsation ω_w of the weak field (w) and on the pulsation ω_G of the gravitational wave. No resonance condition is necessary ; modifications of the absorption spectrum appear independently of any spectral value of ω_G : in this sense the detector can be considered as a broad band one.

In order to calculate P_G , we need to know the behaviour of the gas in the cell when gravitation is taken into account. In the sequel we only sketch the theoretical methods and the leading physical ideas which were used to pick out orders of magnitude.

b) The gravitational correction to the hamiltonian

The effects of a gravitational field on the internal structure of an atom have been broadly discussed in the literature, at least for hydrogen [8]. One can show that they are negligible. Let us consider a gravitational radiation with $h < 10^{-17}$ $\omega_G < 2\pi\, 10^4\ s^{-1}$ which corresponds to most likely situations [9]. In the local coordinates of the nucleus' proper reference frame of a free-falling atom, the metric can be calculated [10]. The corrections to flat spacetime metric do not exceed 10^{-45} thus they will be neglected here.

Usually, when studying the behaviour of an atom in a light field, one uses the hamiltonian

$$H = \frac{p^2}{2M} + \hat{H}_{INT} - \vec{\mu}\vec{E} + \Delta \qquad \text{(II.1)}$$

The different terms are the kinetic energy of the center of mass, the internal hamiltonian, the interaction term between the electric field $\vec{E}$ and the dipole momentum $\vec{\mu}$ and some (relativistic) corrections Δ . As we are looking for the lowest order gravitational term, we neglect Δ in the sequel, and we look only for the corrections to the first three terms. The hamiltonian corresponding to the motion of the center of mass is obtained by standard methods [11] :

$$\text{(II.2)} \quad H_{CM} = \frac{\vec{p}^2}{2M} + \frac{Mc^2}{2} h_{00} + \frac{c}{2}\left[h_{0i} p^i + p^i h_{0i}\right] + \frac{p^i h_{ij} p^j}{2M}$$

Here we assumed for the metric $g_{\mu\nu}$ the relations

$$g_{\mu\nu} = \eta_{\mu\nu} + h_{\mu\nu} \ ; \ \eta_{\mu\nu} = diag\,(1,-1,-1,-1) \ ; \ |h_{\mu\nu}| \ll 1 \ ; \ \mu,\nu = 0,1,2,3 \ ;$$

p^i is the momentum operator ($i = 1,2,3$) and the summation rule on repeated index is used. The next two terms in (II.1) keep the same form in the coordinates of the nucleus' proper reference frame : the Schrödinger's equation for internal states is

$$\text{(II.3)} \quad i\hbar \frac{\partial}{\partial t} |\psi\rangle = \left(\hat{H}_{int} - \vec{\mu}\,\vec{E}^r\right) |\psi\rangle$$

We neglect terms of order of $\frac{v}{c} h$ where v is the velocity of the atom. Thus the proper frame of the nucleus can be defined by the tetrad $e^\mu_i = \delta^\mu_i - \frac{1}{2} h^\mu_i - \frac{1}{2}\delta^\mu_0 h^0_i$; $e^\mu_0 = \delta^\mu_0 (1 - \frac{1}{2} h_{00})$. Then we obtain $(E^r)^i = -e^\mu_i F_{\mu\lambda} e^\lambda_0$, $d\tau = (1 + \frac{1}{2} h_{00})\,dt$ where $F_{\mu\lambda}$ is the Maxwell's tensor. We define $E^i = \eta^{il} F_{l0}$ and we consider E^i as the sum of the usual electric field E^i_0 and a gravitational correction δE^i . Then equation (II.3) becomes

$$\text{(II.4)} \quad i\hbar \frac{d|\psi\rangle}{dt} = \left(\hat{H}_{int} - \vec{\mu}\,\vec{E}_0 + \frac{1}{2} h_{00} \hat{H}_{int} - \vec{\mu}\cdot\vec{\delta E} - \frac{1}{2}\vec{\mu}^j h_{jk} E^k_0\right)|\psi\rangle$$

From(II.2) and(II.4) we obtain the expression for the hamiltonian :

$$\text{(II.5)} \quad H = \frac{\vec{p}^2}{2M} - \vec{\mu}\,\vec{E}_0 + \hat{H}_{int} + \Delta + U$$

$$\text{with} \quad U = \frac{Mc^2 h_{00}}{2} + \frac{c}{2}\left\{h_{0i} p^i + p^i h_{0i}\right\} + \frac{p^i h_{ij} p^j}{2M} + \frac{1}{2} h_{00} \hat{H}_{int} - \vec{\mu}\,\vec{\delta E} - \frac{1}{2}\hat{\mu}^i h_{ij} E^j_0$$

c) The equations

The density operator ρ which describes the gas in the cell satisfies the equation

$$\text{(II.6)} \quad i\hbar \frac{d\rho}{dt} = [H,\rho] + i\hbar R\{\rho - \rho^e\}$$

$\hbar$ = Planck's constant. H is given by (II.5) ; ρ^e is the density operator at thermal equilibrium. R is a relaxation operator defined by the relations

$$\langle\alpha|\langle\vec{p}'|\, R\{\rho-\rho^e\}\, |\vec{p}''\rangle|\beta\rangle = -\Gamma_{\alpha\beta} \langle\alpha|\langle\vec{p}'|\,(\rho-\rho^e)\,|\vec{p}''\rangle|\beta\rangle$$

with the notations $H_{int}|\alpha\rangle = E_\alpha|\alpha\rangle$, $p^i|\vec{p}\rangle = (\vec{p})^i|\vec{p}\rangle$

Now we consider Fermi coordinates of the laboratory with the origin in the neighbourhood of the lasers. The gravitational radiation is defined by : $h_{\mu\nu} = 0$ except $h_{00} = h_{33} = -h_{03} = k(\vec{x},t)$; $k(\vec{x},t) = \frac{1}{2}(x^2 - y^2)\,\ddot{h}_+(ct-z) + xy\,\ddot{h}_\times(ct-z)$

$$(\dot{\ }) = \frac{d}{c\,dt} \ .$$

h_+ and $h_\times$ are arbitrary functions and c is the celerity of light. In this case, as we are looking for the lowest order gravitational correction, we can assume

$$\Delta \simeq 0 \quad ; \quad U \simeq -\frac{Mc^2}{2} k(x,t) \ .$$

We express equation (II.6) in Wigner representation :

$$\rho_{W\,\alpha\beta}(\vec{q},\vec{R},t) = \int \langle\alpha|\langle \vec{R} + \frac{\vec{x}}{2}|\,\rho\,|\vec{R} - \frac{\vec{x}}{2}\rangle|\beta\rangle \exp\left(-\frac{i}{\hbar}\vec{q}\,\vec{x}\right) \frac{d^3\vec{x}}{(2\pi\hbar)^3}$$

then

$$\text{(II.7)} \quad i\hbar\left\{\frac{d}{dt} + \frac{\vec{q}}{M}\cdot\vec{\nabla}_R + i\omega_{\alpha\beta}\right\} \rho_{W\,\alpha\beta}(\vec{q},\vec{R},t) + i\hbar\,\Gamma_{\alpha\beta}\left\{\rho_{W\,\alpha\beta} - \rho^e_{W\,\alpha\beta}\right\} = \frac{1}{(2\pi\hbar)^3} \sum_{\gamma} \iint d\vec{x}\, d\vec{\sigma}\, e^{\frac{i}{\hbar}(\vec{\sigma}-\vec{q})\vec{x}} \left\{V_{\alpha\gamma}(\vec{R}+\frac{\vec{x}}{2},t)\,\rho_{W\,\gamma\beta}(\vec{\sigma},\vec{r},t) - \rho_{W\,\alpha\gamma}\, V_{\gamma\beta}(\vec{R}-\frac{\vec{x}}{2},t)\right\}$$

with $V_{\alpha\beta}(\vec{R},t) = U(\vec{R},t)\,\delta_{\alpha\beta} - \vec{E}_0(\vec{R},t)\,\vec{\mu}_{\alpha\beta}$; $\hbar\omega_{\alpha\beta} = E_\alpha - E_\beta$

One expands $V_{\alpha\beta}(\vec{R} \pm \frac{\vec{x}}{2}, t) = V_{\alpha\beta}(\vec{R},t) \pm \frac{\vec{x}}{2}\vec{\nabla}_R V_{\alpha\beta}(\vec{R},t) + \dots$

Using (II.7), one can show that the lowest order gravitational correction is obtained by solving the equation

$$i\hbar\left\{\frac{d}{dt} + \frac{\vec{q}}{M}\vec{\nabla}_R + i\omega_{\alpha\beta}\right\} + i\hbar\Gamma_{\alpha\beta}\left\{\underset{W}{\rho}_{\alpha\beta} - \underset{W}{\rho}^{c}_{\alpha\beta}\right\}_{\vec{q},\vec{R},t} = \tag{II.8}$$
$$-\vec{E}(\vec{R},t)\sum_{\gamma}\left\{\vec{\mu}_{\alpha\gamma}\underset{W}{\rho}_{\gamma\beta} - \underset{W}{\rho}_{\alpha\gamma}\vec{\mu}_{\gamma\beta}\right\}_{\vec{q},\vec{R},t} - i\hbar\vec{a}(\vec{R},t)\vec{\nabla}_q\underset{W}{\rho}_{\alpha\beta}(\vec{q},\vec{R},t)$$

where $\vec{a}(\vec{R},t) = -\vec{\nabla}_{R} U(\vec{R},t)$

From (II.8) we obtained the power absorbed P_W by using the diagramatic scheme elaborated by C.J. Bordé [12]. The method was completed to take gravitation into account : the corresponding vortex (wavy line) is

$$-\vec{a}\cdot\vec{\nabla}_{\vec{q}}\,\underset{W}{\rho}_{\alpha\beta}(\vec{q},\vec{R},t)\Big|_{\vec{r}=\vec{R}-2\vec{q}}$$

The calculations have been performed by J. Sharma in the case when the gravitational wave is periodic with $h_x = 0$. The significant diagrams for the calculation of P_G are

$P_G =$ 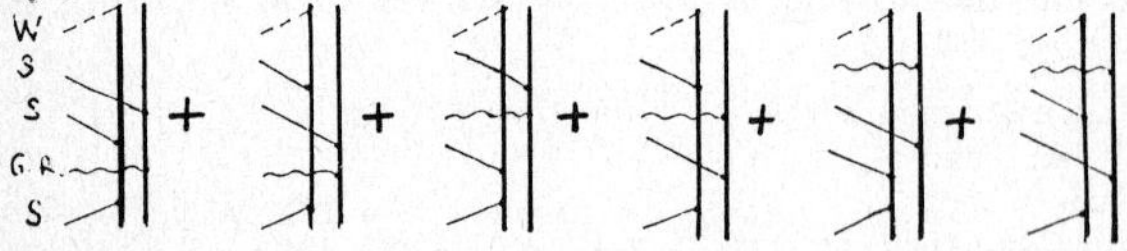

+ complex conjugate

It appears that $P_G \neq 0$ only for $\omega_W = \omega_S \pm \omega_G$ where ω_W and ω_S are the pulsations of the weak field (the probe) and of the strong field. The calculations have been performed for a two levels system in the limit of a large Doppler broadening, the cell being located between $x = 0$ and $x = L$. The results obtained are consistent with those given in ref. [7] when $\underset{W}{\rho}^{0}_{\alpha\beta}$ is the classical Maxwellian distribution.

d) Discussion

The power P_W on the detector is given as a function of ω_W fig. (5).

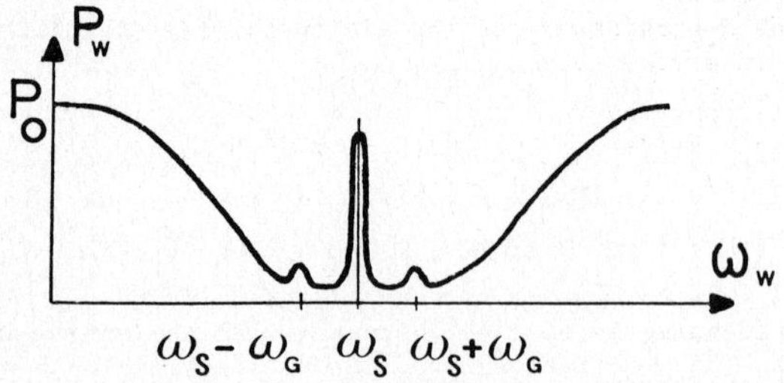

Fig. 5.

The modifications in the absorption spectrum consist in the presence of two side bands at frequencies $\omega_W = \omega_S \pm \omega_G$. For $\omega_W = \omega_S \pm \omega_G$ one finds the following order of magnitude, in the case $\omega_G \geq \Gamma \sim \Gamma_{\alpha\beta}$ and $\omega_W \sim \omega_S \sim \omega$:

$$P_W \simeq P_0 - 2\pi\hbar\omega N F \Omega_W^2 \left\{1 - \frac{\Omega_S^2}{\Gamma\omega_G} - h\frac{L\omega}{2c}\frac{\Omega_S^3}{\Gamma^2\Omega_W}\right\}$$

N is the number of active atoms, Ω_S and Ω_W are the Rabi frequencies of the corresponding light fields and F is the Maxwellian distribution considered as a function of ω : $F \sim \frac{1}{\omega}\sqrt{\frac{Mc^2}{kT}}$ where k is the Boltzmann's constant and T the temperature.

We consider the photon noise for an integration time τ . The signal to noise ratio is $S/N \sim P_G\sqrt{\tau/P_W\hbar\omega}$. We use the following relations : $P_W \geq N\hbar\omega F\Omega_W^2\Omega_S^2/\Gamma\omega_G$ $\omega_G \geq \Gamma$, $\Omega_S \leq \Gamma$ and $\Gamma > \alpha\mathcal{P}$ where $\mathcal{P}$ is the pressure and α of order of $10^3 s^{-1}/P_a$. Then we find

$$S/N \leqslant \left\{ \frac{h^2 L^3 D^2 \omega \omega_G^3 \tau}{\alpha c^2} \sqrt{\frac{Mc^2}{(kT)^3}} \right\}^{1/2} \quad \text{(II.9)}$$

D being the diameter of the light beams.

Let us assume the following optimistic orders of magnitude :

$\Omega_s \sim \alpha \mathcal{P} \sim \Gamma \sim \omega_G \sim 10^3 s^{-1}$; $h \sim 3\,10^{-24}$; $\omega \sim 10^{15} s^{-1}$; $L = 100$ m

$D = 1$ m ; $Mc^2 \sim 10^{11}$ eV ; $T \sim 3$ K

We find the necessary integration time : $\tau \geqslant 2.10^7$ s $\simeq$ 8 months for the detection of a periodic wave.

If the lasers are separated from the cell by a long distance ℓ one has to substitute $\ell^2 L$ for L^3 in (II.9). For a pulse, with the previous orders of magnitude and $\ell \sim 10^4$ m the sensitivity is $h \geqslant 10^{-22}$ Hz$^{-1/2}$.

These orders of magnitude rule out the possibility of using the device studied here in terrestrial experiments at least for broad band pulses. Spectroscopic detectors might be however interesting within the scope of future space experiments with large ℓ ($\ell \omega_G \sim c$).

Some more studies are however necessary in order to obtain definite conclusions. We especially need to take into account the different other sources of noise and the geometry of the beams : transit time [13] and Ramsey fringes for instance. Moreover it is necessary to study the quantum limit whose nature might be different from interferometers'.

CONCLUSION

The laser displacement sensors using active interferometers or the spectroscopic technique seem easier to realize and to operate than the passive Michelson or Fabry-Perot interferometers and they may be of some interest for the measurement of small displacements ($\Delta x/L \geqslant 10^{-20}$ Hz$^{-1/2}$) in geophysics, for instance. But we do not think they can be easily scaled up to the sensitivity $\Delta x/L \simeq 3\,10^{-24}$ Hz$^{-1/2}$, which is necessary for a gravitational wave antenna. The only way we know to reach this goal is passive interferometry.

There is no fundamental physical reason to choose between a Michelson and a Fabry-Perot system. The "best choice" might change as technology evolves, but both systems will likely give similar results, and cost considerations may be decisive.

REFERENCES

[1] R.W.P. Drever, this book.

[2] S.N. Bagayev, V.P. Chebotayev, A.S. Dychkov, V.G. Goldort, Appl. Phys. 25, p. 161, 1981.

[3] R.W.P. Drever, in Quantum Optics and General Relativity, Nato ASI Series (in press).

[4] C.M. Caves, Phys. Rev. D 23, p. 1693 (1981).
See also communications by D.F. Walls and by L. Lugiato at the XIIth Intern. Quant. Electr. Conf., Appl. Phys., B28, p. 109 (1982).

[5] A. Brillet and P. Cerez, J. Phys. (Paris) C8, p. 73 (1981).

[6] B. Cagnac, G. Grynberg, F. Biraben, J. Phys. (Paris) 34, p. 845 (1973).

[7] Yu. E. Nesterikhin et al., J.E.T.P., 48, p. 1 (1978).

[8] P. Tourrenc et J.L. Grossiord, Nuov. Cim., 32B, p. 163 (1976).
L. Parker, Phys. Rev. D22, p. 1922 (1980).

[9] K. Thorne, Rev. Mod. Phys., 52, p. 285 (1980).

[10] W-Q Li and W-T Ni, J. Math. Phys., 20, p. 1473 (1979).

[11] G. Papini, Nuov. Cim., 52B, p. 136 (1967).

[12] C. Bordé, in Advances in Laser Spectroscopy, Nato ASI Series, edited by T. Arrechi, F. Sturmia and H. Walker, Plenum Press (1982).

[13] A.V. Braslavets et al, Sov. J. Quantum Electron, 11, p. 171 (1981).

ELECTROMAGNETICALLY-TRACKED FREE-MASS GRAVITATIONAL WAVE ANTENNAS

Ronald W. Hellings

Jet Propulsion Laboratory
4800 Oak Grove Drive
Pasadena, California
U.S.A.

The response to a gravitational wave of two free masses whose relative motion is monitored with an electromagnetic tracking signal is derived. The results indicate a two-feature signature in one-way data and a three-feature signature in two-way data. The effect is applied to gravitational wave experiments using laser interferometers, spacecraft Doppler tracking, planetary ranging, and pulsar timing analysis. Actual results are presented from spacecraft Doppler experiments and from pulsar timing data analysis, with new upper limits being set on a possible cosmic gravitational wave background via the pulsar data.

INTRODUCTION

When expressed in the most natural coordinate system, the effect of a weak plane gravitational wave on a free test mass is not to move the mass away from its coordinate position but to flex the spacetime around the mass. The most simple gravitational wave detector which could be envisioned would be created by setting up two of these fiducial spacetime markers - free masses - and using an electromagnetic tracking signal passed from one to the other as a probe of the spacetime curvature in the region between them. This is the fundamental idea behind gravitational wave antennas based on laser interferometers, spacecraft Doppler tracking, planetary ranging, or pulsar timing analysis.

In this lecture, I will first derive the details of the effect of a gravitational wave on an electromagnetic tracking signal, a result which would apply to any of the four techniques mentioned. Then, in the third and fourth sections, actual experiments using Doppler tracking and pulsar timing will be described in some detail and their results discussed.

THE EFFECT OF A GRAVITATIONAL WAVE ON AN ELECTROMAGNETIC TRACKING SIGNAL

Consider two free masses, one at the origin of a coordinate system and the other at a distance ℓ from the origin and at an angle θ from the z-axis, as shown in Figure 1. For simplicity, we assume both masses are at rest. Let the mass at the origin be sending out a series of photons of frequency ν_0 while a weak plane gravitational wave is passing through space in the +z direction. The presence of the wave will change the geometry of spacetime from that of flat, Minkowski spacetime to a curved spacetime whose invariant line element is given by:

$$ds^2 = c^2dt^2 - dz^2 - (1 + \hat{h}\cos 2\phi)dx^2 - (1 - \hat{h}\cos 2\phi)dy^2 - \hat{h}\sin 2\phi\, dxdy \qquad (1)$$

where $\hat{h}(t - z/c)$ is the gravitational wave amplitude and where ϕ is the angle between a principal polarization vector of the wave and the x-axis.

If coordinates are rotated so that the second mass is in the x-z plane, then we locate the photon at time t with coordinates (x, z) which may be parametrically related to each other to first order by:

$$x = s\sin\theta \qquad z = s\cos\theta$$

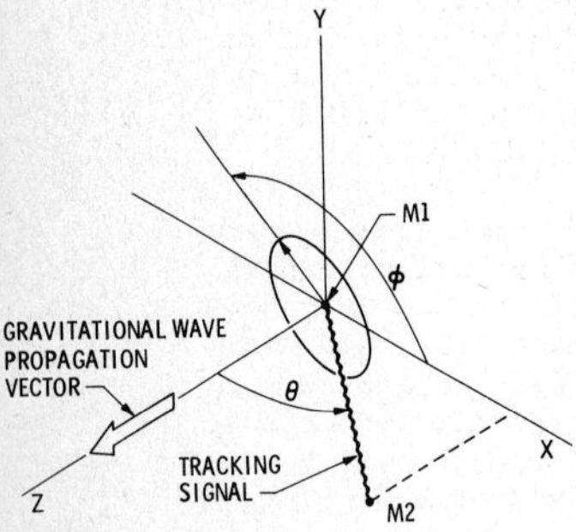

Figure 1

where s is a parameter corresponding to the distance the photon would have traveled if there had been no wave. Along the photon path, the proper time is zero, so the elapsed coordinate time and the distance parameter must obey:

$$c^2dt^2 = (1 + h)dx^2 + dz^2$$

or

$$c^2dt^2 = (1 + h\sin^2\theta)ds^2 \tag{2}$$

where $h = \hat{h}\cos 2\phi$ has been defined to simplify the notation.

By integrating this expression from the time of emission of the photon (t_o) to the time of reception (t_1), the elapsed time of flight may be related to the unperturbed geometrical distance (ℓ) between the two masses

$$\int_{t_o}^{t_1} c\,dt = \int_o^{\ell} (1 + \frac{1}{2} h\sin^2\theta)\,ds, \tag{3}$$

or

$$c(t_1 - t_o) = \ell + \frac{1}{2}\sin^2\theta \int_o^{\ell} h(t - z/c)ds, \tag{4}$$

where h<<1 was used in taking the square root in Equation 3.

Using lowest order expressions for t and z inside the argument of the small quantity h, i.e. using

$$t = t_o + s/c, \quad z = s\cos\theta,$$

Equation 4 becomes:

$$c(t_1 - t_o) = \ell + \frac{1}{2}\sin^2\theta \int_o^{\ell} h(t_o + \frac{s}{c} - \frac{s}{c}\cos\theta)ds,$$

or, defining a new variable, $q \equiv s(1 - \cos\theta)$,

$$c(t_1 - t_o) = \ell + \frac{1}{2}\frac{\sin^2\theta}{1 - \cos\theta}\int_o^{\ell(1-\cos\theta)} h(t_o + q/c)dq \tag{5}$$

If we define H to be the antiderivitive of h, then Equation 5 can be written:

$$c(t_1 - t_o) = \ell + \frac{c}{2}(1 + \cos\theta)[H(\ell/c - \frac{\ell}{c}\cos\theta + t_o) - H(t_o)] \tag{6}$$

Now $c(t_1 - t_o)$ is the apparent range, ρ, which Equation 6 allows us to write as:

$$\rho = \ell + \frac{c}{2}(1 + \cos\theta)[H(t_1 - \frac{\ell}{c}\cos\theta) - H(t_o)], \tag{7}$$

where we have identified $t_o + \ell/c \approx t$, as the time of reception in the argument of H. The Doppler shift in the frequency of photons emitted by the source will be equal to the apparent radial velocity of the source, that is, to the derivation of ρ in Equation 7. Thus, we have:

$$\frac{\nu_1 - \nu_o}{\nu_o} = \frac{1}{c}\frac{d\rho}{dt} = \frac{1}{2}(1 + \cos\theta)[h(t_1 - \frac{\ell}{c}\cos\theta) - h(t_o)]. \tag{8}$$

Equation 8 gives the gravitational-wave induced Doppler shift in a one-way tracking signal and is appropriate for describing the effect which a gravitational wave would have in a record of pulsar timing data. Note that the shift depends only on the amplitude of the wave at the time ($t = t_1$) and position ($z = \ell \cos\theta$) of signal reception and at the time ($t = t_o$) and position ($z = 0$) of signal emission. Equation 8 will be used later in the discussion of pulsar timing gravitational wave experiments.

For the other experiments mentioned in the first section - laser interferometers, Doppler tracking, and planetary ranging - the electromagnetic tracking link is not one-way but two-way. A signal is emitted from one mass, coherently transponded or bounced off of the second mass, and then received back at the first mass a round-trip light-time later. For these experiments, Equation 8 will give the Doppler shift on the first leg, but the second leg remains to be computed.

The computation of the additional shift on downlink follows the same method as that which led to Equation 8, with a few changes in variables. Using s as the approximate distance travelled by the photon from mass 2 to mass 1, we have

$$z = (\ell - s)\cos\theta \qquad t = t_1 + s/c$$

and

$$t - z/c = t_1 - \frac{\ell}{c}\cos\theta + \frac{s}{c}(1 + \cos\theta),$$

The range integral then becomes:

$$\rho = \ell + \frac{1}{2}\frac{\sin^2\theta}{1 + \cos\theta}\int_o^{\ell(1+\cos\theta)} h(q/c + t_1 - \frac{\ell}{c}\cos\theta)dq,$$

where $q \equiv s(1 + \cos\theta)$. This integrates to:

$$\rho = \ell + \frac{c}{2}(1 - \cos\theta)[H(t_1 + \ell/c) - H(t_1 - \frac{\ell}{c}\cos\theta)].$$

The Doppler shift on downlink is, therefore:

$$\frac{\nu_2 - \nu_1}{\nu_1} = \frac{1}{c}\frac{d\rho}{dt} = \frac{1}{2}(1 - \cos\theta)[h(t_2) - h(t_1 - \frac{\ell}{c}\cos\theta)], \qquad (9)$$

where the reception time is $t_2 \approx t_1 + \ell/c$. Writing everything in terms of $t = t_2$, Equations 8 and 9 combine to give a total two-way Doppler shift of:

$$\frac{\nu_2 - \nu_o}{\nu_o} = \frac{1}{2}[(1 - \cos\theta)h(t) - 2\cos\theta h(t - \frac{\ell}{c} - \frac{\ell}{c}\cos\theta) - (1 + \cos\theta)h(t - 2\frac{\ell}{c})]. \qquad (10)$$

This is the same expression which has been derived by another method by Estabrook and Wahlquist[1] and by Hellings[2].

Equation 10 gives the total Doppler shift of a single photon passing over a two-way path. The result depends on the value of the wave amplitude only at the times and positions of emission, bounce, and reception. To see how Equation 10 gives rise to a three-pulse signature in the Doppler record, consider a continuous stream of photons which are emitted from mass 1 while a gravitational wave pulse of duration short compared to the light-time between the masses is passing through space. Then the only photons which will have any Doppler shift at all will be those which happen to be emitted, bounced, or received at the special times when h was non-zero during the event. Since the arguments of h in the three terms in Equation 10 differ by the order of the light-time between the masses, a received photon will only carry information about one of the terms in Equation 10, and the entire record of photons received will spread the information out in time as shown in Figure 2. This unique three-pulse signature will be very useful in increasing confidence in a possible gravitational wave detection by a spacecraft Doppler tracking experiment.

In the last paragraph, it was assumed that the characteristic width of h is short compared to the light-time, as it would be for the waves to be looked for in Doppler tracking experiments and pulsar timing experiments. If the pulse widths are long compared to /c, however, then the three terms in Equation 10 will overlap and cancel to zeroth order, leaving only the first order residue as the signal in the frequency record. This may be seen by expanding h in a Taylor series about t to give:

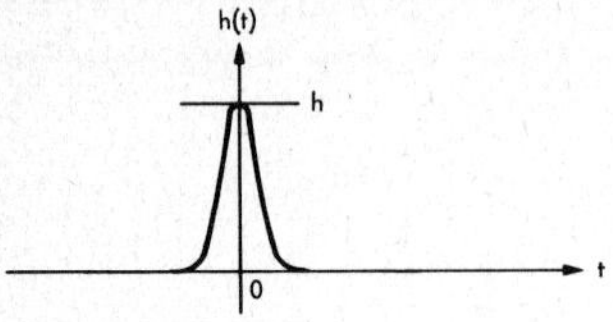

(a) GRAVITY WAVE

$$h(t - \frac{\ell}{c} - \frac{\ell}{c}\cos\theta) \approx h(t) - (1 + \cos\theta)\frac{\ell}{c}\dot{h}(t)$$

$$h(t - 2\frac{\ell}{c}) \approx h(t) - 2\frac{\ell}{c}\dot{h}(t).$$

With these expansions, Equation 10 becomes

$$\frac{\Delta\nu}{\nu} = -\frac{\ell}{c}\dot{h}(t)\sin^2\theta, \tag{11}$$

the integral of which gives an expression proportional to h:

$$\Delta\phi = \nu_o\frac{\ell}{c}\sin^2\theta h(t), \tag{12}$$

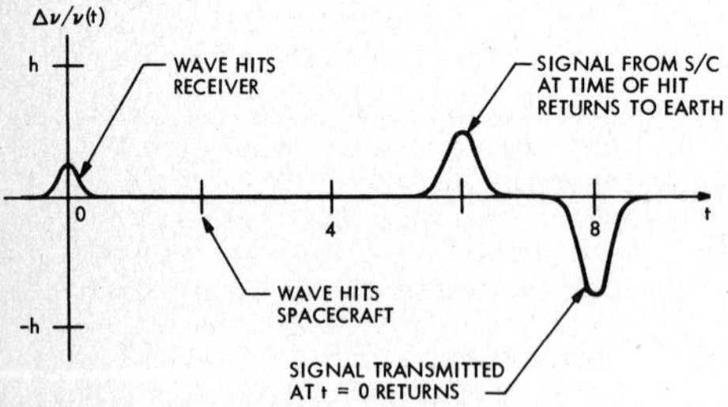

(b) THE DOPPLER SIGNAL

where $\Delta\phi$ is the phase differences in cycles produced by the gravitational wave. This phase offset will be seen as a change in the apparent range between the masses (given by $\Delta\ell = c\nu_o^{-1}\Delta\phi$) so Equation 12 can also be written as the more familiar expression for spatial strain:

$$\frac{\Delta\ell}{\ell} = \sin^2\theta h(t). \tag{13}$$

In the interaction of gravitational waves with the planets, the greatest sensitivity comes at gravitational wave periods comparable to the orbital periods, a period much longer than the light time to the planet, so Equation 13 would be the appropriate equation to use for planetary ranging experiments.

For laser interferometers (discussed by R. Drever in this volume), the long period condition also applies, so the signal in each arm of the interferometr will also most appropriately be given by Equation 12 or 13, while the differenced signal, obtained by letting the signals from the two arms interfere, would be written:

$$\Delta\phi = \nu_o\frac{\ell}{c}h(t)[\sin^2\theta_1 - \sin^2\theta_2]$$

where θ_1 and θ_2 are the orientations of the two interferometer arms to the gravitational wave propagation direction.

SPACECRAFT DOPPLER TRACKING

The Tracking System

The Doppler tracking system is probably most easily understood by reference to Figure 3. The heart of the system is the hydrogen maser clock which both controls the frequency ν of the low-noise transmitter and provides the reference frequency for producing the Doppler shift $\Delta\nu$. The uplink is presently a 220-kW S-band (2.1 GHz) signal radiated from one of the 64-m parabolic antennas in

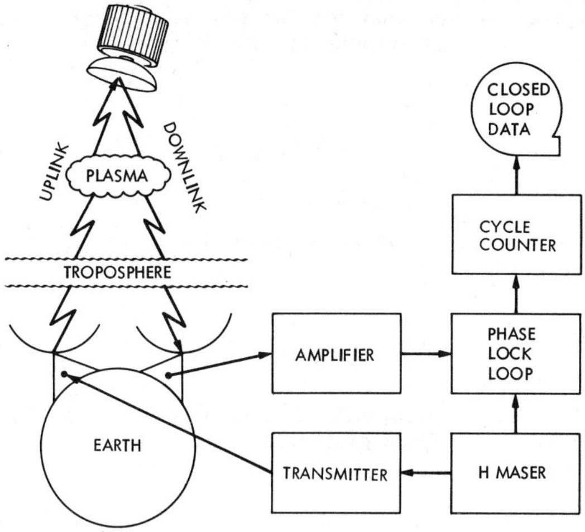

Figure 3

NASA's Deep Space Network (DSN). Both uplink and downlink will be affected by troposphere, ionosphere, and interplanetary plasma scintillation. The signal is tracked in a phase-lock loop on board the spacecraft and coherently transponded at translated S-band (2.3 GHz) and X-band (8.4 GHz) frequencies at powers of a few tens of watts. The downlink may be received by the same station which sent it (in which case it is called "two-way tracking") or by some other station (in which case it is referred to as "three-way tracking"). DSN receiving antennas and low-noise maser amplifiers operate at about 30°K. In normal DSN operation, the received signal is tracked in a phase-lock loop, the hydrogen maser being used to beat the frequency down to the Doppler tone. This low-frequency tone is fed into a cycle counter which integrates the frequency, sampling the count at a specified interval and resolving the last partial cycle at each sampling to the nearest nanosecond. These phase counts are then differenced to calculate phase change and divided by the sample time to calculate average $\Delta\nu$.

Each of the elements in Figure 3 contributes noise to the system, and a comparison of noise levels to possible gravitational wave strengths would lead one to a pessimistic view for the prospects for such an experiment. However, we have as yet made no use of the unique Doppler signature of the gravitational waves (Figure 2).

In searching for a solitary burst of gravitational waves, the best use of this unique signature will probably be to increase confidence that some event which protrudes strongly above the noise is in fact a gravitational wave. However, in a search for a stochastic background of cosmic gravitational radiation, it is possible to use this signature to actually dig into the noise to pull out its gravitational wave component. The key to the use of Equation 10 in improving the signal-to-noise ratio is to notice that, of the three features in the Doppler record produced by each feature in h, the first and last will be separated by a round-trip light-time and will always be in inverse sense to each other with the intermediate feature turning up somewhere in between. A stochastic isotropic combination of waves will smear the intermediate pulse out, but the property that whenever $\Delta\nu/\nu$ is high now it will be low a round-trip light time later will be preserved in the stochastic addition of waves. The existence of gravity-wave noise in the tracking record will, therefore, manifest itself as an anticorrelation in the autocovariance function $A(\tau)$ at a time lag equal to $2\ell/c$. Analytic calculations indicate that the power in the anticorrelated feature will be one-sixth the power in the zero-lag value of $A(\tau)$.

Experimental Results

From January 25 to January 28, 1979, four days of data were taken with Voyager I at a round-trip light time of 4000 sec. The data were all two-way, with an S-band uplink from the 64-m antenna at Deep Space Station (DSS) 63 near Madrid,

Spain, and a coherently transponded S- and X-band downlink received back at DSS 63. From March 6 to March 12, 1980, six days of Voyager I data were taken. The S-band uplink was generated at the 64-m DSS 14 at Goldstone, California, and two-way S- and X-band data were then recorded back at DSS 14. At the same time, the 40-m antenna at Caltech's Owens Valley Radio Observatory (OVRO) was used to receive the transponded X-band signal. The round-trip light-time in 1980 was about 6400 sec. The experiments were timed to occur near solar opposition in order to take advantage of the reported drop in plasma noise when the solar wind is streaming along the line of sight. The two-way S- and X-band data were obtained from the standard Deep Space Network (DSN) Doppler extractors. The "three-way" data (different earth stations receive and transmit) taken at OVRO used parts of the NRAO Mark III VLBI system and a device called the Digital Tone Extractor (DTE). The experiments are discussed in more detail by Hellings, et al[3].

As argued in the last section, the preferred data analysis algorithm in a search for the stochastic background involves the autocovariance function of the Doppler record. Any gravity-wave spectrum which falls off faster at high frequency than the other noise in the Doppler record will then be visible as a more-or-less sharp autocorrelated feature centered at a time lag $\tau = 2\ell$. As long as statistics give a standard deviation σ_A in the autocovariance function which is less than one-sixth the zero-lag autocovariance value, then the gravity wave's one-sixth power feature at a round-trip light-time may be sought for. When the autocovariance statistics are not this good, then only an upper limit to the background may be found, given by the total zero-lag power.

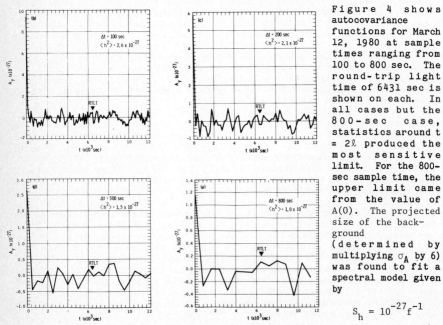

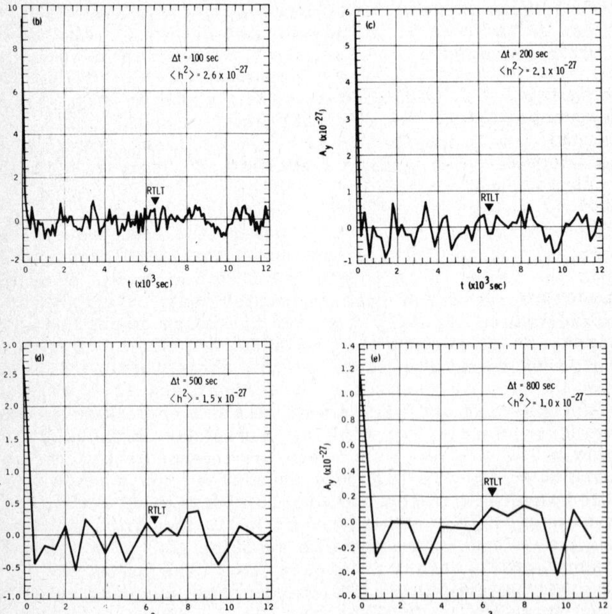

Figure 4 shows autocovariance functions for March 12, 1980 at sample times ranging from 100 to 800 sec. The round-trip light time of 6431 sec is shown on each. In all cases but the 800-sec case, statistics around t = 2ℓ produced the most sensitive limit. For the 800-sec sample time, the upper limit came from the value of A(0). The projected size of the background (determined by multiplying σ_A by 6) was found to fit a spectral model given by

$$S_h = 10^{-27} f^{-1}$$

where it is assumed that the frequency band ran from a low frequency of 2×10^{-4} ($\approx 1/2\ell$) up to a high frequency $f_H = 1/2\tau$, where τ is the sample time. The equivalent energy density spectral density is

$$S_E = 5f(\mathrm{erg} \cdot \mathrm{cm}^{-3} \cdot \mathrm{Hz}^{-1}).$$

In Figure 5 the ability of the autocorrelation algorithm to dig into noise is made apparent by comparing S_h to the Doppler noise spectrum. At low frequencies (long sample times) there are so few data points that statistics do not dig below the rms Doppler noise, but, for high frequencies, the method gives over a 10 dB increase in gravity wave signal-to-noise ratio. In Figure 6, S_E is plotted as a line labeled "Doppler" along with other existing limits on the

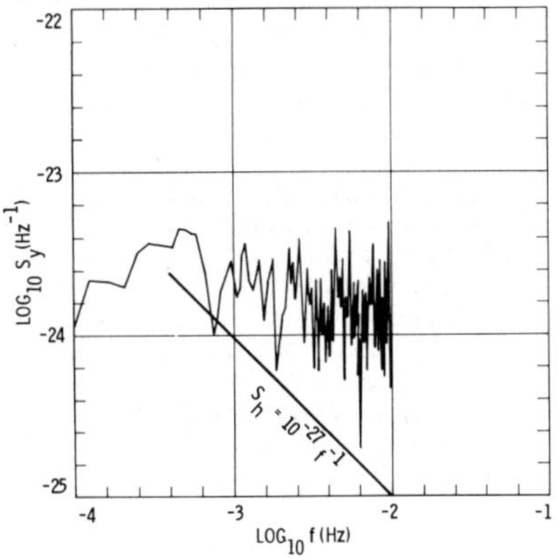

Figure 5

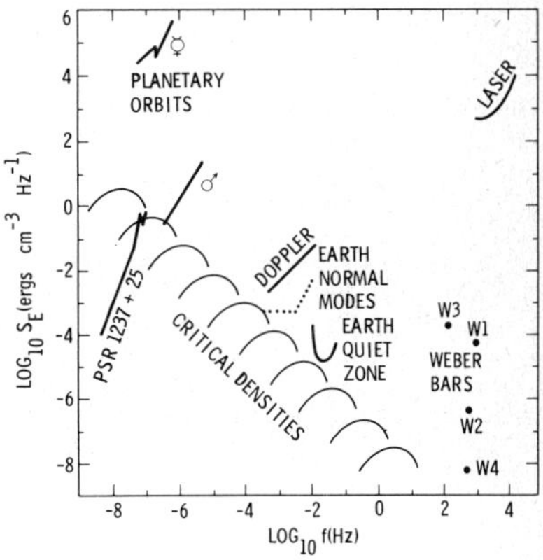

Figure 6

background, both experimental and theoretical. The set of curves labeled "critical densities" represents possible broad band spectra of gravitational radiation whose energy density is the maximum allowed by observational limits on dynamics of cosmological models, as derived by Zimmerman and Hellings[4]. As can be seen, the present results fail by about an order of magnitude in power (a factor of 3 in amplitude) to be at the interesting cosmological level.

PULSAR TIMING DATA

Shortly after the discovery of pulsars in 1968, G. S. Downs at the Jet Propulsion Laboratory (JPL) began a long-term program of regular observations of pulsar pulse arrival times. This data set now contains high-quality S-band data on twenty-four pulsars extending over a period of about twelve years.

Several runs lasting from two to five minutes each are obtained in a typical observing session. During each run, the incoming data are signal-averaged at the current model of the pulsar period. The location of the pulse in each run is found by fitting the pulse shape to a master shape (obtained by averaging many runs) in which the background level, the pulsar strength, and the pulse location are adjusted to achieve the best fit. The location of the pulse, the nominal starting time, and corrections for clock offsets, propagation delays, instrumental delays, and pulse drift due to period mismatch, are combined to produce the topocentric arrival time of the first pulse of the run. These arrival times are reduced to effective solar system barycentric arrival times by using the tracking station locations and earth positions derived from JPL ephemeris DE96. Further details in the experimental techniques can be found in the paper by Downs and Reichley[7].

The expected barycentric arrival time of the nth pulse is computed via the model

$$t_n = t_o + nP_o + \frac{1}{2} n^2 \dot{P}_o P_o,$$

where P_o is the pulsar period at t_o and $\dot{P}_o$ is the first derivative of P at t_o. The parameters t_o, P_o, and $\dot{P}_o$ are fit to the data in a least squares sense and the residuals are computed. Residuals for pulsar PSR 1237 + 25 are shown in Figure 7. The noise sources responsible for the residuals are primarily thought to be variations in the pulse shape due to fluctuations in the pulse-producing mechanism or in the propagation medium, at high frequencies, and unmodelled fluctuations in the physical rotation rate of the pulsar at low frequencies. Hidden in the noise is some small stochastic contribution due to the cosmic gravitational radiation background, producing frequency fluctuations according to Equation 8 (or, more appropriately, Equation 9 for a downlink from the pulsar to earth). In principle, gravitational waves with periods up to the one-way light-time between the pulsar and earth, i.e. $\sim 10^3$ years, could be seen in the data. However, the total period of data extends only over a dozen years, so the upper limit on period would be some fraction of that time, say $\sim 10^8$ secs. It should also be noted, from Equation 9, that data from any pulsar will contain information about h at the time and place of reception (i.e. at earth) and about the value h had at the pulsar at the time of emission of the signal. Thus, data from all pulsars will have a gravitational wave signal in common with all other pulsars (though with an amplitude scaled by $1 - \cos\theta$) as well as signal which will be independent of the others due to long light-times between pulsars compared to the 12-year data span.

An upper limit to the strength of the cosmic gravitational wave background can be derived from the residuals shown in Figure 7 alone. In order to compare with Equation 9, the data were first divided into 50-day bins and then averaged to give the average reception time residual, Δt, in each interval. The data were then differentiated to give:

$$\frac{d}{dt}(\Delta t) = P_o \frac{d}{dt} \frac{\Delta t}{P_o} = \frac{1}{\nu_o} \frac{d(\Delta\phi)}{dt} = \frac{\Delta\nu}{\nu}.$$

The power spectrum of the residuals was then estimated, giving an upper limit to the power spectrum S_h of the stochastic gravitatinal wave amplitude. This limit is shown in Figure 8. Transforming the amplitude spectral density to an energy density spectral density gives the line labelled "PSR 1237 + 25" in Figure 6. As may be seen, this is the first limit on the cosmic gravitational radiation background which enters the cosmologically significant region.

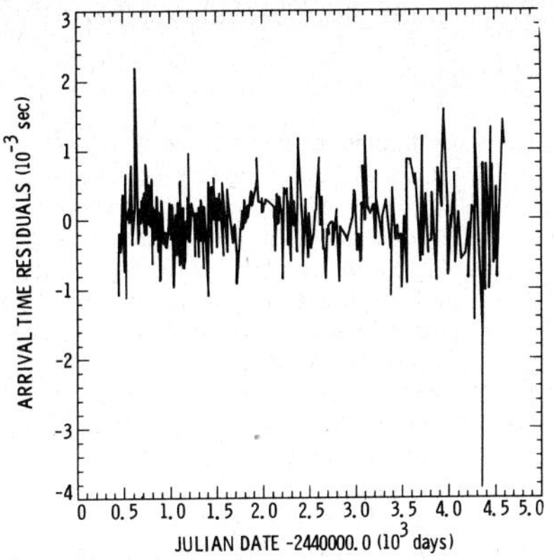

Figure 7

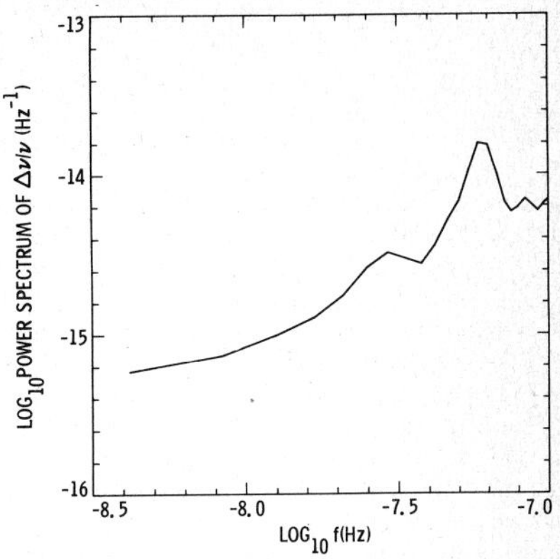

Figure 8

References

[1]. Estabrook, F. B. and Wahlquist, H. D., G.R.G. 6, (1975), 439-447.

[2]. Hellings, R. W., Phys. Rev. D 23, (1981), 832-843.

[3]. Hellings, R. W., et al, Phys. Rev. D 23, (1981), 843-851.

[4]. Zimmerman, R. L. and Hellings, R. W., Ap.J. 241, (1980), 475-485.

[5]. Downs, G. S. and Reichley, P. E., Ap.J. Supplement, (1983), submitted.

A SIMPLE LINEAR MODEL FOR GRAVITY WAVE DETECTOR ANALYSIS

W.G. Unruh

Department of Physics
University of British Columbia
Vancouver, B.C.
Canada

A simple linear model for a gravity wave detector and readout system is presented. This model, using a massless scalar field in one dimension as the readout system, contains the essential feature of giving the readout system an infinite number of degrees of freedom, is exactly solvable in the Heisenberg representation and demonstrates quantum non-demolition measurement by readout state preparation.

The purpose of this lecture is threefold:

1) To introduce a simple linear model system which I believe to be sufficiently rich to describe many of the thermal and quantum effects of a readout system of a gravity wave detector.

2) To solve the model exactly in the Heisenberg representation and discuss some of the advantages of the Heisenberg representation for these problems.

3) To apply the above model to a laser interferometer readout system. Although the laser interferometer is fundamentally non linear, it can be under suitable approximations be reduced to a linear model similar to the above. Unfortunately, I will not have time here to solve the laser model system. For this, the reader is referred to my paper in reference (1).

The usual model for a gravity wave detector is a single or at most a pair of simple harmonic oscillators. The gravity wave is assumed to interact with this oscillator as a classical force. The purpose of the study known as Quantum Non Demolition is to determine the limits placed on the detectable forces especially by the quantum nature of the detector, and to discover the best strategy for measuring the smallest possible force. In measuring the effects of the force, one does not observe the oscillator directly but rather observed it through the intermediary of some sort of readout system. To properly analyse the full quantum properties of the system one should include the readout system in one's analysis. However, this process of including more and more of one's measuring apparatus will very quickly produce such a model of such complexity that it becomes impossible to analyse it. The model should therefore be sufficiently simple that it can be analysed, but sufficiently complex to include all of the relevant possible effects. The simplest such model is to restrict oneself to the analysis of the oscillator alone. A slightly more complex model couples the oscillator to a simple readout system such as another oscillator. The measurement process then consists of quantum measurements in the von Neumann sense of some dynamic variables of the oscillator.[2,3]

In realistic systems, however, the first stage in the readout system is usually a quantum field of some sort. In particular, in the laser interferometer it is the light which plays the role of the primary step in the readout while in the bar detectors it is the modes of the electromagnetic field in the various wires or microwave cavities. I have long felt,[4] therefore, that the treatment of the readout system should be via a model which takes into account the infinite degrees of freedom of a realistic readout system. In particular, the continuous process of reading out data in a real system is at best difficult to mimic by the use of a model in which the readout system contains only a single degree of freedom.

In addition in the usual technique the effects of a heat bath and of damping on the system are usually inserted by postulating a random classical "thermal force" on the oscillator. Again, a true quantum model for the heat bath which contained the essential feature of an infinite number of degrees of freedom in the heat bath would give one more confidence that one had not overlooked some essential feature.

As in any model, one does not expect a simple, solvable model to contain all of the features of the complete system one is studying. The model will be good if it (a) contains the essential features of the real system (which features are essential can of course be a matter of some debate) and (b) it is easily solvable.

My model will be exactly solvable and will contain the feature that the readout system has an infinite number of degrees of freedom.

The model for the detector itself will be a simple harmonic oscillator, with a generalised position variable q, a natural frequency, Ω, and a generalised momentum p. (In an L-C circuit for example, the q could be the charge on the plates of the capacitor while p was the flux in the inductor or in a mechanical oscillator, q could be the amplitude of vibration while p would be the mass times velocity).

The field ψ which is to represent the readout system will be a massless one dimensional scalar field which obeys a wave equation of the form

$$\frac{\partial^2\psi}{\partial t^2} - \frac{\partial^2\psi}{\partial x^2} = 0 \qquad [1]$$

Neither the massless nature of this field nor the one dimensional nature are to be taken as essential features. They are chosen soley to simplify the analysis. Finally the coupling between the field ψ and the detector is chosen to be such as to add a term of the form

$$\int \varepsilon\ \delta(x)\ \dot{\psi}(t,x)\ q(t)dx\ dt \qquad [2]$$

to the action. The interaction is thus localised in x space to the origin x=0 by the delta function. The dot on ψ indicate a time derivative. Again this form of coupling is chosen solely to simplify the analysis. A different form of the coupling (as long as it is linear) should not change any of the essential features of the model but could make the solution very complex and messy.

The full action for the model is to be given by

$$I = \int\{-\tfrac{1}{2}(\dot{\psi}^2 - \psi'^2) + \varepsilon\ \delta(x)\ [\dot{\psi}q + \tfrac{1}{2}(\dot{q}^2 - q^2) + F(t)q]\}\ dxdt \qquad [3]$$

where dots are time derivatives, primes x derivatives, and F(t) is a classical force exerted on the oscillator which in the model is to represent the effect of the gravitational field on the oscillator.

The equations of motion derivable from this action are

$$\frac{\partial^2\psi}{\partial t^2} - \frac{\partial^2\psi}{\partial x^2} = -\varepsilon\,\dot{q}\,\delta(x) \qquad [4]$$

$$\ddot{q} + \Omega^2 q = \varepsilon\,\psi(t,0) + F(t).$$

These classical equations can be solved easily. We find for the scalar field ψ

$$\psi(t,x) = \psi_o(t,x) - \frac{\varepsilon}{4}[q(t-x)\,\theta(x) + q(t,x)\,\theta(-x)] \qquad [5]$$

where $\psi_o(t,x)$ obeys the uncoupled massless scalar wave equation. This gives us an equation for q of the form

$$\ddot{q} + \frac{\varepsilon^2}{4}\dot{q} + \Omega^2 q = \varepsilon\dot{\psi}_o(t,0) + F(t) \qquad [6]$$

Note that although we started with an undamped oscillator, the coupling to the field ψ has introduced a damping term. This equation is solved by

$$q(t) = [q_o\cos\tilde{\Omega}t + \frac{p_o}{\tilde{\Omega}} + \frac{\varepsilon^2}{8}q_o]\,e^{-\varepsilon^2 t/8} \qquad [7]$$

$$+ \int\sin\tilde{\Omega}(t-t')\,e^{-\varepsilon^2(t-t')/8}[\dot{\psi}(t',0) + F(t')]dt'$$

Equations 5 and 7 are the solutions to the classical problem. If I were to solve the quantum problem in the more usual Schroedinger representation, these classical solutions would be of very little help. I would now have to derive the Hamiltonian form the action, and solve the Schroedinger equation for the state of the system, a rather complex procedure. In the Heisenberg representation, however, equations 5 and 7 are also the solutions to the fully quantum equations. All I need do is to reinterpret the symbols in these equations. I let q_o and p_o be operators which represent the position and momentum at the initial time. $\psi_o(t,x)$ will be an operator valued function which I can write in the form

$$\psi_o(t,x) = \int_{\omega>o}(a_{\omega+}\,e^{-i\omega(t-x)} + a_{\omega-}\,e^{-i\omega(t+x)})\,\frac{d\omega}{\sqrt{2\pi\omega}} \qquad [8]$$

$$+ \text{ Herm. conj.}$$

where the operators $a_{\omega\ell}$ (ℓ=+,-) obey the commutation relations

$$[a^{\dagger}_{\omega\ell}, a_{\omega'\ell'}] = \delta(\omega-\omega')\,\delta_{\ell\ell'}$$

$$[a_{\omega\ell}, a_{\omega'\ell'}] = 0 \qquad [9]$$

Since the Heisenberg representation is somewhat unfamiliar to many students, let me remind you of some of its features. In the Heisenberg representation, the operators all obey dynamic equations - they change in time. The state, on the otherhand, does not change during the dynamic evolution of the system. During a measurement on the system, the operators do not change, they continue to obey the same dynamic equations. On the other hand,the state does change during the measurement. If one is measuring the dynamic variable associated with the operator A at time t the state after the measurement will be one of the eigenvectors of the operator A(t). This representation therefore keeps the dynamics and the measurement separate, unlike what happens in the Schroedinger representation. Finally the Heisenberg representation clearly separates the correlations which exist between various variables because of the state chosen, and those which develop due to the dynamic evolution of the system. If A(t) and B(t) both depend on some initial operator C(0) because of the dynamic evolution, there will have been some correlation produced between A and B by that evolution even if they were uncorrelated initially.

The main problem with the Heisenberg representation is that in most problems, the non-commutativity of the various operators makes the solution of the equations impossible. In linear systems however, this problem never arises.

Examining equations 5 and 7 as quantum solutions, we notice one rather interesting feature. The dependence of all of the operators at time t on the initial operators p_o and q_o decays exponentially. After a few decay times, the solutions become completely insensitive to these initial operators. This is true whether or not measurements are being made or the system as measurements do not alter the dynamic equations. By setting the initial time sufficiently far in the past we can completely discard the operators p_o and q_o. Everything now depends only on the field $\psi_o(t,x)$. In particular, the commutation relations between p and q arise out of those satisfied by the field ψ_o, and not out of those for p_o and q_o. (This is one indication that one would obtain inconsistent results if one tried to couple a classical field to a quantum system. The quantum nature of the system would exponentially decay.)

Having completely solved the dynamics of the model, we must now specify the initial state, $|s\rangle$, of the system, and we must specify which measurements we will perform on the readout system, ψ, to determine the force F(t) which acted on the oscillator. Let me answer the second question first. Let us define some orthonormal modes, $h_i(t,x)$, for the field ψ. In particular, these functions will obey the uncoupled wave equation, and will have a temporal spread of τ (i.e. at any point x , $h_i(t,x)$ will be non zero for a time of order τ). These modes are to correspond to the feature of the field which an experimentalist measures during measuring time τ. These $h_i(t,x)$ are assumed to be orthonormal so that

$$\begin{aligned}\delta_{ij} &= \frac{i}{2} \int h_i^*(t,x) \overleftrightarrow{\frac{\partial}{\partial t}} h_j(t,x)\, dx \\ &= \frac{i}{2} \int (h_i^* \dot{h}_j - \dot{h}_i^* h_j)\, dx \quad .\end{aligned} \qquad [10]$$

Furthermore, let us assume that the measurements will be made on the part of the field travelling away from the oscillator at x = 0 and travelling to the right. Then we have

$$h_i(t,x) = h_i(t-x)$$

With each of these modes we can associate a quantum annihilation operator

$$A_i = \frac{i}{2} \int h_i^*(t-x) \overleftrightarrow{\frac{\partial}{\partial t}} \psi(t,x)\, dx \Big|_{t \text{ large}} \qquad [11]$$

which is independent of t for large times t. The operator $A_i^\dagger A_i = N_i$ is the number operator associated with the mode h_i. Measurements of this operator are measurements of how many quanta the field ψ has in mode h_i. I will assume that this is the set of operators which we measure. (Exactly what the functions h_i are for a photomultiplier, for example, is not completely clear. One would have to do a detailed analysis of the quantum behaviour of a photomultiplier to determine this, an analysis which is far outside the aims of this paper.)

We can write A_i in terms of the in field operators a_ω . We find

$$A_i = \int h_i^*(\omega) \left\{ a_{\omega+} + \frac{|\varepsilon^2/4(a_{\omega+} + a_{\omega-}) + \varepsilon F(\omega)/4]}{\Sigma(\omega)} \right\} d\omega \qquad [12]$$

where the Fourier transform $g(\omega)$ of a function $g(t)$ is defined by

$$g(t) = \int g(\omega) \frac{e^{-i\omega t}}{\sqrt{2\pi\omega}} d\omega \qquad [13]$$

and $\Sigma(\omega)$ is defined by

$$\Sigma(\omega) = (-\omega^2 - i\omega\, \varepsilon^2/4 + \Omega^2). \qquad [14]$$

Having decided on which features of the readout ψ we will measure, we must now decide on the initial state of the field ψ. I will assume that this is under the experimentalists control. One possibility would be to place the initial state of the field into its vacuum state, $|0\rangle$, such that $a_{\omega\ell}|0\rangle$. In this case it is easy to use equation 12 to calculate the expectation value of N_i. One finds

$$\langle 0|\, N_i\, |0\rangle = \frac{\varepsilon^2}{4} \left| \int \frac{h_i^*(\omega)\; F(\omega)}{\Sigma(\omega)} d\omega \right|^2 \qquad [15]$$

Let us assume that $F(t)$ is given by an impulse at time $t=0$ so that $F(t)$ was $F_o\ \delta(t)$. Then we have

$$F(\omega) = \sqrt{\frac{\omega}{2\pi}}\, F_o. \qquad [16]$$

If the phase of $h_i(\omega)$ is roughly constant (implying that $h_i(t)$ is non zero for t near 0), we have two possible limiting regimes depending on whether τ the measuring time is larger or smaller than the decay time of the oscillator $8/\varepsilon^2$. Using the crude approximation that $|h(\omega)| \sim \sqrt{\tau}$ and $\Delta\omega$, the bandwidth over which $h(\omega)$ is nonzero, is $1/\tau$, we find

$$\begin{aligned} \langle N_i\rangle &\approx \frac{F^2}{\varepsilon^2\tau\Omega} & \tau >> 8/\varepsilon^2 \\ &\approx \varepsilon^2\tau F_o^2/\Omega & \tau << 8/\varepsilon^2 \end{aligned} \qquad [17]$$

where I have dropped factors of 2, 2π, etc. Since N_i must be an interger, we obtain the measurability limit for F_o with an optimum τ of the damping time of

$$F_o \gtrsim \sqrt{\Omega} \qquad [18]$$

Under the choice of units we have made ($h = M = 1$), this is just the standard quantum limit for the measurability of the force F_o.

Let us therefore choose some other initial state for the field ψ. In particular let us rewrite the initial annihilation operators in terms of some shifted operators $\hat{a}$ so that

$$\hat{a}_{\omega+} = a_+ - \frac{B}{\sqrt{2\pi\omega}}\, \delta(\omega - \Omega) \qquad [19]$$

$$\hat{a}_{\omega-} = a_{\omega-}$$

These shifted operators obey exactly the same commutation relations that $a_{\omega\ell}$ operators do. For example, we could define a "shifted vacuum state by $\hat{a}\ |s\rangle = 0$ for all $\hat{a}$. This state is just a so called coherent state and leads to exactly the same quantum limit as in equation 18. The usual method for improving the accuracy is to alter the coupling between the oscillator and the readout system.[2,3] I will present an alternative which can be called quantum non-demolition by read-out state preparation.[5]

Let us rewrite A_i and N_i in terms of the shifted operators.

$$A_i = B\, h_i^* (\Omega) \left(1 + \frac{\varepsilon^2}{4\Sigma(\Omega)}\right) + \int h_i^* (\omega) \left\{ \hat{a}_{\omega+} + \frac{[\varepsilon^2/4\,(\hat{a}_{\omega+} + \hat{a}_{\omega-}) + \varepsilon F(\omega)/4]}{\Sigma(\omega)} \right\} d\omega \qquad [20]$$

$$N_i = |B|^2 |h_i(\Omega)|^2 \left|1 + \frac{\varepsilon^2}{4\Sigma(\Omega)}\right|^2 + \Bigg\{ B^* h_i(\Omega) \left(1 + \frac{\varepsilon^2}{4\Sigma^*(\Omega)}\right) \times \left[\int h_i^*(\omega) \left\{ \hat{a}_{\omega+} \left(1 + \frac{\varepsilon^2}{4\Sigma(\omega)}\right) + \hat{a}_{\omega-} \frac{\varepsilon^2}{4\Sigma(\omega)} + \frac{\varepsilon F(\omega)}{4\Sigma(\omega)} \right\} d\omega \right] + \text{Herm. conj.} \Bigg\} + (\text{Terms of form } a^\dagger \hat{a} \text{ or } \hat{a}^\dagger F) \qquad [21]$$

If we choose B to be sufficiently large and choose the initial state of field ψ so that the quadratic terms stay relatively small, the number operator will depend linearly on one phase of the force F,

$$\left\{ B^* h_i(\Omega) \left(1 + \frac{\varepsilon^2}{\Sigma^*(\Omega)}\right) \int \varepsilon h_i^*(\omega) \frac{F(\omega)}{4\Sigma(\omega)} d\omega \right\} + \text{c.c}$$

It will also depend on the initial state of the field though the operators

$$D_\omega = B^* h_i(\Omega) \left(1 + \frac{\varepsilon^2}{4\Sigma^*(\Omega)}\right) \left[h_i^*(\omega) \left\{ \hat{a}_{\omega+} \left(1 + \frac{\varepsilon^2}{4\Sigma(\omega)}\right) + \hat{a}_{\omega-} \frac{\varepsilon^2}{4\Sigma(\omega)} \right\} \right] + \text{Herm. Conj.} \qquad [22]$$

If we choose the initial state to be the shifted vacuum for the $\hat{a}$ operators, we find that although the D_ω operators have zero expectation value, their squares do not. This implies that the D_ω operators will contribute a random fluctuating term to the measurement of N_i. This noise will imply that F_o can be measured with no greater accuracy in this way than before. The measurement is still limited by the standard quantum limit.

However, there is nothing to prevent us from putting the initial the ψ field into a state in which the D_ω have both a zero expectation value and their squares also have small expectation values. (i.e. the initial state has a small variance for the D_ω). In this case the limit on measurement of F_o is less than the standard quantum limit by an amount proportional to the decrease in the variance of the D_ω. For a given magnitude for B, the shift quantity, the only limit is given by the fact that a decrease in the variance of the D_ω increases the expectation value and variances of the quadratic terms in N_i which I have neglected. Eventually, as the variances of the D_ω become sufficiently small, these terms will become the dominant source of noise. However, the point at which these take over is inversely proportional to the magnitude of B. We can thus in principle measure one phase of the force F_o arbitrary precision.

In the above analysis I have assumed that the oscillator couples only to the readout field ψ. This is not true in real systems. In particular, most detectors are also weakly coupled to other thermal noise sources, and are damped by mechanisms other than just the readout system. One can take such additional damping and thermal noise sources into account by also coupling the oscillator in the model to additional fields. For example, we can define the scalar massless field ϕ to be a thermal bath which couples to the oscillator. We again choose the model coupling to be of the form

$$\int \tilde{\varepsilon}\ \dot{\phi}(t,x)\ q(t)\ dtdx$$

The solution for this system has almost exactly the same form as before. For example, the expression for A_i is the same as equation 11 with an additional term

$$\int \frac{h_i^*(\omega)\varepsilon^2(b_{\omega+} + b_{\omega-})}{4\ \Sigma(\omega)}\ d\omega$$

and $\Sigma(\omega)$ replaced by

$$\Sigma(\omega) = -\omega^2 - i\omega(\varepsilon^2 + \tilde{\varepsilon}^2)/4 + \Omega^2$$

Here the b annihilation operators are defined by

$$\phi(t,x) = \int (b_{\omega+}\ e^{-i\omega(t-x)} + b_{\omega-} e^{-i\omega(t+x)})\ \frac{d\omega}{\sqrt{2\pi\omega}} .$$

Note that the coupling to any additional field simply increases the damping. In addition, if the field ϕ is in a thermal state, the extra terms will contribute extra noise. In the thermal state, the expectation value of any term linear in b is zero while the quadratic expectation values are

$$< b_{\omega i}\ b_{\omega' j}> = \delta(\omega - \omega')\delta_{ij}\ \frac{e^{-\beta\omega}}{1 - e^{-\beta\omega}} \qquad [24]$$

where β is the inverse temperature 1/kT. One can therefore use this simple model as a model for any thermal noise sources which influence the detector. We also note that the addition of any additional damping of the oscillaotr, other than that provided by the readout system, will invariably introduce extra noise into the oscillator. This additional damping will also compete with the readout system for the changes which the gravity wave induces in the oscillator.

Finally, let us see how we can apply the above model to a laser interferometer[6] type gravity wave detector. In this case, the main barrier is that the interaction between the light (readout system) and the masses (detectors) is not linear. The light affects the masses by means of its radiation pressure - a force which is quadratic in the amplitude of the light amplitude. The mass affects the light by the phase shifts (or equivalently, the doppler shifts) induced when the mirror moves from its equilibrium position. This effect also depends both on the amplitude of the light and the motion of the mirrors. However, we know that in the interferometer, one imposes a strong continuous light beam. What one is interested in detecting are small deviations from the zeroth order situation in which that strong light beam reflects off the mirrors at rest at their equilibrium position. One can thus linearise the problem in terms of these small deviations from the zeroth order situation, and thus produce linear model for the interferometer very similar to the model I have already analyzed.

My model for the mirror mass will be a very low frequency harmonic oscillator to model the effect of the mirror suspension system which has a typical frequency of about a Herz in realistic systems. The light beam will again be modeled by a massless one dimensional scalar field ψ. In the simplest model, I will assume that the interaction between the mirror and the light is that the mirror forces the field to be zero on at the position of the mirror - i.e.

$$\psi(t,q) = 0 \qquad [25]$$

and that the light interacts with the mirror by exerting a force on the mirror equal to its radiation pressure

$$\ddot{q} + \Omega^2 q = -\frac{1}{4}[\dot{\psi}^2 + (\psi')^2] \qquad [26]$$

It is not entirely clear what the first condition would mean as an exact quantum boundary condition. A better model would be to write the interaction between the field ψ and the mirror as a term in the action of the form

$$\int \psi^2(t,x)\ V(x - q)\ dx\ dt \qquad [27]$$

where $V(x)$ was some potential function for the field ψ. However, if $V(x)$ is sufficiently high near $x = 0$ and is non zero only over a sufficiently narrow range about $x = 0$, this model will give results which are identical to the simpler model as long as one is concerned with frequencies ω much less than the height of the potential $V(x)$.

We can write a solution for $\psi(t,x)$ in the form

$$\psi(t,x) = \psi_o(t - x) + \psi_1(t + x) \qquad [28]$$

which obeys the free field equation

$$\ddot{\psi} - \psi'' = 0 \qquad [29]$$

The boundary condition on ψ implies that

$$\psi_1(t + q(t)) = \psi_o(t - q(t)) \qquad [30]$$

Linearising this equation with respect to q we have

$$\psi_1(t) + q(t)\ \psi_1(t) \approx \psi_o(t) - q(t)\ \dot{\psi}_o(t) \qquad [31]$$

A solution accurate to lowest order in q gives

$$\psi_1(t) \approx \psi_o(t) - 2q(t)\ \dot{\psi}_o(t) \qquad [32]$$

Finally let us rewrite ψ_o as the sum of a large "classical" field and a "small" quantum term

$$\psi_o(t) = \frac{B\ e^{-i\omega_o t}}{\sqrt{\omega_o}} + \frac{B^*\ e^{i\omega_o t}}{\sqrt{\omega}} + \hat{\psi}_o(t) \qquad [33]$$

Neglecting terms which are not linear in the "small" quantities $\hat{\psi}$ and q, we finally obtain the linearised expression for ψ in terms of q and the "initial" displaced field $\hat{\psi}$.

$$\psi(t,x) \approx \frac{B}{\sqrt{\omega_o}} e^{-i\omega_o(t-x)} - \frac{B}{\sqrt{\omega_o}} e^{-i\omega_o(t+x)} - \frac{2Bi\omega_o e^{-i\omega_o(t+x)}}{\sqrt{\omega_o}} q(t+x)$$
$$+ \frac{B^*}{\sqrt{\omega_o}} e^{i\omega(t-x)} - \frac{B^*}{\sqrt{\omega_o}} e^{-i\omega(t+x)} + \frac{2B^*}{\sqrt{\omega_o}} i\omega_o e^{i\omega_o(t+x)} q(t+x)$$
$$+ \hat{\psi}_o(t-x) - \hat{\psi}_o(t+x) \qquad [34]$$

Also linearising the pressure term we find

$$\ddot{q} + \Omega^2 q = -\underline{2\omega_o|B|^2} - \underline{2\omega_o}|B|^2\,\dot{q} - \frac{4i\omega_o\mathrm{Im}(B)}{\sqrt{\omega_o}}\,\dot{\hat{\psi}}_o \qquad [35]$$

$$+ \text{ (terms of higher order in } \hat{\psi} \text{ and } q)$$

$$+ \text{ (terms of frequency } e^{\pm 2i\omega_o t})$$

Note that these equations are almost identical to those in our simple model except for the additional hetrodyne factors of the form $e^{\pm i\omega_o t}$. Although these increase the mathematical complexity of the solution, they can be handled without too much difficulty. I refer the reader to my paper in reference 1 for details.

REFERENCES

[1] Unruh, W.G., "Quantum Noise in the Interferometer Detector" in "Quantum Optics, Experimental Gravitation, and Measurement Theory". Edited by P. Meystre and M.O. Scully, Plenum, (to be published).

[2] Caves, C.M., in "Quantum Optics, Experimental Gravitation, and Measurement Theory". Edited by P. Meystre and M.O. Scully, Plenum, (to be published). This paper also has an excellent set of references to the Quantum Non-Demolition literature.

[3] Caves, C.M., et al Rev. Mod. Phys. 52 341 (1980).

[4] Unruh, W., "Quantum Non Demotion" in "Gravitational Radiation, Collapsed Objects, and Exact Solutions" ed. C. Edwards, Springer-Verlag (1980).

[5] Unruh, W.G. "Readout State Preparation and Quantum Non Demolition" in "Quantum Optics, Experimental Gravitation, and Measurement Theory" Edited by P. Meystre and M.O. Scully, Plenum, (to be published).

[6] See for example the description of a laser interferometer detector by R. Drever in this volume.

AUTHOR INDEX

SUBJECT INDEX